Glencoe Health

Mary H. Bronson, Ph.D.

Don Merki, Ph.D.

Contributing Authors

Michael J. Cleary, Ed.D.

Kathleen Middleton, M.S.

Dinah Zike, M.Ed.

TIME

 Learning Solutions

Boston   Burr Ridge, IL   Dubuque, IA   New York   San Francisco   St. Louis
Bangkok   Bogotá   Caracas   Lisbon   London   Madrid
Mexico City   Milan   New Delhi   Seoul   Singapore   Sydney   Taipei   Toronto

About the Authors

Mary H. Bronson, Ph.D., has taught health education in grades K-12, as well as health education methods classes at the undergraduate and graduate levels. As Health Education Specialist for the Dallas School District, Dr. Bronson developed and implemented a district-wide health education program, *Skills for Living*, which was used as a model by the state education agency. She has assisted school districts throughout the country in developing local health education programs. She is also the author of Glencoe's *Teen Health* textbook series.

Don Merki, Ph.D., has taught health education for 35 years. He taught at the University of New Mexico, featuring classes in substance abuse, mental health, adopting a healthy lifestyle, HIV/AIDS and sexually transmitted diseases, and stress and life management skills. He taught students from broad cultural and ethnic backgrounds from elementary to graduate school.

TIME

TIME is the nation's leading news and information magazine. With over 80 years of experience, TIME provides an authoritative voice in the analysis of the issues of the day, from politics to pop culture, from history-making decision to healthy living. TIME Learning Ventures brings the strength of TIME and TIME For Kids' editorial and photographic excellence to educational resources for school and home.

Michael J. Cleary, Ed.D., C.H.E.S., is Professor and School Health Education Coordinator at Slippery Rock University. Dr. Cleary taught at Evanston Township High School in Evanston, Illinois, and later became the Lead Teacher Specialist at the McMillen Center for Health Education in Fort Wayne, Indiana. Dr. Cleary has published and presented widely on curriculum development and portfolio assessment in K-12 health education. Dr. Cleary is the co-author of *Managing Your Health: Assessment for Action.*

Kathleen Middleton, M.S., C.H.E.S., is a nationally recognized expert in health education, curriculum development, and assessment. Kathleen serves as the health education consultant for the CCSSO-SCASS Health Education Assessment Project. She has more then 25 years experience in health education, including teaching at the middle school, high school, and college levels. Ms. Middleton is the author of *Comprehensive School Health Challenge.* She has served as administrator for Health and Physical Education for the Monterey County Office of Education.

Dinah Zike, M.Ed., is an international curriculum consultant and inventor who has designed and developed educational products and three-dimensional, interactive graphic organizers for over thirty years. As president and founder of Dinah-Might Adventures, L.P., Dinah is the author of over 100 award-winning educational publications. Dinah has a B.S. and an M.S. in educational curriculum and instruction from Texas A&M University. Dinah Zike's *Foldables* are an exclusive feature of McGraw-Hill textbooks.

The **McGraw-Hill** Companies

Glencoe Health

2 3 4 5 6 7 8 9 0 VNH VNH 0

ISBN-13: 978-0-07-728826-6
ISBN-10: 0-07-728826-2

Learning Solutions Manager: Aimee Tait
Learning Solutions Representative: Nada Mraovic
Production Editor: Kathy Phelan
Printer/Binder: RR Donnelley

Health and Educational Consultants

Alia Antoon, M.D., F.A.A.P.
Assistant Clinical Professor of Medicine, Harvard
Medical School
Chief of Pediatrics, Shriners Hospital
Boston, Massachusetts

Christine Anne Pedrick Hayashi, J.D.
Reading Specialist
Sylmar, California

Patricia Sullivan
Inclusion Specialist
Meade Middle School
Fort Meade, Maryland

UNIT 1: A Healthy Foundation

Kristen D. Fink, M.A.
Executive Director, Community of Caring
Arlington, Virginia

Betty M. Hubbard, Ed.D., C.H.E.S.
Professor of Health Education
Department of Health Sciences
University of Central Arkansas
Conway, Arkansas

UNIT 2: Physical Activity and Nutrition

Roberta L. Duyff, R.D., C.F.C.S.
Food and Nutrition Education Consultant
St. Louis, Missouri

UNIT 3: Mental and Emotional Health

Betty M. Hubbard, Ed.D., C.H.E.S.
Professor of Health Education
Department of Health Sciences
University of Central Arkansas
Conway, Arkansas

Peter T. Whelley
Adjunct Faculty
University System of New Hampshire
Moultonsborough, New Hampshire

Gordon D. Wrobel, Ph.D.
Consultant, National Association of School
Psychologists
Bethesda, Maryland

UNIT 4: Promoting Safe and Healthy Relationships

Cheryl Page, C.H.E.S.
Health Education Specialist
Salem Keizer Public Schools
Salem, Oregon

Jeanne Title
Coordinator, Prevention Education
Napa County Office of Education and Napa Valley
Unified School District
Napa, California

UNIT 5: Personal Care and Body Systems

Patrick M. Forese, M.S.
Allied Health Educator
Slippery Rock University
Grove City High School
Grove City, Pennsylvania

UNIT 6: Growth and Development

Stephanie S. Allen, M.S., R.N.
Senior Lecturer, Baylor University
Louise Herrington School of Nursing
Dallas, Texas

Alice B. Pappas, Ph.D., R.N.
Associate Dean/Associate Professor
Baylor University
Louise Herrington School of Nursing
Dallas, Texas

UNIT 7: Tobacco, Alcohol, and Other Drugs

Nancy S. Maylath, M.P.H., H.S.D.
Director, Student Wellness Office
Purdue University
West Lafayette, Indiana

Jeanne Title
Coordinator, Prevention Education
Napa County Office of Education and Napa Valley
Unified School District
Napa, California

UNIT 8: Diseases and Disorders

Michael T. Brady, M.D.
Professor and Vice-Chair
Department of Pediatrics
Children's Hospital, Columbus
The Ohio State University
Columbus, Ohio

Health and Educational Consultants (continued)

UNIT 9: Injury Prevention and Environmental Health

David A. Sleet, Ph.D.
Associate Director for Science
Division of Unintentional Injury Prevention
Centers for Disease Control and Prevention (CDC)
Atlanta, Georgia

Teacher Reviewers

Angela Bevilacqua
Health Educator
Lakewood Ranch High School
Bradenton, Florida

Rhoda Booker
Assistant Principal
Fairview High School
Fairview, Tennessee

Pamela R. Connolly
Curriculum Coordinator for Health and Physical
    Education
Diocese of Pittsburgh
North Catholic High School
Pittsburgh, Pennsylvania

Pamela Dobbins, B.S.N., M.Ed.
Healthcare Science Technology Education Teacher
Georgia Association of Educators
Adel, Georgia

Jill English, Ph.D., C.H.E.S.
Assistant Professor
California State University, Fullerton
Fullerton, California

Elizabeth J. Godwin
Family and Consumer Science Teacher
Cape Coral, Florida

Debra C. Harris, Ph.D.
Department Chair, Health and Physical Education
West Linn High School
West Linn, Oregon

Pamela Hoalt, Ph.D.
Professor of Health Education
Malone College
Canton, Ohio

Norma H. Lee
Health Education Consultant
New Market, Tennessee

Michael Rulon
Health/Physical Education Teacher
Pawtucket, Rhode Island

Linda B. Salzman
Health Education Consultant and Trainer
Wilmington, North Carolina

Alan Sewell
Health and Physical Education Teacher
E.A. Laney High School
Wilmington, North Carolina

Contents

Promoting Safe and Healthy Relationships

UNIT 5

Personal Care and Body Systems

UNIT 6

Growth and Development

UNIT 9

Injury Prevention and Environmental Health

Health Skills Activity

Hands-On Health ACTIVITY

Real-Life Application

Resilient TEENS

CHAPTER 1

Living a Healthy Life

Lesson 1 Your Health and Wellness

Lesson 2 Promoting a Healthy Lifestyle

Lesson 3 Your Behavior and Reducing Health Risks

Eye ON THE Media

Teens in the Media

The media plays a part in your overall health. Through the media, you are influenced in some of the following ways:

► **what you eat**

► **how you respond to peer pressure**

► **how you interact with your family and others**

Visit the Eye on the Media section at **health.glencoe.com** to learn more about how media plays a role in your health choices.

FOLDABLES™ Study Organizer

Before You Read

Make this Foldable to help you organize your notes on health, wellness, and the health continuum. Begin with one sheet of plain 8½" x 11" paper or one sheet of notebook paper.

► **Step 1**

Fold the sheet of paper in half along the short axis.

► **Step 2**

Fold in half again along the short axis.

As You Read

Analyze and record your current position on the continuum diagram. Under the tabs, record habits, decisions, and other factors that influence your health.

► **Step 3**

Cut up the inside fold of the front flap. Label the flaps as shown.

Health   Continuum

SPOTLIGHT ON HEALTH

Using Visuals. Make a list of five decisions you've made this week that have had a positive effect on your health.

Your Health and Wellness

Guide to Reading

Building Vocabulary

As you read this lesson, write each new highlighted term and its definition in your notebook.

▶ health (p. 4)
▶ wellness (p. 5)
▶ prevention (p. 6)
▶ health education (p. 7)
▶ *Healthy People 2010* (p. 7)
▶ health literacy (p. 8)

Focusing on the Main Ideas

In this lesson, you will learn how to:

▶ **Explain** how the nation's health goals relate to individual, family, and community health.
▶ **Describe** the criteria for evaluating health information.
▶ **Understand** the importance of health literacy for achieving and maintaining good health.

Reading Strategy

Explain

▶ Write down the Building Vocabulary terms along with a definition describing what each means to you.

What does the word *healthy* mean to you? Write a paragraph describing what being healthy means to you.

▼ Spending time with friends is an important part of health. *Give an example of how relationships can have a positive impact on health.*

Suppose someone asks whether you are healthy. How would you answer? Would you consider only your physical health? For example, would you think of how often you are sick? Throughout this course, you will see that health is much more than just the absence of disease. A state of well-being comes from understanding the relationship among physical, mental and emotional, and social health throughout adulthood.

The Importance of Good Health

What is your usual response to the question, "How are you?" A true description of your health would require much more than a simple "fine" or "okay." **Health** is *the combination of physical, mental/emotional, and social well-being.* It is not an absolute state. Being healthy doesn't mean that you will never be sick. Instead, being healthy means knowing various strategies when making decisions related to health needs and risks of young adults.

4 Chapter 1 Living a Healthy Life

Take the Health Inventory for Chapter 1 at **health.glencoe.com**.

The Health Continuum

Health is dynamic, or subject to constant change. For example, you might be the top performer for your basketball team on Tuesday and sick in bed with the flu on Wednesday. Think of your health at any moment as a point along a *continuum*. This continuum spans the complete spectrum of health from chronic disease and premature death to a high level of health. Along the continuum are many points where your health could be located at any given time.

Changes along the continuum may occur suddenly, such as when you get injured playing a sport. At this time of your life, it's even common for your emotions to shift suddenly from moment to moment. Understanding the health continuum provides you with a method for predicting immediate and long-term impact of health decisions on the individuals who make them. In this way, you can compare the relationship of health to quality of life.

Changes may also be so gradual that you're not even aware that you're moving from one side of the continuum to the other. Take a look at **Figure 1.1.** Where do you fit on the health continuum right now? Where would you like to be in a month? A year?

A person with a balanced life is said to have a high degree of **wellness**, *an overall state of well-being, or total health.* It comes from making decisions and practicing behaviors that are based on sound health knowledge and healthful attitudes. Achieving wellness requires an ongoing, lifelong commitment to physical, mental/emotional, and social health.

When you feel your best, you will perform at your best. *How might maintaining a high level of wellness help you reach your goals?*

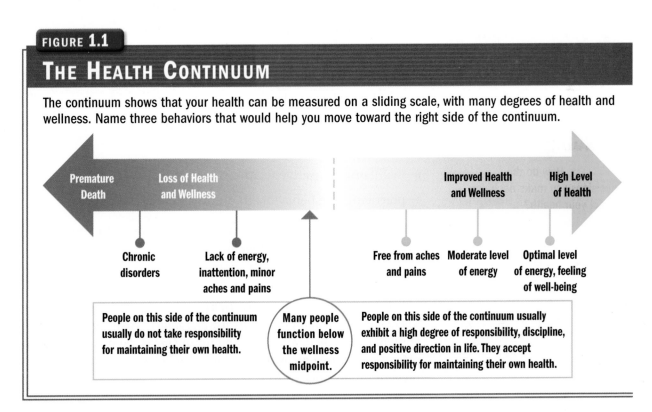

FIGURE 1.1

THE HEALTH CONTINUUM

The continuum shows that your health can be measured on a sliding scale, with many degrees of health and wellness. Name three behaviors that would help you move toward the right side of the continuum.

Premature Death	Loss of Health and Wellness		Improved Health and Wellness	High Level of Health

| Chronic disorders | Lack of energy, inattention, minor aches and pains | Free from aches and pains | Moderate level of energy | Optimal level of energy, feeling of well-being |

People on this side of the continuum usually do not take responsibility for maintaining their own health.

Many people function below the wellness midpoint.

People on this side of the continuum usually exhibit a high degree of responsibility, discipline, and positive direction in life. They accept responsibility for maintaining their own health.

Promoting Your Health

The decisions you make each day affect your health. What you choose to wear, eat, and do can have personal health consequences. For example, not wearing the proper safety gear when participating in a physical activity increases the chances of serious injury in the event of an accident. Eating high-calorie snacks can result in unhealthful weight gain. Making responsible decisions about health shows that you know strategies for maintaining personal, family, and community health.

Lifestyle Factors

Experts have identified habits that affect people's overall health, happiness, and *longevity*, or how long they live. These habits, or *lifestyle factors*, are personal behaviors related to the way a person lives. They help determine your individual control over health risks. Certain lifestyle factors are linked to specific diseases—for example, smoking and lung cancer. Other lifestyle factors promote good health. These include:

▶ getting 8 to 10 hours of sleep each night.

▶ starting each day with a healthy breakfast.

▶ eating a variety of nutritious foods each day.

▶ being physically active for at least 30 minutes most days of the week.

▶ maintaining a healthy weight.

▶ avoiding tobacco, alcohol, and other drugs.

▶ abstaining from sexual activity before marriage.

▶ managing stress.

▶ maintaining positive relationships.

▶ practicing safe behaviors to prevent injuries.

Fitting these health-promoting lifestyle factors into your life will help ensure a high level of wellness.

Wellness and Prevention

A key to your wellness is **prevention**—*practicing health and safety habits to remain free of disease and injury*. Wearing safety belts, applying sunscreen, and avoiding unsafe areas are just a few examples of preventive measures. What other actions could you take to prevent illness and injury?

 Research has shown that teens need more sleep than adults. Establishing a regular sleep schedule can help you get enough sleep each night. *What are two other actions you can take to ensure that you get an adequate amount of sleep?*

Reading Check

Describe How do the decisions you make each day affect your health?

The Importance of Health Education

Health is critical to quality of life. Learning how to become and stay healthy should be a top priority. That's why **health education**—*the providing of accurate health information to help people make healthy choices*—is important. The goal of health education is to show people the relationship of healthful living to their quality of life.

The Nation's Health Goals

Health education affects more than just students. **Healthy People 2010** is *a nationwide health promotion and disease prevention plan designed to serve as a guide for improving the health of all people in the United States.* The plan, which is revised every 10 years, aims to promote health and prevent illness, disability, and early death.

GOALS OF *HEALTHY PEOPLE 2010*

Healthy People 2010 has established two main goals for the future: increase quality and years of healthy life for all Americans and remove health differences that result from factors such as gender, race, education, disability, and location. To reach these goals, individuals, families, and communities must work together.

Reaching the nation's health goals and objectives is related to the health of the individuals in that nation. Studies have shown, for example, that as people become more educated, the general health of a population improves. Therefore, to benefit the health of the larger community, it is up to each individual to be the best he or she can be. Achieving wellness empowers each individual to improve the community in which he or she lives. This, of course, can be extended to global health issues. As more individuals take charge of their own wellness, global health will improve. Individuals, families, and communities each have a role to play:

▶ **Individuals** can take an active role in their own health. You will identify the benefits of setting personal goals for maintaining a healthy body. You will also learn to access reliable health care information and services and to promote the health of others. The information in this book will help you put many of these strategies into action.

▶ **Families** can shape the attitudes and beliefs that result in healthful behaviors. Parents and guardians play an important role in meeting the nation's health goals when they teach their children the values and skills necessary to maintain good health.

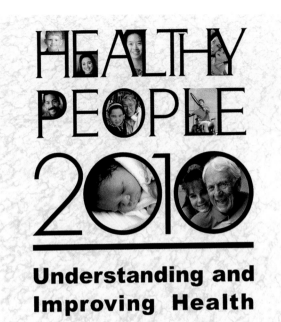

HEALTHY PEOPLE 2010

Understanding and Improving Health

Healthy People 2010 is a plan designed to promote the health of all Americans. *What are the nation's health goals as stated in* Healthy People 2010*?*

Reading Check

Explain What are the two main goals of *Healthy People 2010*?

Goal Setting: Health for All

For class James must set a health goal and explain how reaching his goal will help him, his family, and his community. He has asked his sister to help him.

"Becky, how could a person's health affect anyone else?"

"I can think of lots of ways," Becky says.

"Like what?" James asks.

"Cigarette smoking," Becky replies. "If someone in the family smokes, others in the family are exposed. The community is affected, too. Tobacco use means more illness and more health care needs."

"Yeah," James agrees, "and more fires and litter."

"Do you understand the assignment better now?" Becky asks.

James nods. He wonders what goal to set.

What Would You Do?

Put yourself in James's shoes. Choose a goal that will enhance your health and the health of others. Apply the goal-setting steps to help you reach your goal.

1. Identify a specific goal and write it down.
2. List the steps you will take to reach your goal.
3. Identify potential problems and ways to get help and support from others.
4. Set up checkpoints to evaluate your progress.
5. Reward yourself once you have achieved your goal.

▶ **Communities** can provide health services and offer behavior-changing classes such as tobacco-cessation programs. They can also take steps to ensure a safe environment.

The best chances for success occur when individuals, families, and communities work together. For example, a health care professional can provide information to his or her patients and encourage them to practice healthy behaviors. Individuals can then put that information into practice.

Becoming Health Literate

Health literacy refers to *a person's capacity to learn about and understand basic health information and services and use these resources to promote his or her health and wellnes*s. A health-literate person knows how to access resources from home, school, and the community that provide valid health information.

Reading Check

Describe What are the characteristics of a health-literate person?

A health-literate individual needs to be

▶ **a critical thinker and problem solver**—a person who can develop evaluation criteria for health information before making a decision and who knows how to make responsible, healthy choices.

▶ **a responsible, productive citizen**—someone who acts in a way that promotes the health of the community and who chooses safe, healthful, and legal behaviors that are consistent with family guidelines and that show respect for the individual and others.

▶ **a self-directed learner**—a person who has developed evaluation criteria for health information. These criteria include whether the information is reliable, accurate, and current. Such information is available through various media, through technology such as the Internet, and from health care professionals.

▶ **an effective communicator**—someone who is able to express his or her health knowledge in a variety of ways.

Helping others make healthy choices is part of being a responsible, productive citizen. *List three ways to help others make healthy decisions.*

LESSON | **1** | **REVIEW**

Reviewing Facts and Vocabulary

1. Write a paragraph using the terms *health*, *wellness*, and *health education*.

2. Relate the nation's health goals and objectives to individual, family, and community health: What can an individual do to address the goals and objectives of *Healthy People 2010*?

3. What three criteria can help you evaluate health information?

Thinking Critically

4. **Analyzing.** What is the relationship between promoting healthy behaviors, such as avoiding tobacco, and preventing disease?

5. **Evaluating.** Explain how being health literate helps you achieve and maintain good health.

Applying Health Skills

Practicing Healthful Behaviors. Review the health-promoting lifestyle factors discussed in this lesson. For one week, keep track of how many of them you participate in. Then identify three healthy behaviors that you took part in each day. Also identify one or two factors that you could improve.

After You Read

Identify Cause and Effect. Make a chart listing positive lifestyle factors on one side and how those factors help you achieve and maintain good health on the other side.

 Visit **health.glencoe.com** for the Interactive Study Guide for Lesson 1.

Promoting a Healthy Lifestyle

Guide to Reading

Building Vocabulary

As you read this lesson, write each new highlighted term and its definition in your notebook.

- heredity (p. 12)
- environment (p. 13)
- peers (p. 13)
- culture (p. 14)
- media (p. 15)

Focusing on the Main Ideas

In this lesson, you will learn how to:

- Demonstrate how to take responsibility for your health.
- Analyze how influences such as heredity, environment, culture, media, and technology impact health.
- Compare how health messages are delivered through media and technology.

Reading Strategy

Organize Information

- Draw a triangle, and label each side with one of the three elements: Physical, Mental/Emotional, and Social. As you read, list ways that each element influences your health.

Quick Write

Write a paragraph describing at least two ways you can promote healthy lifestyles at home and at school.

Participating in fun activities with family members enhances your health.

How does staying up late affect you in the morning? How do you feel after engaging in physical activity? The actions you take regarding one aspect of your health have an effect on the other aspects as well.

Your Health Triangle

The three elements of health—physical, mental/emotional, and social—are interconnected, like the sides of a triangle. When one side receives too much or too little attention, the whole triangle can become lopsided and unbalanced. To truly maintain health, you need to take personal responsibility for establishing and implementing health maintenance for all three sides of your health triangle.

Physical Health

Your physical health has to do with how well your body functions. When you are in good physical health, you have enough energy to perform the activities of daily life, to cope with everyday challenges and stresses, to resist diseases, and to avoid injury.

Being physically healthy involves getting adequate sleep and rest, eating nutritious meals, drinking enough water, and being physically active on a regular basis. It also includes using strategies when applying the decision-making process regarding healthy habits. Good physical health also involves paying attention to what you put into your body. It means avoiding harmful substances, such as tobacco, alcohol, and other drugs.

Mental/Emotional Health

Your feelings about yourself, how well you meet the demands of daily life, and your ability to process information are all important parts of your mental/emotional health. People with good mental/emotional health enjoy challenges, such as the increased responsibility in the transition from adolescence to adulthood. They also accept responsibility for their actions and stand up for their beliefs and values.

People with good mental/emotional health are in touch with their feelings and can express them in appropriate ways. They can usually deal with the frustrations of life without being overwhelmed by them. They avoid dwelling on negative thoughts. Instead, they consider their situation and then use positive thoughts and actions to move forward.

Social Health

Your social health involves the way you get along with others. It includes your ability to make and keep friends and to work and play in cooperative ways, seeking and lending support when necessary. It involves communicating well and showing respect and care for yourself and others.

▼ **The health triangle is made up of three elements— physical, mental/emotional, and social health.** *How might something affecting the physical side of your health triangle—an injury, for example—affect the other two sides?*

Keeping a Balance

Each side of your health triangle is equally important to your health. You might think of the three areas of health as the legs of a tripod on which a camera is mounted. If one leg is shorter than the other two, the tripod will tilt or fall. It's much the same with your health. An unbalanced health triangle is likely to cause you problems at some point.

Influences on Your Health

Imagine that the story of your health were made into a movie. The movie might focus on the following questions:

▶ What situations and people affected your health at each stage of your life?

▶ How have influences on your health changed through the years?

▶ How do early influences still affect you today?

There are several important influences on your health. It is important that you learn to identify the value for personal outcomes acquired from lifelong learning about health education. In this lesson, you will learn how hereditary, environmental, and lifestyle factors place you at risk for disease.

People from the same family often share many of the same physical traits. *What physical similarities do the people in this family share? List ways that heredity and environment affect human growth and development.*

Reading Check

Describe What are the three elements of the health triangle?

Heredity

Your **heredity** refers to *all the traits that were biologically passed on to you from your parents.* You probably are familiar with heredity in terms of your physical traits such as eye color, hair color, and height. Heredity also influences your general level of health. Inheriting specific genes may put you at risk for certain illnesses, such as diabetes, requiring you to take steps to reduce your risk or manage the illness. Other genes may strengthen your resistance to disease. Beyond your physical health, it is important to understand how ethnic and cultural diversity both enrich and challenge healthy living. It is important that you learn to evaluate how your genetics and health choices contribute to disease.

Environment

Your **environment** is *the sum of your surroundings*, including your family, your neighborhood, your school, your job, and your life experiences. Environment includes all the places you go to in a given day and the physical conditions in which you live. In this lesson, you'll learn how the environmental conditions of the community influence the health of individuals.

PHYSICAL ENVIRONMENT

Your physical environment influences every aspect of your health. A person who lives in a safe environment is likely to enjoy good physical and mental/emotional health. In contrast, someone who lives in an area with a high crime rate may experience stress. Environmental factors such as air pollution also affect health.

SOCIAL ENVIRONMENT

A person who knows how the social environment influences the health of the community can develop a supportive network of family, friends, and other role models.

As a teen an important part of your social environment is your peers. **Peers** are *people of the same age who share similar interests*. Your peers include your friends and classmates. Loyal and supportive friends who care about their health can have a positive effect on your own health. Peers who take part in dangerous, unhealthy, or illegal behaviors like using tobacco, alcohol, or other drugs could create pressure for you to be "part of the group." Standing up to peer pressure can be challenging. Choosing friends who care about their health and yours supports a positive peer environment.

Reading Check

Explain Name some health influences.

▼ **Climate is one factor that can influence health.** *What other aspects of a person's physical environment can affect his or her health?*

CULTURE

Culture refers to *the collective beliefs, customs, and behaviors of a group*. This group may be an ethnic group, a community, a nation, or a specific part of the world. The language your family speaks, the foods you enjoy, the traditions you have, and the religion you practice are all part of your cultural environment. Your culture gives you a sense of identity. Health-literate consumers know how ethnic and cultural diversity both enrich and challenge healthy living.

Attitude

The way you view situations—your attitude—greatly affects the choices you make. For example, in order to practice good health habits, you must believe that there is some benefit to you and that problems may result if you don't develop these habits.

Attitude can play a major role in health and wellness. Studies have shown that people who tend to see the positive in situations are more likely to have better health than those who see only the negative. Try to view challenging situations positively and think in realistic terms. Doing so will help you make healthful decisions, reach your goals, and successfully manage your life.

Behavior

Although you have no control over your heredity and only limited control over your environment, you have a great deal of control over your behavior. Suppose your family has a history of heart disease. This doesn't mean that you will "follow in their footsteps." You can lower your risk of developing the disease by practicing healthy habits, such as reducing your intake of high-fat foods and engaging in regular physical activity.

Maintaining a sense of humor can help you handle the difficulties that inevitably occur in life.
How can humor be used to ease tension during difficult times?

Hands-On Health ACTIVITY

Health Influences

There are many influences on your health each day. In this activity you will record the influences that affect your health for one day.

What You'll Need

• pencil and paper

What You'll Do

1. Divide a sheet of paper into a grid of 12 rows and 3 columns. Label the columns "Activity," "Element of Health" (physical, mental/emotional, social), and "Influence."

2. Throughout the day, record activities that influence your physical, mental/emotional, or social health. Identify the element of health being affected and whether the influence is positive or negative. For example: *Activity:* Worked hard on my science project. *Element:*

Mental. *Influence:* Positive because I am learning new information and developing my thinking skills. *Activity:* Watched TV and ate cookies. *Elements:* Physical and mental/emotional. *Influence:* Negative because an ad for cookies made me hungry, and I should be physically active instead of sitting on the couch.

3. Compare your grid with that of a classmate. How are your influences the same, and how are they different? Did you respond to similar influences in different ways? If so, why?

Apply and Conclude

In your private health journal, write a paragraph on what you have learned about health influences. What are the major influences in your life?

Your behavior affects not only your physical health but also your mental/emotional and social health. For example, mastering a new skill can give you a sense of accomplishment and enhance your self-esteem. Learning how to resolve conflicts peacefully can have a positive influence on your relationships with others.

Media

The media is a major influence on health. **Media**, or *the various methods of communicating information*, includes radio, television, film, newspapers, magazines, books, and the Internet. Although the media's main purpose has been to provide information and entertainment, it also plays a powerful role in shaping public opinion.

Advances in information delivery systems, such as the Internet, have put access to thousands of information sources at your fingertips. Unfortunately, not all health messages and sources are reliable. For example, some advertisers may make exaggerated claims to try to persuade you to buy a product. For reliable information, stick to

HEALTH Online

TOPIC Learning About Health Promotion

Go to **health.glencoe.com** for eFlashcards, concentration games, and online quizzes.

ACTIVITY Review each of the study tools above for Chapter 1. Write a statement explaining which tool you think will best help you learn about promoting heath, and why.

publications from professional health organizations, such as the American Medical Association and the American Heart Association. It is important to accurately analyze the health messages delivered through the media and technology. Generally, Web sites and publications from accredited universities and government agencies are also reliable sources of information.

Technology

Technology has impacted the health status of individuals, families, communities, and the world. Advances in medical screenings and treatment for diseases such as heart disease, cancer, and AIDS have helped large numbers of people live longer, healthier lives. Other technological advances help keep our air, land, and water clean. However, advances in technology can have a downside. Technology has replaced many of the physical activities that once were part of daily life. People drive or ride instead of walk. They may watch TV or work on the computer instead of being physically active. Recognizing the impact of these influences can help you live a more active, healthy life.

LESSON 2 **REVIEW**

Reviewing Facts and Vocabulary

1. Describe the importance of taking responsibility for establishing and implementing health maintenance for individuals of all ages by keeping the three areas of health in balance.

2. Define the terms *culture* and *media*, and explain how each influences health.

3. Explain how technology has impacted the health status of individuals, families, communities, and the world.

Thinking Critically

4. **Applying.** Select the side of your health triangle that you think is most affected by personal behavior. Explain your choice.

5. **Analyzing.** If you were looking for facts about weight lifting, how might you analyze the health messages delivered through a Web site for a company that sells weight equipment versus information provided by the American Academy of Pediatrics (AAP)?

Applying Health Skills

Analyzing Influences. The United States has many cultures within its population. Investigate which cultures are represented in or near your community. Select one and prepare a presentation on traditions and other factors that might influence the health of people growing up in that particular culture.

After You Read

Identify Cause and Effect. List the three elements of the health triangle in one column. In another column next to each element, list what you can do to keep the health triangle in balance.

Visit **health.glencoe.com** for the Interactive Study Guide for Lesson 2.

Your Behavior and Reducing Health Risks

Guide to Reading

Building Vocabulary

As you read this lesson, write each new highlighted term and its definition in your notebook.

▶ risk behaviors (p. 17)

▶ cumulative risks (p. 19)

▶ abstinence (p. 20)

Quick Write

Your behavior can reduce your health risk. Create a list and briefly describe at least five ways you can reduce your health risk.

Focusing on the Main Ideas

In this lesson, you will learn how to:

▶ Promote your own health and reduce risk.

▶ Describe the consequences of taking risks.

▶ Evaluate the importance of abstinence from risk behaviors, including sexual activity before marriage.

Reading Strategy

Predict

▶ Create a list of at least three points you believe will be presented in this lesson, and write one or two sentences describing each.

P art of becoming an adult is learning how to make responsible decisions. As you move toward adulthood, you become increasingly responsible for decisions regarding your health. Remember, the choices you make during adolescence can affect your health for the rest of your life. It is important, therefore, that you learn to interpret the importance of various health risks.

Understanding Health Risks

T he first step in becoming responsible for your health is to understand the role of individual responsibility regarding personal risk behaviors. **Risk behaviors** are *actions that can potentially threaten your health or the health of others.* A second step is to examine your current behaviors and make any necessary changes.

Wearing protective gear is one way to reduce health risks. *What are other ways to reduce health risks when engaging in physical activity?*

Ⓐ Regular physical activity reduces health risks.

Recognizing Risk Behaviors

The Centers for Disease Control and Prevention (CDC) and other public health agencies routinely survey teens nationwide to monitor their risk behaviors. In the most recent youth risk behavior survey, questionnaires on personal risk factors were gathered from teens in grades 9 through 12 in 33 states. The six categories of personal health risk factors and some of the results are shown in **Figure 1.2.**

When you analyze this data, you'll see that there is encouraging news. Most teens are *not* drinking alcohol or using tobacco. Over two thirds of teens wear safety belts when riding in cars. Where do you fit in? Are you making responsible decisions about your own health and well-being? Throughout this course, you will learn strategies for minimizing many types of risks.

FIGURE 1.2

TEEN RISK BEHAVIORS

The majority of teens are avoiding many risk behaviors or are taking preventive measures to improve their health.

The Youth Risk Behaviors Survey (YRBS) gathers data on the following:

- Behaviors that contribute to unintentional and intentional injuries
- Tobacco use
- Alcohol and other drug use
- Sexual behaviors that contribute to unplanned pregnancy and sexually transmitted infections (STIs) (including HIV infection)
- Unhealthy dietary behaviors
- Physical inactivity

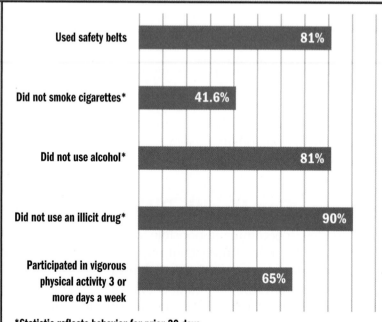

Used safety belts **81%**

Did not smoke cigarettes* **41.6%**

Did not use alcohol* **81%**

Did not use an illicit drug* **90%**

Participated in vigorous physical activity 3 or more days a week **65%**

*Statistic reflects behavior for prior 30 days.

Source: Based on data from the Centers for Disease Control and Prevention (CDC) and the National Household Survey on Drug Abuse (NHSDA)

Real-Life Application

Analyzing Risk Behaviors

Review Figure 1.2 on page 18. Your teacher will provide you with additional information on youth risk behaviors or instruct you on how to access this information.

Choose one category of personal health risk factors:

- Behaviors that may contribute to intentional and unintentional injuries
- Tobacco use
- Alcohol and other drug use
- Sexual behaviors that contribute to unplanned pregnancy, STIs, and HIV
- Unhealthy dietary behaviors
- Physical inactivity

ACTIVITY

Using the statistics in Figure 1.2 and the additional information you obtained, create a convincing poem, poster, song lyric, or cartoon advocating for risk-reducing behavior among your peers. Share your advocacy message with other students in your class or school.

Cumulative Risks and Consequences

The consequences of risk behaviors may add up over time. These **cumulative risks** are *related risks that increase in effect with each added risk.* Smoking one cigarette, for example, is not likely to result in death. Neither is eating one high-fat meal or getting one sunburn. If these behaviors are repeated over time, however, the negative effects accumulate and lead to serious health consequences.

Cumulative risks may also result from combinations of risk factors. For example, driving faster than the posted speed limit is a risk factor that can have deadly results. Another is not wearing a safety belt when you drive or ride in a car. Driving in bad weather is a third risk factor. The combination of these three factors greatly magnifies the potential for harm to yourself and to others. The more risk behaviors you participate in, the more likely you are to experience negative consequences at some point. Cumulative risks can and do occur in all areas of health and safety.

Did You Know ?

Scientists have discovered that the brain undergoes structural changes during the teen years. Some of those changes may mean that it's natural for teens to want to take on new challenges. *Healthy* challenges include running for class president, trying out for a play, and introducing yourself to a new student.

Visit **health.glencoe.com** and use the eFlashcards to review Chapter 1 vocabulary.

Abstaining from Risk Behaviors

The only way to avoid the consequences of some of the most serious risk behaviors is to practice abstinence. **Abstinence** is *avoiding harmful behaviors,* including the use of tobacco, alcohol, and other drugs and sexual activity before marriage.

Abstaining from Tobacco, Alcohol, and Other Drugs

When you abstain from using tobacco, alcohol, and other drugs, you avoid many negative consequences. Using these substances harms all aspects of your health. The physical and psychological effects are well documented; these substances can cause addiction and can seriously harm the body. They can even cause death. Substance use often isolates a person from family and friends, a negative effect on social health. There are legal consequences as well—it is illegal for people under 21 to purchase, possess, or consume alcohol. People under 18 cannot purchase tobacco, and many states restrict purchasing to people over 21. The purchase and use of other drugs are illegal for all people, no matter what their age.

How you behave affects not only yourself but others around you.
What positive effects on others might result from your participation in a campaign that promotes abstinence from substance use?

Abstaining from Sexual Activity

Abstinence from sexual activity is the preferred choice of behavior for unmarried persons of high-school age. Why? Abstinence from sexual activity protects teens against many negative consequences. Even teens who have been sexually active in the past can choose abstinence. Teens who abstain from sexual activity

▶ never have to worry about unplanned pregnancy. Sexual abstinence is the only method that is 100 percent effective in preventing pregnancy.

▶ will not be faced with the difficult decisions associated with unplanned pregnancy, such as being a single parent.

▶ will not have to take on the many responsibilities of caring for a child.

▶ don't have to worry about sexually transmitted infections (including HIV infection).

▶ are free of the emotional problems that usually accompany sexual activity, such as guilt, regret, and rejection.

▶ are making a choice that is always legal.

Explain What are some of the leading teen risk behaviors? How can you prevent them?

With the worry of having a sexual relationship eliminated, you are free to establish nonsexual closeness with members of the opposite gender. Through these relationships you can develop genuine feelings of love, trust, and friendship. When you choose to abstain from sexual activity, you can focus on the real priorities of your life: setting and achieving your goals and following your dreams.

Responsible teens abstain from high-risk behaviors. Choosing abstinence will benefit your lifelong health.

Avoiding high-risk behaviors and choosing friends who do so is one of the best ways to achieve and maintain wellness. *How would you communicate to a friend the importance of practicing abstinence?*

LESSON 3 REVIEW

Reviewing Facts and Vocabulary

1. How are risk behaviors associated with consequences?

2. What are *cumulative risks*? Use this term in a complete sentence.

3. Analyze the importance of abstinence from sexual activity as the preferred choice of behavior in relationship to all sexual activity for unmarried persons of school age.

Thinking Critically

4. **Analyzing.** Why is it important to learn about risk behaviors in the teen years?

5. **Synthesizing.** How can you communicate the importance of practicing abstinence to other teens?

Applying Health Skills

Accessing Information. Choose one of the health-risk behaviors from Figure 1.2 that is of personal concern to you. Research how student trends in this behavior have changed over the last five years. Present your data in a line graph.

After You Read

Compare and Contrast. Risk behaviors are actions that can threaten your health. Abstinence means to avoid harmful behaviors. Make a chart listing risk behaviors on one side and ways to abstain from those risks on the other side.

The Cutting EDGE

HIGH-TECH DOCTORS GIVE NEW MEANING TO LONG-DISTANCE RELATIONSHIPS.

Doctor Mehran Anvari is a specialist in laparoscopy. In this medical procedure, a doctor inserts long-handled instruments and a special camera through tiny incisions in a patient's body. That way, a surgeon can perform an operation while viewing the inside of the body on a video screen. Laparoscopy reduces recovery time from many different types of operations. "For example, gallbladder surgery is now an outpatient operation," Anvari says. "It used to mean three or four days in the hospital."

Telerobotic Surgery

In recent years, Anvari has also used live, long-distance videoconferencing with surgeons while they perform operations. The "telementoring" allows the expert to see what's going on and advise the surgeon through the procedure. Anvari is taking that process a giant step further with a "telerobotics" program. It lets faraway experts physically assist in operations, using a three-armed robotic device. "The goal is not to replace local surgeons but enhance care by increasing the level of support for them," Anvari says.

Telerobotic surgery uses electronic impulses to transmit the movements of a surgeon's hand, wrist, and fingers across space. High-tech robots mirror the surgeon's movements, thus allowing the robot to perform the same operations across the room—or much farther away.

Robotic surgery is common in more than one hundred hospitals around the globe, but only recently has the world's first long-distance operation taken place. Surgeons at a New York City lab successfully removed the gallbladder of a 68-year-old woman in Strasbourg, France.

Anvari's work has caught the attention of NASA, which is looking for ways to deal with any astronaut who needs emergency surgery in space. "Improving in-flight medical capabilities is more important with astronauts flying ever-longer missions," says one NASA researcher. Even the sky may not be Anvari's limit.

TIME to THINK... About Telerobotics

Astronauts are just one group of people who might benefit from the growing technology of telerobotics. Brainstorm at least five other types of workers who might also benefit. List one specific way that each type of worker might find telerobotics useful on the job.

Health Skills Application

1. **Advocacy.** Write a letter to parents informing them of the nation's health goals and objectives and the role of *Healthy People 2010*. Highlight things that they can do individually, as a family, and as a community that relate to the health of all people in the United States. *(LESSON 1)*

2. **Analyzing Influences.** Consider how each of the influences on health affects your own wellness. On a sheet of paper, make two columns—one titled *Positive* and the other *Negative*. Identify the positive and negative aspects of each influence and record them in the appropriate column. *(LESSON 2)*

3. **Goal Setting.** What would be possible consequences of using an illegal drug? Provide an example of how a goal would be negatively affected by these consequences. *(LESSON 3)*

Health Educator

Do you have an interest in improving the health of young people? Do you enjoy working with individuals and groups? If so, it might be worth your time to look into health education as a career.

To be a public school health teacher, you must be credentialed. This includes having a four-year college degree and completing an approved teacher-training program. To find out more about this and other health careers, click on Career Corner at **health.glencoe.com.**

Parent Involvement

Analyzing Influences. With a parent, analyze the influence of laws, policies, and practices on a health-related issue that relates to disease prevention. Topics may include regulations for smoking in public buildings, policies and practices for fire and safety in your school, and traffic laws. Write a brief report that summarizes your findings.

School and Community

Restaurant Inspection. Talk with a health inspector about food-handling requirements and other health codes for restaurant workers. Find out whether you or a small group of students could observe the inspection of a restaurant. Share what you have learned with your class.

After You Read

Use your completed Foldable to help you formulate a plan to increase your level of health and improve your position on the health continuum.

➤ EXPLORING HEALTH TERMS
Answer the following questions on a sheet of paper.

Lesson 1 *Match each definition with the correct term.*

health	health literacy
Healthy People 2010	health education
wellness	prevention

1. The combination of physical, mental/emotional, and social well-being.

2. An overall state of well-being, or total health.

3. The providing of accurate health information to help people make healthy choices.

4. A nationwide health promotion and disease prevention plan designed to serve as a guide for improving the health of all people in the United States.

5. A person's capacity to learn about and understand basic health information and services and use these resources to promote his or her health and wellness.

6. Practicing health and safety habits to remain free of disease and injury.

Lesson 2 *Replace the underlined words with the correct term.*

heredity	media	peers
culture	environment	

7. One part of your <u>culture</u> is where you live.

8. Radio and television are examples of <u>environment</u>.

9. Your <u>heredity</u> influences such things as your language and what you eat.

10. <u>Media</u> is the sum of an individual's traits that were biologically passed along by both parents.

11. People of the same age who share similar interests are your <u>culture</u>.

Lesson 3 *Identify each statement as True or False. If false, replace the underlined term with the correct term.*

risk behaviors	cumulative risks
abstinence	

12. Avoiding harmful behaviors, including sexual activity before marriage and the use of tobacco, alcohol, and other drugs, is known as <u>risk behaviors</u>.

13. <u>Abstinence</u> can potentially threaten your health or the health of others.

14. <u>Cumulative risks</u> are related risks that increase in effect with each added risk.

➤ RECALLING THE FACTS
Use complete sentences to answer the following questions.

1. What is the purpose of *Healthy People 2010*?

2. List five lifestyle factors that promote good health. How are these factors related to preventing disease?

3. What can communities do to address the goals of *Healthy People 2010*?

4. Which aspect of health reflects your ability to enjoy challenges and handle frustrations?

5. Identify six categories of influences on health.

6. Over which influences on health do you have the most control?

7. What is the first step toward becoming responsible for your health?

8. Describe the two ways that cumulative risks occur.

9. List three reasons that it is important to abstain from all sexual activity for unmarried persons of school age.

For more review questions for Chapter 1, go to **health.glencoe.com**.

➤ WRITING CRITICALLY

1. Persuasive. Write copy for a flyer that persuades others to keep their health triangle in balance. In your flyer, provide readers with suggestions for living a healthy lifestyle and ways in which they can keep each side of the health triangle in balance.

2. Narrative. Write a one-page story showing a teen making healthy lifestyle choices. In your story, focus on the teen's environment, his or her family and friends, and other factors that positively influence his or her health on a daily basis. Your story should include at least three characters, a setting, and a plot that tells a clear story.

Standardized Test Practice

 Read the passage below and then answer the questions.

Staying Hydrated

(1) Veronica glanced at the clock as she ran down the hall. (2) "Only ten minutes to get there!" she thought. (3) Veronica was late for her school's soccer game. (4) She gathered her equipment as quickly as she could.

(5) On her way to the field, her mother asked where Veronica's water bottle was. (6) Veronica had forgotten to pack it. (7) "Don't worry, Mom, I'll just borrow a bottle from someone," she said. (8) "Be sure you do," her mother replied, "because the heat wave we're in is even worse because of the humidity." (9) The game was about to begin as they pulled into the parking lot. (10) Veronica raced onto the field, forgetting to get a drink from the nearby water fountain.

(11) Near the end of the first half, Veronica started to feel weak. (12) Then her leg cramped. (13) After resting and drinking a bottle of water, she began to feel better. (14) But her coach refused to let her back into the game. (15) He told her that she had become dehydrated. (16) This surprised Veronica—she hadn't even felt thirsty before her leg cramped.

(17) What Veronica didn't know was that you cannot count on thirst for knowing when you need water. (18) People can become dehydrated before feeling thirsty. (19) Before playing soccer—or any sport—players should drink plenty of non-carbonated fluids.

1. Which sentence includes details that support the author's point of view?

- **A** sentence 2
- **B** sentence 7
- **C** sentence 18
- **D** sentence 10

2. How does the writer show that the purpose of this essay is to persuade?

- **F** The writer emphasizes the use of proper-fitting protective gear.
- **G** The writer contrasts the different types of soccer gear people use.
- **H** The writer explains that soccer's increasing popularity has led to more injuries among players.
- **I** The writer describes what happened to someone who had not drunk enough water.

3. Write a paragraph explaining the importance of drinking plenty of water before and during sports activities.

Building Health Skills and Character

HEALTH Online

Eye ON THE Media

Health Advocacy in the Media

Advocacy organizations raise awareness and funds for issues or causes. The media and media personalities can help gain support for the following types of activities:

► **nonprofit health programs**

► **research**

► **social and political causes**

Visit the Eye on the Media section at **health.glencoe.com** to learn more about how media and advocacy groups work together.

FOLDABLES™
Study Organizer

Before You Read

Make this Foldable to help you organize what you learn about building health skills. Begin with one sheet of plain 8½″ x 11″ paper or one sheet of notebook paper.

►**Step 1**

Fold a sheet of paper along the long axis, leaving a ½″ tab along the side.

►**Step 2**

Turn the paper, and fold into thirds.

►**Step 3**

Cut the top layer along both folds. Then cut each tab in half to make six tabs.

►**Step 4**

Turn the paper vertically and label the tabs as shown.

As You Read

Under the tabs, define terms related to each of the health skills. Record what you learn about health skills as you read and discuss Lesson 1.

SPOTLIGHT ON HEALTH

Using Visuals. What skills are the teens in this photo demonstrating? Which skills do you practice on a regular basis to maintain or improve your health?

Building Health Skills

Guide to Reading

Building Vocabulary

As you read this lesson, write each new highlighted term and its definition in your notebook.

▶ health skills (p. 28)
▶ interpersonal communication (p. 28)
▶ refusal skills (p. 30)
▶ conflict resolution (p. 30)
▶ stress management (p. 31)
▶ advocacy (p. 32)

Focusing on the Main Ideas

In this lesson, you will learn how to:

▶ Demonstrate communication skills to build and maintain healthy relationships.
▶ Describe refusal strategies and conflict resolution skills.
▶ Formulate self-management strategies.
▶ Assess influences on behavior.
▶ Identify evaluation criteria for health information.

Reading Strategy

Organize Information

▶ Make a chart with two columns. List the five health skills from the main headings in this chapter on one side of the chart. As you read, list what you learn about each of the health skills on the other side.

List three skills you need to effectively communicate. Describe how these skills can positively impact your health.

FIGURE 2.1

THE HEALTH SKILLS

Developing and practicing these health skills will provide a lifetime of benefits.

Interpersonal Communication
• Communication Skills
• Refusal Skills
• Conflict Resolution

Self Management
• Practicing Healthful Behaviors
• Stress Management

Analyzing Influences

Accessing Information

Decision Making/Goal Setting

Advocacy

The choices you make and the actions you take can affect your health. Accepting responsibility for your health begins with a commitment to take charge of your actions and behaviors in a way that reduces risks and promotes wellness. The first step is to develop *health skills*. **Health skills**, or life skills, are *specific tools and strategies that help you maintain, protect, and improve all aspects of your health.* **Figure 2.1** presents a basic overview of the health skills.

Interpersonal Skills

One of the traits of a health-literate individual is knowing techniques for communicating care, consideration, and respect of self and others. Effective communication involves not only making yourself heard but also being a good listener. **Interpersonal communication** is *the exchange of thoughts, feelings, and beliefs between two or more people.*

Effective **communication** skills for building and maintaining healthy relationships include:

▶ **Clearly say what you mean.** Use *"I" messages* to state your position, for example, "I feel frustrated when our plans change." This helps you avoid placing blame on others.

▶ **Pay attention to *how* you say something.** Use a respectful tone. Make sure you understand the relationship between verbal and nonverbal communication.

▶ **Be a good listener.** Avoid interrupting the speaker, and show that you are listening by nodding or asking appropriate questions.

Reading Check

Explain What does the phrase *interpersonal communication* mean?

Health Skills Activity

Communication: The Ball's in Your Court

When Mark arrives late at the basketball court, his friend Phillipe throws the ball at him, shouting, "You're a half hour late!"

"Well, excuse me, Mr. Punctual," Mark laughs.

"You're never on time. It's like you assume I have nothing better to do than wait around for you," Phillipe says.

"Sorry, bud, but some things came up," Mark answers.

"Yeah? Well, I'm outta here." Phillipe throws up his hands and turns to walk away.

"Wait, let me explain," Mark says calmly.

Phillipe hesitates, wondering how to respond.

What Would You Do?
How can Mark and Phillipe use effective communication skills to build and maintain their friendship? Write an ending to this scenario, demonstrating the communication skills below.

1. Use "I" messages.
2. Speak calmly and clearly, using a respectful tone.
3. Listen carefully, and ask appropriate questions.
4. Show appropriate body language.

FIGURE 2.2

REFUSAL STRATEGIES

Sometimes you must reinforce your decision to say no.

SAY NO IN A FIRM VOICE.
Do this calmly and clearly. Use expressions such as "I'd rather not."

EXPLAIN WHY.
State your feelings. Tell the other person that the suggested activity or behavior goes against your values or beliefs.

SUGGEST ALTERNATIVES.
Propose a safe, healthful activity to do instead.

USE APPROPRIATE BODY LANGUAGE.
Make it clear that you don't intend to back down from your position. Look directly into the other person's eyes.

LEAVE IF NECESSARY.
If the other person continues to pressure you, or simply won't take no for an answer, just walk away.

CHARACTER CHECK

Respect. When you apply refusal skills to avoid risky situations, you demonstrate respect for yourself and your values. **How can using refusal skills help you uphold your values and the values of your family?**

Reading Check

Identify What factors can promote a positive self-image?

Refusal Skills

Think about how you handle situations in which you are asked to do something that you know is harmful or wrong. In such circumstances, you need to use refusal skills. **Refusal skills** are *communication strategies that can help you say no when you are urged to take part in behaviors that are unsafe or unhealthful, or that go against your values.* Demonstrating these strategies, including the ones shown in **Figure 2.2,** will help you resist risky behaviors.

Conflict Resolution Skills

In addition to practicing effective refusal skills, it is important to develop and apply strategies for dealing with conflicts or disagreements and avoiding violence. **Conflict resolution** is *the process of ending a conflict through cooperation and problem solving.* The key to conflict resolution is respecting others' rights and your own. Willingness to compromise will also help achieve a resolution that satisfies everyone. Follow these steps when dealing with a conflict:

▶ Take time to calm down and think through the situation.

▶ When discussing the conflict, speak calmly and listen attentively, asking questions when appropriate.

▶ Use a polite tone and try to brainstorm solutions where no one loses respect. Work to resolve the conflict peacefully.

Self-Management Skills

When you practice self management, you take responsibility for your health and act in specific ways that promote your wellness. Two self-management skills, practicing healthful behaviors and managing stress, help provide a foundation of good health.

Practicing Healthful Behaviors

Choices you make today will affect your health in the future. Healthful behaviors are more than just actions that can protect you from illness or injury. These behaviors support every aspect of your health. Eating nutritious foods and getting regular medical and dental checkups, as well as avoiding the use of tobacco, alcohol, and other drugs, are all behaviors that help you maintain and strengthen your overall health. Practicing healthful behaviors also involves expressing your feelings in healthful ways, building your self-esteem, and maintaining healthy relationships. It also includes identifying risk behaviors that you should manage.

Managing Stress

Stress, the body's and mind's reactions to everyday demands, is a natural part of life. Being late to class, balancing many activities, and winning an award can all cause stress. Learning strategies for **stress management**, or *ways to deal with or overcome the negative effects of stress,* will help you develop awareness of your own control over stress. Some strategies for managing stress include engaging in physical activity, listening to soothing music, managing time effectively, taking a warm bath, and laughing.

Analyzing Influences

How do you determine what health choices are right for you? Many factors influence your health. *Internal influences,* which include your knowledge, values, likes, dislikes, and desires, are based on your experiences and your perspective on life. You have a great deal of control over your internal influences. *External influences,* which come from outside sources, include your family, your friends and peers, your environment, your culture, laws, and the media. As you become aware of these influences, you will be better able to make healthful choices—about everything from your personal behavior to which health products you buy.

▲ **Practicing healthful behaviors includes making everyday activities safe for you and those around you.** *What healthful behaviors do you practice on a regular basis?*

Reading Check

Identify What are some origins of stress? What can you do to manage stress?

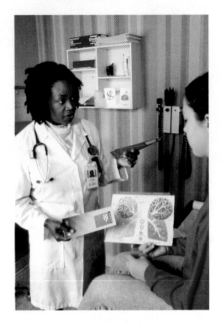

Talking to a health professional can help you obtain accurate, reliable information. *Where else can you find valid health information?*

Accessing Information

Learning how to find resources from home, school, and community that provide valid information will help you be better prepared to make healthful choices. Keep in mind that reliable sources of health information include:

▶ parents, guardians, and other trusted adults.

▶ library resources, such as encyclopedias and nonfiction books on science, medicine, nutrition, and fitness.

▶ reliable Internet sites, such as those posted by government and educational institutions.

▶ newspaper and magazine articles by health professionals or experts.

▶ government agencies, health care providers, and health organizations.

Advocacy

Advocacy is *taking action to influence others to address a health-related concern or to support a health-related belief.* This skill enables you to positively influence the health of those around you. In this responsible role, you can help others become informed and publicly support health causes that concern and interest you. Encouraging family, friends, peers, and community members to practice healthful behaviors is one way to practice health advocacy.

LESSON 1 REVIEW

Reviewing Facts and Vocabulary

1. Define the term *interpersonal communication*, and identify the role of "I" messages.

2. List five refusal strategies.

3. What is *stress management*? Identify three ways to reduce the effects of stress.

Thinking Critically

4. **Analyzing.** What are the advantages of peacefully resolving conflicts?

5. **Applying.** What are two ways you could show support for a health cause or organization?

Applying Health Skills

Stress Management. List all the healthful strategies you used this past week to relieve stress. Which ones helped the most?

After You Read

Identify Cause and Effect. List three ways that your health decisions are influenced by peers, family, and the media. How can you positively influence the health of others?

Making Responsible Decisions and Setting Goals

Guide to Reading

Building Vocabulary

As you read this lesson, write each new highlighted term and its definition in your notebook.

▶ decision-making skills (p. 33)

▶ values (p. 34)

▶ goal (p. 34)

▶ short-term goal (p. 35)

▶ long-term goal (p. 35)

▶ action plan (p. 36)

Focusing on the Main Ideas

In this lesson, you will learn how to:

▶ Apply decision-making skills that promote individual, family, and community health.

▶ Cite the advantages of seeking advice and feedback regarding decision-making skills.

▶ Describe the processes involved in choosing and achieving goals.

Reading Strategy

Predict

▶ Scan the headings and subheadings in this lesson. Write down three topics you think will be covered in this lesson.

Quick Write

Write a brief paragraph describing a goal you set for yourself and the steps you took to reach that goal.

When you make decisions or set goals, you show that you know how to implement a plan for attaining personal health. Making responsible decisions and setting meaningful goals are important skills that can promote individual, family, and community health.

The Decision-Making Process

Decision-making skills are *steps that enable you to make a healthful decision.* The steps are designed to help you make decisions that protect your rights and health while respecting the rights and health of others. The six basic steps for making a decision are described in **Figure 2.3** on page 34. Often, you will find it helpful to seek advice from those with more experience, such as parents and guardians. Doing so can provide valuable feedback and strengthen family bonds and values.

This teen made the decision to study for his exam instead of going out with friends. *What responsible decisions have you made in the past week?*

FIGURE **2.3**

STEPS OF THE DECISION-MAKING PROCESS

Step 1: STATE THE SITUATION

Examine the situation and ask yourself: What decisions need to be made? Consider all the health information and who else is involved.

Step 2: LIST THE OPTIONS

What are the possible choices you could make? Remember that sometimes it is appropriate not to take action. Share your options with parents or guardians, siblings, teachers, or friends. Ask for their advice.

Step 3: WEIGH THE POSSIBLE OUTCOMES

Weigh the consequence of each option. Use the word *HELP* to guide your choice.
- **H** *(Healthful)* What health risks, if any, will this option present?
- **E** *(Ethical)* Does this choice reflect what you and your family believe is right?
- **L** *(Legal)* Does this option violate any local, state, or federal laws?
- **P** *(Parent Approval)* Would your parents or guardians approve of this choice?

Step 4: CONSIDER VALUES

Values are *the ideas, beliefs, and attitudes about what is important that help guide the way you live.* A responsible decision will reflect your values.

Step 5: MAKE A DECISION AND ACT ON IT

Use everything you know at this point to make a responsible decision. You can feel good that you have carefully prepared and thought about the situation and your options.

Step 6: EVALUATE THE DECISION

After you have made the decision and taken action, reflect on what happened. What was the outcome? How did your decision affect your health and the health of those around you? What did you learn? Would you take the same action again? If not, how would your choice differ?

Explain What does the acronym H.E.L.P. from Step 3 of the decision-making process mean?

Setting Personal Health Goals

Consider your plans for the future. What do you want to do with your life? Do your plans include further education and a family? What kind of career are you interested in pursuing? Setting goals can help you shape your life in positive ways by focusing your energy on behaviors that you want to develop or change. A **goal** is *something you aim for that takes planning and work.* Goal setting is also an effective way to build self-confidence, increase your self-esteem, and improve your overall health.

Types of Goals

Every goal involves planning. When you set a goal and plan strategies to reach it, you will need to consider how much time it will take to accomplish the goal. A **short-term goal**, such as finishing a project by Friday or cleaning your room before dinner, is *a goal that you can reach in a short period of time*. A **long-term goal** is *a goal that you plan to reach over an extended period of time*. For example, you show that you know how to implement a plan for attaining personal health goals for the school year and know methods for evaluating progress. A plan of this type will include both short- and long-term goals. A long-term goal may take months or even years to accomplish. Often, short-term goals are steps in a plan to achieve a long-term goal. What kinds of short-term goals might help a person become a physician or a computer technician?

Health Minute
Setting Goals

Some guidelines to remember:

► Make sure that your goals are your own, not someone else's.

► Set a goal because it will help you grow, not because you want to outdo someone.

► If you do not achieve your goal, use what you've learned to set a new goal.

Hands-On Health ACTIVITY

Setting a Personal Health Goal

In this activity, you will set a personal health goal and work to achieve it.

What You'll Need

• notebook   • pencil

What You'll Do

Use your notebook as a personal health goal journal. Record your efforts to reach your goal during the school year. Write a reflective summary of what you learned in the process.

1. **Set a goal.** Do you want to get along better with family members? Eat more nutritiously? Be more active? Set a realistic health goal, and write it down. Explain why you have chosen this goal and what rewards you expect to obtain when achieving the goal.

2. **List steps to meet the goal.** Examine a variety of options to achieve the goal you have set. List the steps you will take to reach your goal.

3. **Evaluate your progress, and adjust plans if necessary.** If there have been obstacles, give yourself more time, and work to overcome them. If you are moving ahead of schedule, you may want to set a more challenging goal.

Apply and Conclude

After a week, examine your progress. Has your plan been effective? How can it be strengthened? Extend your one-week plan to four weeks. Make it a habit to continue to set and work toward new health goals.

V Reaching your goals through hard work brings personal satisfaction.

Achieving Your Goals

To establish and reach your goals, create an **action plan**, or *a multistep strategy to identify and achieve your goals.* Follow these steps:

▶ **Set a specific, realistic goal, and write it down.** State your goal as something positive. This will help motivate you.

▶ **List the steps you will take to reach your goal.** Look for ways to break your larger goal into smaller, short-term goals.

▶ **Identify sources of help and support.** Such sources might include friends, family members, peers, teachers, or neighbors.

▶ **Set a reasonable time frame for reaching your goal.** After deciding on a reasonable time, put it in writing.

▶ **Evaluate your progress by establishing checkpoints.** Periodically check how you are progressing, and make any necessary adjustments that will help you reach your goal.

▶ **Reward yourself for achieving your goal.** Enjoy the personal satisfaction reaching a goal brings. You might celebrate your achievement with your family or friends.

LESSON 2 REVIEW

Reviewing Facts and Vocabulary

1. What are the six steps of the decision-making process?
2. Summarize the advantages of seeking advice and feedback regarding decision-making skills.
3. Explain the difference between short-term and long-term goals, and provide an example of each.

Thinking Critically

4. **Applying.** Identify a major health-related decision that teens might have to make. How can teens access information and use decision-making skills to make an informed choice that promotes individual, family, and community health?
5. **Synthesizing.** Explain and defend this statement: *Decision making and goal setting are interrelated.*

Applying Health Skills

Decision Making. Cari's friends want her to skip school to go to the beach with them. Apply the six steps of decision making to Cari's situation, and help her make a responsible choice based on health information.

After You Read

Identify Cause and Effect. Make a chart that lists the steps of the decision-making process on one side. On the other side of the page, list ways that this process can help you set and achieve your health goals.

Building Character

Building Vocabulary

As you read this lesson, write each new highlighted term and its definition in your notebook.

▶ character (p. 37)
▶ role model (p. 40)

Quick Write

Think about the different consequences of your actions. List three ways you can display good character.

Focusing on the Main Ideas

In this lesson, you will learn how to:

▶ Describe the importance of good character for self, others, and community.

▶ Apply communication skills and practice behaviors that show respect for self, family, and others.

▶ Analyze ways to demonstrate good character.

Reading Strategy

Organize Information

▶ Create a chart with three columns. In the first column, list the six traits of good character. In the second column, list ways to develop your character. In the last column, list some ways to demonstrate good character.

As you have learned, it is important to consider and act on your most important beliefs and values when making a decision. Values shape your priorities, and they help you distinguish right from wrong. The values that help you make healthful, well-informed decisions are also traits of good character. **Character** can be defined as *those distinctive qualities that describe how a person thinks, feels, and behaves.*

What Is Good Character?

Good character is an outward expression of inner values. A person with good character demonstrates *core ethical values,* such as responsibility, honesty, integrity, and respect. These values are held in high regard across all cultures and age groups. People with good character know techniques for communicating care, consideration, and respect for self and others. They know positive strategies for expressing needs, wants, and feelings.

▲ **Character helps shape behavior.** *What values might prompt the teen in the photo to return the found wallet?*

FIGURE **2.4**

TRAITS OF GOOD CHARACTER

A person of good character demonstrates these traits in his or her actions and behaviors.

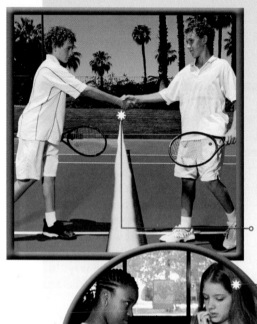

Trustworthiness: If you are trustworthy, you are honest, loyal, and reliable—you do what you say you'll do. You have the courage to do the right thing, and you don't deceive, cheat, or steal.

Respect: Showing respect means being considerate of others and tolerant of differences. It also means using good manners. You make decisions that show you respect your health and the health of others. You treat people and property with care.

Responsibility: Being responsible means using self-control—you think before you act and consider the consequences. You are accountable for your choices and decisions—you don't blame others for your actions. Responsible people try to do their best, and they persevere even when things don't go as planned.

Fairness: If you are fair, you play by the rules, take turns, and share. You are open-minded, and you listen to others. You don't take advantage of others, and you don't assign blame to others.

Caring: A caring person is kind and compassionate. When you care about others, you express gratitude, you are forgiving, and you help people in need.

Citizenship: If you advocate for a safe and healthy school and community, you are demonstrating good citizenship. A good citizen obeys laws and rules and respects authority. Being a good neighbor and cooperating with others are also parts of good citizenship.

TOPIC Good Character

Go to **health.glencoe.com** and click on the Web Links for more information on good character.

ACTIVITY Using these links, list three ways that you can put good character into action.

Character and Health

Because your character plays a significant role in your decisions, actions, and behavior, it impacts all aspects of your health. Developing good character enhances each side of your health triangle. For example, if you know methods for effectively expressing feelings and opinions on health issues, you are more likely to take care of your body by eating nutritious foods and keeping physically active. When you act with responsibility and fairness, both your mental/emotional and social health will improve. Identifying factors that promote a positive self-image helps you feel good about yourself, and your relationships with others are strengthened.

Traits of Good Character

There are several different traits that contribute to good character. **Figure 2.4** identifies six primary traits of good character.

Developing Your Character

Character and core ethical values are learned when you're young and developed throughout your life. To take a more active role in your character development:

▶ Stand up for your beliefs.

▶ Learn from people who demonstrate good character traits. Ask family members for tips on strengthening values.

▶ Join volunteer groups in your school or community. Form friendships with people who exhibit core ethical values.

Reading Check

Describe What are the six traits of good character?

Real-Life Application

Character in Action

A person with good character knows effective techniques for supporting community, state, and federal agencies that advocate healthier communities. The teen showcased here began a pen-pal program that links young people with life-threatening illnesses with other teens around the country.

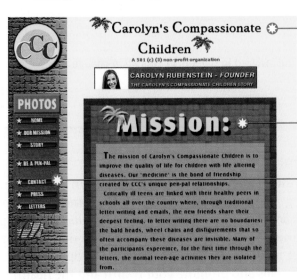

○ **Character Traits:** Compassion, caring, and courage.

○ **Mission:** Create a support network among teens with life-threatening diseases.

○ **Action:** Contact hospitals and other organizations to establish a network.

ACTIVITY

Choose an organization with volunteer opportunities. Research information on the organization's mission and programs. Write a paragraph summarizing your findings.

Resilient TEENS

Shari Schindler is quietly but firmly against the use of drugs and alcohol. "I've seen what drugs can do," she says in a subdued voice.

Shari's voice brightens when the subject changes to teaching. "I've always known I want to be a teacher," she says. "That's why I joined Careers in Education." The organization has helped Shari overcome her natural shyness and gain confidence as a leader and teacher.

Shari Schindler is a member of the Chippewa Indian tribe and will be the first of her family to attend college. She's always been proud of her heritage. "My father and my uncle taught me to appreciate my culture and accept others," she says. "It's okay to be different, and I don't have to do drugs to fit in."

"It's okay to be different, and I don't have to do drugs to fit in."

Reading Check **Explain** How did getting involved in Careers in Education change Shari's life?

Positive Role Models

Having positive role models is important in developing and strengthening good character traits. A **role model** is *someone whose success or behavior serves as an example for others.* Many people look to their families for role models. Parents, grandparents, and other family members are often the people who best support your goals and promote your health and the health of your family. They can inspire and encourage basic values such as working hard, staying focused, planning ahead, being honest, and engaging in safe and healthful behaviors. Other role models may include teachers, coaches, religious leaders, and volunteers.

Think about the character traits that your role models demonstrate. Do you show the same traits in your daily actions? People whose behavior reflects good character are more likely to experience increased feelings of self-worth, satisfaction, and a sense of purpose.

Demonstrating Character

By demonstrating good character, you practice behaviors that have a positive effect both on yourself and others at home, at school, and in your community.

▶ **Make a difference at home.** You demonstrate trust-worthiness and reliability at home when you carry out your responsibilities. By showing respect and caring in daily actions, you will also strengthen your family relationships.

▶ **Make a difference at school.** At this stage in life, you are probably beginning to evaluate the rules that others have set for you. By observing school rules, you show respect for teachers and fellow students.

▶ **Make a difference in your community.** Good citizenship means obeying laws, respecting the needs of others, and being tolerant of differences. Take advantage of the opportunity you have to model good character and be a positive influence on those around you.

Helping out with household tasks is a way to demonstrate good character at home. *How do you contribute to your home, school, and community?*

LESSON | 3 — REVIEW

Reviewing Facts and Vocabulary

1. What is *character*? How is good character related to values?
2. Name the six primary traits of good character.
3. List three ways of demonstrating good character in your home, your school, and your community.

Thinking Critically

4. **Synthesizing.** Why do you think that caring, responsibility, and respect are values that exist across cultures?
5. **Applying.** In what ways can you use communication skills to demonstrate consideration and respect for self, family, and others?

Applying Health Skills

Advocacy. Prepare a message about an important health cause or organization. The message should be appropriate for a specific audience, such as children, teens, parents, or individuals with a disability.

After You Read

Identify Cause and Effect. List three ways that demonstrating good character impacts your health. Write one or two sentences describing the positive impact of each.

Visit health.glencoe.com for the Interactive Study Guide for Lesson 3.

Lesson 3 Building Character **41**

Making A DIFFERENCE

Can teens really have a positive effect on the world? You bet! Here's just one example.

Jennifer Howitt, 16, may use a wheelchair, but she isn't sitting out on life. Paralyzed after breaking her back in a hiking accident at age nine, she has since developed into one of the country's top young disabled athletes. She competed at the World Athletic Championships in track and field and went to the Sydney Paralympics as the youngest member of the 12-person United States women's wheelchair basketball team. Says Jennifer of her experience in Sydney, "It was pretty inspirational. If the entire world can come together to celebrate people overcoming challenges and participating in sports, then it is really possible for us, as a planet, to work out all our problems."

How does staying active help Jennifer? "I got a lot of confidence out of playing basketball," says Jennifer, who started the sport at age 11 when her father took her to a practice. "I didn't want to go," she recalls. "I was sort of in denial about my disability. But once I started playing, I couldn't get enough."

Now Jennifer coaches other young paraplegic athletes at Berkeley's Bay Area Outreach & Recreation Program. When an 11-year-old girl there told Jennifer that she was a role model, "it almost made me cry," says Jennifer.

After high school, Jennifer plans to head to Georgetown University in Washington, D.C., where she'll major in international politics. In the meantime, she's establishing a few international relations of her own: She recently lived for a few months with a family in Costa Rica, and she also coached at a recreation center in Northern Ireland.

How will Jennifer change the world? She hopes "to show young girls with disabilities that they can achieve whatever they want. A disability doesn't get in the way of anything." ■

TIME to THINK... About Positive Role Models

Like Jennifer, many people considered to be positive role models have overcome major life obstacles. Brainstorm with the class names of heroes. Using the Internet or your school's media center, research the life of one person on the list. What problems or challenges did he or she overcome? Report your findings to the class.

Health Skills Application

1. **Communication Skills.** List examples of body language that you or others use when communicating. Pick two examples, and explain how they reinforce verbal messages. *(LESSON 1)*

2. **Decision Making.** Imagine that you are trying to improve your grades to make the basketball team. Which activity would you attend if they occurred at the same time—an extra basketball practice or a study session? Demonstrate how you would use the decision-making steps to make your choice, based on health information. *(LESSON 2)*

3. **Analyzing Influences.** Do all individuals who are famous for their achievements make positive role models? Why or why not? *(LESSON 3)*

Family Counselor

Do you have a keen understanding of how values direct behavior within a family? Are you able to deal with people from varied backgrounds? If so, a career as a family counselor might be for you. These professionals work with entire families or with individual family members to solve problems and improve relationships.

To enter this profession, you'll need a four-year college degree and a master's degree in counseling. Find out more about this and other health careers by clicking on Career Corner at **health.glencoe.com.**

Parent Involvement

Advocacy. Learn more about a nonprofit organization in your community. With your parents, find out how your family could become involved. By volunteering your time, you can help the organization achieve its mission, get

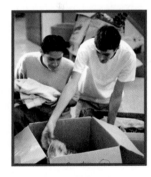

firsthand knowledge of how it operates, and help individuals with special needs in your community.

School and Community

Conduct an Interview. In certain professions—teaching and law, for example—effective communication is especially critical. Interview an individual from one of these professions, and learn about the guidelines he or she uses to ensure good communication.

After You Read

Use your completed Foldable to review main ideas and recall what you know. On the back of your Foldable, write a brief narrative about an experience you have had involving one of the health skills.

► EXPLORING HEALTH TERMS   *Answer the following questions on a sheet of paper.*

Lesson 1   *Replace the underlined words with the correct term.*

conflict resolution   advocacy
refusal skills   stress management
interpersonal communication
health skills

1. "I" messages are a form of <u>refusal skills</u>.
2. <u>Advocacy</u> is a process to help you resolve conflict through cooperation and problem solving.
3. People use <u>conflict resolution</u> to manage the body's reactions to everyday demands.
4. <u>Stress management</u> is a responsible role in which you influence others' health behaviors.

Lesson 2   *Match each definition with the correct term.*

action plan   goal
decision-making skills   values
long-term goal   short-term goal

5. Something you aim for that takes planning and work.
6. A goal that you plan to reach over an extended period of time.
7. A multistep strategy for identifying and achieving your goals.
8. The ideas, beliefs, and attitudes about what is important that help guide the way you live.

Lesson 3   *Fill in the blanks with the correct term.*

character   role model

A person with high standards usually exhibits good (**_9_**). This person often makes a positive (**_10_**).

► RECALLING THE FACTS   *Use complete sentences to answer the following questions.*

1. List the strategies for effective communication.
2. What are refusal skills?
3. What steps should you follow to resolve a conflict?
4. Why are self-management skills important? Give an example of two of these skills.
5. What are decision-making skills?
6. Define the term *value*.
7. Explain how the word *HELP* can assist you in weighing the possible consequences of a decision and making the right choice.
8. What are the six steps of a goal-setting action plan?
9. Describe what it means to demonstrate the character trait of trustworthiness.
10. How does character impact your health?
11. How can you take an active role in your character development?
12. What are some benefits of being a positive role model?

For more review questions for Chapter 2, go to **health.glencoe.com**.

➤ WRITING CRITICALLY

1. Narrative. Write a one-page story in which a teen effectively uses refusal strategies to avoid an unhealthful or unsafe activity. In your story, describe the situation and include dialogue between the teen and the person proposing the activity.

2. Descriptive. Identify a positive role model in your life who exhibits the traits of good character. Write a one-page descriptive biography of your role model explaining how he or she exhibits at least three traits of good character. Your biography should focus on the positive character traits of your role model and the specific ways in which he or she demonstrates these character traits.

Standardized Test Practice

Read the speech below and then answer the questions.

Smoking: The Lasting Impact

Today you will probably make a number of decisions. These decisions may or may not have a lasting effect on your life. One decision that *will* have a lasting effect is the decision not to start smoking. As you know, smoking is dangerous to your health. Smokers have a greater chance than nonsmokers of dying of lung and heart disease. Cigarette smoke is also dangerous to others—passive smoke kills or affects the health of nonsmokers too, including the smoker's friends and family. Do you have a young child in your family? That child could be seriously harmed by passive smoke.

The most important factor in your decision, however, is that smoking is addictive. Tobacco poisons the user at the same time the nicotine in tobacco smoke makes the user want—and need—more poison. Smoking is a habit and an unhealthy one. Many smokers admit that they would like to quit, but they cannot. Starting is easy; quitting is hard. Start smoking now and you may be signing on for a habit that is dangerous to you, your friends and your family.

1. Which sentence from the speech best summarizes the writer's view of smoking?

  A Many smokers admit that they would like to quit but cannot.
  B Smoking is a dangerous and unhealthy habit.
  C Starting is easy, quitting is hard.
  D Smokers have a greater chance than nonsmokers of getting and dying of lung cancer and heart disease.

2. How does the writer support the statement that nicotine is addictive?

  F by explaining that nicotine makes users want more
  G by stating how easy it is to quit smoking
  H by telling how easy it is to start smoking
  I by describing dangers to family members

3. Create a radio ad to encourage teens not to start smoking. Choose the best arguments you can to build your case.

Being a Health-Literate Consumer

Today's "Health Beat"

Many newspapers have a section dedicated to healthy living and health news. This media coverage can affect communities and the world by

► providing health information.

► influencing health advocacy.

Visit the Eye on the Media section at health.glencoe.com to learn more about the health information that newspapers cover.

FOLDABLES™
Study Organizer

Before You Read

Make this Foldable to help you organize what you learn about making consumer choices. Begin with one sheet of plain 8½″ x 11″ paper or one sheet of notebook paper.

Step 1

Fold a sheet of paper into thirds along the short axis.

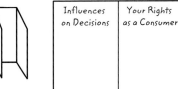

Step 2

Unfold and label as shown.

Influences on Decisions	Your Rights as a Consumer	Today's Consumer Choices

As You Read

Under each label, take notes on what you learn about being a good consumer and making consumer choices.

SPOTLIGHT ON HEALTH

Using Visuals. Write a one paragraph summary telling how you have used information on product labels to decide what to purchase.

Making Consumer Choices

Guide to Reading

Building Vocabulary

As you read this lesson, write each new highlighted term and its definition in your notebook.

► health consumer (p. 48)
► media (p. 49)
► advertising (p. 49)
► comparison shopping (p. 50)
► warranty (p. 50)
► online shopping (p. 52)

Focusing on the Main Ideas

In this lesson, you will learn how to:

► Describe factors that influence consumer decisions about health care products and services.
► Analyze health messages delivered through advertising in the media.
► Assess ways to use criteria to evaluate health products.

Reading Strategy

Predict

► Create a table with three columns labeled K, W, and L. In the K column, list what you know about this lesson's topic. In the W column, list what you want to learn on this topic.

Quick Write

Think about the product labels you have seen. Make a list of the different types of information you remember seeing on product labels.

▲ Part of being a wise consumer involves making informed purchasing decisions about health- and fitness-related products.

Many health care products and services are available to the consumer. Supermarket and drug store shelves are lined with dozens of well-known brands of personal care products. Phone books list hundreds of different types of health care professionals, clinics, and other health services. What information do you need before you make a decision regarding health care products and services?

Being an Informed Health Consumer

In the years to come, you will become more responsible for decisions regarding your health. Although most decisions about health services are still in the hands of your parents or guardians, you are probably already making choices about such products as shampoo, skin cleansers, or deodorant. An informed health consumer knows how to evaluate factors that influence personal selection of health products and services. A **health consumer** is *anyone who purchases or uses health products or services.*

Influences on Your Decisions

Many factors influence your decision to buy specific products and services. Internal factors, such as habit and personal taste, can play a role, as can external factors such as the opinions of family members and friends, and cost. Another important factor is the cost and accessibility of health care services. An important external factor that influences purchasing decisions is the **media**, or *the various methods of communicating information.*

Media and Advertising

Many health products and services are promoted through advertising. **Advertising** is *a written or spoken media message designed to interest consumers in purchasing a product or service.* Advertisements provide information that can help you make purchasing decisions. Remember, however, that the primary purpose of advertising is to make you want to buy the product featured in the ad. **Figure 3.1** lists some of the techniques that advertisers use to convey a certain message to the consumer and persuade him or her to buy a product. By analyzing the messages hidden in ads for health products, you can make a better-informed purchasing decision.

FIGURE 3.1

HIDDEN MESSAGES IN ADVERTISING

Advertisers use several techniques to persuade consumers to purchase their products.

Technique	Example	Hidden Message
Bandwagon	Group of people using a product or service	Everyone is using it—you should too.
Rich and famous	Product displayed in expensive home	It will make you feel rich and famous.
Free gifts	Redeemable coupons for merchandise	It's too good a deal to pass up.
Great outdoors	Scenes of nature	If it's associated with nature, it must be healthy.
Good times	People smiling and laughing	The product will add fun to your life.
Testimonial	People for whom a product has worked	It worked for them, so it will work for you, too.

Comparing Choices

Advertising is one source of information about products and services. However, keep in mind that this information may be misleading, since advertising is designed to persuade you to purchase a product. As a consumer, you need to understand how to analyze the cost and accessibility of health care services. **Comparison shopping** is *a method of judging the benefits of different products by comparing several factors, such as quality, features, and cost.* Here are some criteria to consider as you evaluate products and services.

▶ **Cost.** Decide on a price range for your purchase. Then compare prices of the same brand or similar brands at different stores.

▶ **Features.** Decide which product features are important to you. This will allow you to avoid paying for features that you don't need and will help ensure that you purchase products with features that you find especially useful or desirable.

▶ **Quality.** Well-made products offer superior performance. An inexpensive product is no bargain if it falls apart or doesn't work.

▶ **Warranty.** Before you purchase a product, especially one that is costly, ask about the warranty. A **warranty** is *a company's or a store's written agreement to repair a product or refund your money should the product not function properly.* Always read a warranty in its entirety—including the fine print—and make sure that you understand its terms. Some warranties cover only certain aspects of a product or its use.

▶ **Safety.** Safety considerations should be foremost in your mind when choosing sports, recreation, or home-safety products.

- The **Underwriters Laboratory (UL)** is a product-safety testing and certification organization. The UL logo on electrical appliances, fire extinguishers, and other products indicates that the product has passed strict safety standards.

- **Snell,** a nonprofit foundation, and the **American National Standards Institute (ANSI)** monitor safety standards for helmets and other protective equipment. Look for their logos on any equipment you are thinking of buying.

▶ **Recommendations.** Talk to people who have used the product that you are considering purchasing. Parents or other trusted adults are good sources of information. Independent testing organizations such as the Consumers Union rate products.

Ⓥ **Accessing product information before you go to the store makes comparison shopping easier.** *Where can you find information on the safety and effectiveness of protective equipment?*

Real-Life Application

Reading Product Labels

You can use the information on a product label to make an informed decision about whether to purchase the product. Study the label below, and then complete the activity for practice in evaluating products.

SPF 35 SUNBUSTER LOTION

ACTIVE INGREDIENTS: Avobenzone, Octocrylene, Octyl Salicylate, Oxybenzone

PRODUCT'S INTENDED USE: Provides protection against both UVA and UVB rays to help prevent sunburn, premature aging, and skin cancer.

PRECAUTIONS: Discontinue use if signs of irritation or rash appear. Avoid contact with eyes.

DIRECTIONS FOR USE: Apply liberally to all exposed areas before sun exposure. Waterproof for up to 80 minutes of swimming. Reapply after swimming, excessive perspiration, or vigorous activity.

MANUFACTURER'S CONTACT INFORMATION: Call **800-555-1234** Weekdays 9 a.m. to 9 p.m. Eastern Time.

If two different brands have the same ingredients, which would be the wiser purchase?

Why should a consumer read this section carefully?

How can ignoring this section pose a risk to one's health?

Why might a consumer need this information?

ACTIVITY

Bring in the container or label of a personal care product that you use. Draw the label on a large sheet of construction paper. Using the above sample as a guide, draw arrows and label the different types of information. Use online Internet or library resources to find out more about the product. Write this additional information on the back of the paper. Tell the class about your product. Discuss whether you will continue using this product, and explain why or why not.

PRODUCT LABELS

One way to compare two similar products is to read their labels. Important information on product labels includes the product's name and intended use, directions for use, precautions and warnings, manufacturer's information, and the amount in the container. On most labels you'll find the ingredients listed by weight in descending order. The label will also identify the active ingredients— the ones that make the product effective. This means that when you are comparing two acne medications, for example, you can compare labels to determine which contains more of the active ingredient.

Reading Check

Describe What are the six criteria for comparing product choices?

Your Rights as a Consumer

As a consumer you have certain rights, both before and after you purchase a product or service. **Figure 3.2** summarizes these rights. Usually, consumer rights are recognized and respected. Most stores and service providers strive to keep their customers satisfied. Sometimes, however, consumers need help resolving a complaint. You will learn more about how to handle consumer problems in Lesson 3.

Reading Check

Explain What are your consumer rights?

Today's Consumer Choices

Consumers today have more choices than ever before when it comes to product selection and ways to shop. **Online shopping** involves *using the Internet to buy products and services*. Below are some points to consider when shopping online.

▶ **Price.** Online sources sometimes offer lower prices. However, some of these savings may be lost to the added cost of shipping.

▶ **Convenience.** Items are delivered directly to the home. For many people this convenience outweighs the potential problem of repackaging and mailing items that may need to be returned.

FIGURE 3.2

YOUR CONSUMER RIGHTS

- **The right to safety.** You have the right to purchase products and services that will not harm you or others.
- **The right to choose.** You have the right to select from many products at competitive prices.
- **The right to be informed.** You have the right to truthful information about products and services.
- **The right to be heard.** You have the right to join in the making of laws that govern buying and selling.
- **The right to have problems corrected.** You have the right to seek compensation when you have been treated unfairly.
- **The right to consumer education.** You have the right to learn the skills necessary to help you make wise choices.

▶ **Product information.** Online descriptions provide only limited information about a product, and you can only view a picture of an item—you can't actually examine it or try it on before you buy.

If you decide to purchase products online, there are some safeguards you should consider. First, get permission from your parents or guardians. Next, make sure that the site is secure. This means that information such as credit card numbers will not be accessible to others. Check the organization's return policy, and make sure that you understand it completely. Finally, write down any confirmation numbers or other information related to your purchase. You will need these numbers if a problem arises.

Be sure to get your parents' or guardians' permission before ordering merchandise online. *What else should you consider before placing an online order?*

Reviewing Facts and Vocabulary

1. Why might some health messages delivered through advertising in the media be misleading?

2. What is a *warranty*? Why it is important to read a warranty in its entirety?

3. List three safeguards you should consider when shopping online.

Thinking Critically

4. **Synthesizing.** Demonstrate ways to use criteria to evaluate health products for appropriateness: What factors would you consider when deciding which of two bicycle helmets to buy? List the factors in order of importance.

5. **Analyzing.** Explain the advantages and disadvantages of seeking information about a product from someone who uses the product.

Applying Health Skills

Analyzing Influences. Recall a purchase you have made recently. List all the factors that influenced your decision. Include any advertising you have seen for the product, recommendations of family and friends, safety considerations (if any), and incentives such as coupons or sales. Review your list, circle the most influential factor, and explain why that factor was most important in your purchasing decision.

After You Read

Identify Problems and Solutions. List some of the problems that can occur when purchasing consumer health products. Describe strategies for handling those problems.

Choosing Community Health Services

Guide to Reading

Building Vocabulary

As you read this lesson, write each new highlighted term and its definition in your notebook.

▶ health care system (p. 54)

▶ primary care physician (p. 54)

▶ specialist (p. 54)

▶ preventive care (p. 55)

▶ health insurance (p. 57)

▶ medical history (p. 58)

Focusing on the Main Ideas

In this lesson, you will learn how to:

▶ Compare professional health services, such as primary and preventive care.

▶ Describe health care services in the community that relate to disease prevention and health promotion.

▶ Analyze the cost, availability, and accessibility of health services for people of all ages.

Reading Strategy

Classify

▶ Make a chart with three headings: types of health services, facilities for health services, and ways to pay for health services. As you read, list terms and names in the correct column.

Quick Write

Think about a situation that might require professional health services. Write a brief description of the type of health care professional who would provide the services.

⚑ Most schools require that a student get a physical exam before participating in a sports program.

Being a health-literate consumer means more than being informed about products. It also involves knowing how to analyze the cost and accessibility of health care services.

Types of Health Services

You have probably received immunizations and had health screenings. The health care professionals you have seen are part of a **health care system**, which includes *all the medical care available to a nation's people, the way they receive care, and the method of payment*. Health care can be divided into general care and specialized care. General care includes **primary care physicians**, or *medical doctors who provide physical checkups and general care*, as well as school nurses and dentists. Specialized care includes **specialists**, or *medical doctors trained to handle particular kinds of patients or medical conditions*. **Figure 3.3** lists a variety of health care specialists and the situations requiring their services.

FIGURE 3.3

SOME HEALTH CARE SPECIALISTS

Specialist	Specializes In
Allergist	allergies
Dermatologist	skin diseases
Gynecologist	care of female reproductive system
Neurologist	nervous system problems
Oncologist	cancer
Ophthalmologist	care of eyes
Orthodontist	adjustments of teeth to improve bite and jaw alignment
Orthopedist	skeletal deformities or injuries
Pediatrician	children's health
Psychiatrist	mental health
Urologist	urinary tract problems

 An orthopedist is a specialist who treats injuries to the skeletal system. *Describe the difference between a primary care physician and a specialist.*

Whenever you've seen a doctor for a checkup or a dentist for an oral exam, you've used preventive care. **Preventive care** involves *actions that prevent the onset of disease or injury.* After reading this section, you will know how to access school and community health services for yourself and others. By exercising good preventive health care, you show that you recognize the health concerns that require collaborative decision making.

Facilities for Health Care Services

Communities may have more than one type of health care facility. These facilities may offer health promotion services as inpatient care or outpatient care. *Inpatient care* requires the patient to stay at the facility overnight and is provided for patients with a serious injury or illness. *Outpatient care* allows the patient to be treated and return home the same day. Health care facilities include:

Reading Check

Describe How do the services offered by primary care physicians differ from services offered by specialists?

▶ **Private practices.** Physicians in private practice work for themselves. Most of their patients are seen at an office on an outpatient basis, although the physicians are usually associated with a hospital in case inpatient care is required.

▶ **Clinics.** Physicians may provide outpatient care in a community clinic rather than an office.

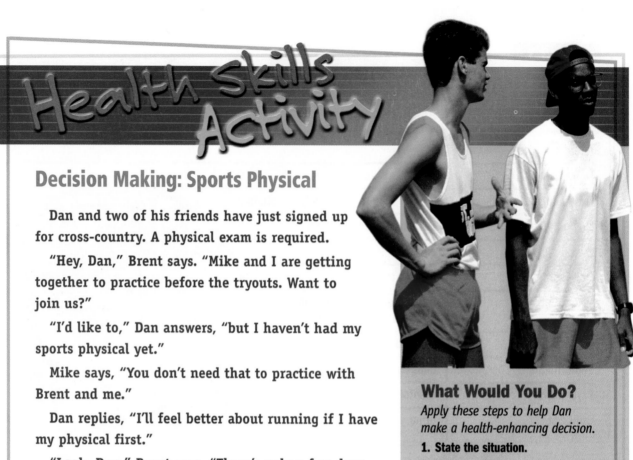

Health Skills Activity

Decision Making: Sports Physical

Dan and two of his friends have just signed up for cross-country. A physical exam is required.

"Hey, Dan," Brent says. "Mike and I are getting together to practice before the tryouts. Want to join us?"

"I'd like to," Dan answers, "but I haven't had my sports physical yet."

Mike says, "You don't need that to practice with Brent and me."

Dan replies, "I'll feel better about running if I have my physical first."

"Look, Dan," Brent says, "There's only a few days left before tryouts. You'd better get in some practice time, or you might not make the team."

Dan wonders what he should do.

What Would You Do?
Apply these steps to help Dan make a health-enhancing decision.
1. State the situation.
2. List the options.
3. Weigh the possible outcomes.
4. Consider values.
5. Make a decision and act.
6. Evaluate the decision.

▶ **Group practices.** Doctors in a group practice share office space, equipment, and support staff. Otherwise, they function in the same manner as those in private practice.

▶ **Hospitals.** Hospitals generally offer both inpatient and out-patient care. Some physicians work at the hospital. Those in private or group practice are there only when required.

▶ **Emergency rooms.** Located within most hospitals, emergency rooms provide care required for potentially life-threatening illnesses or injuries.

▶ **Urgent care centers.** These centers, staffed by primary care physicians, usually handle emergencies that are not life threatening. Patients may go to these centers if their primary care physician is unavailable or if they don't have one.

Knowing how to choose a health service shows that you can analyze the cost and accessibility of health care services.

How People Pay for Health Services

Knowing how to analyze the cost and accessibility of health care services is very important since health care can be a major expense. **Health insurance** is *a plan in which private companies or government programs pay for part or all of a person's medical costs.* The insured person pays a periodic *premium,* or fee, for coverage. In conventional insurance plans, the insured person pays for doctor visits and other forms of treatment out of pocket. An *out-of-pocket expense* is one that the patient must pay for. The patient is then reimbursed by the insurance company for a fixed portion, often 80 percent of the cost of the visit. Hospital care is covered in much the same way. In most insurance plans, members must also pay a *deductible.* This is an amount a member must pay in out-of-pocket expenses before the plan will start reimbursing for health care services.

Managed Care

Some insurance plans are called *managed care plans.* These plans emphasize preventive care and offer reduced physician charges for their members. There are several types of managed care plans:

▶ **Health Maintenance Organizations (HMOs).** Members pay a monthly premium but receive most or all medical services with few or no out-of-pocket expenses. Some HMOs require a small co-payment for an office visit. HMO members can see only those physicians who have signed an agreement with the HMO.

▶ **Preferred Provider Organizations (PPOs).** Medical providers connected with PPOs agree to charge the organization less than their regular fee for member usage. Members pay a monthly premium to use providers in the plan but can choose a provider outside the plan. Using outside providers, however, results in higher out-of-pocket expenses.

▶ **Point of Service (POS) plans.** Members of this type of plan can choose providers inside or outside the plan. Choosing an outside provider often results in higher premiums and higher out-of-pocket expenses.

How do people get health insurance?
There are several ways for people to obtain health insurance. Many people who work are insured through their employers. Often employees can choose from several plans to find the one that best meets their needs. Self-employed people often purchase their own insurance. People who cannot afford insurance may be covered by Medicaid, the federal government's medical insurance program.

Most managed care plans offer preventive health services to their members.
Why is preventive care important?

Trends in Health Care

To help reduce expenses and improve the quality of care, the health community continually updates the types of care available and the procedures used to implement care for people of all ages. Current trends include the following:

▶ **Birthing centers** are homelike settings that involve family members in the delivery of a baby. Birthing centers are usually less expensive than hospitals. However, they are appropriate only for women with low-risk pregnancies.

▶ **Drug treatment centers** specialize in treating people with drug and alcohol problems, usually outside of a hospital setting.

▶ **Continuing care and assisted living facilities** provide short- and long-term care for people who need help with daily tasks but who do not require professional medical care. Many older adults benefit from this kind of care.

▶ **Hospices** provide care for people who are terminally ill. Hospice workers are experts at managing pain and providing emotional support for the patient and his or her family.

▶ **Telemedicine** is the practice of medicine over distance through the use of telecommunications equipment. A medical specialist located hundreds of miles away can be brought into an examination room through a live interactive electronic system.

You and Your Health Care

A good doctor/patient relationship is critical to quality health care. This relationship requires open communication and a sense of trust. A health care professional can treat you and make recommendations for your health, but you need to take an active role in your medical care. Your relationship with your health care provider is a partnership—each of you must apply skills to effectively maintain your health. A good place to start is with an awareness of your own **medical history**, *complete and comprehensive information about your immunizations and any health problems you have had to date.* Most doctors' offices will ask you to fill out a medical history during your first visit. This form usually requires you to provide information about your own health habits, as well as the health of close family members. Ask your parents to help you obtain this information. The information in your medical history gives a health care provider an idea of your overall level of wellness. Health-literate consumers should also prioritize their own health risks and construct a model health risk behavior self-management plan.

Did You Know

▶ You have the right to access your medical records by contacting your doctor. Copies can be made for another health care professional of your choosing and, in some states, for your personal use. Insurance companies and government agencies typically are able to access your records as well. Laws protect your confidentiality by limiting access by other individuals or organizations.

Patient Skills

These tips can help you make the most out of your next medical appointment:

▶ Before you go, write down your reasons for seeing the doctor.

▶ While you are at the office, ask questions about any diagnoses, medications, or procedures that you do not understand or are unsure about.

▶ Inform the staff of any allergies you have or any medications you are taking.

MEDICINE USE

If the physician prescribes a medicine for you, ask the pharmacist any questions you have about the medication. If the doctor recommends an over-the-counter medication, compare products by reading labels and make sure that you understand what symptoms each medicine is intended to treat.

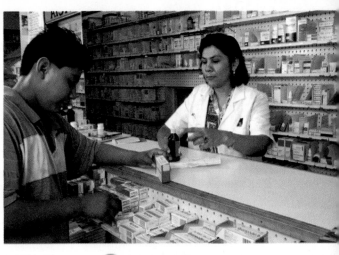

A pharmacist is a reliable source of information about both prescription and over-the-counter medications. *What types of questions might you ask a pharmacist?*

LESSON 2 REVIEW

Reviewing Facts and Vocabulary

1. Distinguish between *primary care physicians* and medical *specialists*.

2. Identify situations requiring primary and preventive care.

3. List three actions that can help you make the most of your next medical appointment.

Thinking Critically

4. **Analyzing.** Compare and analyze the cost, availability, and accessibility of health services for people who don't have health insurance to those who do. How would cost, availability, and accessibility differ for an older person?

5. **Applying.** The incidence of type 2 diabetes is increasing in teens in the United States. Factors that lead to this disease include being overweight and inactive. How might information in a teen's medical history aid in diagnosing this disease?

Applying Health Skills

Accessing Information. Use your local telephone book and other sources to identify available health-related services in your community that relate to disease prevention and health promotion. Make a table that describes and assesses each of these services.

After You Read

Compare and Contrast. Create a two-column table. In one column list different types of managed-care insurance plans. In the second column, list the benefits of the plan.

Managing Consumer Problems

Guide to Reading

Building Vocabulary

As you read this lesson, write each new highlighted term and its definition in your notebook.

▶ fraud (p. 61)

▶ health fraud (p. 61)

▶ malpractice (p. 61)

▶ consumer advocates (p. 63)

Focusing on the Main Ideas

In this lesson, you will learn how to:

▶ Identify potential problems with health care products and services.

▶ Explain methods for addressing critical health issues that result from fraud.

Reading Strategy

Predict

▶ Review the lesson headings and subheadings. Prepare a one page outline showing what information will be covered in the lesson.

Create a list of the steps you would take if you purchased a product that broke the first time you used it.

Most health care products and services you purchase will live up to their claims. However, an informed consumer understands potential controversy regarding the validity of health information, products, and services.

▼ Always keep your sales receipt. Some stores require receipts as part of their return policy, and many manufacturers require receipts to validate a product's warranty.

Problems with Products

Sometimes products are defective. Find out about a seller's return policy before purchasing a product. Many items can be returned to the store from which they were purchased. Others may need to be sent back to the manufacturer. Information in the product warranty will help you determine which course of action to follow. Before you return a product, make sure that you are using the product correctly. If the product is truly defective, you must then decide whether you want a replacement or your money back. Put your reasons for returning the item in a letter, and keep a copy for future reference. Return the item in its original packaging. If you are mailing the item, be sure to get a shipping receipt to prove that you sent it.

Health Fraud

Fraud is *deliberate deceit or trickery.* You can reduce your risk of being a victim of fraud by understanding potential controversy regarding the validity of health information, products, and services. **Health fraud**, also known as quackery, is *the sale of worthless products or services that claim to prevent diseases or cure other health problems.*

Fraudulent Products

Health-literate consumers should apply critical thinking skills to analyze marketing and advertising methods for influencing food and other choices. Several types of products are particularly susceptible to health fraud:

▶ **Weight-loss products.** Ads for some diet pills, fad diets, and exercise equipment claim that a person can lose weight virtually overnight. Weight loss is effectively achieved only through healthful eating habits and regular physical activity.

▶ **Beauty and anti-aging products.** Many tooth whiteners, hair enhancers, and wrinkle creams may work temporarily, but none offer permanent results. Products that aren't approved by the Food and Drug Administration (FDA) may harm you.

Fraudulent Treatments

Another type of health fraud is clinics that specialize in "miracle" cures for ailments such as arthritis or that feature a remarkable and unusual treatment, such as consuming substances extracted from peach pits to cure cancer. These methods are ineffective and may even be dangerous. Check with a health care professional before seeking treatment at such a clinic.

OTHER PROBLEMS WITH HEALTH SERVICES

Some people experience problems with their regular health care providers. Sometimes these problems can be solved by changing health care professionals. Health care professionals can sometimes be negligent or guilty of **malpractice**—*failure by a health professional to meet accepted standards.* To make sure that you are getting the best medical treatment possible, always get a second opinion from another health care professional for any major health concern, such as those involving surgery or other extensive treatment. If you have a critical problem with a health care professional, you may be able to get help from a regulatory organization such as the American Medical Association or from a state licensing board.

Red Flags of Fraud

Look for the phrases below in ads for health care products and services—they may indicate health fraud.

Possible signs of health fraud:

▶ "secret formula"
▶ "miracle cure"
▶ "overnight results"
▶ "all natural"
▶ "available only through mail-order"
▶ "hurry, this offer expires soon"
▶ "one-time offer"

▼ Having an open, trusting relationship with your health care provider can help resolve many concerns about a diagnosis or treatment. *Why should you get a second opinion for any serious health concern?*

Writing a Letter of Complaint

A carefully written letter of complaint can help secure fair treatment for yourself if a product or service does not meet your expectations. Study the letter and answer the questions. Then compose your own letter of complaint.

```
Name of Company
Street Address
City, State, ZIP code

Dear (contact person):

On (date), I (bought, had repaired)
a (name of product) at (location).
Unfortunately, your product has not
performed well. (state the problem).

To resolve the problem, I would appreciate
(state what you want—money back, exchange,
repair). Enclosed are copies (do not send
originals) of my records (include receipts
and other documents).

I look forward to your reply and a reso-
lution to the problem and will wait until
(set a time limit) before seeking help
from a consumer protection agency or the
Better Business Bureau. Please contact me
at (phone number and address).

Sincerely,

Your name (signed)
```

○ Why is it important to provide this information early in the letter?

○ Why do you need to be specific here? Why should you not send the original documents?

○ Why might mentioning a consumer protection agency or the Better Business Bureau make the company more likely to act on your letter?

Source: Federal Consumer Information Center, U.S. General Services Administration.

ACTIVITY

With a partner, identify a health care product with which you might not be or have not been satisfied. Develop a three-part complaint letter about the product, using the sample above as a guide. Read your completed letter to the class. Have your classmates evaluate the letter, and adjust it on the basis of their feedback.

Reading Check

Explain What are some of the types of products that are particularly susceptible to health fraud?

Methods for Addressing Consumer Problems

If you try to resolve a critical health problem with a product and are dissatisfied with the result, seek help from one of these groups:

▶ **Business organizations** such as the Better Business Bureau (BBB) deal with complaints against local merchants. The core services of the BBB include dispute resolution and truth-in-advertising complaints.

► **Consumer advocates** are *people or groups whose sole purpose is to take on regional, national, and even international consumer issues.* Some groups, like the Consumers Union, test products, inform the public, and play a role in protecting consumers when problems arise. Others work to expose fraud and teach consumers about their rights and responsibilities.

► **Local, state, and federal government agencies** ensure that consumers' rights are protected. To protect themselves, consumers should understand the role of governmental agencies in regulating advertising claims related to health. The Federal Trade Commission works to prevent false or deceptive advertising. The Food and Drug Administration ensures that medicines are safe, effective, and properly labeled. The Consumer Product Safety Commission protects consumers against harmful products and can recall dangerous ones. Small claims courts are state courts that handle legal disputes involving amounts of money below a certain limit.

HEALTH Online

TOPIC Consumer Safety

Go to health.glencoe.com for information about the U.S. Consumer Product Safety Commission.

ACTIVITY Using the links, research the history and mission of the U.S. Consumer Product Safety Commission. Share what you learn with your classmates.

LESSON 3 — REVIEW

Reviewing Facts and Vocabulary

1. Define the term *fraud.*
2. Under what circumstances might you want to seek a second medical opinion?
3. When might a person file suit in small claims court?

Thinking Critically

4. **Analyzing.** Why is health fraud considered one of the worst types of fraud?
5. **Evaluating.** List several criteria you would use to distinguish between an effective complaint against a health care product that didn't fulfill its claim and an ineffective complaint.

Applying Health Skills

Communication Skills. Imagine that your aunt sent away for a wrinkle cream that was "guaranteed to make you look ten years younger in only three weeks." After using the product for a month, she finds that not only does she not look younger, but her skin is red and irritated. Write a dialogue in which you explain to your aunt the likelihood that she is a victim of health fraud and explore methods for addressing this critical health issue.

After You Read

Classify. Develop a list of health care products that may be fraudulent (e.g., diet aids, miracle cures, etc.). Write a step-by-step plan of what you can do to protect yourself from false claims.

Understanding Public Health Services

Guide to Reading

Building Vocabulary

As you read this lesson, write each new highlighted term and its definition in your notebook.

▶ public health (p. 64)

▶ epidemiology (p. 65)

Quick Write

List the names of any public health agencies that you are familiar with. Describe what services they provide to the public.

Focusing on the Main Ideas

In this lesson, you will learn how to:

▶ Analyze health services in the community and the world.

▶ Describe the benefits of positive relationships among community health professionals in promoting a healthy community.

Reading Strategy

Classify

▶ Make a chart with three headings: local health agencies, national health agencies, and global health agencies. As you read, list the agencies and organizations in the correct category column.

(A) Nonprofit organizations like the American Red Cross promote community health in various ways.

Due to advances in **public health**, *a community-wide effort to monitor and promote the welfare of the population,* Americans are living longer, healthier lives.

Public Health Agencies

Public health issues are addressed at the local, national, and global level. Health-literate consumers understand how public health policies and government influence health conditions. They can identify appropriate community agencies providing resources for disease information and support.

Health at the Local Level

State, county, and city health departments focus on disease prevention. Nonprofit agencies have local chapters that are devoted to particular health concerns. Nonprofit agencies may provide health-promotion services in these communities.

Health at the National Level

Several agencies work at the national level to protect health.

▶ The **National Cancer Institute (NCI)** is the federal government's principal agency for **cancer** research.

▶ The **Environmental Protection Agency (EPA)** is responsible for protecting the country's air, water, and land.

▶ The U.S. Department of Labor's **Occupational Safety and Health Administration (OSHA)** works to prevent injuries and safeguard the health of workers across the country.

▶ The **United States Department of Agriculture (USDA)** leads the federal antihunger effort with food stamp, school lunch, and school breakfast programs. One agency of the USDA, the **Food Safety and Inspection Service (FSIS),** is responsible for the safety of meat, poultry, and egg products.

▶ The **Department of Health and Human Services (DHHS)** oversees more than 300 health-related programs. These programs are administered by 13 agencies, which include the following:

• The **Centers for Medicare and Medicaid Services (CMS)** administer federal insurance programs, which help provide health care to low-income and elderly Americans.

• The **Food and Drug Administration (FDA)** ensures the safety of food, drugs, and cosmetics.

• The **National Institutes of Health (NIH)** conduct medical research and provide funding for medical research carried out at other institutions.

• The **Substance Abuse and Mental Health Services Administration (SAMHSA)** provides programs that aid substance abusers and people with mental/emotional disorders.

• The **Centers for Disease Control and Prevention (CDC)** conduct research and collect data to help control the spread of diseases. Part of the CDC's job involves **epidemiology**, or *the scientific study of patterns of disease in a population.*

• The **Federal Trade Commission (FTC)** was established to enforce antitrust and consumer protection laws. The FTC works to promote fair competition in the nation's markets and to ensure that consumers are given the right to make informed choices.

Reading Check

Explain How would you match various health needs and problems with the local health services, agencies, or clinics on this page?

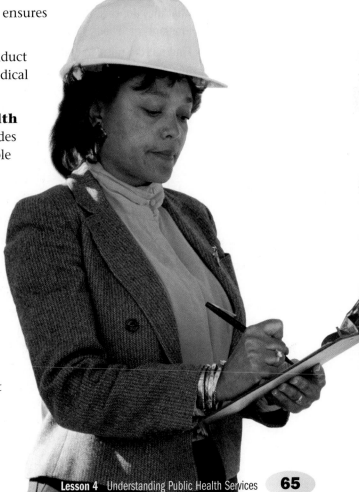

▼ OSHA inspectors work to prevent injuries and protect the health of workers in the United States. *How might periodic inspections of a workplace help ensure workers' safety?*

Raising Awareness of Public Health Programs

In this activity your group will create a public service announcement (PSA) to highlight the mission of a public health agency or program.

What You'll Need

- paper and pen
- telephone directory (one per group)
- Internet access (optional)

What You'll Do

1. In your group, examine the list of agencies in the "Government" section of the phone directory. Agencies will often list specific offices that indicate what they do, such as "Lead Poisoning Program" or "Food Safety."

2. Find out the mission and history of one agency or office. What health problems does this agency seek to address? What services does it provide? If possible, research this information online.

3. Write a PSA script that promotes the agency or office. Make sure that you convey how this agency promotes public health. Target the message to high-school students.

4. Arrange with your teacher and school administrators to present your PSA to your school.

Apply and Conclude

As a class, brainstorm a list of other ways of highlighting the contributions of public-health agencies or programs. Then write a paragraph describing the importance of raising people's awareness of these organizations and programs.

Reading Check

Cause and Effect Name some ways that teens can promote public health in their communities.

Public Health on a Global Scale

Some countries don't have the medical technologies or services that are available in the United States and other developed nations. War, drought, floods, or economic crises can impact world health and lead to starvation, unsanitary living conditions, and uncontrolled disease. Government agencies and private organizations from around the world extend aid to countries in crisis. One key organization leading this effort is the World Health Organization (WHO). An agency of the United Nations with a membership of nearly 200 countries and territories, WHO has programs to explain transmission, prevention, warning signs, and treatment of communicable diseases. Another organization, the International Committee of the Red Cross, provides emergency aid to victims of armed conflict, disease outbreaks, and natural disasters.

FIGURE 3.4

ADVOCATING FOR PUBLIC HEALTH

There are many ways that teens can advocate for public health. Here are just a few:

- Follow all health and safety laws and ordinances; for example, keep your immunizations up to date.
- Set an example by practicing healthful behaviors, such as always wearing a helmet when biking or skating.
- Avoid actions that could endanger the health or safety of others, such as reckless driving.
- Get involved in events that promote public health. Participating in events such as community walks or 10K runs for charity improves your own health as well as the health of others.
- Find out which community groups deal with public health issues. Identify their goals and support them.
- Inform the proper authorities if you notice a condition or activity that threatens public health.

Advocacy—Taking Action for Public Health

Individuals can play a critical role in promoting public health. **Figure 3.4** lists some of the ways you can help promote public health in your own community.

Becoming an advocate in your community shows that you understand how public health policies and government regulation influence health conditions.

LESSON 4 REVIEW

Reviewing Facts and Vocabulary

1. Define the term *public health.*

2. What effect is a poor economy likely to have on a community? What effect is a poor economy likely to have on world health?

3. List two organizations that work to maintain world health.

Thinking Critically

4. **Applying.** Why might restaurant inspections be handled by government agencies rather than the restaurants themselves?

5. **Analyzing.** Analyze the impact of the availability of health services in the community and the world.

Applying Health Skills

Accessing Information. Research public-health agencies in your community. Make a four-column chart in which you list the name of each agency, describe what each one does, tell whether each is a government or private agency, and describe opportunities for volunteering to advocate for public health. Share this information with your class.

After You Read

Compare and Contrast. Write a paragraph comparing and contrasting how health care organizations manage health care needs at the regional, national, and global levels.

 Visit **health.glencoe.com** for the Interactive Study Guide for Lesson 4.

The Trouble
WITH FAT-BURNER PILLS
Be wary of the promises of these supplements— and pay even closer attention to the risks.

Have you seen ads for supplements that claim they can "boost your metabolism and burn away fat"?

There are a lot of these supposed "miracle" supplements. Some are available as liquids; others come in the form of pills. Whatever they look like, they generally promise the same thing: By speeding up your metabolism, they can reduce your fat—a claim that still hasn't been substantiated, or proven. Many studies that do seem to back up manufacturers' claims have been funded by those same companies.

Marketing Makes Millions

Even so, thanks to a marketing blitz, the supplements have become a multibillion-dollar industry. People are bombarded by television ads that show slim people who have supposedly lost weight on supplements. Radio commercials frequently air endorsements by people (sometimes local celebrities) making those same claims.

When makers of these supplements get negative publicity, they often use the media to fight back. They may give their side of the story to rival news organizations or give interviews on their own Web sites. Anyone who logs on to the site becomes a potential customer.

What's distressing is that not only do these supplements not work, they are not risk free.

Most contain the controversial ingredient ephedrine (a Chinese herb also known as ephedra or mahuang). The U.S. Food and Drug Administration has received reports of about 80 deaths and about 1,400 instances of adverse effects that may be associated with the use of the herb. The agency has issued warnings about using products containing ephedrine, citing such potential side effects as heart attack, stroke, seizures, psychosis, and death. The products are even packaged with a long list of user warnings.

If you want to increase your metabolism, there is only one safe and reliable way to do it. Increase your physical activity—whether it's walking briskly, jogging, or playing sports. There are no shortcut pills to a leaner body.

TIME to THINK... | About "Miracle" Drugs

The article mentions that many studies that back up manufacturers' claims about their weight-loss supplements have been funded by the companies themselves. Do you think that such studies are less reliable than studies conducted by independent researchers? Why or why not? Share your opinion with the rest of the class. Be sure to include the reasons you hold that opinion.

Health Skills Application

1. Accessing Information. Investigate a type of health-related product, such as a piece of sports equipment or a sports drink. Choose three similar products in that category and compare costs, quality, and any other appropriate factors. After you have done your research, decide which item you would purchase and explain why. *(LESSON 1)*

2. Practicing Healthful Behaviors. Identify those actions you presently take that could be considered preventive care. What additional actions could you take to protect yourself from disease? *(LESSON 2)*

3. Advocacy. Create an awareness campaign to help educate older adults in your community about the problem of health fraud. You may wish to create a poster, newsletter, or videotape to present your health message. *(LESSON 3)*

4. Accessing Information. Interview the manager of a local restaurant. Find out what state and local health laws the restaurant must follow. Share the information with your class. *(LESSON 4)*

CAREER Corner

Public Health Specialist

Are you interested in a career in health education and wellness? Do you have a real concern for the welfare of your community? If so, then a career as a public health specialist might be a good choice for you.

To enter this profession, you need a bachelor's degree with a specialization in a biological, medical, or physical science; food science or technology; chemistry; nutrition; engineering; epidemiology; or another related scientific field. For more information on this and other health careers, click on Career Corner at **health.glencoe.com.**

BEYOND the Classroom

Parent Involvement

Interpersonal Communication. Sit down with your parents, and discuss their choice of health insurance plans. Talk about the plan's coverage, costs of premiums, choices in physicians, and any out-of-pocket expenses your parents might incur. If your parents have no insurance, discuss with them what you have learned about health insurance plans in class.

School and Community

Community Health Services. Research a health service for people of all ages that is available in your community. Identify its purpose, funding, and programs. Find out what volunteer opportunities, if any, are available at the organization. Summarize your findings in a one-page report that you present to the class.

After You Read

Make another tri-fold Foldable like the one you made at the beginning of the chapter. Design it as a brochure to advise consumers about the importance of comparison shopping.

FOLDABLES™
Study Organizer

► **EXPLORING HEALTH TERMS** *Answer the following questions on a sheet of paper.*

Lesson 1 *Match each definition with the correct term.*

advertising	media
comparison shopping	online shopping
health consumer	warranty

1. Anyone who purchases or uses health products or services.
2. The various methods of communicating information.
3. A method of judging the benefits of different products by comparing several similar factors for each one.
4. Using the Internet to buy products and services.

Lesson 2 *Fill in the blanks with the correct term.*

health care system	preventive care
health insurance	primary care physician
medical history	specialist

5. The _____ includes all the medical care available to a nation's people, the way they receive care, and the method of payment.
6. Actions that prevent the onset of disease or injury are known as _____ .
7. _____ is a plan in which private companies or government programs pay for part or all of a person's medical costs.
8. Complete and comprehensive information about your immunizations and any health problems you have had to date is your _____ .

Lesson 3 *Replace the underlined words with the correct term.*

| consumer advocate | health fraud |
| fraud | malpractice |

9. Deliberate deceit or trickery is <u>malpractice</u>.

10. When a health care professional fails to meet accepted medical standards, he or she is guilty of <u>consumer advocacy</u>.
11. A person or group whose sole purpose is to take on regional, national, and even international consumer issues is a <u>health fraud</u>.

Lesson 4 *Answer each question with the correct term.*

| epidemiology | public health |

12. What is a community-wide effort to monitor and promote the welfare of the population?
13. What is the scientific study of patterns of disease in a population?

► **RECALLING THE FACTS** *Use complete sentences to answer the following questions.*

1. List two internal factors that can influence your buying decisions.
2. List three techniques advertisers use to persuade consumers to buy their products.
3. How are ingredients listed on a product label?
4. Describe the health care that is provided by emergency rooms and urgent care centers.
5. What is a deductible?
6. Why do health care professionals have new patients fill out a medical history?
7. List the steps to follow before you try to return a product.
8. What should you do if you have an unresolved problem with a health care provider?
9. Which government office can recall a dangerous product from the marketplace?
10. What is the focus of state, county, and city health departments?

For more review questions for Chapter 3, go to **health.glencoe.com**.

11. Identify the federal government's principal agency for cancer research.

12. List three ways you can advocate for public health.

___

▶ WRITING CRITICALLY

1. Persuasive. Write a persuasive advertisement telling others why they should use a particular health product and how they would benefit from it. Research a product using sources such as the Internet, product information, or recommendations from experts to include supporting evidence telling why using the product could be beneficial.

2. Expository. Write a news article that could be published in the school or local newspaper exposing a health fraud. Define and explain health fraud in your article, and inform others about the particular types of products that consumers should be cautious of. Inform your readers about what precautions they can take to avoid being a victim of health fraud.

Standardized Test Practice

MATH **Read the paragraph below, and then answer the questions.**

Two families have medical insurance policies through different employers. Both insurance policies contain different costs for different items. The Lopez family pays $250 a month for its plan, and the insurance company will pay 85 percent of the cost of a hospital stay. A family member pays $20 for each doctor visit. This insurance plan does not cover any vision costs.

The plan the Perez family has costs $410 a month, and the company pays for all of a hospital stay. A family member pays $15 for each doctor visit. The plan will pay the entire cost of an eye exam and $100 toward a pair of glasses or contact lenses.

1. Pedro Lopez has to have his gallbladder removed, and his hospital stay costs $4,000. Before the surgery, he needed three doctor's appointments, each of which costs $93. The insurance company pays according to the policy. Which function describes what Pedro has to pay to have his gallbladder removed? (Hint: The variable C is Pedro's cost, H is the cost of the hospital, and D is the cost of each doctor visit.)

(A) $C = H + D$

(B) $C = H + 3D$

(C) $C = 0.15H + 3D$

(D) $C = 0.15H + 3(\$20)$

2. Melisa Perez has an eye exam and needs glasses. The glasses cost $395, and the exam is $95. How much does she have to pay?

(F) $295

(G) $300

(H) $395

(I) $490

3. In one year, both families had the following medical expenses: a hospital stay that cost $12,000, 14 trips to the doctor, four eye exams at $100 each, and two pairs of glasses at $300 each. Which policy would be the best to have under these circumstances? Justify your answer.

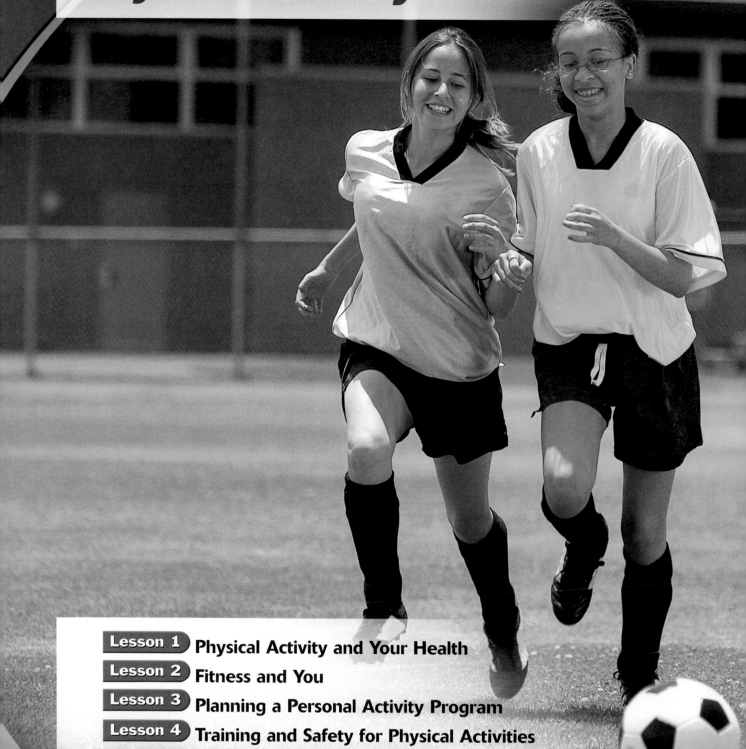

CHAPTER 4

Physical Activity for Life

Eye ON THE Media — Truth in Fitness Advertising?

Fitness ads may be misleading. Advertisers may claim that using their product will help you

▶ lose more weight each week than is healthy.

▶ achieve unrealistic results, such as rock-hard abs in 10 minutes a day.

Visit the Eye on the Media section at health.glencoe.com to learn more about this topic.

FOLDABLES™ Study Organizer

Before You Read

Make this Foldable to record what you learn about the benefits of physical activity and the risks of physical inactivity. Begin with one sheet of 11″ x 17″ paper.

▶ **Step 1**

Fold the short sides of the paper inward so that they meet in the middle.

▶ **Step 2**

Label as shown.

Benefits of Physical Activity | Risks of Physical Activity

As You Read

Under each label, take notes, define terms, record examples and draw your own conclusions about the importance of physical activity and the risks of physical inactivity.

SPOTLIGHT ON HEALTH

Using Visuals. Give two examples of how getting regular physical activity benefits your physical, emotional and social health?

Physical Activity and Your Health

Guide to Reading

Building Vocabulary

As you read this lesson, write each new highlighted term and its definition in your notebook.

- physical activity (p. 74)
- physical fitness (p. 74)
- sedentary lifestyle (p. 77)
- osteoporosis (p. 78)
- metabolism (p. 78)

Focusing on the Main Ideas

In this lesson, you will learn how to:

- Analyze how regular physical activity will enhance and maintain health.
- Describe the effects of regular physical activity on body systems.
- Assess how regular physical activity aids in disease prevention.
- Combine physical activity into your daily life.

Reading Strategy

Predict

- After scanning the lesson headings and subheadings, list three topics that you believe will be covered in this lesson.

Quick Write

Write a brief paragraph describing at least two of the physical activities you enjoy.

What kinds of physical activities do you enjoy? Do you like to play basketball? Maybe you prefer skiing, riding mountain bikes, or playing volleyball. Whatever your preference, regular physical activity enhances your health.

▼ Tasks such as vacuuming, raking leaves, or washing the car can help you fit more physical activity into your life. *What physical activities do you include in your daily routine?*

What Is Physical Activity?

Physical activity is *any form of movement that causes your body to use energy.* It may be purposeful, such as when you exercise or play sports. It may also occur as part of your regular routine—for example, when you wash the car or take the dog for a walk. Many forms of physical activity can improve your level of **physical fitness**, *the ability to carry out daily tasks easily and have enough reserve energy to respond to unexpected demands.* Maintaining a high level of physical fitness shows that you accept responsibility for your own health, and that you value regular physical activity.

What Are the Benefits of Physical Activity?

Physical activity provides health benefits that last a lifetime. Knowing strategies for health enhancement and risk reduction helps strengthen not only the physical but also the mental/emotional and social sides of your health triangle.

Benefits to Physical Health

Physical activity makes your body stronger, increases your energy, and improves your posture. It can reduce chronic fatigue and stiffness and can improve motor responses. It strengthens your muscles and bones and helps reduce the risk of many serious diseases. Health problems associated with inadequate levels of health-related fitness can affect the following body systems:

▶ **Cardiovascular System.** Regular physical activity strengthens the heart muscle, allowing it to pump blood more efficiently.

▶ **Respiratory System.** When you engage in regular physical activity, your respiratory system begins to work more efficiently—you can breathe larger amounts of air, and the muscles used in respiration don't tire as quickly. This helps you perform such activities as running farther without getting out of breath.

▶ **Nervous System.** By helping you respond more quickly to stimuli, physical activity can improve your reaction time. This is especially helpful when driving or cycling.

Reading Check

Name What are two body systems that benefit from regular physical activity?

Ⓥ Participating in a community event such as the one shown here is a good way to be physically active, to help others, and to engage in positive social interaction.

Benefits to Mental/ Emotional Health

Being physically active has many positive effects on your mental/emotional health. It can help reduce stress. Doing some stretching exercises before bed, for example, can help you relax tense muscles and sleep better after a difficult day at school. Physical activity also allows you to manage anger or frustration in a healthy way. By stimulating the release of certain chemicals that affect the brain, physical activity can improve your mood and decrease your

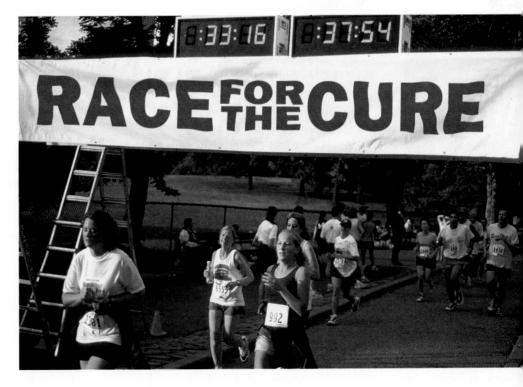

risk of depression. As well as improving your overall health, participating regularly in health-enhancing activities and personally rewarding physical activity outside the physical education class setting can benefit your mental/emotional health by

► helping you look and feel better, which can increase your self-confidence.

► contributing to a positive self-concept by giving you a sense of pride and accomplishment in taking care of yourself.

► reducing mental fatigue by bringing more oxygen to the brain. This improves your concentration, allowing you to think more clearly and work more productively.

► giving you a "can-do" spirit when faced with new challenges.

Hands-On Health ACTIVITY

Promote the Benefits of Physical Activity

In this activity you'll think of ways that different activities benefit all three parts of the health triangle. Then you'll choose an activity and create a plan to try it out.

What You'll Need

- paper and pencil
- markers or colored pencils

What You'll Do

1. Make a four-column chart on a sheet of paper. Label the columns "Activity," "Physical," "Mental/Emotional," and "Social."

2. Work in a group of three. Take turns identifying and recording a physical activity that you enjoy. Then work together to think of a physical, mental/emotional, and social benefit of each activity listed. Record these in the appropriate columns.

3. Choose one of the activities on your chart. Using markers or colored pencils, create an ad that illustrates the physical, mental/emotional, and social benefits of that activity. Present your finished ad to the class.

Apply and Conclude

Based on class presentations, choose an activity that you're interested in but have never tried. Write a plan to try the activity to see if you like it.

Benefits to Social Health

Are you a member of a recreational or school team? Do you swim laps at a neighborhood pool? Do you like hiking or exploring trails in your community? If so, you have probably met—and possibly formed friendships with—others who share your interests. Participating in a fitness regimen with friends can be fun and may motivate you to stick with your fitness program; in turn, you can help motivate your friends. Physical activity can also benefit social health by

▶ building self-confidence, which helps you cope better in social situations, such as when you meet new people.

▶ giving you the opportunity to interact and cooperate with others.

▶ helping you manage stress, which can enhance your relationships with others.

Risks of Physical Inactivity

According to the Centers for Disease Control and Prevention (CDC), some teens do not make physical activity a part of their lives. The CDC's Youth Risk Behavior Surveillance Survey (YRBSS) 2003 includes these troubling facts about the level of physical activity among U.S. teens.

▶ More than one in three teens (35 percent) do *not* participate regularly in vigorous physical activity (that is, for at least 20 minutes three times a week).

▶ Only 55 percent of all U.S. students attend a physical education class one or more days a week.

▶ Only 29 percent of teens attend a daily physical education class—a serious decline from 42 percent in 1991.

Clearly, many teens have a **sedentary lifestyle**, or *a way of life that involves little physical activity.* They may spend much of their time watching TV, playing video games, or working on the computer rather than being physically active. It is important that teens learn to evaluate the benefits of various physical activities in order to reduce the risks of a sedentary lifestyle. The negative effects of a sedentary lifestyle may include

▶ unhealthful weight gain, which is linked to several potentially life-threatening conditions, including cardiovascular disease, type 2 diabetes, and cancer. Cardiovascular disease is the leading cause of death among Americans. **Diabetes** is a serious disorder that prevents the body from converting food into energy.

Responsibility. When you participate in regular physical activity, you take responsibility for your health. By taking care of yourself, you are saying that you are worth investing in. Be positive about the benefits these activities bring you, and don't forget to compliment yourself: "I like how I feel, and I like how I look!" **Write three other positive statements that reflect the benefits you receive from regular physical activity.**

Reading Check

Explain What are the benefits of physical activity?

The number of obese adult Americans doubled between 1980 and 1999. During the same period, the number of overweight teens tripled. In children and teens, these weight increases correspond to higher occurrences of asthma and type 2 diabetes. Eating a well-balanced diet and increasing the amount of physical activity can help reverse these trends.

Reading Check

Name What are some of the risks of a sedentary lifestyle?

▶ an increased risk of **osteoporosis**, *a condition characterized by a decrease in bone density, producing porous and fragile bones.* Porous and fragile bones fracture more easily than healthy bones.

▶ a reduced ability to manage stress.

▶ decreased opportunities to meet and form friendships with active people who value and live a healthy lifestyle.

You can lower your risk of these and many other health problems by including more physical activity in your daily life. For example, when you go shopping, walk to the store or, if you have to drive, park farther away from the entrance. **Figure 4.1** suggests other healthful alternatives to sedentary activities.

FIGURE 4.1

APPROACHES TO EVERYDAY ACTIVITIES

Instead of . . .	Try . . .
• Taking an elevator or escalator	• Taking the stairs
• Playing video or computer games	• Playing soccer, basketball, or tennis
• Getting a ride to a friend's house	• Walking, skating, or riding your bike there
• Using a shopping cart	• Carrying groceries to the car
• Watching TV or taking a nap	• Gardening or mowing the lawn
• Taking the car through a car wash	• Washing the car yourself

---

Physical Activity and Weight Control

The CDC reports that more than one-half of American adults and 14 percent of teens are overweight. This situation can be traced to a sedentary lifestyle and overeating. To stay within a weight range that is healthy for you, it's important to develop good eating habits and be physically active on a regular basis.

Understanding how the food you eat gets converted into energy can help you maintain a healthy weight. **Metabolism** is *the process by which your body gets energy from food.* Food's energy value is measured in units of heat called calories. Your body needs a sufficient number of calories each day to function properly. Additional calories must be burned through physical activity or they will be stored in the body as fat. When you are physically active, your metabolic rate rises and your body burns more calories than when it is at rest. The number of calories burned depends in part on the nature of the activity. When you stop being active, your metabolic rate slowly returns to normal. For several hours afterward, however, you continue to burn more calories than you did before you began the activity.

Hiking is a physical activity that you can enjoy throughout your life. *Name two safety considerations to keep in mind while hiking.*

Fitting Physical Activity into Your Life

Health professionals recommend that teens incorporate 60 minutes of moderate physical activity into their daily lives. Any activities that get you moving count toward your daily total and shows that you have set a personal goal for maintaining a healthy body. For example, walk or bike to school instead of getting a ride. Suggest to your family that you go for a hike or a swim on the weekend. Organize a basketball game with friends. Be sure to include some activities that you can participate in throughout your life. Hiking, swimming, golfing, biking, racquetball, tennis, and bowling are just a few examples of lifelong activities.

LESSON 1 · REVIEW

Reviewing Facts and Vocabulary

1. What is the difference between *physical activity* and *physical fitness*?
2. Examine and briefly describe the effects of regular physical activity on three body systems.
3. Analyze the relationship between regular physical activity, health promotion, and disease prevention.

Thinking Critically

4. **Analyzing.** Explain why watching television and walking affect metabolism differently.
5. **Synthesizing.** Why does it take longer to get the maximum health benefit from a leisurely walk than from swimming laps?

Applying Health Skills

Advocacy. Design a pamphlet with eye-catching headlines and graphics to educate younger students about the importance of physical activity. Your pamphlet should encourage and guide them to determine and then participate in the types of physical activity best suited to their interests and abilities.

After You Read

Compare and Contrast. After reading the lesson, write two brief paragraphs comparing the effects of a physically active lifestyle to those of a sedentary lifestyle.

Fitness and You

Guide to Reading

Building Vocabulary

As you read this lesson, write each new highlighted term and its definition in your notebook.

- cardiorespiratory endurance (p. 80)
- muscular strength (p. 80)
- muscular endurance (p. 80)
- flexibility (p. 81)
- body composition (p. 81)
- exercise (p. 81)
- aerobic exercise (p. 83)
- anaerobic exercise (p. 84)

Focusing on the Main Ideas

In this lesson, you will learn how to:

- Describe the five areas of health-related fitness.
- Improve each of the five areas of health-related fitness.

Reading Strategy

Organize Information

- As you read, use your Foldable to write down key points and define terms while reading this lesson.

Write a brief paragraph describing what being physically fit means to you.

These teens are improving their fitness levels. *Explain how this activity improves cardiorespiratory endurance.*

Do you have trouble running a mile even though you work out three times a week? Does your best friend excel at track but have a hard time doing push-ups? Every person's level of physical fitness is different.

Elements of Fitness

To have total fitness, you need to identify and describe the five health-related components of physical fitness and know how to make positive decisions related to physical activity.

- **Cardiorespiratory endurance**—*the ability of the heart, lungs, and blood vessels to utilize and send fuel and oxygen to the body's tissues during long periods of moderate-to-vigorous activity.*

- **Muscular strength**—*the amount of force a muscle can exert.*

- **Muscle endurance**—*the ability of the muscles to perform physical tasks over a period of time without becoming fatigued.*

▶ **Flexibility**—*the ability to move a body part through a full range of motion.*

▶ **Body composition**—*the ratio of body fat to lean body tissue, including muscle, bone, water, and connective tissue such as ligaments, cartilage, and tendons.*

Various activities and tests can help you assess health-related fitness levels. When you know your strengths and weaknesses, you can take steps to improve your physical fitness through exercise. **Exercise** is *purposeful physical activity that is planned, structured, and repetitive and that improves or maintains personal fitness.*

Measuring Cardiorespiratory Endurance

Cardiovascular disease is the leading cause of death in the United States. Keeping your cardiovascular system healthy is the most effective way of reducing your risk of developing this life-threatening disease. Cardiovascular health depends on maintaining good cardiorespiratory endurance. Can you run a mile without stopping or hike for most of the day without getting tired? If so, you have good cardiorespiratory endurance and recognize the implications of cardiovascular disease on healthy living.

CARDIORESPIRATORY ENDURANCE—STEP TEST

The three-minute step test can be used to measure your cardiorespiratory endurance. This test enables you to determine the rate at which your heart beats following a period of physical activity.

1. Use a sturdy bench about 12 inches high. Fully extending each leg as you step, step up with your right foot and then with your left. Then step down with your right foot first.

2. Repeat at the rate of 24 steps per minute for three minutes.

3. Take your pulse. To do this, find a pulse point on your wrist using the first two fingers of your other hand. *Do not use the thumb, which has its own pulse.* If you have trouble finding the pulse in your wrist, try finding the pulse point in your neck just below your jaw. Count the number of beats you feel for one minute.

4. Find your pulse rate on the chart to evaluate your cardiorespiratory endurance.

Measuring Muscular Strength and Endurance

You need muscular strength for activities that involve lifting, pushing, or jumping, and muscular endurance to perform such activities repeatedly. Having good muscular strength and endurance gives you the necessary power to carry out your daily tasks without becoming fatigued.

As you do the step test, your heart rate increases. *Explain why physical activity causes your heart to beat faster.*

STEP TEST SCORING CHART	
Beats/ Minute	Rating
85–95	Excellent
96–105	Good
106–125	Fair
126 or more	Needs Improvement

▼ **Curl-ups measure abdominal strength.** *How might abdominal strength improve your posture?*

CURL-UPS HEALTHY RANGE SCORING CHART		
Age	Male	Female
13	21 or more	18 or more
14+	24 or more	18 or more

▼ **The arm hang is used to measure upper body strength and endurance.** *What are the benefits of having good upper body strength and endurance?*

ARM HANG HEALTHY RANGE SCORING CHART		
Age	Male (Time in Seconds)	Female (Time in Seconds)
12	7–14	7–14
13–15	12–20	7–14

ABDOMINAL MUSCLE STRENGTH AND ENDURANCE—CURL-UPS

The body has different muscle groups, so there are different ways to measure muscular strength and endurance. Curl-ups often are used to measure abdominal strength.

1. Lie on your back with your knees bent at about a 45-degree angle and your feet slightly apart. Position your arms at your sides.

2. With your heels flat on the floor, curl your shoulders slowly off the ground, moving your arms forward toward your feet as you rise.

3. Slowly return to the original position. Do one curl-up every three seconds; continue until you can't do any more at the specified pace.

4. Find your score on the chart to rate your abdominal strength.

UPPER BODY STRENGTH AND ENDURANCE—ARM HANG

The arm hang is one test that is used to measure upper body strength and endurance. For this test, work with two other people.

1. Grasp the horizontal bar with your palms facing away from you.

2. Raise your body so that your chin is above the bar and your elbows are flexed to hold your chest near the bar. One person should act as a spotter to make sure that you are not swinging as you hang from the bar.

3. Hold the position described in Step 2 for as long as possible. The third person will time you with a stopwatch and will stop the watch if your chin touches the bar, your head tilts backward, or your chin falls below the bar.

4. Compare your score with those in the chart to rate your upper body strength and endurance.

Measuring Flexibility

When sitting on the floor with your legs outstretched, can you reach forward and touch your toes? If so, you have good flexibility. Being flexible can increase your athletic performance, help you feel more comfortable, and reduce the risk of muscle strains and other injuries. It can also help prevent lower back problems. Some track and field events, gymnastics, ballet and other forms of dance, figure skating, and the martial arts require a great deal of flexibility.

BODY FLEXIBILITY—SIT-AND-REACH

You can use the back saver sit-and-reach test, developed by the Cooper Institute of Aerobics Research in Dallas, Texas, to assess the flexibility of your lower back and the backs of your thighs. Before taking the test, do some light stretching to warm up your muscles.

1. Tape a yardstick on top of a 12-inch-high box so that it protrudes 9 inches toward you. The "zero" end should be nearest you. Put the back of the box against a wall.

2. Sit on the floor. Remove your shoes, and fully extend one leg so that the sole of your foot is flat against the side of the box beneath the yardstick. Bend your other knee so that your foot is flat on the floor two to three inches from the side of the extended leg.

3. Place the palm of one hand over the back of the other hand. Extend your arms over the yardstick, reaching forward as far as you can.

4. Repeat Step 3 four times. On the fourth try, hold the position for at least one second and notice where your fingertips are on the yardstick. Record your score to the nearest inch.

5. Switch the position of your legs and repeat the test.

6. Find your scores on the chart to determine your flexibility.

SIT-AND-REACH HEALTHY RANGE SCORING CHART	
Gender	Number of Inches
Male	8
Female	10 (ages 13–14)
	12 (ages 15+)

Measuring Body Composition

Being physically active and eating a balanced diet can improve the way you look. These healthful practices can also help you avoid the health problems associated with being overweight. To look and feel your best, it is helpful to have some idea of your body composition—that is, how much of your body is composed of fat and how much is composed of everything else. In general, males with 25 percent or more body fat and females with 30 percent or more body fat are at risk of developing cardiovascular problems. Carrying too much weight also places added stress on the skeletal system. To maintain a healthy body composition, eat a nutritious, balanced diet and maintain fitness.

The "pinch test" is a common method of determining body composition. It is conducted with a tool called a *skinfold caliper,* a gauge that measures the thickness of the fat beneath a fold of skin. The tester measures folds of skin on three to seven different parts of the body, usually including the back of a shoulder, the back of an arm, the abdomen, hip, and thigh. The average of the measurements is then calculated to estimate the total proportion of body fat.

Improving Your Fitness

You can choose from many different physical activities and exercises to improve your fitness level, but most fall into one of two categories: aerobic exercise or anaerobic exercise. **Aerobic exercise** is *any activity that uses large muscle groups, is rhythmic in nature, and can be maintained continuously for at least 10 minutes three times a day or for 20 to 30 minutes at one time.* Examples of aerobic exercise include running, cycling, swimming, and dancing.

Ⓐ The pinch test is often used to determine how much of a person's body is composed of fat.

Real-Life Application

Targeting Cardiovascular Fitness

Use these steps to find your target heart range—the ideal range for your heart rate during aerobic activity. Then do the activity to help you apply this information.

Target Heart Range

○ **Maximum target heart rate.** Exercising above this rate can result in injury.

○ **Target heart range.** To safely build cardiorespiratory endurance, keep your heart rate within this range. Take your pulse for 6 seconds and multiply this number by 10 to determine the number of beats per minute.

○ **Minimum target heart rate.** Exercising below this rate will not build cardiorespiratory endurance.

ACTIVITY

Prepare a written plan describing how you will apply this information. Include your target heart range (with your calculations), two aerobic activities, how you will check your heart rate while you are doing each activity, and how you will keep your heart rate within the target range.

Finding Your Target Heart Range

1. Sit quietly for five minutes, and then take your pulse. This is your resting heart rate. Suppose that it is 66 beats per minute.
2. Subtract your age from 220 to find your maximum heart rate. For example, if you are 16, your maximum heart rate will be 204.
3. Subtract your resting heart rate from your maximum heart rate. (Example: 204 − 66 = 138)
4. Multiply the number you arrived at in Step 3 by 60 percent and again by 85 percent. Round to the nearest whole numbers. (Example: 138 × 0.60 = 83; 138 × 0.85 = 117)
5. Add your resting heart rate to the numbers you arrived at in Step 4. (Example: 83 + 66 = 149; 117 + 66 = 183) The resulting totals represent your target heart range (between 149 and 183).

Anaerobic exercise involves *intense short bursts of activity in which the muscles work so hard that they produce energy without using oxygen.* Running a 100-meter dash and lifting weights are examples of anaerobic exercises.

Improving Cardiorespiratory Endurance

When you do aerobic exercises, your heart rate increases and your heart sends more oxygen to your muscles to use as energy. Over time, this strengthens the heart muscle, allowing it to pump blood more efficiently. Aerobic exercise also affects your respiratory system by increasing the lungs' capacity to hold air. **Caution:** Don't force yourself to continue an aerobic activity if you become exhausted. Before beginning a fitness program that includes aerobic activities, consult a health care professional. This is especially important if you have asthma or another respiratory disorder. It is also recommended for people with heart disease.

Improving Muscular Strength and Endurance

Anaerobic exercises improve muscular strength and endurance. The more work the muscles do, the stronger they become. Sprinting is an example of an anaerobic activity. Resistance or strength training, which builds muscles by requiring them to move in opposition to a force, is also a form of anaerobic exercise. Free weights, exercise machines, or your own body weight can provide resistance. In addition to building and strengthening muscle, resistance exercises help the body keep blood sugar levels normal and help maintain healthy **cholesterol** levels.

As indicated in **Figure 4.2,** there are three types of resistance training exercise. Exercises such as these tone muscles, improve muscular strength, and increase muscular endurance.

Improving Flexibility

When you have good flexibility, you can easily bend, turn, and stretch your body. You can improve your flexibility through regular

Reading Check

Describe What are the three types of resistance exercise?

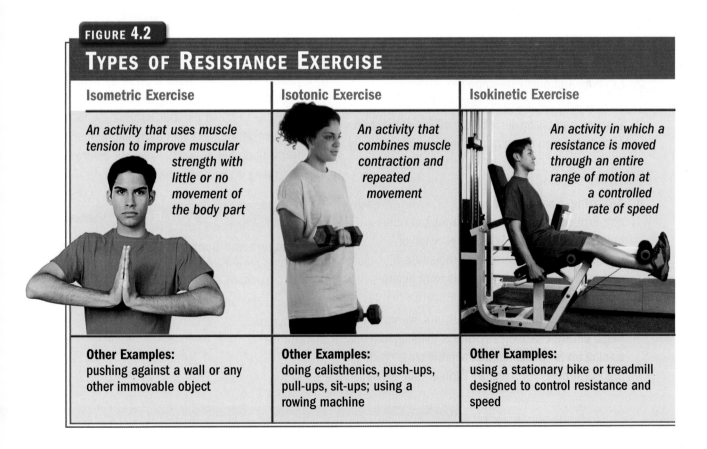

FIGURE 4.2

TYPES OF RESISTANCE EXERCISE

Isometric Exercise	Isotonic Exercise	Isokinetic Exercise
An activity that uses muscle tension to improve muscular strength with little or no movement of the body part	*An activity that combines muscle contraction and repeated movement*	*An activity in which a resistance is moved through an entire range of motion at a controlled rate of speed*
Other Examples: pushing against a wall or any other immovable object	**Other Examples:** doing calisthenics, push-ups, pull-ups, sit-ups; using a rowing machine	**Other Examples:** using a stationary bike or treadmill designed to control resistance and speed

Regular, gentle stretching of muscles and joints helps increase flexibility.

What exercises do you include in your routine to increase your flexibility?

stretching exercises. Just be sure to move slowly and gently. For example, to stretch the muscles of your upper body, stand with your arms extended behind your back, hands clasped; raise your arms until you feel tightness in your shoulders and chest; and hold for 20 seconds.

Improving and Maintaining Bone Strength

The health behaviors you engage in relating to physical activity and nutrition can affect the health of your skeletal system now and later in life. You probably already know that calcium—found in dairy products and certain green vegetables—is essential for building strong bones. Resistance training and weight-bearing aerobic activities—those that force you to work against gravity, such as walking and stair climbing—can also help increase bone mass, strengthening your skeletal system.

It's very important to complete a health-related fitness test and assess your personal level of physical fitness, including monitoring your heart. Learning your fitness level and taking steps to improve it shows that you accept responsibility for your own health.

LESSON 2 REVIEW

Reviewing Facts and Vocabulary

1. Identify and describe the five areas of health-related fitness.

2. Examine and briefly describe the relationship among body composition, diet, and fitness.

3. Examine and briefly describe the effects of resistance training on the muscular and skeletal systems.

Thinking Critically

4. **Analyzing.** Sam has been doing 50 curl-ups each day. Explain what area of health-related fitness this exercise benefits. What other types of physical activities or exercises should Sam add to his routine to improve his total health-related fitness?

5. **Evaluating.** Keesha, who has asthma, wants to begin an exercise program. She is thinking of signing up for a high-impact aerobic class. Is this a good strategy for Keesha? Explain your answer.

Applying Health Skills

Practicing Healthful Behaviors. Help family members determine their target heart ranges. Then make a list of aerobic activities you could do together. Determine how you all could use this information to improve your cardiorespiratory endurance. Remember: get a health screening before beginning an exercise program.

After You Read

Compare and Contrast. Describe the difference between aerobic and anaerobic exercise. Write a few sentences explaining how each contributes to a physical activity program.

Planning a Personal Activity Program

Guide to Reading

Building Vocabulary

As you read this lesson, write each new highlighted term and its definition in your notebook.

▶ overload (p. 90)
▶ progression (p. 90)
▶ specificity (p. 90)
▶ warm-up (p. 90)
▶ workout (p. 90)
▶ F.I.T.T. (p. 90)
▶ cool-down (p. 91)
▶ resting heart rate (p. 92)

Focusing on the Main Ideas

In this lesson, you will learn how to:

▶ Establish realistic fitness goals.
▶ Develop a personal physical activity program.
▶ Describe the basic principles of a physical activity program.

Reading Strategy

Predict

▶ Scan the main headings, subheadings, figures, and photographs. Based on your current knowledge, what do you think this lesson is about?

Quick Write

List at least six activities you have tried or would like to try. Categorize those activities as aerobic or anaerobic based on your current knowledge.

Participating in a school sports program may inspire you to set fitness goals and begin a physical activity program.

Knowing the many health benefits of physical activity may inspire you to begin a personal activity program—but having a reason or goal for being physically active is even more inspiring. Developing a plan for attaining personal fitness goals and methods for evaluating progress will help you succeed. It is important that your plan demonstrates the relationship between physical activity, nutrition, and weight management.

Setting Physical Activity Goals

How can you be sure to include physical activity in your daily routine? The first step is to set realistic fitness goals. Then you can develop a plan to meet your goals. To meet the U.S. Department of Agriculture (USDA) recommendations, teens should get 60 minutes of physical activity every day. This may include all sorts of activities, from participating in physical education classes and playing sports to doing household tasks such as mowing the lawn and cleaning your room. Your school or community may offer programs that provide a variety of fun and healthful physical activities.

Getting Started

Figure 4.3 provides suggestions about how to design a personal fitness plan and set goals based on the health-related fitness assessment results that will lead to or maintain a satisfactory fitness level. To help you reach your fitness goals, it is recommended that you divide your time when doing various types of physical activity.

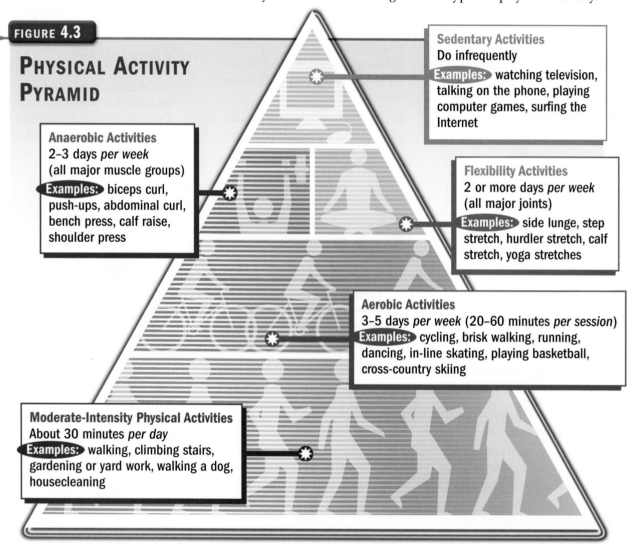

FIGURE 4.3

PHYSICAL ACTIVITY PYRAMID

Sedentary Activities
Do infrequently
Examples: watching television, talking on the phone, playing computer games, surfing the Internet

Anaerobic Activities
2–3 days *per week*
(all major muscle groups)
Examples: biceps curl, push-ups, abdominal curl, bench press, calf raise, shoulder press

Flexibility Activities
2 or more days *per week*
(all major joints)
Examples: side lunge, step stretch, hurdler stretch, calf stretch, yoga stretches

Aerobic Activities
3–5 days *per week* (20–60 minutes *per session*)
Examples: cycling, brisk walking, running, dancing, in-line skating, playing basketball, cross-country skiing

Moderate-Intensity Physical Activities
About 30 minutes *per day*
Examples: walking, climbing stairs, gardening or yard work, walking a dog, housecleaning

Choosing Activities

Including different types of physical activities in your fitness program can help make it more enjoyable. As your fitness level increases, you can alter your program to promote individual health. Other factors that may affect your decision making include:

▶ **Cost.** Some activities require specialized—and possibly expensive—equipment. Think about what you can afford, and keep in mind that you may discover after a time that an activity just doesn't suit you.

▶ **Where you live.** For convenience you'll want to choose activities that you can do locally, without spending a lot of time traveling. Think about the features of your local area. Is the land flat or hilly? What type of climate do you live in? To what activities does the region best lend itself?

▶ **Your level of health.** Some health conditions have risks that need to be considered when planning physical activities. For example, some types of physical activity can aggravate **asthma**, a disease of the respiratory system.

▶ **Time and place.** Build your program into your daily routine. Don't schedule jogging at 6:00 A.M. if you're not a morning person. Design your schedule to help you achieve your goals.

▶ **Personal safety.** Think about your **personal safety** as you develop a fitness program. If you plan to run long distances, avoid going through unsafe areas or running after dark.

▶ **Comprehensive planning.** Select activities that address all five areas of health-related fitness.

Reading Check

Describe What are the recommendations for dividing your time when doing various types of physical activity?

Health Skills Activity

Goal Setting: Starting a Physical Activity Program

William wants to start a physical activity program, but he's not sure where to begin. He really wants to improve his cardiorespiratory and muscle endurance, and he knows that his flexibility and muscle strength need work, too. He's also thinking about signing up for soccer; tryouts are in three months. What can William do to improve his fitness level and make the soccer team?

What Would You Do?
Apply the five goal-setting steps to William's situation.

1. Identify a specific goal and write it down.
2. List the steps you will take to reach your goal.
3. Identify potential problems and ways to get help and support from others.
4. Set up checkpoints to evaluate your progress.
5. Reward yourself once you have achieved your goal.

Cross Training

Engaging in a variety of physical activities to strengthen different muscle groups is known as cross training. Jumping rope, swimming, jogging, and cycling are good cross-training activities for athletes.

Basics of a Physical Activity Program

To plan your physical activity program, use goals and logical steps to develop an action plan to organize resources in order to be physically active. Because it focuses on *your* goals and interests, your fitness program is unique. However, all effective fitness programs are based on these three principles:

▶ **Overload**, *working the body harder than it is normally worked,* builds muscular strength and contributes to overall fitness. It is achieved by increasing repetitions or by doing more sets (groups of 6 to 12 repetitions) of an exercise.

▶ **Progression** is *the gradual increase in overload necessary to achieve higher levels of fitness.* As an activity becomes easier to do, increase the number of repetitions or sets or increase the amount of time spent doing the activity.

▶ **Specificity** indicates that *particular exercises and activities improve particular areas of health-related fitness.* For example, resistance training builds muscular strength and endurance, while aerobic activity improves cardiorespiratory endurance.

To gain the most benefit from an exercise program, you'll want to include three basic stages for each activity. These are the *warm-up,* the *workout,* and the *cool-down.* Include each stage in every session even when you're in a hurry.

The Warm-Up

The **warm-up**, *an activity that prepares the muscles for work,* is the first stage in any physical activity routine. Begin the warm-up by taking a brisk walk to raise your body temperature. Then, slowly stretch large muscles to increase their elasticity and reduce the risk of injury. After stretching individual muscles, perform the physical activity slowly for about five minutes. Warming up allows your pulse rate to increase gradually. A sudden increase in pulse rate places unnecessary strain on the heart and blood vessels.

The Workout

The part of an exercise program when the activity is performed at its highest peak is called the **workout**. To be effective, the activity needs to follow the **F.I.T.T.** formula—*frequency, intensity, time/ duration,* and *type of activity*—outlined in **Figure 4.4.**

Health Minute

Avoiding Boredom in Your Workout Routine

If your workout becomes boring:

▶ Vary your routine by cross training. For example, skate one day and swim the next.

▶ Work out with a friend. This can be more fun than working out alone and can help you both stay motivated.

▶ Try listening to music while working out. When you have something else to focus on, the workout session may seem to pass more quickly. (**Note:** Listen to music only when participating in indoor activities. When exercising outdoors, you need to be alert to possible dangers.)

▶ Take a break to give your body time to recharge.

FREQUENCY

You should schedule workouts three to four times each week, with only one or two days between sessions. The frequency of your workouts depends partly on your fitness goals and the type of activity you do—as well as on your schedule and possibly even the weather. Exercising more than three times each week for six months should help *get* you physically fit. To *maintain* your fitness level, continue your program at least three times each week.

INTENSITY

Working your muscles and cardiorespiratory system at an intensity that allows you to reach overload will help you improve your fitness level. Begin slowly to build endurance. Doing too much too soon is harmful and can cause chronically sore muscles.

When weight training, start with a light weight and build to heavier weights. For aerobics, work toward your target heart range. If you are out of shape, it may take about six months before you can work out for 20 to 30 minutes within your target heart range.

TIME/DURATION

Slowly build up the amount of time you spend doing aerobic exercises. The goal in aerobics is to work within your target heart range for 20 to 30 minutes. When weight training, do the exercises slowly, taking at least two seconds to lower a weight. Rest for one or two minutes between sets. Also, vary the exercises to strengthen your muscles in the full range of motion.

TYPE

To get the maximum health benefits from your workout routine, devote 75 to 80 percent of your workout time to aerobic activity and 20 to 25 percent to anaerobic activity. Choose activities that you enjoy, or you may find it difficult to complete your workouts.

The Cool-Down

Ending a workout abruptly can cause your muscles to tighten and may make you feel dizzy. To avoid these effects, you need to cool down after a workout. The **cool-down** is *an activity that prepares the muscles to return to a resting state.*

FIGURE 4.4

THE *F.I.T.T.* FORMULA

Include each of these elements in your workout.

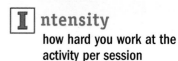

F requency
how often you do the activity each week

I ntensity
how hard you work at the activity per session

T ime/duration
how much time you devote to a session

T ype
which activities you select

Reading Check

Define What does the acronym F.I.T.T. mean?

The warm-up is an important part of any physical activity routine. *Explain how stretching prepares muscles for exercise and prevents injuries.*

Y Using a calendar or journal can help you keep track of your fitness program.

Begin the cool-down by slowing down the activity. Continue the activity at this slower pace for about five minutes, then stretch for five minutes.

Monitoring Your Progress

To monitor your progress, keep a fitness journal. In your journal, list your goals and note the frequency, intensity, duration, and type of each activity in which you participate. At the end of 12 weeks, and every 6 weeks after that, compare the figures to evaluate your progress.

Resting Heart Rate

Your **resting heart rate** is *the number of times your heart beats in one minute when you are not active.* Your resting heart rate can also be used to evaluate your progress. A person of average fitness has a resting heart rate of about 72 to 84 beats per minute. Just four weeks of a fitness program can decrease that rate by 5 to 10 beats per minute. A resting heart rate below 72 indicates a good fitness level.

LESSON 3 REVIEW

Reviewing Facts and Vocabulary

1. How can using the Physical Activity Pyramid help you meet your fitness goals?
2. Identify and define the three principles upon which all effective fitness programs are based.
3. What do the letters in the *F.I.T.T.* formula stand for?

Thinking Critically

4. **Analyzing.** How is your resting heart rate an indication of your level of fitness?
5. **Synthesizing.** Maria is a runner. Describe how she could include the three stages of an effective exercise program in her fitness routine.

Applying Health Skills

Goal Setting. Use the goal-setting steps to develop a personal fitness program. Synthesize information from this lesson and apply critical-thinking and decision-making skills to determine what activities to include and how you will incorporate them into a formal plan. Think of obstacles that could prevent you from following your plan, and apply problem-solving skills to figure out how to overcome these obstacles.

After You Read

Compare and Contrast. Using Figure 4.4, write a summary describing how you would incorporate the F.I.T.T. formula into your personal activity plan.

Visit **health.glencoe.com** for the Interactive Study Guide for Lesson 3.

Training and Safety for Physical Activities

Guide to Reading

Building Vocabulary

As you read this lesson, write each new highlighted term and its definition in your notebook.

- ▶ training program (p. 93)
- ▶ hydration (p. 94)
- ▶ anabolic steroids (p. 94)
- ▶ health screening (p. 95)

Quick Write

Prepare a list of safety equipment needed for at least three activities you enjoy.

Focusing on the Main Ideas

In this lesson, you will learn how to:

- ▶ Explain how health-promotion strategies can enhance a training program.
- ▶ Describe how safety concerns related to various physical activities, including preventive health screenings, enhance a training program.

Reading Strategy

Make Inferences

- ▶ This lesson provides information on how training programs help you stay safe while getting physical activity. Write a brief paragraph describing what you now think are the benefits of training programs.

△ A physical education teacher or coach can help you establish your goals for a training program.

Beginning a new physical activity can be exciting. Knowing how to make positive decisions related to physical activity and injury-prevention can help you stay safe.

Training and Peak Performance

The first step in becoming fit is to take good care of your body. Eat nutritious foods and drink plenty of fluids, especially water. Getting adequate rest is essential. To keep your body in top form, it is also important to learn methods for predicting the immediate and long-term impact of health decisions and to apply proper safety practices as related to exercise and physical activity.

The next step in improving fitness often involves beginning a training program for your chosen activity. A **training program** is *a program of formalized physical preparation for involvement in a sport or another physical activity.* Consult your physical education teacher, coach, or another trusted adult to help you set your training goals.

Nutrition and Hydration

What you eat and drink is an important part of any training program. Food provides the energy necessary for peak performance. You will learn more about nutrition in Chapter 5. It is important that you demonstrate and evaluate the importance of regular physical activity and proper diet. Equally important is hydration, especially when you are engaged in vigorous physical activity. **Hydration** is *taking in fluids so that the body functions properly.* When you are adequately hydrated, you are more alert and focused, your reaction time is faster because your muscles respond more quickly and are less likely to cramp, and your endurance is greater. To stay hydrated, drink plenty of water before, during, and after vigorous physical activity.

Adequate Rest

Sleep, which helps your body rest and reenergize, is also essential for any training program. Getting too little sleep can disrupt the nervous system, causing slowed reaction time, lack of concentration, forgetfulness, irritability, and even depression. On average, teens need 8 to 10 hours of sleep every night to function at their best.

Avoiding Harmful Substances

Avoiding harmful substances such as tobacco, alcohol, anabolic steroids, and other drugs is another part of maintaining an athletic training program. Avoiding these substances also shows that you understand the potential controversy regarding the validity of health information, products, and services.

ANABOLIC STEROIDS

Anabolic steroids are *synthetic substances that are similar to the male hormone testosterone.* Because these substances cause the body to make muscle tissue, some athletes take them to increase muscle mass and enhance performance. However, anabolic steroids have very harmful effects, including increased risk of cancer and heart disease; sterility, or the inability to produce children; skin problems such as acne and hair loss; unusual weight gain or loss; sexual underdevelopment and dysfunction; and violent, suicidal, or depressive tendencies.

It is illegal to use anabolic steroids without a prescription, and those who test positive for steroid use are disqualified from competitions.

NUTRITIONAL SUPPLEMENTS

Nutritional supplements are nonfood substances that contain one or more nutrients that the body needs, such as vitamins or minerals. The best way to get nutrients is from food, but sometimes a multiple vitamin and mineral supplement may be appropriate.

Drinking water is important before, during, and after vigorous physical activity.
Explain why hydration is so important during any physical activity.

Reading Check

Explain Why is staying hydrated important to your training program?

Resilient TEENS

In many ways, 18-year-old Brady Borslien's life seems perfect. He's a star athlete, a member of the choir, drama, and LEO clubs, and vice president of his school.

What is not immediately apparent about Brady Borslien is his struggle to overcome depression. He became depressed after a particularly rough year. It started, he says, when both his grandparents died of cancer. Brady had been particularly close to his grandfather.

Before experiencing it himself, Brady thought depression was something a person should just get over. "I know better now," he says. "It's like a cloud that covers your whole life." Fortunately, Brady has help from friends and counselors at school. He takes medication to treat the physical effects of the depression and speaks about his condition to other kids. "It's hard, but I'm glad I'm doing it," he says. "No one should have to feel this way."

"It's like a cloud that covers your whole life."

 Reading Check **Describe** What actions can you take if you are feeling depressed?

A health care provider can advise you about whether you need this type of supplement. It's important to take the recommended dosage of any supplement. High doses, or *megadoses,* of a nutritional supplement can be harmful.

Safety First!

Safety should be a major concern when you participate in sports and other physical activities. You can reduce your risk of injury by

▶ visiting a health care professional for a health screening before beginning a new activity. A **health screening** is *a search or* *check for diseases or disorders that an individual would otherwise not have knowledge of or seek help for.* This preventive health care helps ensure that you don't have a health condition that could make the activity dangerous for you.

▶ using the proper safety equipment for your chosen activity.

▶ being alert to the surrounding environment, including other players and spectators.

▶ playing at your skill level and knowing your physical limits.

▶ warming up before and cooling down after every activity.

▶ staying within areas that have been designated for physical activities, such as skateboarding parks and bicycle paths.

▶ obeying all rules and restrictions—for example, those that restrict swimming to certain areas or that prohibit skateboarding on sidewalks.

▶ practicing good sportsmanship.

If you should become injured or ill during physical activity, tell a physical education teacher, coach, or another adult immediately. Recognizing and applying safety techniques, practices, and guidelines as related to fitness and nutrition will help you remain healthy.

Personal Safety

You can reduce risks to your personal safety by selecting the right time and place for your activity. This is especially true if you work out alone. If you run or jog, choose a well-used area during daylight hours, when other people are there. If you can't avoid nighttime physical activity, wear reflective clothing so that others can see you. Wearing a whistle that you can blow to attract attention if you are in danger is also a good idea. Also, be aware of the effects of weather: bicycling or running—and even walking—can be a health risk when it's wet and slippery outside.

To avoid sports injuries, choose the proper athletic gear. *Match each piece of equipment with an appropriate sport or other physical activity.*

Using Proper Equipment

Before you begin any new physical activity, learn to use the equipment involved. Check the equipment to make sure that it fits and is in good condition. Always wear the safety gear recommended for that particular activity. Many sports have strict requirements for protective equipment. These tips may also help.

▶ Wear a helmet when bicycling, skateboarding, or skating. Also, when skateboarding or skating, wear knee and elbow pads, gloves, and wrist guards.

▶ Avoid riding at night, if possible. If you must, make sure your bike has reflective tape, a rear reflector, and a headlight. Skateboards and skates also should be outlined with reflective tape. When participating in any outdoor activity at night, wear light-colored clothing with reflective patches on the front and back so that drivers and pedestrians can see you more easily.

▶ Males participating in contact sports—such as football and hockey—should wear athletic supporters or cups to protect the groin area. Females should wear sports bras to prevent stretching of the ligaments that support the breasts.

Proper footwear and clothing also are important. Athletic shoes should be comfortable and should have a cushioned heel, good arch support, and ample toe room. Laced shoes are best for proper control of your foot in the shoe. Wear socks to cushion your feet and keep them dry. In general, choose comfortable, nonrestrictive clothing. When it's warm outside, dress lightly. In cool weather, wear several loose-fitting layers that you can easily remove as you warm up.

Whatever activity you choose, it's essential to use the proper safety equipment. *What safety equipment are the teens pictured here using?*

LESSON 4 REVIEW

Reviewing Facts and Vocabulary

1. Define the term *hydration.*
2. What are *anabolic steroids*? Name three ways they can harm health.
3. Why is beginning a physical activity program a situation requiring preventive health care?

Thinking Critically

4. **Evaluating.** How can practicing good sportsmanship help you stay safe when participating in a sport?
5. **Analyzing.** Enrique wants to play on the school football team in the fall. To prepare, he plans to participate in a training program in the spring and summer. List five things Enrique should do before and during his training program.

Applying Health Skills

Accessing Information. Working with a classmate, search the Web for three schools that have adopted the policy of random drug testing of school athletes. Compare your school's policy with theirs, noting both similarities and differences.

After You Read

Identify Problems and Solutions. Develop a list of at least two activities you enjoy. For each of those activities, describe some of the problems associated with the activities, and potential solutions to those problems.

Physical Activity Injuries

Guide to Reading

Building Vocabulary

As you read this lesson, write each new highlighted term and its definition in your notebook.

▶ overexertion (p. 99)

▶ heat cramps (p. 99)

▶ heatstroke (p. 99)

▶ frostbite (p. 100)

▶ hypothermia (p. 101)

▶ muscle cramp (p. 102)

▶ strain (p. 102)

▶ sprain (p. 102)

Focusing on the Main Ideas

In this lesson, you will learn how to:

▶ Analyze weather-related risks associated with various physical activities.

▶ Describe how to prevent and respond to minor injuries related to physical activities.

▶ Assess physical activity injuries that require professional health services.

Reading Strategy

Organize Information

▶ As you read, use your Foldable to create a graphic organizer listing minor and major injuries. Note which of these injuries require medical attention.

Write a paragraph describing how you prepare differently for hot-weather and cold-weather activities based on your current knowledge.

▲ These teens are taking specific precautions to prevent sports injuries. *What safety precautions did you take in your most recent outdoor activity?*

With any activity that involves movement, there is always a risk of accident or injury. The risk of injury during physical activity increases when a person is not in good physical condition or has not sufficiently warmed up or cooled down. Knowing injury-prevention and injury-management strategies can reduce the risk of injury during physical activity. Attempting physical activities that are beyond your level of ability also increases the risk of injury.

Weather-Related Risks

Taking your physical activity routine outdoors can be a great change of pace, but some weather-related health problems need to be taken into consideration. These problems can be avoided by not participating in outdoor physical activity when temperatures are extremely high or extremely low. Factors such as wind, humidity, and air pollution can increase your risk of injury or illness. Be aware of wind chill factors, ultraviolet (UV) indexes, and air quality alerts. You also should pay attention to weather warnings. Stay inside if there is a threat of tornadoes, thunderstorms, flash floods, or blizzards.

Hot-Weather Health Risks

Two concerns during hot weather are dehydration, or excessive loss of water from the body, and poor air quality. Smog can damage the lungs, so if you live in an area where smog is a concern, avoid outdoor physical activities during smog alerts. To avoid dehydration, drink plenty of water before, during, and after physical activity.

Many hot-weather health problems are related to **overexertion**, or *overworking the body*. For example, heat exhaustion—an overheating of the body that results in cold, clammy skin and symptoms of shock—is caused by overexertion in a hot, humid atmosphere. Other symptoms include dizziness, headache, shortness of breath, and nausea. Heat exhaustion may be preceded or accompanied by **heat cramps**, *muscle spasms that result from a loss of large amounts of salt and water through perspiration*. If you experience any of these symptoms, move to a cool place and lie down with your feet elevated. Take small sips of water as you start to recover. If symptoms are severe, or if vomiting occurs, get medical help immediately.

Continuing to exercise with the symptoms of heat exhaustion and dehydration can lead to **heatstroke**, *a condition in which the body loses the ability to rid itself of excessive heat through perspiration*. This causes hyperthermia, a sudden increase in body temperature, which can be life-threatening. A person suffering from heatstroke may have difficulty breathing and may collapse suddenly. If heatstroke occurs, immediately call for medical help. Then move the person to a cool place, and sponge him or her with cold water until help arrives.

Cold-Weather Health Risks

When participating in cold-weather activities, dress in three layers to keep warm. The first layer should pull moisture and perspiration away from your body. Many synthetic fabrics have been specifically developed to help keep the skin dry. The middle layer should provide insulation. Wool or synthetic fleece fabrics can help keep you warm even if they get wet. A coated nylon windshell as the top layer will help keep warmth in and water and wind out. A hat is also a must—70 percent of the body's heat is lost through the head. Removing layers as you warm up or adding them as the temperature drops can help you adjust to changes in the weather.

When you begin any cold-weather activity, start slowly and be sure to warm up your muscles. Staying hydrated is as important in

Staying hydrated is essential when working out in hot or cold weather. *What other steps can this player take to protect himself from health problems associated with working out in hot weather?*

Helmets, goggles, and gloves are proper equipment when snowboarding.

cold weather as it is in hot weather. Two specific health risks from cold weather are particularly important to keep in mind: frostbite and hypothermia.

▶ **Frostbite** is *a condition that results when body tissues become frozen,* and it requires professional medical treatment. You can avoid frostbite by dressing warmly and covering all exposed skin—especially the ears, face, feet, and fingers, where frostbite most often occurs. An early warning sign of frostbite, called frostnip, is a whitening of the skin of the toes, fingers, nose, or ears. If this happens or if you notice a lack of feeling in any exposed area, get indoors right away and warm the area with warm water.

Real-Life Application

Being Safe While Physically Active

Sports and recreational activities are the second most frequent cause of injury for teens. Many such injuries can be prevented by being cautious and by wearing proper equipment. Examine the graph, and choose a sport or recreational activity in which you or your friends participate. Using reliable online and print resources, research your sport to find injury statistics. For example, what injuries are most common for this sport? How many teens are injured each year in this sport? How many of these injuries are treated in emergency rooms? What protective equipment and precautions can reduce injury in this sport?

Frequency (%) of High School Sport Injuries

Major | Moderate

% of injuries

| Baseball | Basketball | Football | Soccer | Volleyball | Wrestling |

Major: Baseball 10.3, Basketball 8.5, Football 8.4, Volleyball 5.6, Wrestling 13
Moderate: Baseball 12.7, Basketball 13.5, Football 11, Soccer 12, Volleyball 12, Wrestling 15.4

Source: Based on data from the National Athletic Trainers' Association

ACTIVITY

Using the activity you have researched, create a poster that explains how teens can get injured while participating in the activity and presents ways of staying safe. Make your poster colorful and attention-getting to appeal to a teen audience. Be sure to give it a catchy title.

▶ **Hypothermia** is *a condition in which body temperature becomes dangerously low.* It is usually associated with cold weather, but it also can result from lengthy exposure to wind or rain or from submersion in cold water. When hypothermia occurs, the body loses the ability to warm itself. As body temperature drops, the brain cannot function and body systems begin to shut down. A person with this condition may become disoriented and lose motor control. Because hypothermia can lead to death, it requires immediate medical attention.

When participating in cold-weather activities, pay attention to your body. Shivering is a sign that your body is losing heat. If you begin to feel cold or to shiver, go to a warm, dry place; wrap yourself in a blanket; and drink warm liquids to slowly raise your body temperature.

Protecting Yourself from Sun and Wind

Prolonged exposure to sun and wind is another weather-related risk of outdoor physical activity. Windburn occurs when skin is exposed to freezing wind, causing it to become red, tight, and sore to the touch. Reduce the risk of windburn by wearing protective clothing and using lip balm. The sun's UV rays cause *sunburn,* a burning of the outer layers of the skin. Mild sunburn makes your skin red and slightly sore. Severe sunburn causes blistering of the skin, swelling, and pain. In addition to increasing the risk of sunburn, repeated or prolonged exposure to the sun speeds the skin's aging process and increases your risk of developing **skin cancer.** The most dangerous hours for UV exposure are from 10:00 A.M. to 4:00 P.M. To protect yourself against sunburn:

▶ Cover as much of the body with clothing as possible when outdoors and wear broad-brimmed hats on sunny days.

▶ Use sunscreen and lip balm with a sun protection factor (SPF) of *at least* 15. The SPF number indicates the sunscreen's ability to screen out the sun's harmful UV rays. Because UV rays penetrate clouds, you need to wear sunscreen on cloudy days, too.

▶ Apply sunscreen 30 minutes before you go outside, spreading it liberally and evenly over all areas of your skin that will be exposed. Reapply it at least every two hours.

UV rays can also damage your eyes. A *cataract,* a cloudy covering over the lens of the eye, is caused in part by sun exposure. Wear a visor or a hat with a brim, and use sunglasses, even during the winter months. Because sunlight is reflected off snow, those participating in winter sports need to wear goggles to protect their eyes from both UV exposure and glare.

▼ **Apply sunscreen frequently when you participate in outdoor activities.** *Why is it important to use sunscreen in both hot and cold weather?*

Reading Check

Describe What are two ways you can protect yourself from sunburn?

▼ Ligaments are strong bands of tissue that connect the bones to one another at a moveable joint. Sprains result if these bands are stretched or torn.

Minor Injuries

Have you ever had sore muscles after a physical activity or experienced the pain of a twisted ankle? Muscles are often sore 24 to 48 hours after a strenuous workout. Warming up, cooling down, and stretching can prevent or reduce muscle soreness. Other minor injuries that affect the skeletal or muscular systems include muscle cramps, strains, and sprains. A **muscle cramp** is *a spasm or sudden tightening of a muscle.* It happens when a muscle is tired, overworked, or dehydrated. A **strain** is *a condition resulting from damaging a muscle or tendon.* A **sprain** is *an injury to the ligament surrounding a joint.* Symptoms of a sprain include pain, swelling, and difficulty moving. Severe sprains require medical treatment.

Treatment for Minor Injuries

Minor injuries such as muscle cramps, strains, and some sprains are easily treated. Muscle cramps can be relieved through light massage. An effective response strategy for these minor accidental injuries is the *P.R.I.C.E.* procedure described in **Figure 4.5**.

Major Injuries

Pain—especially extreme pain—may signal that you have a major injury. If you experience extreme pain, numbness, or disorientation or hear a "cracking" sound during a fall, get appropriate medical treatment immediately. Doing so shows that you know how to analyze situations requiring professional health services.

▲ Many minor sports injuries can be treated by following the *P.R.I.C.E.* procedure. *Which part of the P.R.I.C.E. procedure is pictured here?*

FIGURE 4.5

THE *P.R.I.C.E.* PROCEDURE

Protection Protect the area from further injury.

Rest Avoid using the affected muscle or joint. This may mean not using the affected area for several days.

Ice Ice helps reduce pain and swelling. Place ice cubes in a plastic bag, and wrap the bag in a towel. Hold the towel-wrapped bag on the affected area for 20 minutes. Remove the bag for 20 minutes, and then reapply the bag for another 20 minutes. Repeat this process every three waking hours over the course of 72 hours.

Compression Light pressure through the use of an elastic bandage can help reduce swelling. The bandage should not be so tight that it cuts off the blood supply to the area, and it should be loosened at night.

Elevation Raising the affected limb above the level of the heart helps reduce pain and swelling, especially at night.

Major injuries include:

This teen's safety gear helps protect him from serious injury. *What type of serious injury might the face mask prevent?*

▶ **Fractures and Dislocations.** Fractures are any break in a bone. A fracture causes swelling and often extreme pain, and it usually requires immobilization to heal properly. Dislocations result when a bone is forced from its normal position at a joint. A dislocation sometimes causes a "popping" sound when it occurs. A physician must put the bone back into place and immobilize the joint so that the tissue can heal.

▶ **Tendonitis.** This is a condition in which the tendons, bands of fiber that connect muscles to bones, are stretched or torn from overuse. Treatment includes rest, medication, and physical therapy.

▶ **Concussions.** Concussions result from blows to the head and can cause swelling of the brain, resulting in unconsciousness or even death. Concussions can also lead to serious neurological problems. If you receive any blow to the head and experience headache, dizziness, or loss of memory or consciousness, see a health care professional immediately.

LESSON 5 | **REVIEW**

Reviewing Facts and Vocabulary

1. What is *hypothermia*? With which types of weather is this condition often associated?

2. Analyze and describe strategies for preventing and responding to the accidental injuries described in this lesson.

3. Identify which injuries described in this lesson require the attention of professional health services.

Thinking Critically

4. **Evaluating.** Explain why muscle cramps might be more dangerous for a swimmer than for a jogger.

5. **Analyzing.** On a hot day, a runner begins to have trouble breathing and also becomes pale, dizzy, and nauseated. From what condition is this runner likely to be suffering? Analyze and describe strategies for responding to this condition.

Applying Health Skills

Communication Skills. Imagine that your friend has suffered a minor sprain to her ankle while in-line skating. Analyze and describe how she could use the *P.R.I.C.E.* procedure to respond to this accidental injury.

After You Read

Describe. List two hot- or cold-weather related risks and write one or two sentences describing the effects of these risks.

Visit **health.glencoe.com** for the Interactive Study Guide for Lesson 5.

Lesson 5 Physical Activity Injuries **103**

What Is Everyone Walking About?

It's simple, it's cheap, and studies show that walking may be one of the best forms of exercise.

Walking may be the perfect exercise. For starters, it's one of the safest things you can do with your body. It's much easier on the knees than running and, beyond an occasional stitch in the side, doesn't trigger negative side effects. Researchers believe that if everyone in the United States were to walk briskly 30 minutes a day, we could cut the incidence of many diseases 30 to 40 percent.

Brisk walking provides many of the same benefits as more intense activities, like jogging or aerobics. Just walk at a reasonably vigorous pace (3 to 4 miles per hour) for about half an hour, five or six times a week. You may not feel the benefits all at once. Evidence, however, suggests that over the long term, a regular walking routine can do a world of preventive good—from lowering the risk of stroke and diabetes to helping combat arthritis and high blood pressure.

Before you begin, a few pointers can help you get the most out of your walking routine. First, pay attention to your shoes. Walkers spend more time with the entire foot on the ground than do runners, so shoes for walking need more room at the front for the feet to spread.

Second, keep a record of your efforts, including how long you walked and how far you went. There's nothing like tracking your improvements to keep you motivated.

Third, prepare yourself properly. The best way to avoid muscle aches is to start slowly and incorporate gentle stretches into your pre-exercise warm-up and post-exercise cool-down.

Finally, set realistic goals. Remember: You don't need to win any races to get healthy. The secret to success is to keep a steady course. ◾

TIME to THINK... About Walking

Create a schedule of your typical school day. Find at least three ways that you can increase the amount of walking that you do—for instance, taking the stairs rather than the elevator. Share your ideas with the class.

1. Practicing Healthful Behaviors. Identify three sedentary activities from your daily life and suggest a physical activity you could do in place of each. *(LESSON 1)*

 2. Goal Setting. Identify two areas of your health-related fitness that need improvement. Use the goal-setting steps to develop a plan for improving these areas. *(LESSON 2)*

 3. Advocacy. Prepare a short presentation in which you encourage teens to develop their own fitness programs based on the principles of overload, progression, and specificity. *(LESSON 3)*

 4. Refusal Skills. With a classmate, role-play a scenario in which you refuse a friend's offer of an herbal supplement that claims to enhance athletic performance. *(LESSON 4)*

 5. Accessing Information. Locate three sources in your community from whom you can request information about sports injuries. Summarize the information you receive from each source, and share your findings with the class. *(LESSON 5)*

Sports Medicine

Would you like to work with athletes and others who lead physically active lives? If so, you may enjoy a career in sports medicine. Physicians specializing in sports medicine treat injuries related to sports and other physical activities.

To enter this profession, you will need to complete a four-year college program, four years of medical school, and from one to seven years of residency training. Learn more about this and other related health careers by clicking on Career Corner at **health.glencoe.com.**

After You Read

On the back of your completed Foldable, use the information you have learned in this chapter to outline a personal plan to increase your weekly level of physical activity.

FOLDABLES™
Study Organizer

► EXPLORING HEALTH TERMS
Answer the following questions on a sheet of paper.

Lesson 1 *Replace the underlined words with the correct term.*

physical activity	**osteoporosis**
physical fitness	**sedentary lifestyle**
metabolism	

1. Watching television and taking naps are characteristic of a <u>physical activity</u>.
2. <u>Physical fitness</u> is a condition characterized by a decrease in bone density.
3. <u>Osteoporosis</u> refers to the process by which your body gets energy from food.

Lesson 2 *Fill in the blanks with the correct term.*

body composition	**muscular endurance**
exercise	**muscular strength**
flexibility	**aerobic exercise**
cardiorespiratory endurance	**anaerobic exercise**

Purposeful physical activity that is planned, structured, and repetitive and that improves or maintains fitness is (_4_). (_5_) is any rhythmic activity that uses large muscle groups and can be maintained continuously for 20 to 30 minutes at one time. (_6_) involves activities in which the muscles produce energy without using oxygen.

Lesson 3 *Replace the underlined words with the correct term.*

overload	**workout**
progression	**cool-down**
specificity	**F.I.T.T.**
warm-up	**resting heart rate**

7. The part of an exercise program when the activity is performed at its highest peak is called the <u>overload</u>.
8. A <u>workout</u> prepares the muscles for work.
9. An activity that prepares the muscles to return to a resting state is a <u>progression</u>.

Lesson 4 *Match each definition with the correct term.*

health screening	**hydration**
training program	**anabolic steroids**

10. A program of formalized physical preparation for involvement in a sport or another physical activity.
11. Taking in fluids so that the body functions properly.
12. A search or check for diseases or disorders that an individual would otherwise not have knowledge of or seek help for.

Lesson 5 *Identify each statement as True or False. If false, replace the underlined term with the correct term.*

overexertion	**hypothermia**
heatstroke	**muscle cramp**
heat cramps	**strain**
frostbite	**sprain**

13. Many hot-weather health problems, such as heat exhaustion, are related to <u>hypothermia</u>.
14. <u>Frostbite</u> is a condition that results when body tissues become frozen.
15. A <u>muscle cramp</u> is an injury to the ligament surrounding a joint.

► RECALLING THE FACTS
Use complete sentences to answer the following questions.

1. Examine and briefly describe the effects of regular physical activity on the nervous system.
2. Analyze the relationship between regular physical activity, health promotion, and disease prevention: How can engaging in regular physical activity reduce your risks of cardiovascular disease?
3. What is muscular strength, and how is it measured?
4. Examine and briefly describe how aerobic exercise affects the cardiovascular and respiratory systems.

For more review questions for Chapter 4, go to health.glencoe.com.

5. In the context of physical activity, what is meant by the term *progression*?

6. What three elements should be part of every physical activity session?

7. Why are proper nutrition and adequate rest important factors in a physical activity training program?

8. Why is starting a fitness program a situation that requires preventive health care?

9. Describe and analyze a strategy for responding to minor strains and sprains.

10. What symptoms signal a major injury that requires treatment from professional health services?

➤ WRITING CRITICALLY

1. **Descriptive.** Interview a coach at your school. Write a descriptive article that could be published in a newspaper or newsletter providing advice from the coach on how to develop a personal physical activity program. Include quotes from the coach describing how he or she feels fitness has improved their life.

2. **Persuasive.** Write a public service announcement that persuades others to begin a regular physical activity program. Make sure you include some of the positive benefits of fitness.

Standardized Test Practice

Read the passage below and then answer the questions.

The Cyclist

(1) Ingrid hunched over her handlebars and tried to pedal faster. (2) She had ridden a good race so far, and she didn't need to lose her concentration now. (3) At last, she was approaching the three leading riders. (4) And here came the last two miles of the race—a slow incline, followed by a curve, then a straight push to the finish line. (5) Ingrid switched gears and focused on a point ahead of her. (6) She passed one rider without even looking at him, concentrating instead on keeping a smooth and even pace. (7) Ingrid allowed herself to think about how she would feel if she lost. (8) Half a mile left and there were still two riders ahead! (9) "Steady, faster, steady faster," she thought. (10) Ingrid searched deep for the strength to increase her pace. (11) She passed another cyclist. (12) Concentrating, visualizing victory, she passed the third, final competitor and crossed the finish line. (13) Ingrid won!

---

1. Which sentence is not necessary to the overall organization of this passage and should be deleted?

   Ⓐ sentence 5
   Ⓑ sentence 7
   Ⓒ sentence 9
   Ⓓ sentence 13

2. The writer wants to add the following detail to the paragraph:

   With luck, her competitors would lose their concentration.

   Based on the organization of this paragraph, after which number on the list should this detail be added?

   Ⓕ after number 2
   Ⓖ after number 6
   Ⓗ after number 11
   Ⓘ after number 13

3. Write a paragraph that describes Ingrid's feelings and actions now that the race is over.

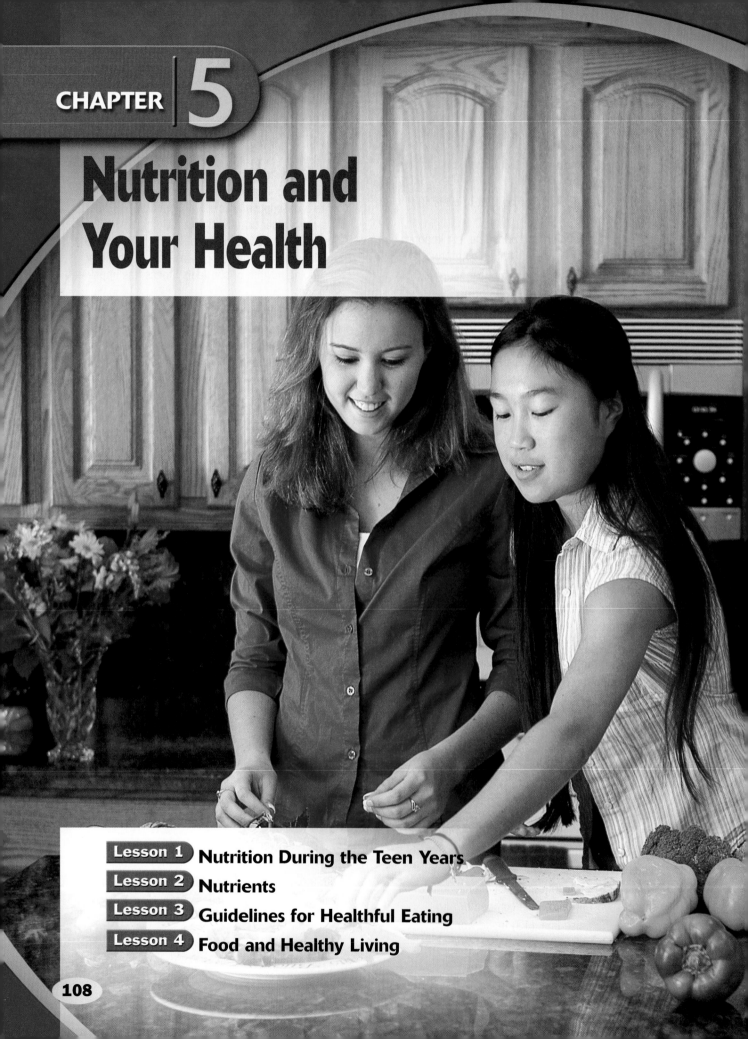

CHAPTER 5

Nutrition and Your Health

Analyzing Food Ads

Your choice of foods can be influenced by media advertisements. Food industry advertisers create ads targeting certain groups of people:

► **teens and children**

► **young adults**

► **married or unmarried people**

Visit the Eye on the Media section at **health.glencoe.com** to learn more about how advertisers try to influence what you eat.

FOLDABLES™
Study Organizer

Before You Read

Make this Foldable to record what you learn about the benefits of physical activity and the risks of physical inactivity. Begin with one sheet of plain 8½" x 11" paper or one sheet of notebook paper.

► **Step 1**

Fold a sheet of paper along the long axis.

► **Step 2**

Turn the paper, and fold into thirds.

► **Step 3**

Cut the top layer along both folds. Label the tabs as shown.

Hunger & Appetite | Food & Emotions | Food & Environment

As You Read

Write down any questions you have about how each of these three factors influences your eating habits. As you read the chapter, write answers to your questions under the tabs.

SPOTLIGHT ON HEALTH

Using Visuals. Food and social activities often go together. Describe how friends and family influence your eating habits and food choices.

Nutrition During the Teen Years

Guide to Reading

Building Vocabulary

As you read this lesson, write each new highlighted term and its definition in your notebook.

▶ nutrition (p. 110)
▶ calories (p. 110)
▶ nutrients (p. 110)
▶ hunger (p. 111)
▶ appetite (p. 111)

Focusing on the Main Ideas

In this lesson, you will learn how to:

▶ **Analyze** the relationship between nutrition, quality of life, and disease.
▶ **Evaluate** various influences on food choices.
▶ **Describe** the immediate and long-term benefits of nutrition on body systems.

Reading Strategy

Organize Information

▶ List the terms Calories, Nutrients, Hunger, Appetite, Emotion, and Environment on a sheet of paper. As you read, list the relevant factors under each term.

Quick Write

List five foods you like to eat. Describe why you like to eat each food.

Choosing fresh fruit as a snack is a good way to supply your body with the nutrients it needs.
What's your favorite healthful snack?

Picture yourself biting into a crisp, juicy apple or a slice of cheese pizza with zesty tomato sauce. Do these foods appeal to you? In this lesson, you will learn about the relationship between eating habits and total health. Enjoying a wide variety of healthful foods is an important part of good **nutrition**—*the process by which the body takes in and uses food.* Because not all foods offer the same benefits, making healthful food choices shows that you understand the impact of personal health behaviors on body systems.

The Importance of Good Nutrition

Good nutrition enhances your quality of life and helps prevent disease. It provides you with the calories and nutrients your body needs for maximum energy and wellness. **Calories**, or more correctly, kilocalories, are *units of heat that measure the energy used by the body and the energy that foods supply to the body.* **Nutrients** are *substances in food that your body needs to grow, to repair itself, and to supply you with energy.* Making healthy food choices will provide your body with the nutrients it needs to help you look your best and perform at your peak.

Take the Health Inventory for Chapter 5 at **health.glencoe.com**.

What Influences Your Food Choices?

Have you ever wondered why you choose the foods you do? Taste, of course, plays an important part in your choice of foods. You probably won't eat a food—even if you know it's healthful—if you don't like its taste. To gain insight into your eating habits, it's important to understand the difference between your physical *need* for food and your psychological *desire* for food—between hunger and appetite. Distinguishing between the two can help you make more healthful food choices. It is also important that you apply critical thinking skills to analyze marketing and advertising methods for influencing food choices.

Hunger and Appetite

Hunger, an unlearned, inborn response, is *a natural physical drive that protects you from starvation.* When your stomach is empty, its walls contract, stimulating nerve endings. The nerves signal your brain that your body needs food. When you eat, the walls of the stomach are stretched and the nerve endings are no longer stimulated. You have satisfied your physical need for food.

The physical need for food isn't the only reason people eat. Have you ever eaten something "just to be sociable" or in response to a familiar sensation—for example, the aroma of freshly baked bread? In such cases you are eating in response to appetite rather than to hunger. **Appetite** is *a desire, rather than a need, to eat.* Whether you are responding to hunger or to appetite when you eat, many factors influence your food choices and eating habits, including your emotions and a number of factors in your environment.

Food and Emotions

Food is sometimes used to meet emotional needs. For example, do you tend to eat more—or less—when you feel stressed, frustrated, or depressed? Do you sometimes snack just because you're bored? Do you reward yourself with a food treat when you've achieved a goal? Using food to relieve tension or boredom or to reward yourself can result in overeating and unhealthful weight gain. On the other hand, if you lose interest in eating whenever you're upset, you may miss getting enough of the nutrients your body needs. Recognizing when emotions are guiding your food choices can help you break such patterns and improve your eating habits.

Food and Your Environment

A number of environmental factors influence food choices:

▶ **Family, friends, and peers.** Many of your eating habits were shaped as you were growing up, when adults planned your meals. Now you may prefer certain foods because you've grown up eating them. Friends and peers can influence you to try new foods.

Health Minute

Managing Your Eating Habits

To manage your eating habits:

▶ **Try not to be overly influenced by others in making food choices.** Make choices with your health in mind—not just your appetite.

▶ **Pay attention to quantity.** Start off with reasonably sized servings, and, if possible, use a smaller plate. Listen to your body's "hunger clock" rather than to your appetite. When you feel full, stop eating. It takes 20 minutes for your stomach to signal your brain that it is satisfied.

▶ **Make something other than food the focus of social occasions.** If you are getting together with friends, for example, consider a setting other than a restaurant, such as a park or community center.

Reading Check

Describe What is the difference between hunger and appetite?

Resilient TEENS

When 14-year-old Ali Hoy's mother and father split up, she was relieved. The late night arguments and shouting stopped. Ali admits to being confused and embarrassed by all that was happening in her life. "I was really sad and worried at first," she says. "Then Mom took me to a counselor, and things got better."

Today, Ali's outlook is different. Her mother remarried and she's now part of a busy, happy family. She's studying oil painting, pottery, and guitar. She's involved in a variety of clubs and activities, including 4H and basketball. She's also become the family cook, preparing healthy dinners most evenings that are ready when her family comes home.

Ali has decided to become a professional chef. In her spare time, she writes away to culinary schools throughout the United States, requesting applications so that she can start right after she finishes high school in a couple of years. "I think all that stuff with the divorce made me tough," she says. "I know I'm strong."

"I was really sad and worried at first, then Mom took me to a counselor, and things got better."

Reading Check   **Describe** How did Ali use her love of cooking to bring her family together?

▶ **Cultural and ethnic background.** Your food choices may reflect your cultural heritage or ethnic background. Ethnic and cultural diversity both enrich and challenge healthy living. Some ethnic groups may eat more fruits and vegetables. Others may rely on using oils and salt.

▶ **Convenience and cost.** Convenience and cost of foods may be top priorities for some people. For example, busy families may rely on foods that can be prepared quickly, such as microwavable meals.

▶ **Advertising.** Advertisers spend millions of dollars each year to influence your decisions about food. Part of being an informed consumer involves carefully analyzing the health messages delivered through food advertisements in the media. Then you, rather than advertisers, will control your food choices.

Nutrition Throughout the Life Span

Good nutrition is essential for health throughout life but particularly during adolescence—one of the fastest periods of growth you'll experience. Healthful eating provides you with the nutrients you need for growth and development, gives you energy for sports and other activities, enables you to stay mentally alert, and helps you feel good and look your best. A healthful and balanced eating plan also helps prevent unhealthful weight gain, obesity, and type 2 diabetes— conditions that have become more common among children and teens in recent years. Making healthful food choices now also lowers your risk of developing many life-threatening conditions as you get older. These conditions include heart disease, stroke, certain cancers, and osteoporosis.

ⓥ Eating nutritious meals as a family can contribute to the health of all family members.

LESSON 1 REVIEW

Reviewing Facts and Vocabulary

1. Briefly explain the relationship between nutrition, quality of life, and disease.
2. Define the term *appetite.*
3. Name three influences—other than family—on people's food choices.

Thinking Critically

4. **Evaluating.** Give examples of how your family has influenced your food choices.
5. **Applying.** How does what you eat now affect your health, both now and as you grow older?

Applying Health Skills

Analyzing Influences. Look through magazines and other printed media to find five food advertisements that contain specific health claims. Analyze the health message that each ad delivers about its product. How might it influence your food choice? Present your findings in the form of a table.

After You Read

Describe. Write a list of three influences on your food choices. For each influence, list at least two ways that it can have a positive or negative effect on what you eat.

LESSON 2

Nutrients

Guide to Reading

Building Vocabulary

As you read this lesson, write each new highlighted term and its definition in your notebook.

- carbohydrates (p. 114)
- fiber (p. 115)
- proteins (p. 116)
- lipid (p. 117)
- vitamins (p. 119)
- minerals (p. 120)

Focusing on the Main Ideas

In this lesson, you will learn how to:

- Describe the functions of the six basic nutrients in maintaining health.
- List nutrients in a variety of foods.
- Explain the relationship between nutrition, health promotion, and disease prevention.

Reading Strategy

Organize Information

- Write the word *nutrients*. Surround it with six circles titled Carbohydrates, Proteins, Fats, Vitamins, Minerals, and Water. As you read, list the relevant factors in each circle.

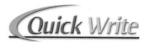 Quick Write

Write a brief paragraph describing a nutritious meal that you would enjoy.

Each of these foods is rich in one or more nutrients. *Which of these foods do you eat regularly?*

To survive, the human body needs the nutrients found in food. These nutrients are classified into six groups: carbohydrates, proteins, fats, vitamins, minerals, and water. Each plays a unique part in maintaining the normal growth and functioning of your body. Health-literate teens understand how nutrient and energy needs vary in relation to gender, activity level, and stage of life.

Carbohydrates

Carbohydrates are *the starches and sugars present in foods.* Made up of carbon, oxygen, and hydrogen, carbohydrates are the body's preferred source of energy, providing four calories per gram. Your body uses energy from carbohydrates to perform every task, including sitting and reading the words on this page. Depending on their chemical makeup, carbohydrates are classified as either simple or complex. Most nutritionists recommend that 55 to 60 percent of your daily calories come from carbohydrates, mainly complex carbohydrates.

Simple and Complex Carbohydrates

Simple carbohydrates are *sugars,* such as fructose and lactose (found in fruit and milk, respectively). You're probably most familiar with the simple carbohydrate sucrose. It occurs naturally in many plants, such as sugarcane and sugar beets, and is refined to make table sugar. Sugars are added to many manufactured food products.

Complex carbohydrates, or *starches,* are found in whole grains, seeds, nuts, legumes (dried peas and beans), and tubers (root vegetables such as potatoes). The body must break down complex carbohydrates into simple carbohydrates before it can use them for energy.

The Role of Carbohydrates

Your body converts all carbohydrates to glucose, a simple sugar that is the body's main source of energy. Glucose that your body does not use right away is stored in the liver and muscles as a starch-like substance called glycogen (GLI-coh-jen). When more energy is needed, your body converts the glycogen back to glucose. However, it's possible to take in more carbohydrates than your body can use right away or can store as glycogen. When this happens, your body converts and stores the excess carbohydrates as body fat. You can avoid consuming excess carbohydrates by learning to make informed food choices and maintaining healthful eating habits.

Fiber

Fiber is *an indigestible complex carbohydrate* that is found in the tough, stringy parts of vegetables, fruits, and whole grains. Although it can't be digested and used as energy, fiber helps move waste through the digestive system and thereby helps prevent intestinal problems such as constipation. Eating enough fiber throughout your life may promote health by reducing your risk of heart disease. Some types of fiber have also been shown to help control diabetes by reducing blood glucose levels.

To stay healthy, eat 20 to 35 grams of fiber each day. Fruits and vegetables with edible skins and whole-grain products such as bran cereals, oatmeal, and brown rice are excellent sources of fiber.

Health Minute
Getting More Fiber into Your Diet

To get 20–35 grams of fiber daily:

► Start your day with a whole-grain breakfast cereal, such as oatmeal.

► Choose whole fruit instead of fruit juice.

► Make sure you eat at least five servings of fruits and vegetables each day.

► Select high-fiber snacks (popcorn, raw vegetables, nuts, and fruit with edible skins).

► Eat legumes at least two or three times a week.

► Substitute whole-grain ingredients (whole-wheat flour, bran) for low-fiber ingredients (white flour) in recipes whenever possible.

▼ **Each of these foods is a rich source of carbohydrates.**

Proteins

A vital part of every cell in your body, **proteins** are *nutrients that help build and maintain body cells and tissues.* Proteins are made of long chains of substances called amino acids. Your body can manufacture all but 9 of the 20 different amino acids that make up proteins. The 9 that your body can't make are called *essential amino acids*—you must get them from the foods you eat.

Complete and Incomplete Proteins

The proteins in food are classified into two groups, *complete proteins* and *incomplete proteins.*

▶ **Complete proteins** contain adequate amounts of all nine essential amino acids. Animal products—such as fish, meat, poultry, eggs, milk, cheese, and yogurt—and many soybean products are good sources of complete proteins.

▶ **Incomplete proteins** lack one or more of the essential amino acids. Sources include beans, peas, nuts, and whole grains. Consuming a combination of incomplete proteins, for example, rice and beans or peanut butter and bread, is equivalent to consuming a complete protein. You don't have to combine the incomplete proteins in one meal to get this benefit, you just need to eat them both over the course of the day.

The Role of Proteins

Proteins have many functions. During major growth periods, such as infancy, childhood, adolescence, and pregnancy, the body builds new cells and tissues from the amino acids in proteins. Throughout your life your body replaces damaged or worn-out cells by making new ones from protein. The body also uses protein to make enzymes, hormones, and antibodies. Enzymes are substances that control the rate of chemical reactions in your cells. Hormones regulate the activities of different cells, and antibodies help identify and destroy disease-causing organisms. Proteins also supply the body with energy, although they are not the body's main energy source. Like carbohydrates, proteins provide four calories per gram and excess protein is converted to body fat.

Reading Check

Explain What is fiber?

Each of these foods is a good source of protein. *Which of these foods contain complete proteins? Which contain incomplete proteins?*

Fats

Some fat in the diet is necessary for good health. Fats are a type of **lipid** (LIHP•ehd), *a fatty substance that does not dissolve in water.* Fats provide more than twice the energy of carbohydrates or proteins—9 calories per gram.

The building blocks of fats are called fatty acids, molecules made mostly of long chains of carbon atoms, with pairs of hydrogen atoms and single oxygen atoms attached. Fatty acids that the body needs, but cannot produce, are called *essential fatty acids.* Depending on their chemical composition, fatty acids are classified as either saturated or unsaturated. Most fats are a mixture of these two types.

Saturated and Unsaturated Fatty Acids

A *saturated fatty acid* holds all the hydrogen atoms it can. Fats high in saturated fatty acids are usually solid at room temperature. Animal fats and tropical oils—such as palm oil, palm kernel oil, and coconut oil—have a high proportion of saturated fatty acids. Fats in beef, pork, egg yolks, and dairy foods are higher in saturated fatty acids than are the fats in chicken and fish. A high intake of saturated fats is associated with an increased risk of heart disease.

Most vegetable fats—including olive, canola, soybean, corn, and cottonseed oils—contain a high proportion of unsaturated fatty acids. An *unsaturated fatty acid* has at least one unsaturated bond—a place where hydrogen can be added to the molecule. Unsaturated fats are usually liquids (oils) at room temperature. In contrast to saturated fats, unsaturated fats have been associated with a reduced risk of heart disease.

The Role of Fats

Besides providing a concentrated form of energy, fats are essential for other important health functions. They transport vitamins A, D, E, and K in your blood and serve as sources of *linoleic* (lih•noh•LAY•ihk) *acid,* an essential fatty acid that is needed for growth and healthy skin. Fats also add flavor and texture to food, and, because they take longer to digest than carbohydrates or proteins, they help satisfy hunger longer than other nutrients do. Foods that are high in fats also tend to be high in calories, and consuming excess amounts of fat increases your risk of unhealthful weight gain and obesity. Most nutritionists recommend eating only moderate amounts of fat—no more than 20 to 30 percent of your total daily calorie intake.

The foods pictured here all contain fat. *Classify each food shown here as a source of saturated fat or unsaturated fat.*

Reducing Your Intake of Fats

Consuming too much fat can increase the risk of heart disease and unhealthful weight gain. Most teen boys need no more than 84 grams of fat each day. Most teen girls need no more than 66 grams each day. Analyzing the amount of fat in fast foods and snacks can help you see how to reduce your consumption of fats.

What You'll Need

• paper and pencil

What You'll Do

1. List every fast-food and snack item you eat and the portion size of each over the next three days. Next to each item, record how many grams of fat were in that portion. You can find fat grams in snacks by reading the label on packaged food products or by using a computerized dietary analysis program. Fast-food restaurants can provide a list of nutritional information about their products.

2. Determine the total number of fat grams you consumed over the three-day period. Then divide by three to find your daily average. What did you discover? Were there any surprises?

3. Using your dietary analysis as a guide, set a goal to consume a healthy intake of fat for the next three days. Write a detailed plan describing the steps you will take to reach your goal.

Apply and Conclude

Follow your plan for three days. As a class, share low-fat foods that you tried and enjoyed.

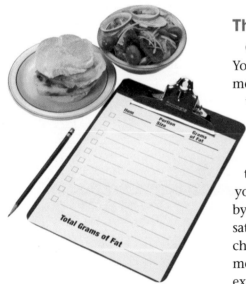

The Role of Cholesterol

Cholesterol is a waxy lipidlike substance that circulates in blood. Your body uses the small amount it manufactures to make cell membranes and nerve tissue and to produce many hormones, vitamin D, and bile, which helps digest fats. Excess blood cholesterol is deposited in arteries, including the arteries of the heart. This increases the risk of heart disease.

High cholesterol may be hereditary, and cholesterol levels tend to rise as people age. Although heredity and age are out of your control, you can significantly reduce your risk of heart disease by eating a diet low in saturated fats and cholesterol. A high intake of saturated fats is linked to increased cholesterol production. Dietary cholesterol is found only in animal products such as egg yolks, meats (especially organ meats), and high-fat milk products. Losing excess weight can also lower cholesterol levels.

Vitamins

Vitamins are *compounds that help regulate many vital body processes, including the digestion, absorption, and metabolism of other nutrients.* Vitamins are classified as either water- or fat-soluble.

Water-soluble vitamins, listed in **Figure 5.1,** dissolve in water and pass easily into the blood during digestion. The body doesn't store these vitamins, so you need to replenish them regularly through the foods you eat. Fat-soluble vitamins are absorbed, stored, and transported in fat. Your body stores these vitamins in your fatty tissue, liver, and kidneys. Excess buildup of these vitamins in your body can be toxic. **Figure 5.2** on page 120 provides more information about fat-soluble vitamins.

Reading Check

Compare and Contrast
What is the difference between water-soluble and fat-soluble vitamins?

FIGURE 5.1

WATER-SOLUBLE VITAMINS

Vitamin/Amount Needed Each Day	Role in Body	Food Source
C (ascorbic acid) Teen female: 60 mg Teen male: 60 mg	protects against infection, helps form connective tissue, helps heal wounds, maintains elasticity and strength of blood vessels, promotes healthy teeth and gums	citrus fruits, cantaloupe, tomatoes, cabbage, broccoli, potatoes, peppers
B₁ (thiamine) Teen female: 1.1 mg Teen male: 1.5 mg	converts glucose into energy or fat, contributes to good appetite	whole-grain or enriched cereals, liver, yeast, nuts, legumes, wheat germ
B₂ (riboflavin) Teen female: 1.3 mg Teen male: 1.8 mg	essential for producing energy from carbohydrates, fats, and proteins; helps keep skin healthy	milk, cheese, spinach, eggs, beef liver
Niacin Teen female: 15 mg Teen male: 20 mg	important for maintenance of all body tissues; helps in energy production; needed by body to utilize carbohydrates, to synthesize body fat, and for cell respiration	milk, eggs, poultry, beef, legumes, peanut butter, whole grains, enriched and fortified grain products
B₆ Teen female: 1.5 mg Teen male: 2.0 mg	essential for amino acid and carbohydrate metabolism, helps turn the amino acid *tryptophan* into serotonin (a messenger to the brain) and niacin	wheat bran and wheat germ, liver, meat, whole grains, fish, vegetables
Folic acid Teen female: 180 mcg Teen male: 200 mcg	necessary for production of genetic material and normal red blood cells, reduces risk of birth defects	nuts and other legumes, orange juice, green vegetables, folic acid-enriched breads and rolls, liver
B₁₂ Teen female: 2.0 mcg Teen male: 2.0 mcg	necessary for production of red blood cells and for normal growth	animal products such as meat, fish, poultry, eggs, milk, and other dairy foods; some fortified foods

FIGURE 5.2

FAT-SOLUBLE VITAMINS

Vitamin/Amount Needed Each Day	Role in Body	Food Source
A Teen female: 800 mcg Teen male: 1,000 mcg	helps maintain skin tissue, strengthens tooth enamel, promotes use of calcium and phosphorous in bone formation, promotes cell growth, keeps eyes moist, helps eyes adjust to darkness, may aid in cancer prevention	milk and other dairy products, green vegetables, carrots, deep-orange fruits, liver
D Teen female: 5 mcg Teen male: 5 mcg	promotes absorption and use of calcium and phosphorous, essential for normal bone and tooth development	fortified milk, eggs, fortified breakfast cereals, sardines, salmon, beef, margarine; produced in skin exposed to sun's ultraviolet rays
E Teen female: 8 mg Teen male: 10 mg	may help in oxygen transport, may slow the effects of aging, may protect against destruction of red blood cells	vegetable oils, apples, peaches, nectarines, legumes, nuts, seeds, wheat germ
K Teen female: 55 mcg Teen male: 65 mcg	essential for blood clotting, assists in regulating blood calcium level	spinach, broccoli, eggs, liver, cabbage, tomatoes

(Y) You get many of the minerals your body needs from these types of foods.

Minerals

Minerals are *substances that the body cannot manufacture but that are needed for forming healthy bones and teeth and for regulating many vital body processes.* Several key minerals are described in **Figure 5.3.**

Water

Water is vital to every body function. It transports other nutrients to and carries wastes from your cells. Water also lubricates your joints and mucous membranes. It enables you to swallow and digest foods, absorb other nutrients, and eliminate wastes. Through perspiration, water helps maintain normal body temperature. It's important to drink at least 8 cups of water a day to maintain health. Plain water, milk, and juice are the best sources of this nutrient. Beverages containing caffeine, such as tea, coffee, and some soft drinks, are not good choices—they cause you to lose some water through increased urination. Certain foods, such as fruits and vegetables, also contain some water.

FIGURE 5.3

SOME IMPORTANT MINERALS

Mineral/Amount Needed Each Day	Role in Body	Food Source
Calcium Teen female: 1,300 mg Teen male: 1,300 mg	building material of bones and teeth (skeleton contains about 99% of body calcium), regulation of body functions (heart muscle contraction, blood clotting)	dairy products; leafy vegetables; canned fish with soft, edible bones; tofu processed with calcium sulfate
Phosphorous Teen female: 1,250 mg Teen male: 1,250 mg	combines with calcium to give rigidity to bones and teeth, essential in cell metabolism, helps maintain proper acid-base balance of blood	milk and most other dairy foods, peas, beans, liver, meat, fish, poultry, eggs, broccoli, whole grains
Magnesium Teen female: 360 mg Teen male: 410 mg	enzyme activator related to carbohydrate metabolism, aids in bone growth and muscle contraction	whole grains, milk, dark green leafy vegetables, legumes, nuts
Iron Teen female: 15 mg Teen male: 12 mg	part of the red blood cells' oxygen and carbon dioxide transport system, important for use of energy in cells and for resistance to infection	meat, shellfish, poultry, legumes, peanuts, dried fruits, egg yolks, liver, fortified breakfast cereal, enriched rice

LESSON 2 | REVIEW

Reviewing Facts and Vocabulary

1. Compare the energy provided to the body by carbohydrates, proteins, and fats.
2. Analyze the relationship between good nutrition, health promotion, and disease prevention: How can reducing your saturated fat intake help lower your risk of heart disease?
3. What are *vitamins*?

Thinking Critically

4. **Analyzing.** Your friend Steve wants to cut down on his intake of saturated fats and cholesterol. What advice would you give him?
5. **Synthesizing.** What are the benefits of eating a variety of fruits and vegetables?

Applying Health Skills

Goal Setting. Copy your school's weekly lunch menus, and examine each day's options. Using what you've learned about nutrients in this lesson, list the most healthful food choices available each day. Then set a goal to eat healthful school lunches for the next week. Use the goal-setting steps to help you create a plan.

After You Read

Explain. Write a summary explaining why it's important to eat a well-balanced diet that includes all of the nutrients listed in this lesson.

Visit **health.glencoe.com** for the Interactive Study Guide for Lesson 2.

Lesson 2 Nutrients **121**

Guidelines for Healthful Eating

Guide to Reading

Building Vocabulary

As you read this lesson, write each new highlighted term and its definition in your notebook.

▶ *Dietary Guidelines for Americans* (p. 122)

▶ MyPyramid (p. 124)

Focusing on the Main Ideas

In this lesson, you will learn how to:

▶ Apply balance, variety, and moderation when making food choices.

▶ Describe the effects of healthful eating behaviors on body systems.

▶ Formulate healthful meals and snacks as part of a balanced diet.

Reading Strategy

Predict

▶ Scan the headings, sub-headings, and pictures in this lesson. Write at least three questions that you believe will be answered in the reading.

Quick Write

Write a brief paragraph about the importance of eating a variety of different foods.

Ⓐ Choosing nutritious foods from the thousands of products available can be a challenge. *What are some factors to consider when shopping for food?*

Guidelines for Healthful Eating

No single food provides all the nutrients your body needs at all stages of your life.

Dietary Guidelines for Americans

The U.S. Department of Agriculture (USDA) and the Department of Health and Human Services (DHHS) have published the ***Dietary Guidelines for Americans***. The guidelines are *recommendations about food choices for all healthy Americans age 2 and over*. The guidelines highlight three keys to a healthy lifestyle:

▶ Make smart choices from every food group.

▶ Find a balance between food and physical activity.

▶ Get the most nutrition out of your calories.

Making Smart Choices from Every Food Group

The best way eat a balanced variety of nutrient-rich foods is by carefully choosing foods from every food group every day.

▶ Focus on a variety of fruits, whether fresh, frozen, canned, or dried. Try fruits other than the usual apples, bananas, oranges, and strawberries. Mango, guava, cantaloupe, papaya, and kiwi can add variety to your diet. To ensure adequate fiber intake, eat whole fruits rather than juice.

▶ Vary your veggies by eating more dark green and leafy vegetables and orange vegetables. Legumes are especially rich in fiber and should be consumed several times a week.

▶ Make half your grains whole. Look to see that grains are referred to as "whole" in the list of ingredients.

▶ Eat calcium-rich foods—such as low-fat or fat-free milk, yogurt, or cottage cheese. If you don't or can't consume milk, choose lactose-free milk products and/or calcium fortified foods and beverages.

▶ Go lean on meat protein and add more beans—such as pinto beans, kidney beans, black beans, garbanzo beans, and lentils. Eat more poultry and fish.

Choosing a variety of fruits and vegetables each day is an important part of building a healthy base. *What fruits and vegetables would you choose as an afternoon snack?*

Balancing Food and Physical Activity

As well as healthful eating, regular physical activity is important to staying well. Physical activity helps you control body weight by balancing the calories you take in as food with the calories you expend every day. The following guidelines will help you find balance between these needs.

▶ Aim for a healthy weight. Maintaining your weight helps you look and feel good. It also lowers your risk for heart disease, some cancers, and diabetes.

▶ Be physically active for 60 minutes every day, or almost every day.

▶ For even greater health benefits and to help control body weight, increase the intensity or the amount of time that you are physically active. About 60 minutes a day may be needed to prevent weight gain.

MyPyramid

MyPyramid is the USDA's food pyramid, shown in **Figure 5.4,** and is a useful tool for making healthful food and activity choices. Each of the colored bars that runs down the length of the pyramid depicts one of the food groups, including grains, vegetables, fruits, milk, and meat and beans. Fats, oils, and sweets are not a food group and should be consumed sparingly. The width of each bar shows you how much of that food you should eat in comparison to the other foods listed on the pyramid. A wider bar means that you should choose more of the foods in that group. As you can see, the grains and vegetables bars are the widest on the pyramid. The meat and beans bar is among the narrowest on the pyramid. This means that a larger percentage of the foods you eat should fall into the grains and vegetables categories rather than meats and beans.

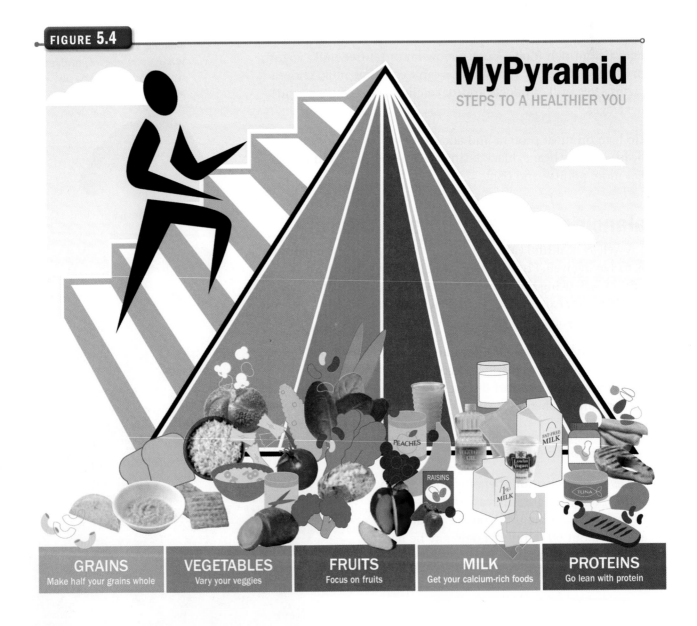

FIGURE 5.4

MyPyramid
STEPS TO A HEALTHIER YOU

| GRAINS | VEGETABLES | FRUITS | MILK | PROTEINS |
| Make half your grains whole | Vary your veggies | Focus on fruits | Get your calcium-rich foods | Go lean with protein |

FIGURE 5.5

CALORIE LEVELS

Age	Females			Males		
	Sedentary*	Mod. Active*	Active*	Sedentary*	Mod. Active*	Active*
14	1800	2000	2400	2000	2400	2800
15	1800	2000	2400	2200	2600	3000
16	1800	2000	2400	2400	2800	3200
17	1800	2000	2400	2400	2800	3200
18	1800	2000	2400	2400	2800	3200

*The number of calories you consume each day is directly related to your activity level. Sedentary means less than 30 minutes of moderate physical activity each day. Moderately Active refers to at least 30 to 60 minutes a day of moderate physical activity. Active means 60 or more minutes a day of moderate physical activity.

Understanding Serving Sizes

In addition to making smart food choices, it's important to make sure that you don't eat more than the correct portion size. Understanding portion sizes will help you see how much food is actually being recommended and will help you practice control. A portion is how much of a food you eat in one meal. Visualizing some common objects can help you estimate portion sizes and control the number of servings you eat. A medium apple, or one portion, is about the size of a tennis ball. One serving of meat is about the size of a regular computer mouse. A piece of meat twice this size equals two servings.

Getting the Most Nutrition from Your Calories

The amount of food you eat is directly related to your activity level. Active teens can eat more without gaining weight than inactive teens. To determine your range of recommended calories, see **Figure 5.5.**

The *Dietary Guidelines* define active as a lifestyle that includes physical activity equivalent to walking more than three miles per day at a pace of three to four miles per hour. When making food choices, consider your activity level and how many calories you believe you will use during the day. You could use up your entire calorie requirements for a day on a few high-calorie items.

CHARACTER CHECK

Citizenship. Citizenship means doing what you can to improve your community. For example, there may be people in your community who go hungry. **Find out how to organize an effort to collect nonperishable food items for a local food bank or homeless shelter. How could this benefit the whole community?**

Reading Check

Explain How can the *Dietary Guidelines* help you make healthy food choices?

Moderation in Fats

To maintain good health, it is necessary to consume some dietary fats. However, the type of fat makes a difference to heart health, and the total amount consumed is also important. The *Dietary Guidelines* recommend that teens keep their total fat intake to no more than 35 percent of daily calories. The *Guidelines* also recommend that most fats come from sources such as fish, nuts, and vegetable oils. Eating less fat, especially saturated and trans fats, will lower your risk of developing cardiovascular disease. If you eat high-fat foods at one meal, eat foods that are lower in fats at other meals.

Moderation in Sugar

You might think that you don't eat much added sugar, but sugars are hidden many foods, including prepared foods. You can moderate your sugar intake by

▶ learning to identify added sugars by their names on food packages. Corn syrup, honey, and molasses are all types of sugar, as are ingredients ending with –ose, such as sucrose, fructose, and maltose.

▶ balancing foods that have added sugars with those that have less added sugars.

▶ limiting your intake of foods that have added sugars but few other nutrients. For example, choose 100 percent fruit juice or water instead of regular soda.

▶ choosing fresh fruits or canned fruits packed in water or juice.

Moderation in Salt

Sodium is an essential mineral. It helps transport nutrients into your cells and helps move wastes out. It also helps maintain normal blood pressure and nerve function. However, most Americans consume far too much salt. Consuming less salt can reduce your chances of developing high blood pressure and may also benefit your skeletal system by decreasing the loss of calcium. Try these tips to moderate your salt intake.

▶ Read the Nutrition Facts panel on food labels to learn how much sodium a serving contains. Choose foods that are low in sodium (less than 140 mg or 5 percent of the Daily Value [DV]).

▶ When eating at restaurants, ask for foods that are prepared without salt or salty flavorings or with reduced amounts of them.

▶ Taste foods before you salt them, and then go easy with the salt shaker. Better yet, season foods with herbs and spices instead of with salt.

▶ Choose fresh fruits and vegetables often.

Real-Life Application

Smart Snacking

Eating several small snacks each day can help growing teens get the nutrients they need. You can choose snacks that promote good health without adding too much fat or too many calories.

Nutrition Facts

Serving Size 1 cookie (17g)
Servings Per Container about 27

Amount Per Serving

Calories 90	Calories from Fat 45

% Daily Value*

Total Fat 5g	**8%**
Saturated Fat 2.5g	**13%**
Trans Fat	
Cholesterol 5mg	2%
Sodium 80mg	3%
Total Carbohydrate 11g	4%
Dietary Fiber 0g	0%
Sugars 6g	
Protein 1g	

Vitamin A	0% •	Vitamin C	0%
Calcium	0% •	Iron	2%

* Percent Daily Values are based on a 2,000 calorie diet. Your daily values may be higher or lower depending on your calorie needs:

ACTIVITY

In small groups, examine the snack labels that your group or teacher has brought to class. Read labels to identify snacks that are low in fat and sugar. In a paragraph, explain other ways the information on labels can help you choose nutritious snacks.

Calories from Fat
Look at this section of the Nutrition Facts panel to find out how much fat is in the snack you are choosing.

Total Fat
This gives you an overview of the fat in the snack. The amount of fat is listed in grams. Remember that fats provide 9 calories per gram, so even small amounts of fats can add many calories.

Saturated Fat
This tells how much of the fat in the snack is saturated. Remember, limiting saturated fats can help reduce the risk of heart disease.

***Trans* Fat**
This tells how much of the fat in the snack is *trans* fat. Keep consumption of *trans* fat low: 5% or less is low; 20% or more is high.

Total Carbohydrate
Under this heading you'll find information about sugars. These, too, are listed in grams. Carbohydrates provide 4 calories per gram.

Healthful Eating Patterns

Whether you eat three meals a day or even more "mini-meals," *variety, moderation,* and *balance* are the foundation of a healthful eating plan. Many people, including teens, find making healthful food choices particularly challenging when having break-fast, snacking, and eating out. Keep in mind that nutrition guide-lines apply to all of your daily food choices, not to just a single meal or food. Any food that supplies calories and nutrients can be part of a healthful eating plan. You don't have to deprive yourself of your favorite foods. With a little planning, you can fit them into your diet.

Reading Check

Cause and Effect How does healthful eating help you stay healthy?

Many types of foods can be part of a healthy breakfast. *Name three nontraditional breakfast foods that you might like to try.*

The Importance of Breakfast

You've probably heard the saying, "Breakfast is the most important meal of the day." While you sleep, your body uses energy for functions such as breathing and keeping your heart beating. By the time you wake up, your body needs a fresh supply of energy. Studies show that eating a nutritious breakfast improves mental and physical performance and reduces fatigue later in the day. If you eat breakfast, you tend to perform better in school, get better grades, and miss fewer days of school. Eating breakfast may also help you maintain a healthy weight. Skipping this meal may cause you to overeat later in the day.

Breakfast foods don't have to be "traditional," such as cereal or eggs. Try eating peanut butter on toast, or a stuffed tomato. To get enough vitamin C, add citrus juice, fruit, or tomato juice to your meal. Breakfast is also a good time to eat a high-fiber cereal and get one calcium-rich serving of milk, cheese, or yogurt.

Nutritious Snacks

A healthful eating plan can include sensible snacks. When you think about snacks, you might think of potato chips, soft drinks, and candy bars. These foods contain a lot of calories but very few nutrients. They may also be high in fat, added sugars, or salt. More healthful snacks include whole-grain products, fruits, and vegetables. If you have practice or a game after school, pack some fresh fruit, cut-up vegetables, string cheese, or a handful of unsalted nuts to avoid eating less healthful snacks. **Figure 5.6** lists some healthful snack items.

FIGURE 5.6

SENSIBLE SNACKS

Food	Food Group	Total Calories per Serving	Calories from Fat
Air-popped popcorn, 3 cups (plain)	Grains	23	0
Apple, 1 medium	Fruit	80	0
Bagel, ½ (small, 2 oz.)	Grains	83	10
Bread stick, 1	Grains	42	6
Frozen juice bar, 4 oz.	Fruit	75	0
Skim milk, 1 cup	Milk	90	0
Sugar-free gelatin (½ cup) with ½ cup sliced banana	Fruit	76	0
Graham cracker squares, 3	Grains	80	15
Pretzel sticks, 50 small	Grains	60	9
Fat-free, sugar-free yogurt, 6 oz.	Milk	86	0

Eating Out, Eating Right

It's important that you learn to develop a personal healthful eating plan that incorporates food choices outside the home setting. This shows that you know various strategies when applying the decision-making process regarding healthy habits. Be aware that many menu items may be fried or topped with mayonnaise, butter, or high-fat sauces. For less fat, order foods that are grilled, baked, or broiled, and ask that high-fat sauces not be used at all or be served on the side. Many fast-food restaurants list the calorie counts and other nutrition information for the foods they serve. You can ask to see this list before placing your order.

When eating out, remember to watch portion sizes. Most restaurant meals are much larger than the serving sizes recommended in the *Dietary Guidelines* and My Pyramid. You may want to eat only part of a portion and take the rest home to enjoy later. As an alternative, offset the larger meal with a smaller meal later.

When eating out, don't hesitate to ask how a particular dish is cooked or what ingredients it contains. *Name two other ways to make healthy food choices when eating out.*

LESSON 3 REVIEW

Reviewing Facts and Vocabulary

1. Define the *Dietary Guidelines for Americans.*
2. Examine the effects of healthful eating behaviors on body systems: How can decreasing salt intake benefit the cardiovascular and skeletal systems?

Thinking Critically

3. **Analyzing.** Why might a person eat fewer servings than recommended by the MyPyramid and still gain an unhealthy amount of weight?
4. **Evaluating.** For lunch Josh had a cheeseburger, fries, and a nondiet soft drink. What could he choose for his afternoon snack and dinner to balance out his high-fat, high-sugar, high-salt meal?

Applying Health Skills

Advocacy. Work with a partner to create a poster that encourages teens to adopt healthful eating habits. Use pictures cut from magazines, computer graphics, or your own drawings to illustrate your poster.

After You Read

Identify Problems and Solutions. Create a one-day menu incorporating the advice in the *Dietary Guidelines*. Write down at least three obstacles you may face by following this menu. Provide solutions for each problem.

Visit **health.glencoe.com** for the Interactive Study Guide for Lesson 3.

Lesson 3 Guidelines for Healthful Eating **129**

Food and Healthy Living

Guide to Reading

Building Vocabulary

As you read this lesson, write each new highlighted term and its definition in your notebook.

▶ food additives (p. 131)

▶ food allergy (p. 133)

▶ food intolerance (p. 134)

▶ foodborne illness (p. 134)

▶ pasteurization (p. 135)

▶ cross-contamination (p. 136)

Focusing on the Main Ideas

In this lesson, you will learn how to:

▶ Analyze the information on food labels.

▶ Compose eating plans to meet changing nutritional requirements, such as special dietary needs and food allergies.

▶ Describe the causes and prevention of foodborne illness.

Reading Strategy

Predict

▶ This lesson contains information on nutrition labeling and foodborne illnesses. Select one of these topics and write a one-page summary describing the type of information you believe will be contained in the lesson.

Quick Write

Make a list of the types of information on a food label that could help you make a healthy food choice.

The labels on packaged food products contain valuable information for the consumer.

Using the *Dietary Guidelines* is one good way to assess the nutritional contribution of a particular food to your overall eating pattern. Similarly, the information on packaged and prepared foods can help you determine whether or not a particular product meets your nutritional needs. Know strategies for health enhancement and risk reduction. Part of health literacy also involves understanding and evaluating food product claims.

Nutrition Labeling

Examine almost any food package, and you'll find a Nutrition Facts panel. The law requires that these information panels be placed on packages of food that are intended for sale. The information provided in a Nutrition Facts panel is shown in **Figure 5.7.**

FIGURE 5.7

NUTRITION FACTS

Nutrition Facts
Serving Size 30g (about 12 pretzels)
Servings Per Container 30 ✺

Amount Per Serving	
Calories 110	Calories from Fat 10 ✺

	% Daily Value*
Total Fat 1g	**2%**
Saturated Fat 0g	**0%**
Trans Fat 0g	**0%**
Cholesterol 0mg	**0%**
Sodium 300mg	**13%**
Total Carbohydrate 23g	**8%**
Dietary Fiber 1g	**4%**
Sugars Less than 1g	
Protein 3g	

Vitamin A	0% •	Vitamin C	0%
Calcium	0% •	Iron	4%

* Percent Daily Values are based on a 2,000 ✺ calorie diet. Your daily values may be higher or lower depending on your calorie needs:

Total Fat	Less Than	65g	80g
Sat Fat	Less Than	20g	25g
Cholesterol	Less Than	300mg	300mg
Sodium	Less Than	2,400mg	2,400mg
Total Carbohydrate		300g	375g
Dietary Fiber		25g	30g

Calories per gram:
Fat 9 • Carbohydrate 4 • Protein 4

Serving Size and Servings Per Container
- Nutrient and calorie content is calculated according to serving size. The serving size on the label may differ from sizes in the *Dietary Guidelines*. The number of servings in the package is also listed.

Calories and Calories from Fat
- The number of calories in one serving and how many of these calories come from fat is given here.

Nutrients (Top section)
- The amounts of total fat, saturated fat, *trans* fat, cholesterol, and sodium per serving are listed in either grams (g) or milligrams (mg).
- The amounts of total carbohydrates, dietary fiber, sugars, and protein per serving are given.

Nutrients (Bottom section)
- Major vitamins and minerals are listed with their Percent Daily Values.

Percent Daily Value
- This section tells you how much the nutrients in one serving contribute to your total daily eating plan. The general guideline is that 20% or more of a nutrient is a lot and 5% or less isn't very much. Choose foods that are high in fiber, vitamins, and minerals and low in fat, cholesterol, and sodium.

The Footnote (Lower part of Nutrition Facts Panel)
- This information is the same from product to product. It contains advice about the amounts of certain nutrients that should be eaten each day.

Ingredients List

Most food labels also list the food's ingredients by weight, in descending order, with the ingredient in the greatest amount listed first. However, food labels that list several similar ingredients can be confusing. For example, when three sweeteners—sugar, honey, and corn syrup—are used in the same product, each is listed separately; therefore, they appear lower on the list than they would if they were counted as one ingredient, "sugars." This may give the impression that the product contains less sugar than it really does.

FOOD ADDITIVES

Some ingredients are **food additives**, *substances intentionally added to food to produce a desired effect.* Additives may be used to enhance a food's flavor or color or lengthen its storage life.

Reading Check

Explain Why is it important to read the Nutrition Facts panel on foods?

SUGAR AND FAT SUBSTITUTES

In response to the public's concerns about excess calories in foods, the food industry has developed a number of substitutes for sugar and fat. Many diet drinks, for example, are sweetened with *aspartame,* which is essentially calorie-free. Fructose, the natural sugar in fruit, is sometimes used as a sweetener. Because fructose is sweeter than table sugar, less sweetener is needed and fewer calories are added to the food. Some potato chips are made with fat replacers so that they supply few calories from fat. An example of a fat replacer is *olestra,* which passes through the body undigested. Because olestra is not absorbed, some people find that its consumption can produce gastrointestinal problems such as diarrhea.

Product Labeling

Along with nutrition information, food labels may state the potential health benefits of a food. In some cases the label may also detail the conditions under which the food was produced or grown—for example, whether or not a food is organic or contains organic ingredients.

Nutrient Content Claims

Product labels may advertise a food's nutrient value. Claims such as "100% Fat-Free" or "Light in Sodium" describe the nutrient content of a food. Some specific terms include the following:

▶ **Light or Lite.** The calories have been reduced by at least one-third, or the fat or sodium has been reduced by at least 50 percent.

▶ **Less.** The food contains 25 percent less of a nutrient or of calories than a comparable food.

Claims on food products must meet strict guidelines. Check the Nutrition Facts panel for more specific information. *What do the labels on each of these food products tell you?*

- **Free.** The food contains no amount, or an insignificant amount, of total fat, saturated fat, *trans* fat, cholesterol, sodium, sugars, or calories.

- **More.** The food contains 10 percent more of the Daily Value for a vitamin, a mineral, protein, or fiber.

- **High, Rich In, or Excellent Source Of.** The food contains 20 percent or more of the Daily Value for a vitamin, a mineral, protein, or fiber.

- **Lean.** The food is a meat, poultry, fish, or shellfish product that has less than 10 grams of total fat, less than 4 grams of saturated fat, and less than 95 mg of cholesterol per 3-ounce serving.

Open Dating

Many food products have *open dates* on their labels. The open dates on products such as milk and canned goods reflect their freshness. Canned foods eaten after these dates are safe, but they may not taste as fresh. Open dates on food such as meat can help you make decisions about the food's safety. Below are some common types of open dating you may see on product labels.

- **Expiration date.** The last date you should use the product.

- **Freshness date.** The last date a food is considered to be fresh.

- **Pack date.** The date on which the food was packaged.

- **Sell-by date (or pull date).** The last date the product should be sold.

Milk containers are labeled with a sell-by date. *What does this date indicate?*

Food Sensitivities

Do you know anyone who feels ill after eating certain foods? This person may have a special sensitivity to the food or to an additive in the food.

Food Allergies

A **food allergy** is *a condition in which the body's immune system reacts to substances in some foods.* These substances, called **allergens,** are proteins that the body responds to as if they were pathogens, or foreign invaders. Allergies to peanuts, tree nuts, eggs, wheat, soy, fish, and shellfish are most common. Scratch tests, in which tiny amounts of suspected allergens are injected under the skin, are a common test for allergies. A simple blood test can also indicate whether a person is allergic to a specific food.

People with allergies have different types of allergic reactions. These reactions may include rash, hives, or itchiness of the skin;

Did You Know?

Lactose intolerance, the inability or reduced ability to digest the natural sugar in milk, is a manageable condition. Small amounts of milk consumed more frequently may be easier to digest. Drinking milk with food helps, too. Another option is to get milk's nutrients from yogurt or cheese, which usually don't cause a problem. Health care professionals can provide lactase enzymes and can explain how to use them. Also, lactose-reduced milk and other products containing the same nutrients as milk are offered at many supermarkets.

vomiting, diarrhea, or abdominal pain; or itchy eyes and sneezing. If you eat something and experience any of these symptoms, consult a health care professional. Serious allergic reactions, such as difficulty breathing, can be deadly. If you or someone else experiences a severe allergic reaction, call for medical help immediately.

Food Intolerances

Food intolerances are more common than food allergies. A **food intolerance** is *a negative reaction to a food or part of food caused by a metabolic problem, such as the inability to digest parts of certain foods or food components.* Food intolerance may be associated with certain foods, such as milk or wheat, or with some food additives. Some types of food intolerance may be hereditary, such as the reduced ability to digest lactose (milk sugar) or gluten, a protein in some grain products.

Foodborne Illness

You've seen the signs in restaurant restrooms: "Employees must wash their hands before returning to work." Restaurants have this policy because handwashing after using the restroom is one strategy to prevent **foodborne illness**, or *food poisoning.* Foodborne illness may result from eating food contaminated with pathogens (disease-causing organisms), the poisons they produce, or poisonous chemicals. Many times the contaminant can't be seen, smelled, or tasted. The best way to protect yourself is to become knowledgeable about the causes of such illnesses and ways to keep food safe.

Allergic Reaction

Foods that can cause allergic reactions include milk products, soy products, peanuts, wheat, and shellfish. *What should you do if you have a severe reaction to any food?*

Causes and Symptoms of Foodborne Illness

According to the Centers for Disease Control and Prevention (CDC), bacteria and viruses cause most common foodborne illnesses. Bacteria that contaminate food include *Campylobacter*, *Salmonella*, and *E. coli* O157:H7. Viruses include the Norwalk and Norwalk-like viruses. Foods become contaminated with these pathogens in two main ways:

▶ Food may be contaminated with pathogens spread by an infected person. This means foodborne illness is a type of **communicable disease.**

▶ Animals raised or caught for food may harbor disease-causing organisms in their tissues. If meat or milk from such an animal is consumed without being thoroughly cooked or pasteurized, the organism may cause illness. **Pasteurization** is *the process of treating a substance with heat to destroy or slow the growth of pathogens.*

Common symptoms of foodborne illness include nausea, vomiting, diarrhea, and fever. Most people recover from these symptoms in a few days. However, foodborne illnesses can be very serious for older adults, very young children, people who are malnourished, or those with weakened immune systems. Individuals who have a fever greater than 101.5°F, who experience prolonged vomiting or diarrhea, or who show signs of dehydration—a decrease in urination, a dry mouth and throat, or dizziness when standing up—should consult a doctor.

Minimizing Risks of Foodborne Illness

Most cases of foodborne illness occur in the home, where pathogens can contaminate food products, kitchen surfaces, cooking and serving dishes, and eating utensils. Practicing good food safety habits, including food storage, cooking, and sanitation shows that you understand the role of individual responsibility regarding personal risk behaviors. To help keep food safe to eat, follow the practice recommended by the Partnership for Food Safety Education: clean, separate, cook, and chill.

Washing your hands after using the bathroom and before handling or eating foods greatly reduces your risk of foodborne illness and the risk of passing pathogens to others. *What are some of the symptoms of foodborne illness?*

Reading Check

Compare and Contrast
What are the differences between a food allergy and a food intolerance?

▶ **Clean.** Before preparing food and after using the bathroom, handling pets, changing diapers, or touching any other obvious source of pathogens, wash your hands thoroughly in hot, soapy water. To prevent **cross-contamination**, *the spreading of bacteria or other pathogens from one food to another,* wash your hands, cutting boards, utensils, plates, and countertops with hot, soapy water after preparing each food item. It is also recommended that you use cutting boards made of nonporous materials, such as plastic or glass, for preparing foods. When possible, use disposable paper towels instead of dishcloths to clean kitchen surfaces. Also, remember to wash fruits and vegetables before you eat them.

▶ **Separate.** To avoid cross-contamination, separate raw meat, seafood, and poultry from other items in your shopping cart. At home, store these foods separately from other foods. The bottom shelf of the refrigerator is a good place to keep these foods because their juices won't run onto other foods. Use separate cutting boards for raw meats and raw vegetables or foods that are ready to be eaten. Never place cooked food on a plate that previously held raw meat, seafood, or poultry. After contact with raw meats, wash cutting boards and other utensils (as well as your hands) in hot, soapy water.

▶ **Cook.** Cook foods to a safe temperature: 160°F for ground beef, 170°F for roasts and poultry, and 145°F for fish. Use a meat thermometer to make sure meats and fish are cooked thoroughly. When thoroughly cooked, meat or poultry juices should run clear. Properly cooked fish should be opaque and flake easily with a fork. Don't eat raw ground beef or ground beef that is still pink after being cooked. Avoid dishes that contain partially cooked or raw eggs. Sauces, soups, and gravies should be brought to a boil before serving.

▶ **Chill.** Cold temperatures slow the multiplication of bacteria. Refrigerate or freeze perishable foods as soon as you get home. Foods that need to be kept cold should be refrigerated quickly at temperatures of 40°F or less. Frozen foods should be stored at 0°F. Refrigerate or freeze prepared foods and leftovers within two hours after a meal—even sooner on a hot day. Divide leftovers into small, shallow containers to help them cool more quickly. Remove any stuffing before freezing meats or poultry. Don't over-pack the refrigerator; air needs

Wash cutting boards in hot, soapy water. *How can using different cutting boards for raw meats and raw vegetables help protect you from foodborne illness?*

to circulate around the food to keep it cool. Don't defrost foods on a kitchen counter. Instead, thaw these foods in a refrigerator, under cold running water, or by using a microwave's defrost function. At a picnic, keep hot foods hot and cold foods cold. Thoroughly cook meats at the picnic site. Discard foods that have been sitting out for two hours—one hour if the temperature is above 85°F.

Proper preparation of picnic foods will help ensure that these foods remain safe to eat. *Why should you discard any picnic food that's been sitting out for two hours?*

LESSON 4 | REVIEW

Reviewing Facts and Vocabulary

1. What can the ingredients list of a food product tell you?
2. How does a *food allergy* differ from a *food intolerance*?
3. What is *pasteurization*?

Thinking Critically

4. **Analyzing.** How does the policy that requires food service workers to wash their hands help prevent communicable disease?
5. **Applying.** Develop a strategy to store food that's left over from dinner.

Applying Health Skills

Accessing Information. Find three to five reliable online sources of information about practices related to preventing foodborne illness. Use these resources to create a pamphlet titled "Preventing Foodborne Illness."

After You Read

Cause and Effect. Make a chart with two columns. List the causes and symptoms of foodborne illness on one side. List the ways to minimize the risks of foodborne illness on the other side.

Visit **health.glencoe.com** for the Interactive Study Guide for Lesson 4.

Lesson 4 Food and Healthy Living **137**

Cracking a
Tough
PROBLEM

Could relief be in sight for those suffering from peanut allergy?

A peanut allergy can be very dangerous. Unlike hay fever, an even more common allergy, an allergic reaction to peanuts can quickly kill a person. Of the nearly 1.5 million Americans who suffer from peanut allergy, more than 150 of them die each year from exposure to peanuts or peanut products. Problems occur when the body overreacts to the presence of peanuts—a process called anaphylaxis. The body's airways clamp down, which can lead to suffocation in some cases. Fortunately, anaphylaxis can be reversed—if it is recognized in time. A peanut allergy is tricky: There's no way to predict who is prone to anaphylaxis and who isn't. Many people who develop anaphylaxis might have had only a mild reaction to eating peanuts in the past. Plus, it is difficult to avoid peanuts or peanut oil—which may be found in plain chocolate candies, sunflower seeds, and other foods.

The Origin of the Allergy

Why do certain people have peanut allergy? Researchers point to a molecule named IgE. One of many compounds produced by the body's immune system, IgE may have evolved to help our ancestors fight off parasitic worms. These days, parastic worms aren't so common, and IgE has become a nuisance. The higher the level of IgE in your body, the more likely you will develop allergic reactions to otherwise harmless stuff, like peanuts. IgE-related allergies also may play a role in some cases of asthma.

Over the past decade, researchers have developed compounds to block the action of IgE and dampen the body's allergic reactions. What does this mean? There may one day be a treatment—or even cure—for peanut allergy.

So for now, at least, folks with peanut allergy have to do what they have always done: Avoid peanuts in any form and try to lead as normal a life as possible. ▮

TIME to THINK...   About Peanut Allergy

Take a poll of your classmates to find out how many students have allergies and what they are allergic to. Then tally the responses in various categories and answer these questions:
1. What percentage of the class has allergies?
2. What is the most common allergy in the class?
3. What percentage of students has that allergy?

1. **Advocacy.** Watch 30 minutes of television and keep a record of the food commercials shown. Analyze the health messages delivered through this media. Then write a script for an advertisement that encourages viewers to try a particular healthful food. *(LESSON 1)*

2. **Goal Setting.** Develop a table that summarizes what you have learned about the nutrients your body needs. Include in your table the name of each type of nutrient, why your body needs the nutrient, and what foods you can eat to make sure you include enough of the nutrient in your eating plan. Then set a goal to improve your intake of one or more of these nutrients. Use the goal-setting steps to reach your goal. *(LESSON 2)*

3. **Accessing Information.** Use reliable online resources to do more in-depth research on the relationship between nutrition and heart disease. How can good nutrition prevent this disease and improve quality of life? Summarize your findings in a one-page report. *(LESSON 3)*

4. **Practicing Healthful Behaviors.** Analyze how healthful practices might reduce the risk of foodborne illness, a communicable disease. Then develop a plan that features safe cooking strategies to reduce the spread of foodborne pathogens. *(LESSON 4)*

Dietetic Technician

Do you enjoy planning meals and cooking? Do you like interacting with others? If so, you may enjoy a career as a dietetic technician. This career allows you to assist dietitians in the planning of healthful meals.

To enter this field, you must first complete a two-year associate's degree program. You'll also need to complete an accredited dietetic technician program and pass a national exam. To maintain certification, you'll need to stay up-to-date on nutrition trends. Find out more about this and other health careers by clicking on Career Corner at **health.glencoe.com.**

Parent Involvement

Accessing Information. Work with your family to list the foods you most enjoy eating. Then look through cookbooks to find recipes for similar foods that contain less fat, sugar, and salt. Make a recipe booklet of these healthful alternatives, and set a goal to try one new recipe each week.

School and Community

Meals on Wheels. Many communities have organizations, such as Meals on Wheels, that provide nutritious meals to older adults or physically challenged individuals who are unable to prepare meals for themselves. Find out whether your community has such an organization and how you and your classmates can become involved.

After You Read

Use your completed Foldable to review what you have learned about the ways that appetite, emotions, and environment influence your eating habits.

FOLDABLES™
Study Organizer

▶ EXPLORING HEALTH TERMS *Answer the following questions on a sheet of paper.*

Lesson 1 *Fill in the blanks with the correct term.*

hunger	nutrition	calories
nutrients	appetite	

The process by which the body takes in and uses food is (**_1_**). (**_2_**) are the units of heat that measure the energy used by the body and the energy that foods supply to the body. The substances in food that your body needs to function properly are (**_3_**).

Lesson 2 *Match each definition with the correct term.*

vitamins	lipid	carbohydrates
proteins	fiber	minerals

4. The starches and sugars present in foods.
5. An indigestible complex carbohydrate.
6. Nutrients that help build and maintain body cells and tissues.
7. A fatty substance that does not dissolve in water.

Lesson 3 *Fill in the blanks with the correct term.*

MyPyramid
Dietary Guidelines for Americans

8. The _____ is a set of recommendations for healthful eating and active living prepared by the USDA and DHHS.
9. _____ is a guide for making healthful daily food choices.

Lesson 4 *Match each definition with the correct term.*

food allergy	pasteurization
food additives	cross-contamination
foodborne illness	food intolerance

10. Substances intentionally added to food to produce a desired effect.
11. Another name for food poisoning.
12. The spreading of bacteria or other pathogens from one food to another.

▶ RECALLING THE FACTS *Use complete sentences to answer the following questions.*

1. How does hunger differ from appetite?
2. Give an example of how friends and peers can influence food choices.
3. Why is good nutrition especially important during the teen years?
4. What is the relationship between glucose and glycogen?
5. How does water benefit the body?
6. List three minerals that are important for health.
7. What three elements form a healthful eating pattern?
8. How many servings should you eat each day from the Milk Group? From the Meat and Beans Group?
9. What does the Percent Daily Value column of a food label tell you?
10. What are some symptoms of a food allergy?
11. How can you keep picnic foods safe to eat?

For more review questions for Chapter 5, go to **health.glencoe.com**.

➤ WRITING CRITICALLY

1. **Descriptive.** Prepare a meal menu for a family celebrating a holiday or birthday. Include foods that are unique to your family's culture or ethnic group. Provide detailed descriptions of any ethnic foods served including how they taste and how the tradition began for serving them at particular times of the year or at certain family functions.

2. **Descriptive.** Louis Pasteur discovered the process of pasteurization in 1822. Conduct further research on Louis Pasteur and his discovery and write a one-page biography about him. In your biography, focus primarily on his discovery of pasteurization.

Standardized Test Practice

 Read the passage below and then answer the questions.

Food for Healthy Living

(1) What do you eat when it's the middle of the afternoon and you're hungry? (2) Suppose that you go to the kitchen to look for a snack. (3) In the refrigerator you find nothing to eat but a few old apple slices and some lettuce. (4) A box of cookies sits on the counter next to the refrigerator, so you finish off the box that's half full.

(5) Everyone gets cravings between meals, especially teens. (6) The middle of the morning, the afternoon stretch between lunch and dinner, and late at night might not be the best times to eat an entire meal, but they are good opportunities for a few nutrients. (7) The challenge with snacking is not when you eat, but what you eat.

(8) Prepare for a snack attack by having something besides candy, chips, or cookies on hand. (9) Beat your craving for a cookie by substituting a pretzel, breadstick, popcorn, or even a carrot stick. (10) Make sure that when you open the refrigerator door you find things. (11) Fill the refrigerator with healthy snacks-not the high-fat, high-salt, and high-calorie foods you see advertised. (12) Even half a baked potato is better than a bag of chips!

1. Which detail should the writer add after sentence 9 to support the topic of the third paragraph?

(A) Yogurt has a smooth texture.

(B) There are many different kinds of chips.

(C) It's hard to think clearly when you're hungry.

(D) The crunchy texture may satisfy your craving.

2. Which words should replace the word "things" in sentence 10 so the reader knows specifically what the writer had in mind?

(F) assorted items

(G) a pitcher of water

(H) breakfast, lunch, and dinner

(I) fruits, vegetables, and yogurt

3. Write an advice column for your school newspaper that outlines your own helpful ideas for healthy eating.

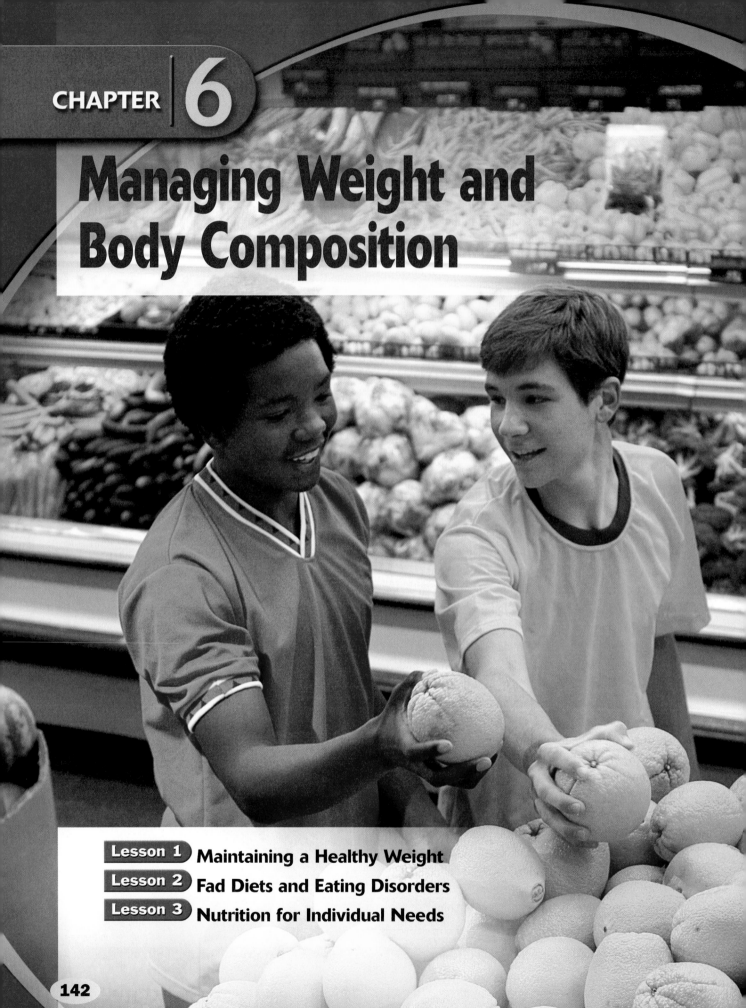

Managing Weight and Body Composition

Eye ON THE Media

Body Image in Teen Magazines

Magazines create the impression that everyone must look a certain way by featuring thin models in their ads. Readers with different types of bodies may develop a negative self-image if they feel that they

► **are too fat or skinny.**

► **are too short or tall.**

► **do not look the right way.**

Visit the Eye on the Media section at **health.glencoe.com** to learn more.

FOLDABLES™ Study Organizer

Before You Read

Make this Foldable journal to record what you learn about health consumer habits. Begin with two sheets of notebook paper.

► **Step 1**

Fold one sheet of notebook paper in half from top to bottom. Cut about 1″ along the fold at both ends, stopping at the margin lines.

► **Step 2**

Fold the second sheet in half from top to bottom. Cut or shave off the fold between the margin lines.

► **Step 3**

Roll up the first sheet, slip it halfway through the cut in the second sheet, and open it up.

► **Step 4**

Fold the pages in half to make a bound journal. Label as shown.

Maintaining a Healthy Weight

As You Read

Label the inside pages of your journal with the following titles: Body Image, The Weight-Calorie Connection, Determining Your Appropriate Weight Range, Body Composition, Weight-Related Health Risks, and Healthful Ways to Manage Weight. Use your journal to take notes as you read the chapter.

SPOTLIGHT ON HEALTH

Using Visuals. What healthy choices are these teens making?

Maintaining a Healthy Weight

Guide to Reading

Building Vocabulary

As you read this lesson, write each new highlighted term and its definition in your notebook.

▶ body image (p. 144)
▶ body mass index (BMI) (p. 145)
▶ overweight (p. 146)
▶ obesity (p. 146)
▶ underweight (p. 147)
▶ nutrient-dense foods (p. 148)

Focusing on the Main Ideas

In this lesson, you will learn how to:

▶ Associate the relationships between body composition, diet, and fitness.
▶ Describe the importance of maintaining a healthy weight to promote health and prevent disease.
▶ Demonstrate healthful ways to manage weight.

Reading Strategy

Predict

▶ After scanning the headings, subheadings, and pictures, write a few sentences describing the conclusion you have drawn about the information that will be presented in this lesson.

 Quick Write

Write a brief paragraph describing factors that might influence the way a person feels about his or her looks.

Media images can have an effect on a person's body image. *How might messages sent by media images negatively affect body image?*

When you look in the mirror, how do you feel about what you see? Are you happy with the way you look, or do you wish some things were different? *The way you see your body* is called your **body image**. Body image is affected by several factors, including media images and the attitudes of family and friends.

For many people body image is tied to perception of weight. Your own healthy weight probably won't be the same as the weight of a fashion model, a bodybuilder, or your best friend. However, you can use some general guidelines to assess your weight and keep it within a healthy range.

The Weight-Calorie Connection

To understand how to manage your weight effectively, it's important to understand calories. As you've learned, calories are units used to measure energy—both the energy in food and the energy your body uses for life processes and physical activities. Maintaining a healthy weight, even while you're growing, is a matter of energy balance: the calories you consume must equal the calories your body burns.

Calories: Their Source

Some foods have more calories than others. The specific number of calories depends on portion size as well as the amounts of carbohydrates, proteins, and fats in the food. Both carbohydrates and proteins supply 4 calories per gram. Fats supply more than twice that number—9 calories per gram. For this reason, even small amounts of fat in a food greatly increase its calorie content. The way a food is prepared or cooked also affects the calorie count.

The Energy Equation

Tipping the balance of the energy equation will result in weight loss or gain. If you take in fewer calories than you burn, you lose weight. If you take in more calories than you burn, you gain weight.

Understanding the relationship between personal nutrition and energy is simple. One pound of body fat equals about 3,500 calories. Eating 500 fewer calories per day than you need to maintain your weight will result in the loss of one pound of body fat after one week (500 calories per day × 7 days = 3,500 calories). Burning an additional 500 calories per day through physical activity would result in a similar weight loss.

Determining Your Appropriate Weight Range

Your appropriate weight is influenced by several factors, including gender, age, height, body frame, growth rate, metabolic rate, and activity level. As a teen you are still growing, so you need more calories than an adult does. Tall and large-framed people need more calories than short and small-framed people. Because an active person burns more calories than a sedentary person does, he or she can consume more calories.

Body Mass Index

One way to evaluate whether your weight is within a healthy range is to determine body mass index. **Body mass index (BMI)** is *a ratio that allows you to assess your body size in relation to your height and weight.* Because BMI for children and teens takes age and gender into account, different charts are used for males and females. **Figure 6.1** on page 146 explains how to determine your BMI. A different chart is used for adults.

As you calculate your BMI, keep in mind that many different ratios of height to weight can be healthy. Teens grow at different rates and in different ways. There is no single size, shape, or growth pattern that's normal for everyone.

Height and gender are two factors that need to be considered when evaluating a person's weight.

FIGURE 6.1

DETERMINING BMI

Use this formula to find your BMI:

BMI = weight (in pounds)
× 703/[height (in inches)]²

Here's how to find the BMI for a 16-year-old male who weighs 145 pounds and is 69 inches tall:

BMI = 145 × 703 / 69²

BMI = 101,935 / 4,761

BMI = 21.41 or 21.4

Find this result in the chart. This teen's BMI indicates that he is within an appropriate weight range.

Source: Adapted from CDC information

BMI Chart for Boys

BMI Chart for Girls

 If your BMI falls above the 85th percentile or below the 5th percentile, consult a health care professional for further evaluation. However, keep in mind that this does not necessarily mean that you are over- or underweight.

Reading Check

Cause and Effect How does calorie consumption affect your weight?

Body Composition

Body composition, or the ratio of body fat to lean body tissue, needs to be taken into account when assessing weight. Diet and fitness affect a person's body composition. For example, a weight-lifting program will increase muscle mass. A high-calorie diet can increase the amount of stored body fat.

Body Weight versus Body Fat

The terms *overweight* and *obese* are often used interchangeably, but they are not the same. **Overweight** is *a condition in which a person is heavier than the standard weight range for his or her height.* **Obesity** refers specifically to *having an excess amount of body fat.* Both can endanger health, but in certain cases being overweight may not pose health risks. Athletes such as bodybuilders or football players may be overweight because of excess muscle tissue rather than excess body fat.

Weight-Related Health Risks

BMI for adults serves as a general guide for evaluating some health risks. Adults with high BMIs are at increased risk of cardiovascular disease; type 2 diabetes; cancer; high blood pressure; and osteoarthritis, a joint disease. Maintaining a healthy weight can help promote health and prevent the development of these diseases.

Overweight: A Health Risk

Being overweight is a serious problem in the United States. The latest findings from the CDC indicate that 15 percent of teens are overweight. Excess body fat strains the muscles and the skeletal system. It forces the heart and lungs to work harder and increases the risk of high blood pressure and high blood cholesterol. Being overweight or obese also increases the risk of type 2 diabetes, asthma, and some cancers.

Why are some people overweight? Genetics may play a role, but being overweight or obese usually results from consuming excess calories and from physical inactivity. To maintain a healthy weight and avoid the health risks associated with overweight and obesity, follow the recommendations in the *Dietary Guidelines for Americans:*

▶ Consume a balanced diet rich in nutrient-dense foods and beverages.

▶ Get at least 60 minutes of exercise daily.

▶ Avoid foodborne illnesses by washing your hands frequently and keeping surfaces where foods are prepared clean.

Underweight: A Health Risk

Some teens are very thin while they are growing. Being thin may also be normal because of genetics or a fast metabolism. Other people, however, diet or exercise excessively to stay thin. A person who is too thin has little stored fat to provide the body with an energy reserve and may not be consuming enough calories and nutrients for health and growth. This may lead to fatigue and a decreased ability to fight illness. How do you know whether you are underweight? **Underweight** refers to *a condition in which a person is less than the standard weight range for his or her height.* A health care professional can help you determine whether you are underweight.

Ⓥ **Physical activities such as swimming burn calories and can help you manage your weight.** *What other physical activities can help you manage your weight?*

FIGURE 6.2

THE BEST WEIGHT-LOSS STRATEGY

Eat Fewer Calories
Eat more foods that are high in nutrients and low in calories.

Burn More Calories
Burn more calories through physical activity.

Reading Check

Explain What are some healthful ways to manage weight?

Healthful Ways to Manage Weight

The teen years are a period of rapid growth and change, so some fluctuations in your weight are normal during this time. If you want to begin a formal weight-management plan, these strategies can help:

▶ **Target your appropriate weight.** Speak with a health care professional to determine a weight range that is healthy for you.

▶ **Set realistic goals.** Gaining or losing one-half pound to one pound per week is a safe and realistic goal.

▶ **Personalize your plan.** Think about your food preferences and lifestyle when designing your weight management program.

▶ **Put your goal and plan in writing.** You might also find it helpful to keep a journal of what and when you eat to become more aware of your eating habits.

▶ **Evaluate your progress.** Track your progress by weighing yourself weekly at the same time of day. Remember that time periods when your weight does not change are normal.

Healthy Weight-Loss Strategies

A health care provider is your best source of information about your appropriate weight. If he or she recommends that you lose weight, use the best weight-loss strategy, illustrated in **Figure 6.2.** Here are some other tips for losing weight.

▶ **Eat 1,700 to 1,800 calories daily to meet your body's energy needs.** To reach this goal, follow the recommendations of the *Dietary Guidelines for Americans.* Eating fewer than 1,400 calories a day may cause you to miss out on essential nutrients.

▶ **Include your favorites in moderation.** Eat smaller portions of your favorite high-calorie foods, and eat them less frequently. Instead of giving up ice cream altogether, for example, have a small scoop once a week.

▶ **Eat a variety of low-calorie, nutrient-dense foods. Nutrient-dense foods** are *foods that are high in nutrients as compared with their calorie content.* Whole-grain products, vegetables, and fruits are examples of low-calorie, nutrient-dense foods.

▶ **Drink plenty of water.** Eight glasses a day will help keep your body functioning at its best.

Resilient TEENS

Taryn Schaeffer was in seventh grade when her ballet instructors began encouraging her to lose weight. "I was already 5'8", which is really tall for a dancer," says Taryn. "So I weighed more than the smaller girls." Taryn began to whittle her body down to an "acceptable" size. She joined the cross-country team, and put herself on a strict diet.

Finally, a youth counselor noticed how thin Taryn had become. She encouraged Taryn to talk about what was bothering her. "She just pointed out that there's a reason we're all different, and I had nothing to prove."

Taryn has since stopped dancing and runs only for fun now. "I still struggle sometimes when I've had a bad day," says Taryn. "I've learned you have to be who you're meant to be, and that's a gift."

"I've learned you have to be who you're meant to be, and that's a gift."

 Reading Check **Explain** What does Taryn mean when she says, "You have to be who you're meant to be"?

Healthy Weight-Gain Strategies

Follow these tips to gain weight healthfully:

▶ **Increase your calorie intake.** Choose foods high in complex carbohydrates, such as breads, pasta, and potatoes. Limit foods high in fat and sugar.

▶ **Eat often and take second helpings.** Choose more than the minimum number of servings from each food group.

▶ **Eat nutritious snacks.** Snack two to three hours before meals to avoid spoiling your appetite.

▶ **Build muscle.** A supervised resistance-training program will help you gain weight by increasing muscle mass.

HEALTH *Online*

TOPIC Healthy Weight Management

Go to **health.glencoe.com** to learn more about the basics of healthy weight management.

ACTIVITY List ten facts you know or have heard about maintaining healthy weights. Use the information you find to determine which are myth and which are fact.

Y Fruit and vegetable drinks are nutrient-dense snacks that can be part of a healthy weight-management plan. *What are some other examples of nutrient-dense snacks?*

Physical Activity and Weight Management

Whether you want to lose, gain, or maintain weight, regular physical activity should be part of your plan. Aerobic exercise burns calories and helps you lose fat. Weight lifting or resistance training will increase muscle mass and produce a firm, lean body shape. Also, since muscle is more efficient than fat at burning calories, having more lean muscle tissue increases the number of calories your body burns, even at rest. Here are some added benefits of regular physical activity:

▶ It helps relieve the stress that often leads to over- or undereating.

▶ It promotes a normal appetite response, which helps you gain, lose, or maintain weight.

▶ It increases self-esteem, which helps keep your plan on track.

Research consistently shows that regular physical activity, combined with healthy eating habits, is the most efficient and healthful way to manage your weight and live a healthy life. Choose activities that you enjoy and that fit your personality. You will soon discover your body's capabilities and begin to look and feel your best.

LESSON 1 REVIEW

Reviewing Facts and Vocabulary

1. List three factors that influence what an individual's appropriate weight should be.
2. Explain the difference between the terms *overweight* and *obesity*.
3. Examine and briefly describe the relationship among body composition, diet, and fitness.

Thinking Critically

4. **Analyzing.** How can keeping a food journal help a person manage his or her weight?
5. **Hypothesizing.** Why is it important to eat a variety of low-calorie, nutrient-dense foods if you're trying to lose weight?

Applying Health Skills

Practicing Healthful Behaviors. Vicki wants to be sure that she maintains a healthy weight range as she moves through her teen years. How can Vicki show that she knows various strategies when making decisions related to her health needs and risks? Write a short story that shows how Vicki practices these behaviors.

After You Read

Compare. Create a chart with two columns. List weight-related health risks on one side. Compare them to healthful ways to manage weight on the other side.

Fad Diets and Eating Disorders

"Miracle patch lets you lose weight without dieting!" Are you familiar with promises like this? They often appear in print ads, radio, TV, and on the Web. It's important that you learn to analyze a variety of weight management plans for sound nutritional practices and their lifelong effects on health.

Risky Weight-Loss Strategies

A number of weight-loss strategies not only fail to produce long-term results but also can cause serious health problems. Part of being a health-literate consumer means that you can make positive decisions related to nutrition.

Fad Diets

If you see an ad like the one shown here, be wary. Such ads are often for **fad diets**, *weight-loss plans that are popular for only a short time*. These diets often are hard to stick with because they limit food variety. They do not offer information on healthy eating patterns. Fad diets that severely restrict the foods a dieter eats fail to provide the body with the nutrients it needs for health and growth. Any weight lost on fad diets is usually regained.

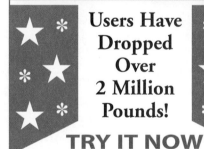

"I Lost 100 Pounds Easy! Eating My Favorite Foods!!!"
"This Is The Greatest Diet Ever!"

Users Have Dropped Over 2 Million Pounds!

TRY IT NOW

 Fad diets may promise quick and easy weight loss. *What would you look for when evaluating specific diet plans found in popular magazines and books?*

Reading Check

Explain How can fad diets harm your health?

ⓨ **Effective weight management involves making healthy lifestyle choices.** *What steps can a person take to successfully manage his or her weight?*

Liquid Diets

A person on a liquid diet replaces all of his or her food intake with a special liquid formula. These very low-calorie diets generally do not meet the body's energy needs. As a result, they often leave the dieter feeling fatigued. Many liquid diets do not provide the body with fiber and needed nutrients. Relying on high-protein, low-carbohydrate liquids as the only source of nutrients can cause serious health problems and even death. Because of the potential dangers associated with liquid diets, the U.S. Food and Drug Administration (FDA) requires these products to carry warning labels and recommends that they be used only under close medical supervision.

Fasting

To fast is to abstain from eating. Although this may seem like a sure way to lose weight, fasting for more than short periods deprives your body of needed nutrients and energy. Without a fresh supply of nutrients each day, your body begins breaking down protein stored in muscle tissue for energy. If the person who is fasting also avoids liquids, he or she may become dehydrated.

Some religious and cultural rituals involve brief periods of fasting. Such fasting is not dangerous for the average person because the fast is of limited duration. However, fasting may not be advisable for those with diabetes or other health conditions. If you are unsure about how cultural or religious fasting may affect a medical condition, consult a health care professional for advice.

Diet Pills

Many diet pills work by suppressing appetite. They may cause drowsiness, anxiety, a racing heart, or other serious side effects. Diet pills may also be addictive. Some cause the body to lose more water than normal, which can lead to dehydration. Diet pills may claim to "burn," "block," or "flush" fat from the body, but a low-risk pill that meets these claims has not yet been developed.

Weight Cycling

Some diet plans or products may seem to help people lose weight quickly, but the weight loss is usually from water, not body fat. Water weight loss is quickly regained. *The repeated pattern of loss and regain of body weight* is called **weight cycling**. Weight cycling is common in people who follow fad diets. Some reports have suggested that weight cycling is harmful, although other studies do not support this finding. It is important to learn how to design a plan for personal weight management based on a realistic and healthful body image. In general, slow and steady weight loss is the best strategy for long-lasting results.

Fad Diets Harm Health

In a society obsessed with weight and appearance, the promise of quick weight loss is hard to resist. However, fad diets are not only ineffective in producing long-term weight loss, they're also potentially harmful. In this activity you will create a poster advocating against fad diets.

What You'll Need

- poster board
- markers

What You'll Do

1. As a class, brainstorm potentially harmful effects of fad diets.
2. In groups of two or three, come up with a simple concept that conveys the message that fad diets can harm health. Your concept should be relevant to high school students.
3. Make a poster illustrating your message. Include supporting information about healthful weight-loss strategies in the poster.
4. Ask permission to display your posters at school.

Apply and Conclude

Is your poster persuasive? What advocacy techniques did you use to persuade others? How will your poster have a positive effect on the health of your audience? Why is this an important health issue for teens?

The Risks of Eating Disorders

Sometimes a person's concerns about weight and efforts to lose weight can get out of control. Becoming obsessed with thinness can lead to eating disorders. An **eating disorder** is *an extreme, harmful eating behavior that can cause serious illness or even death.* The exact cause of eating disorders is unknown. They may be brought on by mental or emotional factors such as poor body image, social and family pressures, and perfectionism. Some scientists think that the cause may be partly genetic. Teens with a family history of weight problems, depression, or substance abuse may be more at risk for developing an eating disorder.

About 90 percent of those with eating disorders are female. It's estimated that about one percent of females ages 16 to 18 have this illness. Eating disorders are a serious health problem, and people who suffer from them need professional help.

Anorexia Nervosa

Anorexia nervosa is *a disorder in which the irrational fear of becoming obese results in severe weight loss from self-imposed starvation.* Anorexia nervosa is a psychological disorder with emotional and physical consequences. The disorder relates to an individual's self-concept and coping abilities. Outside pressures, high expectations, a need to be accepted, and a need to achieve are characteristics associated with the development of anorexia. Medical specialists have also found that genetics and other biological factors may play an equally powerful role in the development of this disorder. Hormones and certain brain chemicals have been shown to trigger the illness in some people.

Anorexia develops most often in teenage girls and young women. Symptoms include extremely low caloric intake, an obsession with exercising, emotional problems, an unnatural interest in food, a distorted body image, and denial of an eating problem.

HEALTH CONSEQUENCES OF ANOREXIA NERVOSA

Physical consequences of anorexia are related to malnutrition and starvation. A drastic reduction of body fat may cause females with anorexia to stop menstruating. Other consequences include loss of bone density, low body temperature, low blood pressure, slowed metabolism, and reduction in organ size. People with anorexia may develop serious heart problems, including an irregular heartbeat that can lead to cardiac arrest and sudden death.

Treatment for anorexia nervosa may include a stay at a clinic or hospital where the person can receive nutrients to regain weight and strength. Anorexia nervosa also requires psychological treatment to address the problems that lead to the disorder.

Bulimia Nervosa

Bulimia nervosa is *a disorder in which some form of purging or clearing of the digestive tract follows cycles of overeating.* A person with bulimia often fasts or follows a strict diet and then *binges*, or quickly consumes large amounts of food. After eating, the person may vomit or take laxatives to purge the food from the body. Following a binge, the person may again try dieting. Other symptoms can include distorted body image and an unnatural interest in food. The exact cause of bulimia is unknown, but societal pressures, self-esteem issues, and family problems may be factors.

People with anorexia often see themselves as overweight even when they are very thin. *What type of help does an individual with an eating disorder need?*

HEALTH CONSEQUENCES OF BULIMIA NERVOSA

Repeated binging, purging, and fasting can cause serious health problems or even death. Frequent vomiting and diarrhea can lead to dehydration, kidney damage, and irregular heartbeat. Vomiting also destroys tooth enamel; causes tooth decay; and damages the tissues of the stomach, esophagus, and mouth. Frequent use of laxatives disrupts digestion and absorption and may cause nutrient deficiencies. Laxative abuse can also change the composition of the blood. Treatment of bulimia nervosa usually includes both medication and psychological counseling.

Binge Eating Disorder

People with **binge eating disorder**, *a disorder characterized by compulsive overeating,* consume huge amounts of food at one time but do not try to purge. This disorder may signal the use of food as a coping mechanism for strong emotions or depression. Treatment involves professional psychological counseling and sometimes medication.

Reading ✓ Check

Demonstrate What can you do if you suspect a friend has an eating disorder?

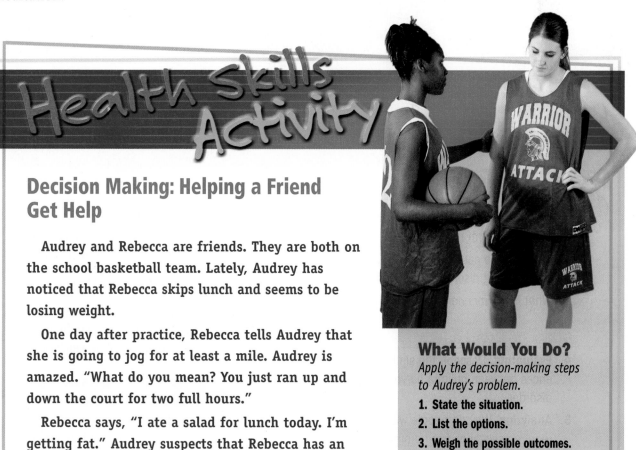

Health Skills Activity

Decision Making: Helping a Friend Get Help

Audrey and Rebecca are friends. They are both on the school basketball team. Lately, Audrey has noticed that Rebecca skips lunch and seems to be losing weight.

One day after practice, Rebecca tells Audrey that she is going to jog for at least a mile. Audrey is amazed. "What do you mean? You just ran up and down the court for two full hours."

Rebecca says, "I ate a salad for lunch today. I'm getting fat." Audrey suspects that Rebecca has an eating disorder and wonders how to help her.

What Would You Do?
Apply the decision-making steps to Audrey's problem.
1. State the situation.
2. List the options.
3. Weigh the possible outcomes.
4. Consider values.
5. Make a decision and act.
6. Evaluate the decision.

Psychologists and clinics that specialize in the treatment of eating disorders may offer support groups for people with these disorders. *Why might support groups be helpful to individuals with eating disorders?*

HEALTH CONSEQUENCES OF BINGE EATING DISORDER

Binge eating disorder often results in unhealthful weight gain, which contributes to health problems such as type 2 diabetes, heart disease, and stroke. Gallbladder problems, high blood pressure, high cholesterol, and increased risk of certain types of cancer have also been associated with this disorder.

Help for Eating Disorders

It's important that you understand the impact of personal health behaviors on body systems. People with eating disorders need professional medical and psychological help. All eating disorders are serious. If you believe a friend might be developing an eating disorder, you may want to discuss the problem with a trusted adult such as a parent, a counselor, or a school nurse. You can also help by encouraging your friend to seek professional help and by being supportive.

LESSON 2 REVIEW

Reviewing Facts and Vocabulary

1. Define the term *fad diets.*

2. Describe the causes, symptoms, and treatment of the eating disorder anorexia nervosa.

3. What is *bulimia nervosa*?

Thinking Critically

4. **Evaluating.** Describe the similarities and differences between bulimia nervosa and binge eating disorder.

5. **Analyzing.** Why do people with eating disorders require assistance from professional health services?

Applying Health Skills

Advocacy. Think of ways to inform teens about the dangers of fad diets and other risky weight-loss strategies. With a group of classmates, plan and create a video or public service announcement (PSA) that tells teens about these dangers and gives tips for healthy weight loss.

After You Read

Cause and Effect. Create a chart with two columns. List risky weight-loss strategies and eating disorders on one side. List the possible effects of these dangerous diets and the health consequences of eating disorders on the other side.

Nutrition for Individual Needs

Guide to Reading

Building Vocabulary

As you read this lesson, write each new highlighted term and its definition in your notebook.

▶ electrolytes (p. 158)
▶ rehydration (p. 158)
▶ vegetarian (p. 159)
▶ vegan (p. 160)
▶ dietary supplement (p. 161)
▶ megadose (p. 161)
▶ herbal supplement (p. 161)

Focusing on the Main Ideas

In this lesson, you will learn how to:

▶ **Assess** the specific nutritional needs of different groups.
▶ **Describe** the proper nutrition for pregnant women, mothers, babies, and young children.
▶ **Demonstrate** health-promoting behavior that will enhance and maintain wellness.

Quick Write

Write a brief paragraph describing how your nutritional needs have changed as you have grown into your teen years.

Reading Strategy

Organize Information

▶ Write the words "Individual Nutrition." Surround them with six circles titled Performance, Vegetarian, Supplements, Pregnancy, Infants/Children, and Older Adults. As you read, fill each circle with the appropriate facts.

▲ Eating well-balanced meals and snacks each day is an important part of any training program. *Why is it important for physically active people to have a well-balanced eating plan?*

Does it seem to you that everyone has a different idea about proper nutrition? Some friends may tell you that eating meat is unhealthy. What can you believe? In truth, nutrient and energy needs vary in relation to gender, activity level, and stage of life.

Performance Nutrition

Do you play on a sports team or take aerobics classes? Learning to modify your personal diet relative to your special needs can help you perform your best in any physical activity.

The Training Diet

The best eating plan for athletes is one that is balanced, moderate, and varied. Your body's need for protein, vitamins, and minerals does not change greatly when training for sports or competition. However, because physical activity burns calories, athletes and other active individuals need to eat more calories from nutrient-dense foods to maintain their weight and energy levels when training.

HYDRATION

Your body naturally loses fluids through perspiration, breathing, and waste elimination. The amount of fluids lost increases during physical activity, especially in hot weather. These fluids must be replaced to avoid dehydration and **heatstroke.** Becoming dehydrated can lead to an imbalance of **electrolytes**, *minerals that help maintain the body's fluid balance.* The minerals sodium, chloride, and potassium are all electrolytes.

To maintain your body's electrolyte balance, you must take in as much water and electrolytes as you lose through perspiration and body wastes. Drink 16 to 24 ounces of fluids two to three hours before a heavy workout and 6 to 12 ounces of fluids every 15 to 20 minutes during heavy workouts. **Rehydration**, or *restoring lost body fluids*, is important after physical activity and competition. Drink 16 ounces of fluid for every pound of body weight lost through sweat. It's best to drink plain water to replenish fluids lost during exercise.

"Making Weight"

In sports such as wrestling and boxing, participants compete in specific weight classes, so maintaining a certain weight is important. Always compete at a weight that's right for you. To do this, you may need to develop a specific eating plan to meet changing nutritional requirements, such as special dietary needs, athletic training, pregnancy, and food allergies.

LOSING WEIGHT

Competing in a weight class that is below your healthy weight can be dangerous. Fasting, crash dieting, or trying to sweat off extra weight before weigh-in can cause dehydration and harm your performance and your health. Over time, such practices may also lead to a loss of muscle mass. Athletes who need to lose weight should follow a sensible plan and try to lose only one-half pound to one pound each week.

GAINING WEIGHT

A program that combines balanced nutrition and exercise is the healthful way to gain weight. A supervised resistance-training or weight-lifting program can help build muscle mass. The extra calories you need for gaining weight should come from nutrient-dense foods, not from protein supplements. For best results, a slow, steady weight gain of no more than one to two pounds per week is recommended. Using **anabolic steroids** or other bodybuilding drugs to build muscle mass is not healthy. Many of these drugs have dangerous side effects ranging from acne and breast development in men to heart attacks and liver cancer. Use of these substances is illegal; athletes who test positive for steroids and similar drugs are often disqualified from their sport.

Resistance training helps build muscle mass.

Reading Check

Explain Why is rehydration important?

Eating Before Competition

Eating three to four hours before competition allows the stomach to empty yet gives an athlete the necessary energy and keeps him or her free from hunger pangs while competing.

Before competing, choose a meal that's high in carbohydrates and low in fat and protein, both of which stay in the digestive system for a longer period of time. Pasta, rice, vegetables, breads, and fruits are good sources of carbohydrates. Also, remember to drink plenty of water before, during, and after competing.

Vegetarianism

A **vegetarian** is *a person who eats mostly or only plant foods.* Some people choose to become vegetarians for religious or cultural reasons. Others make this choice because of their concern for the environment or for how food animals are raised or slaughtered. Many people become vegetarians for health reasons. By cutting out the saturated fats and cholesterol found in many or all animal products, vegetarians may reduce their risk of cardiovascular disease and some cancers. Also, vegetarians may consume more fruits, vegetables, and whole grains—foods that are linked to a reduced risk of many health problems. **Figure 6.3** describes four vegetarian eating styles.

FIGURE 6.3

VEGETARIAN EATING PLANS

No matter which plan a person follows, a vegetarian eating style still involves choosing nutritious foods.

Plan Name	Foods Included
Lacto-ovo vegetarianism	• Dairy *(lacto)* foods and eggs *(ovo)* in addition to foods from plant sources.
Lacto vegetarianism	• Dairy foods in addition to foods from plant sources.
Ovo vegetarianism	• Eggs and foods from plant sources. Fortified soy milk and soy cheese are often substituted for dairy products.
Vegan	• Foods from plant sources only. Fortified soy milk and soy cheese are often substituted for dairy products.

Meatless Meals

Some people have chosen to become vegetarians. A little planning can ensure that vegetarian meals contain sufficient amounts of nutrients.

MyPyramid
STEPS TO A HEALTHIER YOU

GRAINS	VEGETABLES	FRUITS	MILK	PROTEINS
Make half your grains whole	Vary your veggies	Focus on fruits	Get your calcium-rich foods	Go lean with protein

ACTIVITY

Plan a full day's menu for a vegetarian. Plan a breakfast, a mid-morning snack, a lunch, a mid-afternoon snack, and an evening meal.

MEETING NUTRIENT NEEDS

Vegetarians need to eat a variety of incomplete proteins in a way that will yield complete protein over the course of a day. They must also make sure they get enough iron, zinc, and B vitamins, nutrients often found in animal products. For vegetarians the key to getting complete proteins and enough vitamins lies in eating adequate amounts of various nutrient-dense foods, including fruits, vegetables, leafy greens, whole grains, nuts, seeds, and legumes, as well as dairy foods or eggs. A **vegan** is a *vegetarian who eats only plant foods.*

Because vegans consume no meat or dairy products, they must obtain vitamin D, vitamin B_{12}, and calcium from other sources.

Dietary Supplements

Do you take a multivitamin and mineral supplement regularly? These tablets are one type of **dietary supplement**, *a non-food form of one or more nutrients*. Dietary supplements may contain vitamins, minerals, fiber, protein, or herbs. Supplements can be in pill, capsule, powder, or liquid form.

Eating healthful meals and snacks based on the *Dietary Guidelines for Americans* can provide you with all the nutrients your body needs. However, taking a multivitamin and mineral supplement may sometimes be appropriate. A health care provider may recommend these supplements to people with certain lifestyles or medical conditions.

Vitamin and mineral supplements may also be recommended for older adults, pregnant or nursing women, people receiving certain medical treatments, and those recovering from illness. If you are in doubt about your own requirements, ask a health care provider.

Risks of Dietary Supplements

Dietary supplements must be used carefully. Learning to analyze the reliability of various sources of food and nutrition information can help you stay healthy. Taking a **megadose**, or *a very large amount of a dietary supplement,* can be dangerous. Vitamins A, D, E, and K, for example, are stored in body fat and may cause toxicity if taken in large amounts.

An **herbal supplement** is a *chemical substance from plants that may be sold as a dietary supplement.* These substances are often sold as "natural" nutrition aids. However, the safety and nutritional claims of many of these products are not based on conclusive scientific evidence. Currently, manufacturers of herbal products are responsible for product safety and label claims unless the product is known to be dangerous. The Center for Food Safety and Applied Nutrition (CFSAN) of the U.S. FDA alerts consumers to potentially dangerous dietary supplements. One such supplement, ephedra or ma huang, was banned from sale in 2004.

Are herbal products safe because they're natural?
Just because something is natural doesn't mean it's harmless. Certain herbs are poisonous. Others may be harmless on their own, but may interact dangerously with prescription or over-the-counter drugs. Consult a health care provider before taking any herbal supplement.

Labeling laws require manufacturers to include information about a supplement's ingredients. *Where would you go to find reliable information about supplements?*

Explain What is the difference between a dietary supplement and an herbal supplement?

Nutrition Throughout the Life Span

People have different nutritional needs at different stages of life. Many children and most teens, for example, need more calories each day than less active adults. While the nutritional needs of these groups vary slightly, most people can get all the calories and nutrients they need each day by following the recommendations from the *Dietary Guidelines for Americans*.

Nutrition During Pregnancy

A developing fetus depends on its mother for all its needs, so it's important for pregnant females to eat healthfully and to avoid harmful substances such as tobacco, alcohol, and other drugs. In addition to eating properly, pregnant females are encouraged to increase their intake of foods rich in the nutrients listed below. It is important to learn how to differentiate between healthful and harmful dietary habits. A health care provider may also recommend that a pregnant female take a multivitamin and mineral supplement to help meet these nutrient needs.

▶ **Folate.** Getting enough folate, or folic acid, early in pregnancy can prevent spinal defects in the developing fetus. Sources of this B vitamin include fruits, dark green leafy vegetables, and fortified grain products.

▶ **Iron.** Increased blood volume during pregnancy produces an increased demand for this mineral. Found in meat, poultry, fish, dark green leafy vegetables, and enriched grain products, iron helps build and renew hemoglobin, the oxygen-carrying compound in blood cells.

▶ **Calcium.** Calcium helps build the bones and teeth of the developing fetus and replaces any calcium taken from the mother's bones. Calcium is found in most dairy products, dark green leafy vegetables, canned fish with edible bones, and calcium-fortified cereals and juices.

Proper nutrition is important for promoting optimal health for both the mother and the baby. *Explain why proper nutrition is important for breastfeeding mothers.*

Nutrition for Infants and Young Children

Breastfeeding is the best way to feed infants. If breastfeeding isn't possible, fortified formulas provide the nutrients that infants need. As a baby grows through its first year, breast milk or formula is supplemented with a variety of solid foods, usually starting with cereal grains, then vegetables and fruits, and then meat or poultry.

After a child's first birthday, many parents substitute whole milk for formula or breast milk. The fats in whole milk provide essential nutrients for a child's developing nervous system. By this time most children are eating a variety of foods. This variety provides the energy and nutrients needed for growth and encourages the child to enjoy different foods.

Between a child's second and fifth birthdays, parents should gradually replace whole milk with lowfat or nonfat milk to meet calcium and vitamin D needs while reducing fat intake.

Nutrition and Older Adults

Most older adults can get all the calories and nutrients they need each day by following the recommendations in the *Dietary Guidelines for Americans*. Older adults may be advised to follow a special diet if they have a specific health problem.

In certain cases, health care providers might recommend that older adults take a dietary supplement to help meet their nutrient needs. For example, some older adults may take medications that interfere with nutrient absorption.

Proper nutrition and active lifestyles help many of today's older adults remain in good health.

LESSON 3 REVIEW

Reviewing Facts and Vocabulary

1. What type of meal should an athlete eat before competing?

2. Define the term *vegetarian*.

3. Explain what a *megadose* is and why it may be dangerous.

Thinking Critically

4. **Synthesizing.** Explain why proper nutrition is especially important in promoting optimal health for pregnant women, mothers, babies, and young children.

5. **Analyzing.** How does good nutrition enhance and maintain personal health throughout life?

Applying Health Skills

Advocacy. Many people think that taking vitamins, minerals, and herbal supplements will improve their health. Develop a pamphlet to educate others about the best ways of getting the nutrients needed for good health. Include information on the safe use of supplements.

After You Read

Analyze a Graph. Using Figure 6.3 on page 159, write a summary of the differences between vegetarian eating plans. What foods are restricted from each diet? How do vegetarians following each of these plans get protein?

Visit **health.glencoe.com** for the Interactive Study Guide for Lesson 3.

Lesson 3   Nutrition for Individual Needs   **163**

Vegans, Pescos, and Pollos

Vegetarians come in many forms, from the strict to the laid back. Here's a guide to the various flavors.

Ovo-Vegetarianism This group eats vegetables plus unfertilized eggs, on the theory that the hen would lay them even if we didn't eat them.

Lacto-Vegetarianism Vegetables and dairy products are eaten but not eggs. You can have, for example, butter, cheese, whipped cream, milk shakes, and ice cream.

Ovo-Lacto-Vegetarianism The most commonly practiced vegetarian regimen, it includes vegetables, eggs, and dairy. The diet is appealing because it has great variety yet uses no animal meat.

Pesco-, Pollo-, and Semi-Vegetarianism Pesco-vegetarians eat fish (because, they say, fish don't have advanced nervous systems). Pollo-vegetarians eat chicken. The newcomer to the list, semi-vegetarianism, is for people who frequently—but not totally—avoid meat and dairy. These three forms may represent a healthy diet, but they are not, by definition, vegetarian.

Veganism This group avoids all meat, dairy, eggs, or other animal products—even honey. These vegetarian diets can have many health benefits. Certainly, that's the conclusion of studies presented at the International Congress on Vegetarian Nutrition. Reports stated that vegetarians have a healthier total intake of fats and cholesterol. They also indicated that older vegetarians use less medication than do older meat-eaters.

With knowledge about nutrition, you can eat like a king from the vegetable world. Ordinary people, however, are not nutrition professionals. People on vegetarian diets need to be smart eaters to get all their nutrients, while avoiding a high-fat, high-calorie diet of starches and cheeses. A meatless (or nearly meatless) diet can be healthful, but researchers advise that vegetarians should always keep caution on the menu. ◢

TIME to THINK... About Vegetarianism

In a poll of 10,000 Americans, 4 percent reported that they considered themselves to be vegetarians. Of that 4 percent, this graph shows how they described themselves:

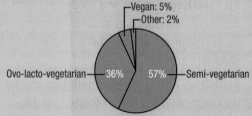

Vegan: 5%
Other: 2%
Ovo-lacto-vegetarian—36%
57%—Semi-vegetarian

Take an in-class poll. How do your results compare to our poll?

1. Analyzing Influences. Many factors, including media messages, influence body image. Identify the three factors that you think have the greatest effect on a teen's body image. Explain what role you think each factor plays in determining body image and whether the effect is positive or negative. *(LESSON 1)*

2. Communicating. Your friend Amy confides that she maintains her weight by alternating periods of fasting with eating large amounts of food. After eating, she vomits to rid her body of the food. Amy says that this practice is not harmful and helps her control her weight. Write a script describing what you would say to Amy. With a partner, role-play your scenario for the class. *(LESSON 2)*

3. Accessing Information. Use reliable online and print resources to find information on at least three dietary supplements known to have harmful side effects. Make a two-column chart that lists in the first column the health claims the supplement manufacturers use to promote their products and, in the second column, the potential side effects of using or abusing the product. Ask permission to post your findings in the weight-training room at your school. *(LESSON 3)*

Registered Dietitian

Are you interested in the special nutritional needs of athletes, older adults, or pregnant women? Would you like to help others make healthful food choices? If you answered yes, you may enjoy a career as a registered dietitian.

Registered dietitians use a variety of skills in their jobs. They must be critical thinkers to analyze eating habits. They must base their nutritional advice on sound science. Good communication skills are necessary. Registered dietitians must show sensitivity to people's needs, cultures, and lifestyles. Find out more about becoming a registered dietitian or working in a related field by clicking on Career Corner at **health.glencoe.com.**

Parent Involvement

Goal Setting. Sometimes it's easier to set and achieve goals if you work with others. With family members, draw up a plan for achieving a specific nutritional health goal. For instance, your goal may be to lose weight or to eat more fruits and vegetables. Use the goal-setting steps to help you reach your goal.

School and Community

Overeaters Anonymous. Overeaters Anonymous (OA) offers support to those who are trying to overcome eating problems. Contact a branch of this organization in your community. Find out what services OA provides and how "sponsors" are used to help support people in recovery. Share your findings in a brief report.

After You Read

Use your completed Foldable to review what you have learned about managing weight and maintaining healthy body composition. List ways that you might use what you have learned in your daily life.

FOLDABLES
Study Organizer

➤ EXPLORING HEALTH TERMS *Answer the following questions on a sheet of paper.*

Lesson 1 *Replace the underlined words with the correct term.*

Body Mass Index (BMI)   underweight
overweight   obesity
nutrient-dense foods   body image

1. The way you see your body is your <u>BMI</u>.

2. The ratio of weight to height used to assess body size is <u>body image</u>.

3. Fruits and vegetables are <u>nutrient-poor foods</u>.

4. <u>Obesity</u> refers to weighing less than the standard weight range for a certain height.

Lesson 2 *Identify each statement as True or False. If false, replace the underlined term with the correct term.*

bulimia nervosa   eating disorder
fad diets   anorexia nervosa
weight cycling   binge eating disorder

5. The repeated pattern of loss and regain of body weight is <u>bulimia nervosa</u>.

6. An extreme, harmful eating behavior that can cause serious illness or even death is an <u>eating disorder</u>.

7. <u>Anorexia nervosa</u> is a condition in which the irrational fear of becoming obese results in severe weight loss from self-imposed starvation.

8. Compulsive overeating is called <u>weight cycling</u>.

Lesson 3 *Match each definition with the correct term.*

dietary supplement   rehydration
electrolytes   vegan
herbal supplement   vegetarian
megadose

9. Restoring lost body fluids.

10. A person who eats only plant foods.

11. A nonfood form of one or more nutrients.

12. A chemical substance from plants that may be sold as a dietary supplement.

➤ RECALLING THE FACTS *Use complete sentences to answer the following questions.*

1. Explain the relationship between energy balance and a healthy weight.

2. Analyze the relationship between maintaining a healthy weight and disease prevention. Name three diseases that can be prevented by maintaining a healthy weight.

3. List three weight-management strategies.

4. How does regular physical activity help promote a healthy weight?

5. What are some risks of long-term fasting?

6. Name three risks associated with diet pills.

7. Describe the causes, symptoms, and treatment of the eating disorder bulimia nervosa.

8. Describe the causes, symptoms, and treatment of binge eating disorder.

9. Explain how dehydration and electrolyte imbalance are related.

10. How can a vegetarian diet benefit health?

11. Why might taking an herbal supplement be risky?

12. Why is proper nutrition important for mothers and babies?

For more review questions for Chapter 6, go to **health.glencoe.com**.

► WRITING CRITICALLY

1. **Expository.** Write a public service announcement that warns others about the potential health risks associated with fad diets. Make sure that your announcement explains why fad diets are unhealthy and describes the possible consequences of fad diets.

2. **Narrative.** Write a script of dialogue between a pregnant female and her health care provider focusing on proper nutrition during pregnancy. In your script, have the health care provider make recommendations regarding nutritional needs during pregnancy. Make sure that your script also includes advice on what should be avoided during pregnancy.

Standardized Test Practice

 Read the passage below and then answer the questions.

Feeling Better

We were all hungry after band practice yesterday. As we gathered up our instruments, a friend suggested that we get a snack from the vending machine down the hall. I didn't know what kind of snacks were in the machine, so I said okay.

I looked over the selections as my friends put coins into the machine. Here's what I saw: candy, chips, and cookies. Everything in the machine was high in either fat, salt, or sugar. Nothing looked good to me, so I put my money back into my purse. That's when the questions from my friends began. "What's wrong with a bag of chips?" "Do you think chocolate is bad for you?" "Everyone likes cookies—why don't you?"

Here's why. Last year my dad found out that he has high blood pressure. He's a bit overweight, so his doctor told him to cut out foods high in salt and fat. My parents haven't told me that I have to stop eating snacks like chips and cookies. But Dad's condition helped me understand that what I eat can affect my health.

So I decided to support Dad by cutting back on fat, salt, and sugar. I feel so much better now! I've also become better at answering questions about my diet change, so my friends' questions don't bother me anymore. I just tell them how much better I feel!

1. What was the author's purpose in writing this passage?

   (A) to tell people that jokes can hurt
   (B) to explain that eating better can affect how one feels
   (C) to persuade everyone to eat cookies rather than chips
   (D) to tell people that healthy snacks taste better than unhealthy snacks

2. Which sentence best represents the main idea of the third paragraph?

   (F) Different cultures have different beliefs.
   (G) Everyone should become a vegetarian.
   (H) Some people prefer to eat salty snacks.
   (I) Eating healthy food can help you feel better.

3. Write a paragraph giving your best suggestions for lifetime weight management. Provide details to explain your main points.

Achieving Good Mental Health

HEALTH Online

Eye ON THE Media

Emotional Health in Television Programs

Actors depict an array of emotions in both healthy and unhealthy ways. Some viewers may feel that it is okay to copy unhealthy behaviors, such as

► anger.

► sadness.

► frustration.

Visit the Eye on the Media section at **health.glencoe.com** to learn more about how to examine healthy and unhealthy behaviors in television programs.

FOLDABLES™ Study Organizer

Before You Read

Use this Foldable to help you organize what you learn about achieving good mental/emotional health. Begin with three sheets of 8½" x 11" paper.

► **Step 1**

Place three sheets of paper on top of each other, with the top edges ¾" apart. Keep the side edges straight.

► **Step 2**

Fold up the bottom half of the stack of papers ¾" from the top half. All tabs should be the same size.

As You Read

As you read and discuss the material in the chapter, use your Foldable to record supporting facts under the appropriate tabs.

► **Step 3**

Crease the stack of papers to hold the tabs in place. Staple together along the fold.

► **Step 4**

Cut the sides of the papers to form a triangle. Label the tabs as shown.

Your Mental/ Emotional Health
Level 5
Level 4
Level 3
Level 2
Level 1

SPOTLIGHT ON HEALTH

Using Visuals. How do friendships and good family relationships help your mental health?

Your Mental and Emotional Health

Guide to Reading

Building Vocabulary

As you read this lesson, write each new highlighted term and its definition in your notebook.

▶ mental/emotional health (p. 170)

▶ hierarchy of needs (p. 172)

▶ self-actualization (p. 174)

▶ personality (p. 175)

▶ modeling (p. 175)

Focusing on the Main Ideas

In this lesson, you will learn how to:

▶ Identify the characteristics of good mental and emotional health.

▶ Develop ways to meet your needs in healthful ways.

▶ Associate abstinence with emotional health.

▶ Compare the relationship between mental health promotion and disease prevention.

Reading Strategy

Classify

▶ Draw a pyramid and divide it into the five levels shown in Figure 7.2. As you read, record the appropriate facts under each level heading.

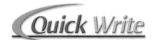

Quick Write

Write a brief paragraph describing the characteristics you think are important for a person with good mental health.

Ⓐ A person with good mental/emotional health has positive self-esteem. *What are some of the positive feelings you have about yourself?*

How do you see yourself? Would you describe yourself as serious, friendly, confident, or shy? Do you think you have a positive outlook? Are you generally a happy person? Do you look forward to facing life's challenges? At the conclusion of this lesson, you'll understand techniques for communicating care, consideration, and respect for self and others.

The Characteristics of Good Mental/Emotional Health

Mental/emotional health is *the ability to accept yourself and others, adapt to and manage emotions, and deal with the demands and challenges you meet in life.* Someone who is mentally and emotionally healthy can usually handle a wide variety of feelings and situations. They know strategies for replacing negative thoughts with positive. Someone who is mentally and emotionally healthy is able to identify factors that promote a positive self-image.

People with good mental/emotional health demonstrate the following characteristics:

Reading Check

Explain What are some of the characteristics of good mental/emotional health?

▶ **Positive Self-Esteem.** Your feelings of confidence and self-esteem are directly related to your general level of wellness. A person with positive self-esteem is better able to accept challenges and take failure in stride.

▶ **Sense of Belonging.** Having emotional attachment to family members, friends, teachers, and other people around you provides comfort and assurance.

▶ **Sense of Purpose.** Recognizing your own value and importance enables you to set and achieve goals and engage in activities that are personally rewarding, such as working hard in school, participating in sports, or doing community service.

▶ **Positive Outlook.** Seeing the bright side and having hope about life reduces stress and increases your energy level. It also increases the possibility of success.

▶ **Autonomy.** Having the confidence to make responsible and safe decisions promotes self-assurance and a sense of independence.

How would you assess your own mental/emotional health? Many of the attributes of good mental/emotional health listed in **Figure 7.1** can help students understand the characteristics of good mental health.

FIGURE 7.1

SIGNS OF GOOD MENTAL/ EMOTIONAL HEALTH

In general, teens with good mental/emotional health
- are realistic about their strengths and weaknesses.
- are responsible for their personal behavior.
- avoid high-risk behaviors, such as using tobacco, alcohol, or other drugs.
- are open-minded, flexible, and able to see several sides of an issue.
- are fun-loving and able to relax alone or with others.
- respect both their own needs and the needs of others.
- respect each person's value as a human being—including their own.
- invest time and energy in developing nurturing relationships.
- express their emotions in ways that do not hurt themselves or others.
- put their talents and abilities to good use.
- view change as a challenge and an opportunity.

A Pyramid of Needs

Many theories have been developed to explain human development and mental health by examining behavior. One important theory was created by Abraham Maslow, a pioneer in psychology. Maslow organized human needs in the form of a pyramid, as shown in **Figure 7.2.** This **hierarchy of needs** is *a ranked list of those needs essential to human growth and development, presented in ascending order, starting with basic needs and building toward the need for reaching your highest potential.*

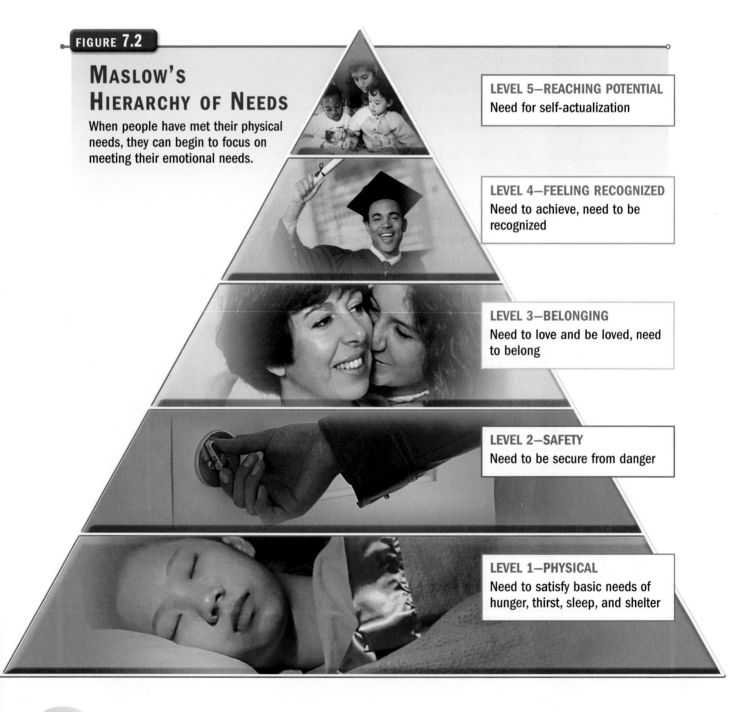

FIGURE 7.2

MASLOW'S HIERARCHY OF NEEDS

When people have met their physical needs, they can begin to focus on meeting their emotional needs.

LEVEL 5—REACHING POTENTIAL
Need for self-actualization

LEVEL 4—FEELING RECOGNIZED
Need to achieve, need to be recognized

LEVEL 3—BELONGING
Need to love and be loved, need to belong

LEVEL 2—SAFETY
Need to be secure from danger

LEVEL 1—PHYSICAL
Need to satisfy basic needs of hunger, thirst, sleep, and shelter

Physical Needs

Survival needs such as food, water, sleep, and shelter from the elements are among the needs at the bottom of the pyramid. People who are denied these basic needs become physically weak and may develop illnesses. It is important that students learn to identify basic human needs. There are many people for whom food, clean water, and shelter are not easily obtained. For example, social issues like homelessness can be related to health and physical needs.

Need for Safety

Satisfying the need for safety includes more than just safeguarding yourself against physical harm. In fact, the safety needs that are essential to your personality can also be psychological in nature. You need the safety of familiar places and people that help you feel secure, such as your home, your family, or trusted friends.

Need to Be Loved and to Belong

Everyone needs to give love and to know that he or she is loved in return. Babies who are denied emotional attention may fail to thrive, and they may even develop behavioral problems later.

Humans are social beings. We need to interact with other people and to know that we are valued members of a group that enhances our physical, mental, and social health. Most people generally want to belong to a community, such as a family, a circle of friends, or a social group such as a school club or a sports team. Feeling a sense of belonging can increase your confidence and strengthen your mental/emotional health.

Need to Be Valued and Recognized

Most of us feel a need to be appreciated, to be personally valued by family, friends, and peers. One way you might meet this need is by participating in productive activities, such as studying hard for exams, playing an instrument or sport, volunteering at a hospital, or writing short stories. By being able to do something well, you gain respect and a feeling of self-worth.

Participating in team sports can give teens a sense of belonging. *What other positive actions can teens take to fulfill this need?*

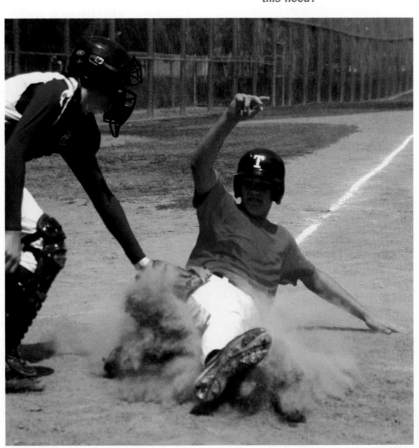

Need to Reach Your Potential

At the top of the pyramid is the need to reach your full potential as a person. This quest for **self-actualization**—*the striving to become the best you can be*—includes having goals that motivate and inspire you. Self-actualization means having the courage to make changes in your life in order to reach your goals. During your teen years, you begin to recognize your potential and set goals for your future. Self-actualization is a lifelong process. Part of the process is learning the self-discipline you need to reach your goals.

Meeting Your Needs

The ways you choose to meet your needs affect your mental/emotional health. For example, meeting the need for affection by building and maintaining respectful, loving relationships with people you care about will strengthen your mental/emotional health. It's also important that you know methods for effectively expressing feelings and opinions on mental/emotional health issues. Sometimes people choose risky ways to fulfill their needs. Some teens may decide to join a gang to feel a sense of belonging or engage in sexual activity in an attempt to feel loved. Such decisions carry dangerous consequences. Gang membership can lead to physical harm and trouble with the law. Sexual activity can result in unplanned pregnancy and sexually transmitted diseases. Practicing **abstinence** and finding healthful ways to meet emotional needs are strategies to avoid these risk behaviors.

▼ Practicing abstinence and meeting needs in healthy ways will strengthen your mental/emotional health. *What other decisions can you make to promote your health?*

Understanding Your Personality

Your **personality** is *a complex set of characteristics that makes you unique*. It's what makes you different from everyone else and determines how you will react in certain situations. Personality is an important factor in how you choose to meet your needs. Thus, it plays a major role in your overall mental health.

Influences on Your Personality

Personality includes an individual's emotional makeup, attitudes, thoughts, and behaviors. It is composed of tendencies that you were born with and characteristics that you have developed in response to life situations and experiences. The two main influences on your personality are heredity and environment.

PERSONALITY AND HEREDITY

Just as you inherit physical traits such as hair and eye color, you inherit some personality traits from your biological parents and ancestors. Heredity plays a role in determining a person's basic intellectual abilities and temperament, or emotional tendencies. There is also evidence that heredity may influence behaviors such as risk-taking and talents such as athletic or artistic abilities. This doesn't mean that you have no control over how successful you become or what you do. Your inherited brain chemistry is only one of the many factors contributing to your personality and behavior.

PERSONALITY AND ENVIRONMENT

Your environment includes everything that surrounds you in your day-to-day life. This means your family, friends, peers, home, neighborhood, school, and every other person, place, object, event, or activity in your life. All of these influences can have an impact on your developing personality.

Among the people in your environment are some who serve as role models for your behavior. Most people naturally engage in **modeling**, or *observing and learning from the behaviors of those around you*, sometimes without even thinking about it. If the behavior of your role model is healthful, the effect on your developing personality will also be healthful. The values you learn from your role models help shape the person you become and the way you live your life.

Reading ✓ Check

Explain What can influence your personality?

Many influences can help shape personality traits, such as a sense of self-discipline and the desire to excel. *Who are the role models in your life who have helped shape your personality?*

Resilient TEENS

Anthony Bonna is quietly matter-of-fact about the difficulties he faced as a child. His father was violent. For Anthony, the solution was politics. His interest began in the first grade when he was given a book about the American Presidents. He memorized all their names and insisted on writing the current President a letter. Anthony went on to study government and form opinions about all kinds of issues. "By the time the 2000 election rolled around I had an opinion about all the candidates and all the issues on the ballot and would talk to anyone who would listen," he says.

After the election the principal of Anthony's school suggested that he apply to be a page with the state House of Representatives in Tallahassee. Anthony got the job and went on to serve as a page at the federal level as well. "I've been living my dreams," says Anthony, "and I think it's because I have a 'yes I can' attitude. Sure there are things I can't change, but there are also things I can."

These days Anthony is busy mentoring other students and helping to create and implement a constitution at his school. "I think I'd like to go into politics," says Anthony when asked about his plans for the future, "but I'm open to pursuing anything that will help me make positive changes."

"I've been living my dreams, and I think it's because I have a 'yes I can' attitude. Sure there are things I can't change, but there are also things I can."

Explain What characteristics of good mental/emotional health did Anthony rely on to get through difficult times?

Personality and Behavior

The one aspect of your personality over which you have the most control is your behavior. How you make decisions, what decisions you make, whether you recognize the consequences of those decisions, and what actions you take can make a great difference in the quality of your life and in your levels of physical and mental/emotional health.

Promoting Mental/Emotional Health

Knowing positive strategies for expressing needs, wants, and feelings will help you choose behaviors that improve health. Being mentally and emotionally healthy can promote your physical health and help prevent some diseases. For example, meeting needs in healthful ways by abstaining from risk behaviors such as gang involvement and sexual activity will protect you from physical harm. People who are able to cope with their emotions and deal with the stress in their lives are also less susceptible to illnesses such as colds and other upper-respiratory infections. Engaging in behaviors that promote mental/emotional health may help prevent disease, and it will strengthen all three sides of your health triangle.

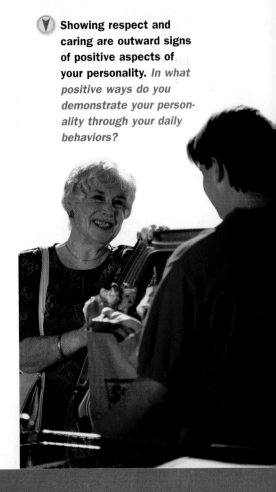
Showing respect and caring are outward signs of positive aspects of your personality. *In what positive ways do you demonstrate your personality through your daily behaviors?*

LESSON 1 — REVIEW

Reviewing Facts and Vocabulary

1. Define the term *mental/emotional health*. Identify three characteristics of a mentally and emotionally healthy person.
2. List the needs in Maslow's hierarchy of needs.
3. How does heredity influence personality?

Thinking Critically

4. **Evaluating.** Analyze the importance and benefits of abstinence as it relates to emotional health.
5. **Analyzing.** Explain how homelessness is a health-related social issue.

Applying Health Skills

Practicing Healthful Behaviors. The need to belong and to be loved is a basic human need. What are some healthy choices that provide positive ways for meeting this need? What are the consequences of meeting this need in negative ways? Make a two-column table to organize your thoughts.

After You Read

Explain. Review Figure 7.2. Write a paragraph explaining what you believe Maslow's Heirarchy of Needs means. Why do you think physical needs must be met before addressing emotional needs?

Developing a Positive Identity

Guide to Reading

Building Vocabulary

As you read this lesson, write each new highlighted term and its definition in your notebook.

▶ personal identity (p. 178)

▶ developmental assets (p. 179)

▶ constructive criticism (p. 183)

Focusing on the Main Ideas

In this lesson, you will learn how to:

▶ Define developmental assets.

▶ Construct strategies for developing a healthy identity.

▶ Correlate how self-esteem and a positive outlook benefit your mental/emotional health.

Reading Strategy

Organize Information

▶ Create a T chart listing each of the developmental assets on one side. On the other side, list some of the attributes of each developmental asset.

Quick Write

Write a brief paragraph describing your special qualities, talents, and abilities.

Your personal identity is made up of many different pieces. *What are some aspects of your identity that make you unique?*

If you were to write an essay describing who you are, you might begin by giving your name and age. Then you might identify your various roles, such as a son or daughter, brother or sister, student. You might also describe your talents, interests, hobbies, and accomplishments. These elements define your **personal identity**, *your sense of yourself as a unique individual.*

Your Personal Identity

During the teen years, you begin to develop a stronger sense of who you are. You learn about yourself through your interactions and relationships with other people. The knowledge you gain from your experiences will help you see yourself more clearly. Developing your personal identity is like putting a jigsaw puzzle together. The pieces of this puzzle include

▶ your interests.

▶ your likes and dislikes.

▶ your talents and abilities.

▶ your values and beliefs.

▶ your goals.

Your Developmental Assets

As you mature, it is important to recognize the developmental assets that will help you build a healthy, positive identity. **Development assets** are *the building blocks of development that help young people grow up as healthy, caring, and responsible individuals.* These assets, listed in **Figure 7.3,** can help you achieve wellness as you mature into an adult. Remember that developmental assets can be found in many aspects of your life and that you can always work to strengthen these assets.

Reading Check

Explain What elements define your personal identity?

FIGURE 7.3

DEVELOPMENTAL ASSETS

The Search Institute, a nonprofit organization, compiled this list of 40 assets that can help young people make healthful decisions on the road to adulthood.

Support—family support, positive family communication, relationships with other adults, caring neighborhood, caring school climate, parental involvement in schooling

Empowerment—being valued by adults in the community; serving a purpose by having a role in the community; feeling safe at home, at school, and in the neighborhood

Boundaries and Expectations—family boundaries (clear rules and consequences), school boundaries, neighborhood boundaries, adult role models, positive peer influences, high expectations

Constructive Use of Time—creative activities, youth programs, time at home, sports

Commitment to Learning—being motivated to achieve, being involved at school, doing homework, reading for pleasure

Positive Values—compassion, equality and social justice, integrity, honesty, responsibility, self-control

Social Competencies—planning and decision making, interpersonal communication, having knowledge and tolerance of different cultures, resistance skills, peaceful conflict-resolution skills

Positive Identity—personal power, self-esteem, sense of purpose, positive view of personal future

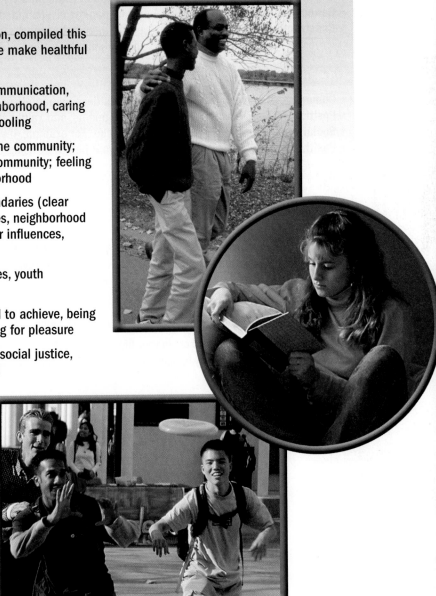

Real-Life Application

Identify and Strengthen Your Developmental Assets

Developmental assets increase the likelihood that a person will behave in ways that will enhance his or her health. Use the chart and questions to help you analyze how information from peers, family, and the community influences personal health.

External Assets	
• **Support** • **Empowerment** • **Boundaries and Expectations** • **Constructive Use of Time**	External developmental assets are the positive experiences that support and empower you. They include the standards set by parents or guardians, the expectations and encouragement of teachers, and the laws and rules of the community.

Internal Assets	
• **Commitment to Learning** • **Positive Values** • **Social Competencies** • **Positive Identity**	Internal developmental assets are the personal strengths, commitments, and values that you use to guide the decisions you make. For example, if you respect yourself, you will not harm your health by using tobacco, alcohol, or other drugs.

ACTIVITIES

1. Identify the external developmental assets in each of the following areas, and describe at least one way that each asset provides a positive influence in your life: family relationships, peer relationships, the school environment, the community environment.

2. Identify your internal developmental assets, and explain why these are personal strengths. Consider the following: accomplishments, strengths, and values.

3. Write a summary about the assets in your life. Reflect on the positive influences these assets have on the decisions you make. Use the following sentence beginnings in your summary:

   I learned that . . . I am proud that . . . I was surprised that . . . I would like to improve . . .

Working Toward a Healthy Identity

Once you recognize your developmental assets as important influences on your personal identity, you can take active steps to strengthen these assets and build a healthy identity. This process requires both self-acceptance and self-improvement.

Recognize Your Strengths and Weaknesses

An essential step in developing a healthy identity is viewing your strengths and weaknesses in honest, realistic ways. Accept and take pride in your strengths and accomplishments. Whether you are a caring family member, a trustworthy friend, an honor student, a good basketball player, or a talented singer, you should feel proud of the positive aspects of your identity.

At the same time, assess your weaknesses without being overly self-critical, and set goals for improvement. For example, if you tend to put things off, or procrastinate, try to develop new work habits that will lessen the pressure of having to do everything at the last minute. You may be able to use one of your strengths to help you address a weakness. For example, your strength might be that you are a fast learner and will quickly learn new work habits. By recognizing your strengths and weaknesses, you will be able to develop appropriate coping and resistance skills. Using your strengths and addressing your weaknesses helps you develop competence and effectiveness.

Demonstrate Positive Values

Your values, or your beliefs and ideas about what is important in your life, guide your actions and influence the decisions you make. You can demonstrate your values in many ways. For instance, you show honesty and integrity when you don't cheat on tests. When you comfort a sad friend, you demonstrate caring and compassion. Making sure that your behavior reflects your personal values and standards will reinforce your positive identity.

Develop a Purpose in Your Life

Think of having a sense of purpose as a framework for your mental health as you grow toward adulthood and work to build a healthy identity. Having a sense of purpose means establishing goals and working to achieve them. Some of the goals you establish will be short-term, such as studying for and passing an exam. Others will be long-term, such as making plans for higher education and acquiring job skills.

Form Meaningful Relationships

Relationships provide one means of developing a sense of purpose in your life. Family and friends enable you to express yourself and share your experiences, beliefs, and feelings. Positive relationships with family, friends, teachers, and coaches also give you a support system that will help you build confidence and develop a sense of security and belonging.

Reading Check

Cause and Effect How can your developmental assets help you build a healthy, positive identity?

The relationship between this coach and her team is part of a caring school climate. *Explain how having this asset can help teens build a healthy identity.*

People with high self-esteem:

▶ take responsibility for their behavior.

▶ generally have a positive outlook on life.

▶ like and accept who they are overall.

▶ try to learn from their successes as well as from their mistakes.

▶ build and maintain healthy relationships.

To improve self-esteem:

▶ think of appropriate ways to share your positive attributes.

▶ engage in behaviors that will promote your health.

Contribute to the Community

Your community is an extended support system for you and your family; it provides services and resources to meet many of your needs. Giving back to the community is part of being a good citizen, and it helps you feel a sense of accomplishment. For example, you might help out a neighbor or participate in a community clean-up campaign. Apply your strengths to improving others' quality of life, and strengthen your sense of belonging in the process.

Avoid Unhealthful Risk Behaviors

Risk-taking is a normal part of growing up—it helps define and develop identity. A health-literate consumer understands the potential impact of common risk behaviors on the quality of life. Healthful risk-taking has a positive effect on development. Engaging in sports, artistic or creative activities, public speaking, travel, and making friends all involve some risk. Such risks challenge you to develop skills and mature in new ways.

Unhealthful risk-taking, such as using tobacco, alcohol, or other drugs; reckless driving; and gang affiliation, can be dangerous.

Self-Esteem and Positive Outlook

When you have a healthy identity, you will experience increased self-esteem and a higher level of mental/emotional health. Self-esteem comes from the understanding that you are a unique and valuable human being. How you feel mentally and physically and how you take care of yourself are all affected by what you think of yourself. Teens with high self-esteem know positive strategies for expressing needs, wants, and feelings. They are able to identify socially acceptable ways of resolving interpersonal conflict by practicing nonabusive behavior.

▶ Teens find many ways to contribute to their community, including building houses for the homeless. *How does helping others contribute to a positive identity?*

Along with self-esteem, having a positive outlook is also directly related to your general level of wellness. Studies have shown that people with a positive outlook live longer and are healthier, both mentally and physically. Remind yourself that no matter what happens, there is always hope. Then, when something goes wrong, make a plan to address the problem. Try to see challenges as opportunities for growing and learning.

Realistic Patterns of Thinking

In order to increase your self-esteem and develop a positive outlook on life, it is essential to see events realistically. Some people fall into a pattern of seeing events as worse than they actually are. For example, a teen who has just failed an exam may think that he or she is stupid and will always fail. By looking at the situation realistically, the teen will realize that he or she was simply unprepared for that day's work and will resolve to study harder next time.

Sometimes, to help yourself see events more realistically, you might seek **constructive criticism**, or *nonhostile comments that point out problems and encourage improvement*. Constructive criticism can help you view a situation more objectively, without the emotional influences that can alter your perception and thinking.

ANALYZING YOUR SELF-TALK

Listen to your self-talk. Replace negative messages with constructive criticism. If you make a mistake, tell yourself that all people make mistakes; learn from yours and move on. Also, don't be afraid of telling yourself "Good job!" when you've done something that deserves praise. Such positive self-talk will benefit your self-esteem, your general outlook on life, and your mental/emotional health.

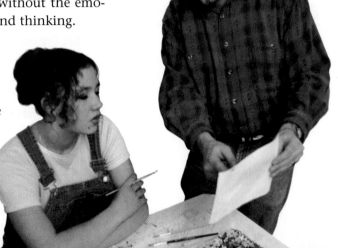

This teen uses constructive criticism from the teacher to improve her skills and thus raise her self-esteem. *Why is self-esteem important to mental and emotional health?*

LESSON 2 — REVIEW

Reviewing Facts and Vocabulary

1. Define *personal identity*. List five elements that contribute to one's personal identity.
2. Name three of the positive values listed as developmental assets.
3. List three strategies for building a positive identity.

Thinking Critically

4. **Synthesizing.** Why do you think developmental assets increase the likelihood that a person will not engage in risk behaviors?
5. **Analyzing.** Describe how positive identity and high self-esteem can help you with goal setting, developing relationships, and contributing to your community.

Applying Health Skills

Goal Setting. Evaluate aspects of your identity. Is there an area you would like to improve? Make a specific goal to strengthen one aspect of your identity. Using the steps of goal setting, write down plans and strategies to help you achieve your goal.

After You Read

Analyze. Carefully read the list of developmental assets in Figure 7.3. As you read the rest of the chapter, make a list of ways to strengthen your developmental assets and develop a healthy identity.

Visit **health.glencoe.com** for the Interactive Study Guide for Lesson 2.

Lesson 2 Developing a Positive Identity **183**

Understanding Emotions

Guide to Reading

Building Vocabulary

As you read this lesson, write each new highlighted term and its definition in your notebook.

► emotions (p. 184)

► hormone (p. 185)

► empathy (p. 186)

► hostility (p. 187)

Focusing on the Main Ideas

In this lesson, you will learn how to:

► Identify the emotions that influence your overall health.

► Examine changes that occur during adolescence.

Quick Write

List as many emotions as you can. In a brief paragraph, describe the emotions you think are most common.

Reading Strategy

Organize Information

► Write the word emotion. Surround it with seven circles and label them Happiness, Sadness, Love, Empathy, Fear, Guilt, and Anger. As you read, fill in each circle with the appropriate information.

Actors portray strong emotions by using body language and changes in their voices. *What emotions are these actors trying to express?*

A rt imitates life. This familiar phrase is particularly true in regard to drama. Acting requires the performer to express a character's emotions both verbally and physically.

Understanding Your Emotions

Emotions are *signals that tell your mind and body how to react.* Sometimes referred to as feelings, emotions are your responses to certain thoughts and events. Learning about your emotions will help you understand the relationship among physical, mental and emotional, and social health throughout adulthood.

► Joy can prompt the release of brain chemicals that cause you to experience warmth and a sense of well-being. Feeling this way promotes mental/emotional health and positively influences your relationships and thus your social health.

► Fear can trigger physical changes, including increased perspiration, an increase in heart rate, and a tightening of muscles. This "fight-or-flight" response enables you to defend yourself or flee the scene.

▶ Strong emotions like anger can cause both physical and mental responses, such as an increase in heart rate and feelings of distress. Inappropriate responses, such as lashing out, can be harmful to you or to people around you.

Identifying Your Emotions

Sometimes you know exactly what you are feeling and why. At other times, you may experience emotions that seem to have no apparent cause. Moreover, the many changes brought on by hormones during puberty can affect your emotions. A **hormone** is *a chemical secreted by your glands that regulates the activities of different body cells.* Hormones may cause you to swing quickly between extreme emotions such as elation and depression. Mixed emotions, such as when you feel both jealous of and happy for a friend, also can be challenging. Learning skills for communicating effectively with family, friends, and others is an important first step toward knowing how to respond in a healthy way.

Happiness

Think of other words that might describe how you feel when you are happy. You might say you are pleased or that you feel good or carefree. Happiness can be described as being satisfied or feeling positive. When you are happy, you usually feel energetic, creative, and sociable.

Sadness

Sadness is a normal, healthy reaction to difficult events. Causes of sadness can range from being disappointed or rejected to experiencing the loss of a loved one. Feelings of sadness may be mild and fleeting, or they may be deep and long-lasting. When you are sad, you may feel easily discouraged and have less energy.

Love

Love involves strong affection, deep concern, and respect. It includes supporting the growth and individual needs of another person and respecting that person's boundaries and values. Love can be expressed through words or actions, such as good deeds. It comes in many forms, such as caring about family and friends, loyalty to siblings, and a deep sense of being connected to your community and country.

Reading ✓ Check

Explain How do hormones affect your emotions?

▼ Sadness may bring feelings of hurt, isolation, or help-lessness. *How can you comfort a friend who is feeling down?*

Reading Check

Describe What physical and mental responses may be caused by emotions?

Empathy

Empathy is *the ability to imagine and understand how someone else feels.* When you feel empathy, you feel connected to another person's emotions. An empathetic person listens attentively and communicates understanding toward others. Demonstrating empathy can help build and maintain your relationships.

Fear

When you are startled by someone or something, you probably feel some degree of fear. Feelings of fear can increase your alertness and help you escape from potentially harmful situations. However, fear that results from an imagined threat can prevent people from leading normal lives. For example, an exaggerated fear of being in a crowd can result in a life of solitude. This type of fear is called a **phobia** and requires professional help.

Communication: Expressing Your Feelings

Tara feels a knot in her stomach when she sees her friend Suzanne. The last time she agreed to go to a concert with Tara, Suzanne failed to show up. It hurt Tara's feelings that Suzanne didn't care enough about their friendship to show up.

Suzanne says excitedly, "Tara, did you see who's playing this weekend? Let's get there early, okay?"

Tara feels torn between two choices. She could ignore her feelings by keeping them bottled up. Her other option would be to communicate her hurt and disappointment, but that would risk hurting Suzanne's feelings.

What Would You Do?

Use the following communication skills to write a dialogue in which Tara expresses her hurt and disappointment in a way that builds and maintains her relationship with Suzanne.

1. Use "I" messages.
2. Keep your tone respectful.
3. Provide a clear, organized message that states the problem.
4. Listen to the other person's side without interrupting.

Guilt

Guilt often results from acting against one's values or from failing to act when action might have brought about a better outcome. Although guilt can eat at you, it can also act as your conscience and motivate you to make some positive changes in your behavior. Sometimes, people may feel guilty for things they have no control over. For example, some teens blame themselves when parents divorce even though they are not the cause of the separation. Being able to recognize when you are not responsible for a negative outcome will save you from needless guilt.

Anger

Anger is a common reaction to being emotionally hurt or physically harmed. When anger isn't handled in constructive ways, it can result in violence, bringing physical and emotional harm to you and others. **Hostility**, *the intentional use of unfriendly or offensive behavior,* can be particularly damaging, not only to others but also to the hostile person. People who show chronic hostile behavior are four to seven times more likely to die of heart disease than those who are not prone to hostility. Knowing strategies for overcoming barriers when communicating information, ideas, feelings, and opinions can help you gain control over feelings such as anger.

HEALTH Online

TOPIC Emotions

Go to health.glencoe.com to explore more about emotions and the role they play in our lives.

ACTIVITY Use the information you find to write a poem about a specific emotion. Make sure that the tone of your poem conveys the emotion you are writing about.

LESSON 3 | **REVIEW**

Reviewing Facts and Vocabulary

1. How can emotions influence your overall health?
2. Define *empathy.* How can a person demonstrate empathy toward others?
3. How might guilty feelings lead to positive results?

Thinking Critically

4. **Evaluating.** Appraise the significance of changes occurring during adolescence: What effects do changing hormone levels have on emotions?
5. **Synthesizing.** List three situations that may cause a teen to feel anger. Then, explain how each of these situations can be dealt with in healthful ways.

Applying Health Skills

Conflict Resolution. Write a skit in which unpleasant emotions cause a conflict between two friends. Your skit should demonstrate positive communication skills that aid the teens in handling their strong emotions and resolving their differences.

After You Read

Explain. Write a paragraph explaining how you can identify your emotions.

Visit **health.glencoe.com** for the Interactive Study Guide for Lesson 3.

Lesson 3 Understanding Emotions **187**

Managing Emotions

Guide to Reading

Building Vocabulary

As you read this lesson, write each new highlighted term and its definition in your notebook.

▶ defense mechanisms (p. 189)

▶ suppression (p. 189)

Quick Write

List three emotions. Describe how to express these emotions in a positive way.

Focusing on the Main Ideas

In this lesson, you will learn how to:

▶ **Compare** and contrast the positive and negative effects of peers, family, and friends on emotional health.

▶ **Demonstrate** strategies for communicating emotions and needs in healthful ways.

Reading Strategy

Explain

▶ Before reading the lesson, describe what you think the term *defense mechanism* means. Describe one or two behaviors that you believe may be related to a defense mechanism.

Healthful expression of feelings increases your ability to enjoy life. *What are some positive ways to express emotions?*

Emotions are neither good nor bad. Learning skills for communicating effectively with family, friends, and others can strongly influence your overall level of health. Learning to recognize emotions and dealing with them in healthful ways are especially important to good mental health.

Dealing with Emotions in Positive Ways

As you were growing up, you learned various positive and negative ways of expressing your emotions from your environment, from your experiences, and from others. Health literate people know positive strategies for expressing needs, wants, and feelings. Maybe your friends express themselves indirectly with looks or smiles or with behaviors such as laughing or hugging. Perhaps some of your peers don't talk about or express feelings much, and you've learned from their example that emotions are private. Regardless of what you have learned, it is important to evaluate strategies for communicating emotions and needs and practice healthful ways of expression.

Negative ways of dealing with feelings do nothing to solve problems. Exaggerating emotions for effect, pretending that feelings are not there at all, or intentionally hurting another person while expressing feelings can worsen the situation and create new problems.

Responding to Your Emotions

You can use some of the following strategies for interpreting and responding to most emotions.

▶ Look below the surface of your emotion. Ask yourself: What am I really reacting to? Does the intensity of my emotion match the situation?

▶ Consider whether or not the situation to which you are reacting will matter tomorrow, next week, or next year.

▶ Don't take action on a strong feeling until you have thoroughly considered the possible consequences of your action.

▶ Use positive feelings to inspire yourself. Relieve negative or upsetting feelings by engaging in physical activities or by talking to a family member or trusted friend.

▶ If a negative feeling doesn't go away, seek help from a parent, another trusted adult, or a health care professional.

Managing Difficult Emotions

You've probably been overwhelmed by strong emotions at one time or another. Intense emotions can affect your attitude and behavior in ways that are upsetting. However, you can learn to manage strong emotions by learning strategies for solving interpersonal conflicts without harming yourself and others. When you feel your emotions building, recognize the feeling and manage it by taking slow, deep breaths and relaxing. You might also get away from the situation to compose yourself. Sometimes you can control your feelings by analyzing the situations that cause them. Writing in a private journal, playing music, or talking your feelings over with a parent or trusted friend can help you reflect on both your emotions and the situation that led to them.

Defense Mechanisms

Because of the way emotions affect you, you may try to avoid the ones that cause you discomfort by using **defense mechanisms**. These are *mental processes that protect individuals from strong or stressful emotions and situations.* **Figure 7.4** on page 190 lists some of the most common defense mechanisms. Sometimes, these responses occur unconsciously and may help protect you from feeling too much emotional pain. For instance, the use of **suppression**, *holding back or restraining,* can provide a temporary escape from an unpleasant situation. In the long run, however, defense mechanisms may keep you from facing what is really troubling you.

 Creating art is a healthful way to handle your emotions. *The next time you feel a strong emotion, try doing something creative.*

Reading ✓ Check

Explain What positive actions can you take in response to your emotions?

FIGURE 7.4

COMMON DEFENSE MECHANISMS

- **Repression.** Involuntary pushing of unpleasant feelings out of conscious thought.
- **Suppression.** Conscious, intentional pushing of unpleasantness from one's mind.
- **Rationalization.** Making excuses to explain a situation or behavior rather than directly taking responsibility for it.
- **Regression.** Reverting to behaviors more characteristic of an earlier stage of development rather than dealing with the conflict in a mature manner.
- **Denial.** Unconscious lack of acknowledgement of something that is obvious to others.
- **Compensation.** Making up for weaknesses and mistakes through gift-giving, hard work, or extreme efforts.
- **Projection.** Attributing your own feelings or faults to another person or group.
- **Idealization.** Seeing someone else as perfect, ideal, or more worthy than everyone else.

Handling Fear

Fear is an emotion many people work to overcome. Overcoming fear requires a strategy. The first step is to identify your fear. Analyzing the situation that causes the fear often helps. Talking about your fear with someone you trust may also give you a fresh outlook. This person may remind you of other fears you have faced successfully or know of resources that can help you. Some fear is healthy and natural; only when fear is irrational or uncontrollable should you consider it a problem.

Dealing with Guilt

Guilt can be a very destructive emotion. When you feel guilty about something, try to get at the underlying source and address that issue. If you have hurt someone, for example, admit your mistake and make amends. Learn from the experience, and resolve to be more careful and responsible in the future. Discussing the situation with family or friends can also help make you feel better. Keep in mind that some situations may not be in your control. Viewing such circumstances realistically and honestly will help you see that you are not responsible and should not feel guilty for them.

Managing Anger

Anger can be one of the most difficult emotions to handle. The first step in constructively dealing with anger is similar to dealing with guilt—you must try to get at the underlying source and address it. Even if there is nothing you can do about the source of your anger, you can find ways to cope with your feelings. Refer to the Hands-On Health Activity for some general anger-management techniques.

Reading Check

Explain How do people use defense mechanisms?

Hands-On Health ACTIVITY

Managing Anger

In this activity you'll develop a comic strip showing healthy strategies to handle anger.

What You'll Need

- pencil and paper

What You'll Do

Write one of the following headings on your paper:

- Do something to relax.
- Rechannel your energy.
- Talk to someone you trust.
- Get some physical activity.

Draw two boxes under the heading. In one box, draw a comic strip showing a situation that makes you angry. In the second box, draw a comic strip showing how to apply the heading at the top of the paper.

Apply and Conclude

Create a comic strip that illustrates at least one effective anger management skill.

LESSON 4 REVIEW

Reviewing Facts and Vocabulary

1. List three strategies for interpreting, responding to, and communicating an emotion or need in healthful ways.
2. What are five common defense mechanisms?
3. Give four examples of anger-management techniques.

Thinking Critically

4. **Analyzing.** Evaluate the positive and negative effects of various relationships on emotional health: In what ways do peers, family, and friends influence how you express and manage emotions?
5. **Explaining.** Describe the results that may occur when you take time to reflect before responding to a strong emotion.

Applying Health Skills

Communication Skills. Write a one-act play. Focus on someone using the strategies listed at the beginning of this lesson to decide how to react to and express a specific feeling.

After You Read

Problems and Solutions. Make a chart with two columns. On one side, list some difficult emotions. On the other side, write some ways to manage difficult emotions.

Visit **health.glencoe.com** for the Interactive Study Guide for Lesson 4.

Lesson 4 Managing Emotions **191**

Five Ways
TO BOOST YOUR SELF-CONFIDENCE

1. ACCENTUATE THE POSITIVE

Remind yourself what you're good at—whether it's a talent like drawing or a personality trait such as being outgoing. This is a great way to ward off that nagging voice of negativity in your head, says Michael Riera, Ph.D., a psychologist in Berkeley, California. Make a list of your strengths and read it aloud every day until you really believe it.

2. REACH OUT

When you feel overwhelmed by school, family, or social pressures, don't ride it out alone: Call a friend to calm your nerves. Don't make the mistake of thinking that asking for support is a sign of weakness. Checking in with someone who cares will make you feel less alone and better able to understand what's making you feel bad about yourself.

3. GIVE YOURSELF A PUSH

Challenging yourself to tackle uncomfortable situations can boost your self-esteem, no matter what the outcome. If you want to talk to your teacher about an extension on an assignment, don't imagine the 12,000 ways that it could go wrong. Instead, says Riera, "see yourself getting through it. Then, even if the teacher says no, acknowledge that by giving it a try you succeeded."

4. HAVE A CHEERLEADING SQUAD

Find a "support network who believes in you," advises Riera, whether that includes friends, family, or a school guidance counselor, and lean on them when you're feeling insecure. They'll be able to see you—and your problems—more clearly than you can see yourself.

5. TRY, TRY AGAIN

You may not reach all your goals the first time you go out for them, but by being realistic about your ambitions, you can pace yourself—and be proud of your improvements along the way. ◢

TIME to THINK... About Self-Esteem

Create a personal "to do" pamphlet. On each page, write one of the above tips. Write two ways that you can use each tip in your daily life. Draw an empty box next to each example, and add a check mark as you accomplish each one.

Health Skills Application

1. **Analyzing Influences.** Make a list of the factors that you think have the strongest influence on your personality. Identify which of these are hereditary influences and which are environmental influences. *(LESSON 1)*

2. **Communication Skills.** Think of a person in your life who has given you constructive criticism or positive feedback. Write a thank-you letter to this person. Indicate how this feedback has affected your feelings of self-esteem. *(LESSON 2)*

3. **Advocacy.** Create a small booklet that promotes emotional health by explaining positive ways for teens to deal with difficult emotions or mood swings. *(LESSON 3)*

4. **Practicing Healthful Behaviors.** For one week, maintain an "anger log." After each instance of anger, rate the experience from 1 (mildly irritated) to 10 (hostile). Include the trigger for your anger, what you felt like doing at the time, and how you actually handled the emotion. If necessary, determine ways to improve your anger-management skills. *(LESSON 4)*

School Counselor

Do you have empathy, and do you like helping others? Are you interested in teaching and working with students and their families? If so, a career as a school psychologist or counselor might be for you. These professionals assist students with personal, family, educational, and mental health problems.

To enter this profession, you'll need a four-year college degree and at least a two-year graduate degree. Find more information about this and other health careers by clicking on Career Corner at **health.glencoe.com.**

Parent Involvement

Advocacy. Learn more about local charities and shelters in your community. With your parents or guardians, find out what items and experience are needed and what volunteer positions are available. Use this information to make leaflets or posters that inform others of ways they can help individuals meet their needs.

School and Community

Service Learning. Find out whether your school has a service-learning program. If it does, determine what community volunteer opportunities exist. If not, search the Web for the Corporation for National and Community Service. Use their Web site to locate specific opportunities in your community.

After You Read

Use the notes you have made on your Foldable to review what you have learned about mental/emotional health. On the back of your Foldable, state whether you feel you are achieving good mental/emotional health, and describe why or why not.

► EXPLORING HEALTH TERMS *Answer the following questions on a sheet of paper.*

Lesson 1 *Match each definition with the correct term.*

hierarchy of needs   **self-actualization**
mental/emotional health   **modeling**
personality

1. A complex set of characteristics that make you unique.
2. A ranked list of those needs essential to human growth and development.
3. Striving to become the best you can be.
4. Observing and learning from the behavior of others.

Lesson 2 *Replace the underlined words with the correct term.*

constructive criticism   **personal identity**
developmental asset

5. <u>Constructive criticism</u> is made up of elements such as interests, abilities, values, and goals.
6. A <u>personal identity</u> is a building block of development that helps you grow up as a healthy, caring, and responsible individual.
7. Giving thoughtful recommendations on how a friend can improve a skill is an example of <u>developmental asset</u>.

Lesson 3 *Fill in the blanks with the correct term.*

emotion   **hormone**
empathy   **hostility**

A(n) (_8_) tells your mind and body how to react. A change in the level of a(n) (_9_) can affect how you react to situations and thus can affect your emotions. Anger sometimes results in (_10_), which can damage a relationship.

Lesson 4 *Identify each statement as True or False. If false, replace the underlined term with the correct term.*

suppression   **defense mechanisms**

11. People sometimes use <u>defense mechanisms</u> to avoid dealing with an unpleasant emotion.
12. <u>Projection</u> is holding back or restraining.

► RECALLING THE FACTS *Use complete sentences to answer the following questions.*

1. In general, teens with good mental/emotional health demonstrate what characteristics?
2. Why is it important to meet needs in positive ways?
3. List four environmental influences that can affect the development of someone's personality.
4. Identify the eight categories of developmental assets.
5. What does it mean to develop a sense of purpose?
6. How can healthful risk-taking have a positive effect on development?
7. How do high self-esteem and a positive outlook affect a person's health?
8. List seven basic emotions.
9. Identify two causes of guilt.
10. Why is it harmful to feel hostile often?
11. What are some ways of managing strong emotions?
12. Identify two strategies for dealing with guilt.

For more review questions for Chapter 7, go to **health.glencoe.com**.

➤ WRITING CRITICALLY

1. **Persuasive.** Maslow's Hierarchy of Needs shows that people cannot focus on their emotional needs until their physical needs such as hunger, sleep, and shelter have been met. Conduct research on public and private agencies that help combat hunger and homelessness. Then, using the knowledge gained from your research, write a news article advocating for the homeless. Persuade others to volunteer to combat homelessness with supporting evidence, facts, opinions, and examples.

2. **Personal.** Write a letter to someone you know who has hurt your feelings in the past. In your letter, identify your emotions and express them in a healthy and respectful way using positive communication skills.

Standardized Test Practice

 The purpose of persuasive writing is to convince the reader to accept your opinion or to take a specific action. The *Writing Situation* focuses on the effect of anger on a person and those around him or her. The *Directions for Writing* suggests that you think about these effects and convince your friend to try some of your anger management techniques.

PROMPT

Writing Situation: You have a friend whose anger has become a problem for him and others. Assume the part of a person who used to have a problem with anger.

Directions for Writing: Think about the techniques you practice now that keep your anger from exploding out of control.

Now write to convince your friend why it is worth trying your techniques for anger management.

Managing Stress and Anxiety

Eye ON THE **Media**

Advertising Stress Relief

Ads on stress relief may be misleading. Consumers should learn to assess the validity of advertising claims. For instance, some advertisers may claim that using their product will

▶ relieve tension.

▶ reduce stress.

▶ cure illness.

Visit the Eye on the Media section at **health.glencoe.com** to learn more about how to evaluate claims made in ads.

FOLDABLES™ Study Organizer

Before You Read

Use this Foldable to help you organize what you learn about the causes and effects of stress. Begin with a sheet of 8½″ x 11″ paper.

▶ **Step 1**

Fold the sheet of paper into thirds along the short axis.

▶ **Step 2**

Unfold. Fold a long end of the sheet down to form a 1″ tab.

Stress	Cause	Effect

▶ **Step 3**

Unfold and label as shown.

As You Read

As you read and discuss the material in the chapter, use your Foldable to record examples of stress you experience, to analyze the cause of the stress, and to note the effects of the stress on your life.

SPOTLIGHT ON HEALTH

Using Visuals. Exercise can help relieve stress. What else can you do to relieve stress?

Effects of Stress

Guide to Reading

Building Vocabulary

As you read this lesson, write each new highlighted term and its definition in your notebook.

▶ stress (p. 198)
▶ perception (p. 198)
▶ stressor (p. 199)
▶ psychosomatic response (p. 202)
▶ chronic stress (p. 204)

Focusing on the Main Ideas

In this lesson, you will learn how to:

▶ **Examine** the causes and effects of stress.
▶ **Differentiate** how stress can affect physical, mental/emotional, and social health.
▶ **Show** how substance abuse harms mental/emotional health.

Reading Strategy

Explain

▶ Write a paragraph explaining what you think the differences are between stress and chronic stress.

Quick Write

Write a brief paragraph describing situations that are particularly a source of stress for teens.

 Disagreements with friends can be a source of stress that affects all aspects of your health triangle.

How does your perception change the way an event affects you?

Everyone experiences stress—it's a natural part of life. **Stress** is *the reaction of the body and mind to everyday challenges and demands.* You might experience stress during your daily routine, such as when you're running late or when you can't find your keys. Taking an important exam, playing in a state championship basketball game, or arguing with a friend can all be sources of stress. Understanding the relationships among physical, mental and emotional, and social health throughout adulthood is an important part of staying healthy.

Stress in Your Life

How much stress you feel depends in part on your perception of events that cause stress. **Perception** is *the act of becoming aware through the senses.* One way to manage stress is to change how you perceive and react to events that cause it. Imagine, for example, that you and your best friend have just had an argument. You believe that this disagreement has destroyed your friendship. Your friend, on the other hand, sees the argument as a simple disagreement that you will eventually work out. Because of your perception of the event, you are more likely to experience a higher level of stress than your friend.

Reacting to Stress

Stress is not necessarily good or bad in and of itself, but it can have positive or negative effects. It can motivate you to do your best and give you the extra energy you need to reach your goals. For example, some people may perform better under the stress of competition. However, the effects of stress can be unhealthy at times. Losing sleep after arguing with a friend or being so worried about a test that you don't perform well are examples of the negative effects of stress. It may be difficult to talk about what stresses you. That's why it is important to know strategies for overcoming barriers when communicating information, ideas, feelings, and opinions on health issues.

 The stress of competition motivates this teen to practice every day. *In what other ways can stress have a positive effect on teens?*

What Causes Stress?

Knowing strategies for managing stress shows that you know what causes it. A **stressor** is *anything that causes stress.* People, objects, places, events, and situations are all potential stressors. Some stressors affect almost everyone in a similar way. The sound of a siren, for example, heightens alertness in most people. Other stressors affect different people in different ways. Going to a new school, for example, can cause anticipation in some people but a sense of anxiety in others. Psychologists have identified five general categories of stressors:

► **Biological stressors,** such as illnesses, disabilities, or injuries

► **Environmental stressors,** such as poverty, pollution, crowding, noise, or natural disasters

► **Cognitive, or thinking, stressors,** such as the way you perceive a situation or how it affects you and the world around you

► **Personal behavior stressors,** such as negative reactions in the body and mind caused by using tobacco, alcohol, or other drugs or by a lack of physical activity

► **Life situation stressors,** such as the death of a pet, the separation or divorce of parents, or having trouble in relationships with peers

Part of how you perceive these stressors has to do with your past experiences. If you had a positive experience the first time you participated in a school play, you'll probably look forward to future performances. On the other hand, if you experienced stage fright, you may feel anxious about being involved in similar events.

Reading Check

Infer How can your perception of an event affect the amount of stress you feel?

The Body's Stress Response

When you perceive a situation or event to be a threat, your body begins a stress response. For example, if a car alarm suddenly goes off as you walk by, you may jump at the sound or feel your heart start to race. The sudden, loud noise is a stressor that affects you instantly, without you even thinking about it.

Two major body systems, the **nervous system** and the **endocrine system,** are active during the body's response to stressors. This response is largely involuntary, or automatic. It happens in three stages and can occur regardless of the type of stressor.

Alarm

Alarm is the first stage in the stress response. This is when the body and mind go on high alert. This reaction, illustrated and explained in **Figure 8.1,** is sometimes referred to as the "fight-or-flight response" because it prepares the body to either defend itself or flee from a threat.

FIGURE 8.1

THE ALARM RESPONSE

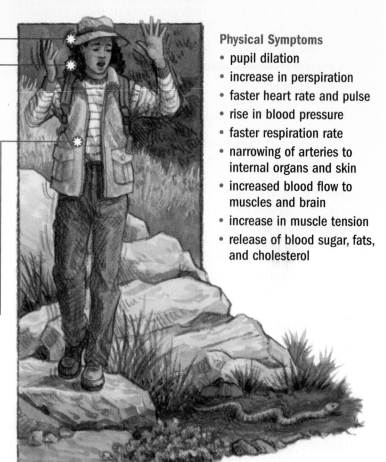

1. Alarm begins when the hypothalamus, a small area at the base of the brain, receives danger signals from other parts of the brain. The hypothalamus releases a hormone that acts on the pituitary gland.

2. The pituitary then secretes a hormone that stimulates the adrenal glands.

3. The adrenal glands secrete adrenaline. Adrenaline is the "emergency hormone" that prepares the body to respond to a stressor.

Physical Symptoms
- pupil dilation
- increase in perspiration
- faster heart rate and pulse
- rise in blood pressure
- faster respiration rate
- narrowing of arteries to internal organs and skin
- increased blood flow to muscles and brain
- increase in muscle tension
- release of blood sugar, fats, and cholesterol

Resistance

If exposure to a stressor continues, the next stage of the stress response is *resistance*. During this stage, your body adapts to the rush created by alarm and reacts to the stressor. This is the stage in which you "fight" or take "flight." Your body is briefly able to perform at a higher level of endurance. In the case of "fight," your ability to resist a physical challenge or attack may be enhanced. In the case of "flight," you may be able to run faster and farther than normal in order to escape from danger. The resistance stage is why people in extremely high-stress situations have been known to accomplish incredible feats, such as lifting an automobile to save a child trapped underneath.

Fatigue

When exposure to stress is prolonged, the body is affected and loses its ability to adapt to the situation and fatigue may set in. During *fatigue*, the third stage of the stress response, a tired feeling takes over that lowers your level of activity. In this stage, your ability to effectively manage other stressors is very low. Both the mind and body have become exhausted. Fatigue can affect the body in several ways.

▶ **Physical fatigue** results when the muscles work vigorously for long periods, often leading to soreness and pain. Reaction time becomes impaired, and muscles tire very quickly.

▶ **Psychological fatigue** can result from constant worry, overwork, depression, boredom, isolation, or feeling overwhelmed by too many responsibilities.

▶ **Pathological fatigue** is tiredness brought on by overworking the body's defenses in fighting disease. Anemia, the flu, being overweight, and poor nutrition can all bring on pathological fatigue. Use of drugs such as alcohol can intensify the feeling of fatigue.

It is important that you learn to analyze stress and its effects on all aspects of health and wellness. Prolonged or repeated stress can lead to stress-related illnesses caused by the changes that take place in your body during these three stages. Although a stress-related illness can be minor, such as sleeplessness or upset stomach, it can also be life threatening, such as high blood pressure, heart disease, or stroke.

▼ Prolonged illness can overwork the body's immune system and result in pathological fatigue. *What can you do to reduce stress and speed recovery during an illness?*

Stress and Your Health

Stress is an unavoidable part of life. Sometimes stress can make life fun, exciting, enjoyable, and challenging. Excessive or prolonged stress, however, can have negative effects on all aspects of your health.

Physical Effects

Sometimes stress can lead to a **psychosomatic response**. This is *a physical reaction that results from stress rather than from an injury or illness. Psycho* means "of the mind," and *somatic* means "of the body." Psychosomatic responses may include sleep disorders, skin disorders, and stomach and digestive problems. Other health problems that may sometimes be stress-related include:

▶ **Headache.** Headache caused by stress is the most common type of headache. It is estimated that, in any given year, about 70 percent of all people worldwide will have at least one stress headache. Many headaches are related to tension. When stressed, the muscles in the head and neck contract. Migraine headaches, which affect about one in ten people, may also be triggered by stress. During a migraine attack, inflamed blood vessels and nerves around the brain cause severe throbbing, which is often accompanied by nausea and vomiting.

▶ **Asthma.** For some people, stress can trigger an **asthma** attack. During an asthma attack, breathing becomes difficult as the bronchioles, or air-carrying tubes of the lungs, constrict. The person may cough, wheeze, or fight to get air. If untreated, some cases of asthma can be life threatening. If you have asthma, it is important to discover what sets off your attacks and how to avoid or manage these triggers.

▶ **High blood pressure.** Prolonged stress can cause an increase in a person's levels of cholesterol, the fatty substance that can block arteries. High cholesterol levels can result in high blood pressure, a condition that contributes to heart disease and stroke.

▶ **Weakened immune system.** Extended exposure to stress can reduce the body's ability to fight disease by weakening the immune system. When your immune system is weakened, you may be more prone to colds, flu, or more severe infections.

Mental/Emotional and Social Effects

Stress can also have an effect on mental/emotional and social health. It can interfere with daily activities and relationships.

▶ **Difficulty concentrating.** It can be hard to focus during stressful situations. This can cause negative self-talk and the distorted belief that failure is inevitable.

Some headaches are caused by psychosomatic responses to stress. *What healthful behaviors can help protect you from the negative effects of stress?*

Resilient TEENS

Listening to Antonio Burton talk about his interest in music and painting, it's hard to believe that anger is a problem for him. But Antonio freely admits he has a temper. "I can't stand seeing people mistreated, or to have someone deliberately push my buttons," he says.

The one time his temper got out of control, Antonio's mother insisted he attend an anger management program. "I learned to identify what triggers my anger and to avoid problems before they occur."

Antonio sees himself as an introvert who has had to learn to be around people. Born with severe asthma that limited his physical activity, he was both overweight and depressed as a child. "My mom and family pushed me to deal with what I was feeling and surround myself with positive people," he says. "I'm still a little different, but now I don't mind. My dream is to change the world by helping one person at a time."

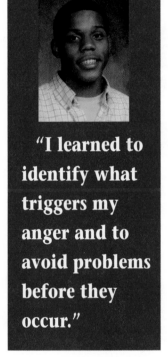

"I learned to identify what triggers my anger and to avoid problems before they occur."

 Reading Check

Describe What can you do to control anger?

▶ **Mood swings.** Feeling happy one moment and sad the next is a common reaction to stress. Teens may experience mood swings as a result of the hormonal changes of adolescence as well as social and academic pressures. These emotional shifts may put a strain on relationships with family and friends.

▶ **Risks of substance abuse.** Stress can increase a person's vulnerability to **drug use.** Many people give stress as the reason they started drinking or smoking. However, use of these substances actually increases stress and leads to even bigger problems.

 Reading Check

Describe What are some of the physical effects of stress?

Taking Control of Chronic Stress

One type of prolonged stress is **chronic stress**, or *stress associated with long-term problems that are beyond a person's control.* The body's reaction to chronic stress is less intense than a fight-or-flight response, but it lasts longer, sometimes for months. Symptoms can include upset stomach, headache, insomnia, change in appetite, and feeling anxious.

Fortunately, even if you can't eliminate the cause of stress, you *can* do something to reduce its effects. Taking care of yourself and keeping the three sides of your health triangle in balance is a good start. Here are some strategies for controlling the effects of stress:

▶ **Engage in physical activity.** Physical activities, such as tennis and swimming, improve your body's health and also affect your brain chemistry, helping to calm you down.

▶ **Look for support among your friends and family.** Chances are, they know exactly how you feel. Go to a movie or eat out together. Talk about what's bothering you.

▶ **Find a hobby or activity that relaxes you.** You might learn something new and make new friends.

▶ **Avoid using tobacco, alcohol, and other drugs.** These substances can lead to addiction and cause other problems.

Hobbies are a great way to relax and reduce your level of stress. *What do you do to relax?*

LESSON 1 | REVIEW

Reviewing Facts and Vocabulary

1. List the five general categories of stressors.
2. Describe the three stages of the body's response to stress.
3. Define *psychosomatic response.* Examine this effect of stress.

Thinking Critically

4. **Analyzing.** What healthful alternatives would you recommend to a teen who is thinking about using drugs to deal with stress? Explain the importance of alternatives to substance abuse.
5. **Applying.** Why is it important to practice healthful behaviors and protect yourself from prolonged or excessive stress?

Applying Health Skills

Decision Making. Describe a scenario in which a teen feels overwhelmed by a stressor. Then, use the six steps of decision making to demonstrate how the teen can handle the stressful situation in an effective way.

After You Read

Cause and Effect. Make a chart with two columns. In the first column, list the causes of stress. In the other column, list the physical, mental/emotional, and social effect of stress.

Visit **health.glencoe.com** for the Interactive Study Guide for Lesson 1.

Managing Stress

Guide to Reading

Building Vocabulary

As you read this lesson, write each new highlighted term and its definition in your notebook.

▶ stress-management skills (p. 208)

▶ relaxation response (p. 209)

Focusing on the Main Ideas

In this lesson, you will learn how to:

▶ **List** personal causes of stress.

▶ **Apply** refusal strategies for avoiding some stressful situations.

▶ **Discover** strategies for managing stress.

▶ **Develop** healthful behaviors that help reduce stress.

Reading Strategy

Explain

▶ Describe at least two of your stressors. Under what conditions do you feel stress?

Quick Write

Write a brief paragraph describing your personal causes of stress. Describe how you are managing your stress.

Identifying stressors and managing stress shows that you know strategies for health enhancement and risk reduction. Although it is impossible to live completely free of stress, it *is* possible to develop and practice effective coping skills for managing stress to prevent self-destructive behaviors.

Identifying Personal Causes of Stress

To help identify your personal stressors, look at what is happening around you right now. Is any of the following causing you stress?

▶ **Life events.** These can include getting a driver's license; graduation; moving or relocating; addition of family members by marriage, birth, or adoption; major illness; and parents' divorce or separation.

▶ **Physical stressors.** These can include pollution, excessive noise, physical injury, lack of rest, drug use, and excessive dieting or exercise.

▶ **Daily hassles.** These may include time pressures, too many responsibilities, deadlines, and conflicts with fellow students.

If you can identify your stressors, you have a better chance of controlling them. *What positive behaviors would help you control the stress of a particularly busy week?*

Avoiding Stress with Refusal Skills

Demonstrating refusal strategies may help you avoid certain stressful situations altogether. Sometimes, just walking away from a tense situation will calm you down. Say no at appropriate times when you see the possibility of stress, conflict, or threat. For example, you can avoid the potentially stressful situation of being at a party at which there will be no adult supervision by simply refusing to go.

Ways to Manage Stress

Sometimes, you can manage stress by changing the way you perceive or react to the stressor. You may be able to get a new perspective on a stressful situation by thinking of it as a learning opportunity instead of a threat. Other ways to manage stress include planning ahead, getting enough sleep, engaging in regular physical activity, eating nutritious food, and avoiding tobacco, alcohol, and other drugs.

Plan Ahead

When you plan ahead, you decide in advance what you want to accomplish and what steps you'll take. Thinking through a situation in advance also helps you recognize where variations to your plan may occur. This better prepares you for unexpected changes. A well-thought-out plan is not a rigid series of steps to follow but rather a flexible map with many ways of reaching your goal. **Figure 8.2** shows ways to reduce stress as you plan for and take your next test.

HEALTH Online

TOPIC Time Management

Go to **health.glencoe.com** and click on Tech Projects to learn about ways to manage time using graphs.

ACTIVITY After you have completed the tech project, write a sentence or two stating whether you think time management is an effective way to manage and reduce stress. Explain your position.

FIGURE **8.2**

OVERCOMING TEST ANXIETY

- Plan for tests well in advance, studying a little bit each night.
- Learn to outline material, highlighting and numbering important points so you can spot them quickly.
- During the test, do some deep breathing. Get comfortable in your chair. Give yourself a quick positive message like, "I can do this!"
- Answer all the questions you are sure of; then go back to answer the ones that are more difficult.
- After getting your corrected test back, examine your mistakes and try to understand why you made them. If you don't understand them, ask questions.

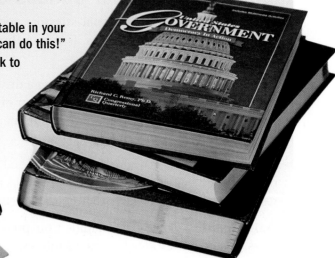

Hands-On Health ACTIVITY

Managing Your Time

When you manage your time well, you reduce your stress. In this activity, you'll develop a time-management plan for the coming week.

What You'll Need

- pencil
- large sheet of paper

What You'll Do

1. Divide your paper into seven columns, one for each day of the week. Create and label 24 rows, one for every hour of the day.

2. Pencil in the week's activities, including time for school, work, exercise, sleep, family, and friends. Include specific goals or deadlines, such as "History paper due." Include preparation time, such as "Go to library to research history paper."

3. Analyze your schedule. Are you surprised at how much time you spend on some activities? Where do you see conflicts? Are there things you'd like to do that you are not doing? Do you have adequate time to relax? To eat healthful meals and get plenty of physical activity?

4. Prioritize your tasks. Write "A" next to any task you need to do, "B" next to any you would like to get done, and "C" for any that can wait.

5. Rework your schedule. Be flexible, and remember that you may not be able to do everything. Try to consolidate tasks and delete low-priority activities.

Apply and Conclude

Keep your time-management schedule on hand as you go through the week. At the end of the week, evaluate your schedule and change it if necessary.

Get Adequate Sleep

Not getting enough sleep can affect your ability to concentrate. This in turn becomes a source of stress because it can interfere with schoolwork, athletics, and even relationships with others. To avoid the stress caused by lack of adequate sleep, manage your time wisely so that you get enough rest each night. Getting eight to nine hours of sleep will help you face the challenges and demands of your day. You will be in a better mood, you will think more clearly, and you will improve your chances of success.

Reading Check

Explain How can refusal skills help you avoid stress?

Get Regular Physical Activity

Participating in regular **physical activity** is another helpful technique for managing stress. When you are under stress, your body has an excess of nervous energy. Engaging in physical activities, such as jogging, walking, or even cleaning your room, can release this pent-up energy. As a result, you will feel more relaxed.

Eat Nutritious Food

Balanced **nutrition** is important for overall health, but it's also important in dealing with stress. Poor eating habits can actually be a source of stress by causing fatigue, weakness, and a reduced ability to concentrate. Inappropriate dieting and over- or undereating can also put the body under additional stress. Too much stress can cause poor absorption of vitamins and minerals, which can lead to deficiencies.

To help reduce stress and feel more energetic, eat a variety of different foods, drink plenty of water, and eat fresh food whenever possible. Eating healthful foods and getting regular exercise shows that you have developed and practice effective coping skills for managing stress to prevent self-destructive behaviors. Here are a few nutrition tips that will help you when you are dealing with stress.

▶ **Eat regular meals.** Common reactions to stress can be either snacking all day or not wanting to eat at all.

▶ **Limit "comfort" foods.** Although foods such as brownies and cookies may make you feel good or even bring back happy memories, they are loaded with fat and sugar.

▶ **Limit caffeine.** The stimulant effect of caffeine causes a rise in blood pressure. Thus, caffeine will actually increase the physical effects of stress on the body.

Avoid Tobacco, Alcohol, and Other Drugs

Some people make the mistake of turning to tobacco, alcohol, or other drugs to relieve stress. However, using these substances does not relieve stress; it increases one's problems and harms one's health. Substance use makes the body more prone to disease and has dangerous long-term effects.

Stress-Management Techniques

To reduce the effects of stress, it's important to know strategies for managing stress. Developing and practicing **stress-management skills**, or *skills that help an individual handle stress in a healthful, effective way*, is one of the steps to good mental health.

Health Minute

Sweat Your
Stress Away

When you're feeling stressed:

▶ Go running, bicycling, or skating.

▶ Play soccer, volleyball, or basketball.

▶ Participate in aerobic dance or martial arts.

Physical activity will:

▶ calm you down.

▶ improve your mood.

▶ improve your appearance.

▶ increase your ability to handle physical and emotional stress.

▶ aid digestion and help you sleep better.

▶ help you maintain a healthy weight.

▶ improve immune system function.

▶ remind you that you are in control of your responses to life.

Successful techniques for managing stress include the following:

▶ **Redirect your energy.** Working on a creative project or going jogging will release your nervous energy.

▶ **Relax and laugh.** The **relaxation response** is *a state of calm that can be reached if one or more relaxation techniques are practiced regularly.* Some relaxation techniques include deep breathing, thinking pleasant thoughts, and stretching. Laughing can help, too.

▶ **Keep a positive outlook.** A positive outlook can help relieve stress because the way you think often determines how you feel.

▶ **Seek out support.** Confide in someone you trust, such as a parent, guardian, sibling, teacher, or close friend. Just talking with someone about your problem may help you feel better about it.

▶ **Express yourself.** Learn positive strategies for expressing needs, wants, and feelings. Share your feelings with someone you trust. Set goals for your future, and share those goals with family members and friends.

Spending quality time with a parent or other family member can help relieve stress. *In what ways can family members help during stressful times?*

LESSON 2 REVIEW

Reviewing Facts and Vocabulary

1. List three personal causes of stress.
2. Name three ways to protect yourself from stress.
3. Define the term *relaxation response*, and identify three relaxation techniques.

Thinking Critically

4. **Applying.** To help reduce the effects of stress, Cathy drinks milk, fruit juice, or water instead of cola drinks. Why is this an effective stress-management technique?

5. **Synthesizing.** Jarod has a big biology test on Friday. As he is heading to his room to study, his friend Ben calls and asks him to go bowling. Use the techniques discussed in this lesson to help Jarod balance his activities and manage his stress.

Applying Health Skills

Stress Management. Make a "How to Survive" flyer advising teens on ways to manage the stress of one of the following life events: moving to a new school, not making a team, getting a failing grade, winning a major award, receiving a scholarship.

After You Read

Identifying Problems and Solutions. After reading the lesson, create a two-column chart. On one side, list some of your stressors. On the other side, list some new strategies you will try to relieve stress.

Visit **health.glencoe.com** for the Interactive Study Guide for Lesson 2.

Lesson 2 Managing Stress **209**

Anxiety and Teen Depression

Guide to Reading

Building Vocabulary

As you read this lesson, write each new highlighted term and its definition in your notebook.

▶ anxiety (p. 210)

▶ depression (p. 211)

Quick Write

In a brief paragraph, describe what anxiety is and describe what depression is.

Focusing on the Main Ideas

In this lesson, you will learn how to:

▶ Identify symptoms of anxiety and depression.

▶ Apply strategies for coping with anxiety and depression.

▶ List warning signs of major depression that should prompt individuals to seek professional help.

Reading Strategy

Predict

▶ Write a brief paragraph describing what you think you'll learn about anxiety and depression in this lesson. Do you think anxiety and depression affects young people?

▲ Anxiety can have many sources. *What are some common sources of anxiety for teens?*

The teen years bring new pressures, challenges, and responsibilities that can sometimes seem overwhelming. This is also a time when you are making major decisions that affect your future. It is no mystery that these stressors can cause anxious feelings, sleeping difficulties, or even mild depression.

What Is Anxiety?

Everyone feels anxious. Brief feelings of worry, insecurity, fear, self-consciousness, or even panic are common stress responses. Occasional anxiety in life is natural. **Anxiety** is *the condition of feeling uneasy or worried about what may happen.* Sometimes anxious feelings can have positive results, such as motivating you to work hard on a school presentation or keeping you alert in risky situations. Other times, anxiety can get in the way of a person's performance. For example, someone giving a speech may feel so nervous and stumble on a few lines. Some symptoms of anxiety include

▶ feelings of fear or dread.

▶ perspiration, trembling, restlessness, or muscle tension.

▶ rapid heart rate, lightheadedness, or shortness of breath.

Some teens experience another form of anxiety when they strive for perfection. They may think that they should get perfect grades or be the best on the team. A perfectionist's anxiety comes from believing that nothing he or she does will be good enough. Placing this type of pressure on oneself can lead to frustration and unhappiness. Having realistic expectations and taking a positive view of your accomplishments can help you avoid the anxiety caused by perfectionism.

Strategies for Coping with Anxiety

Stress-management techniques, such as redirecting your energy or doing relaxation exercises, can be used to reduce the day-to-day anxieties of life. Some people try to escape their anxiety by turning to alcohol or other drugs. They don't realize that such drugs produce only a temporary, false sense of relaxation. These substances cause problems that will make it even harder for the person to function. There are much healthier, more effective strategies for coping with anxiety, including engaging in physical activity and getting support from family and friends.

What Is Depression?

Nearly everyone experiences the occasional sad mood that lasts for a few days. These are natural feelings that can usually be managed by following these suggestions:

▶ Write your feelings in a private journal.

▶ Draw, dance, or engage in some other creative activity.

▶ Talk about your feelings with your family and friends.

▶ Do something nice for someone else. It will take the focus away from you and your feelings.

Sometimes, however, these feelings indicate a more serious condition known as depression. **Depression**, *a prolonged feeling of helplessness, hopelessness, and sadness*, is much stronger than the occasional sad mood and is not as easy to manage. It is important that you learn to recognize the symptoms of depression, and to seek help.

There are two types of depression, depending on the cause of the feeling and the length of time it lasts.

▶ **Reactive depression** is a response to a stressful event, such as the death of a friend. While this type of depression can last longer than a case of the "blues," most times it eventually goes away as the person finds a way to manage his or her response to the event.

Health Minute

Overcoming Social Anxiety

Social anxiety is the condition of feeling uneasy or extremely shy in certain social circumstances.

Someone with social anxiety is:

▶ more likely to avoid others.

▶ less likely to participate in extracurricular activities.

▶ less likely to speak up in class.

▶ more likely to have difficulty initiating casual conversations.

To overcome social anxiety:

▶ Practice replacing self-critical thoughts with more supportive ideas.

▶ Start small, such as by smiling, nodding, and greeting people.

▶ Speak in a louder voice, and use frequent eye contact.

▶ As a listener, ask open-ended questions during conversation.

▶ Become more knowledgeable about current events or another area of interest so you'll have some conversation starters.

▶ Practice conversation and positive-thinking skills often.

Reading Check

Explain What is anxiety and how can you cope with it?

▶ **Major depression** is a medical condition requiring treatment. It is more severe and lasts much longer than reactive depression. Major depression may develop from reactive depression, or it may be the result of a chemical imbalance in the brain or a genetic tendency. Major depression will be discussed in greater detail in the next chapter.

Symptoms of Teen Depression

Although depression is a common emotional problem among teens, the characteristics of depression should be examined. Many young people who are suffering from depression don't act sad or seem outwardly different to their family or friends. Symptoms of depression can include an irritable or restless mood; withdrawal from friends and activities that were previously important or enjoyable; a change in appetite or weight; feelings of guilt or worthlessness; and a sense of hopelessness.

Reading Check

Compare and Contrast
What is the difference between reactive depression and major depression?

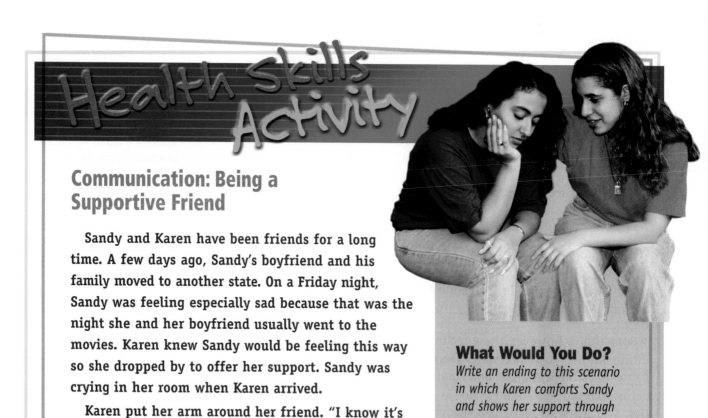

Health Skills Activity

Communication: Being a Supportive Friend

Sandy and Karen have been friends for a long time. A few days ago, Sandy's boyfriend and his family moved to another state. On a Friday night, Sandy was feeling especially sad because that was the night she and her boyfriend usually went to the movies. Karen knew Sandy would be feeling this way so she dropped by to offer her support. Sandy was crying in her room when Karen arrived.

Karen put her arm around her friend. "I know it's hard. I'm here if you want to talk."

"He hasn't even been gone a week and I'm feeling so lost. We always went out on Friday nights. I don't know how I'm going to get through this," Sandy cried.

What Would You Do?
Write an ending to this scenario in which Karen comforts Sandy and shows her support through strong communication skills.

1. Use "I" messages.
2. Speak calmly and clearly.
3. Listen carefully.
4. Show respect and empathy.

Many people experience a few of these symptoms once in a while. This is normal. It's *not* normal to experience several of them at the same time for two weeks or more. In addition, if depression causes a person to start using drugs or to have thoughts about suicide, professional help is needed.

Getting Help for Anxiety and Depression

Strategies for coping with mild forms of anxiety and depressive feelings include talking with supportive people, getting more physical activity, or volunteering. If anxiety or depression persists, it is important that you know how to identify appropriate community resources providing information for mental health and suicide prevention. Changes in mood, sleep patterns, or energy levels may occur as a result of anxiety or depression. It's important that you know how to analyze situations requiring professional health services as they arise.

Both anxiety and depression are very treatable. Talk to a parent or other trusted adult, and seek help from a counselor, school psychologist, or other health care professional.

Some teens and their parents visit the school counselor for confidential help regarding emotional health. *Who else might you turn to for help with a mental or emotional problem?*

LESSON 3 REVIEW

Reviewing Facts and Vocabulary

1. Define the term *anxiety*. What might be a positive result of anxiety? What might be a negative result?

2. List two strategies for managing day-to-day anxieties.

3. What is *depression*? Under what circumstances should a depressed teen seek professional help?

Thinking Critically

4. **Evaluating.** Why might participating in activities such as volunteering help relieve mild depression?

5. **Analyzing.** Why might a teen experiencing anxiety turn to alcohol or other drugs? Why is this dangerous?

Applying Health Skills

Analyzing Influences. Divide a sheet of paper into three columns. Head one column *Family*, one *Friends*, and one *School*. In each column, list how anxiety could affect your relationships and responsibilities.

After You Read

Compare and Contrast. Write a brief paragraph describing the differences between anxiety and depression. What should you do to get help if you recognize the signs of anxiety or depression in yourself or someone else?

Visit **health.glencoe.com** for the Interactive Study Guide for Lesson 3.

Lesson 3 Anxiety and Teen Depression   **213**

Being a Resilient Teen

Guide to Reading

Building Vocabulary

As you read this lesson, write each new highlighted term and its definition in your notebook.

▶ resiliency (p. 214)

▶ protective factors (p. 216)

Focusing on the Main Ideas

In this lesson, you will learn how to:

▶ Define what it means to be resilient.

▶ Develop strategies to promote resiliency throughout the life span.

▶ Formulate methods for developing protective factors.

▶ Explain how protective factors help people avoid risk behaviors.

Reading Strategy

Explain

▶ What do you think the word *resiliency* means?

Quick Write

Write a brief paragraph describing ways that a teen can bounce back from a difficult situation.

▼ When difficult events occur, seeking and giving support is one way to cope. *What else can help a person bounce back from disappointments or crises?*

Everyone goes through times of stress, disappointments, and difficulty. Sometimes, people have no control over events that can change their lives. A natural disaster may strike, or a loved one may die. When hardships and tragedies happen, it can be hard for people to cope with the situation and with their feelings.

What Is Resiliency?

Some people find it easier than others to bounce back from events that have hurt them in some way. The event may be a personal disappointment, such as failing a test or breaking up with a boyfriend or girlfriend. In some cases, a large number of people may be involved in or affected by an event, such as a big earthquake or a war. Being able to overcome disappointments and survive traumatic events is a sign of resiliency. **Resiliency** (ri-ZIL-yuhn-see) is *the ability to adapt effectively and recover from disappointment, difficulty, or crisis.* Resilient people are able to handle adversity in healthful ways and achieve long-term success in spite of negative circumstances.

Factors That Affect Resiliency

Many factors can influence a person's level of resiliency. Having some of the **developmental assets** discussed in Chapter 7 will very likely strengthen a person's resiliency. For example, having a supportive family and a strong sense of self-worth can help an individual bounce back from setbacks or other difficulties. It's also important to know positive strategies for expressing needs, wants, and feelings, and for communicating effectively with family, friends, and others. The factors that affect a person's resiliency can be divided into two categories: external and internal.

External Factors

These factors include your family, your school or community, and your peers. They may also include elements that are less concrete, for example, opportunities to participate in school projects or community events. Although you may have little control over these factors, you can work to strengthen some of them. For example, you could join a community youth program in order to have access to more opportunities and to form healthy peer relationships.

Internal Factors

Internal factors are the ones you have control over. Making a conscious effort to strengthen these factors will increase your resiliency and improve your mental/emotional health. Your attitudes, perceptions, and behaviors make up your internal factors, which also include:

▶ **Commitment to learning.** Being actively engaged in your education increases your self-esteem and gives you a sense of belonging in the school community.

▶ **Positive values.** You demonstrate positive values through your words and actions. For example, you show caring when you help a younger sibling study for a test. By understanding the potential impact of common risk behaviors and avoiding those behaviors, you show that you take responsibility for your health.

Reading Check

Compare and Contrast
List the differences between external factors and internal factors.

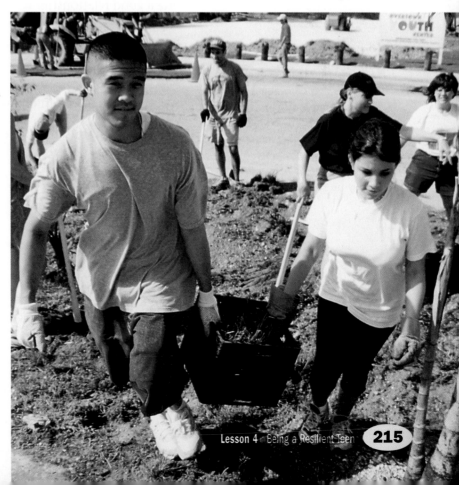

▼ By contributing to the community, these teens are also building their protective factors. *How might helping others strengthen a teen's resiliency?*

Responsibility. Although you can't control external events, you *can* control how you respond to them. For example, you can choose to adapt to and learn from each situation and challenge. **Think about a recent disappointment or difficulty. How did you bounce back from the situation? How can you apply what you learned about yourself to similar events in the future?**

▶ **Social competency.** Being socially competent means that you have empathy and friendship skills. It also means that you can resist negative peer pressure and resolve conflicts nonviolently.

▶ **Positive identity.** Having a positive identity gives you a sense of control over what happens to you. It indicates positive self-esteem and a sense of purpose. You are also likely to have a positive view of your future, an asset that allows you to recover more easily from setbacks.

Resiliency and Your Protective Factors

In addition to strengthening your resiliency, your developmental assets also protect you from risk behaviors such as drug use, sexual activity, and gang involvement. For this reason, developmental assets are often seen as **protective factors**, *conditions that shield individuals from the negative consequences of exposure to risk*. These factors can reduce the possible harmful effect of a difficult event or risky situation. They may also influence a person to respond to a situation in a healthy way.

Building Resiliency by Strengthening Your Protective Factors

Teens who do not have all their external protective factors in place can strengthen the ones they do have. For example, developing a good relationship with the adult members of your family can enhance positive family communication. Teens can also find support from teachers, coaches, clergy, or other caring adults. Internal protective factors can also be improved. Actions you can take include the following:

▶ Become involved in extra-curricular activities at school.

▶ Make a commitment to learning by reading for pleasure at least three hours per week.

▶ Stand up for your beliefs, and refuse to act against your values.

▶ Be honest with yourself and others.

▶ Resist negative peer pressure, and avoid dangerous situations.

▶ Learn about people from other cultures or ethnic backgrounds.

▶ Develop a sense of purpose.

▶ Develop a positive outlook about your future.

Ⓥ **Teens who respect themselves and care about their futures are better able to resist pressure to engage in high-risk behaviors.** *What other protective factors might help a teen say no to risky behaviors?*

Real-Life Application

The Power of Assets

Developmental assets strengthen your resiliency, and they can protect you from participating in risk behaviors. The more assets you have in place, the more equipped you are to avoid unsafe behaviors. This graph illustrates how teens with more than 30 assets steer clear of activities that will harm their health.

ACTIVITY

Make a two-column table. Next, review the list of developmental assets in Chapter 7 and select five assets. List these in the left column of your table. In the right column, explain how you think each specific asset can protect you from the risk behaviors in the graph shown here.

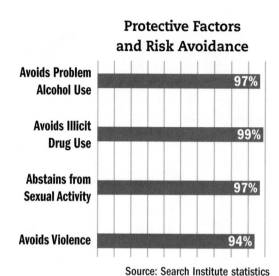

Protective Factors and Risk Avoidance

Avoids Problem Alcohol Use	97%
Avoids Illicit Drug Use	99%
Abstains from Sexual Activity	97%
Avoids Violence	94%

Source: Search Institute statistics

LESSON 4 REVIEW

Reviewing Facts and Vocabulary

1. Define *resiliency*. Why is it important?
2. List three external factors and three internal factors that can affect a person's resiliency.
3. How do protective factors help a person avoid risk behaviors?

Thinking Critically

4. **Analyzing.** Make a list of at least five of your personal stressors. What protective factors do you have or can you develop to help you deal with each one?
5. **Synthesizing.** How does developing a positive outlook strengthen your resiliency?

Applying Health Skills

Goal Setting. Review your protective factors. Is there an area you would like to strengthen? Using the steps of goal setting, make a plan to develop a specific protective factor. Then, put your plan into action!

After You Read

Organize Information. Make a word web. Write the word *resiliency*. Surround it with all the different factors that affect resiliency (e.g., various external factors, internal factors, protective factors, etc.).

Visit **health.glencoe.com** for the Interactive Study Guide for Lesson 4.

Lesson 4 Being a Resilient Teen **217**

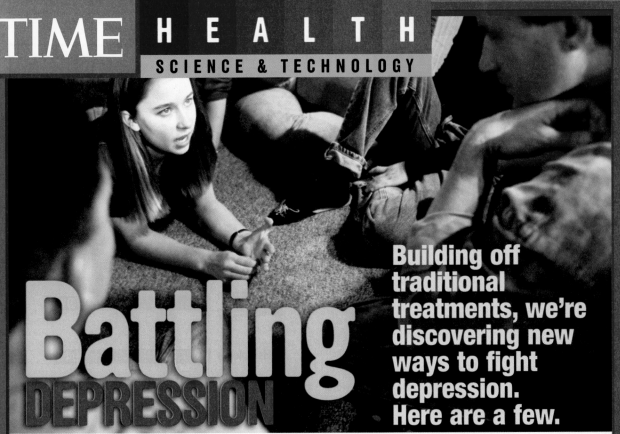

Battling DEPRESSION

Building off traditional treatments, we're discovering new ways to fight depression. Here are a few.

Talking Cures

Today's Treatments Many therapists encourage patients with depression to probe the unconscious roots of their problems by simply talking. Once they are out in the open, these problems can be easier to handle. Newer techniques like cognitive therapy teach patients to recognize destructive patterns in their lives and develop steps for changing bad mental habits.

On the Horizon Meditation has long been used to relieve stress. Now many believe that it may help people with depression by lowering levels of cortisol, a hormone released during stress.

Medicines

Today's Treatments Most antidepressants work by adjusting levels of various neurotransmitters, the chemicals that carry signals in the brain. Unfortunately, many of these drugs produce unwanted side effects.

On the Horizon Researchers are exploring certain molecules that are responsible for 90 percent of chemical signaling in the brain. Because they control so much of the brain's activity, their

levels must be fine-tuned in ways that relieve depression without affecting other brain functions.

Alternative Therapies

Today's Treatments Many patients help themselves using over-the-counter supplements, such as St. John's wort. On the down side, these can have side effects. Researchers are still investigating how effective these supplements are.

On the Horizon Omega-3 fatty acids (found naturally in fish oils) may promote the health of nerve-cell membranes. Scientists hope to discover how these fatty acids can help those suffering from depression. ■

TIME
to **THINK...**

About Treating Depression

The hormone cortisol is mentioned in the above article. Using the Internet or your school's media center, investigate this substance. What part of the body produces it and why? How can it have a negative effect on health? Report your findings to the class.

Health Skills Application

1. **Accessing Information.** Using library resources or the Internet, research the relationship between stress and disease. Write a paragraph explaining what you learned. Identify your sources, and explain why you think they are reliable. *(LESSON 1)*

2. **Refusal Skills.** Describe a scenario in which demonstrating refusal strategies could help you avoid a potentially stressful situation. Then, write three effective refusal statements you could use to avoid the situation. *(LESSON 2)*

3. **Communication Skills.** Suppose you have a friend who is showing symptoms of depression and has withdrawn from activities you used to share and enjoy. How would you talk with your friend? How could you identify whether he or she needed professional health services in this situation? *(LESSON 3)*

4. **Analyzing Influences.** Consider the protective factors in your life. Which have the strongest influence on your health behaviors? Why do you think this is so? *(LESSON 4)*

CAREER Corner

Time Management Consultant

Are you a good organizer? Are you able to handle many tasks efficiently? If so, time management may be the career for you. Many time management consultants have business degrees with an emphasis on project management. In their work, they apply their time management skills to get more done in less time.

Time management consultants can be found in almost every industry. To become a time management consultant, you will need an undergraduate degree in business. You can find out more about this and other health careers by clicking on Career Corner at **health.glencoe.com.**

BEYOND the Classroom

Parent Involvement

Accessing Information. With a parent, investigate stress-management resources in your community. Make a list of agencies and their services. Discuss which resource your family members would most likely use if daily stress were to become a health concern. Which resource would be most helpful in dealing with a highly stressful event?

School and Community

Stress Management Classes. Contact a wellness center in a hospital in your area. Ask whether there are stress-management seminars or classes that you could observe. Attend a session and report to your class on what you have learned.

After You Read

Review the information you have recorded in your Foldable about the causes and effects of stress. Write a short paragraph explaining why it is important to learn how to manage stress and anxiety.

> ## EXPLORING HEALTH TERMS
Answer the following questions on a sheet of paper.

Lesson 1 Match each definition with the correct term.

stress	perception
stressor	psychosomatic response
chronic stress	

1. The act of becoming aware through the senses.
2. An event or situation that causes stress.
3. A physical reaction that results from stress rather than from injury or illness.

Lesson 2 Fill in the blanks with the correct term.

relaxation response
stress-management skills

Redirecting your energy, keeping a positive outlook, and seeking out support are examples of (_4_). Using techniques such as laughing and deep breathing exercises can cause a (_5_).

Lesson 3 Identify each statement as True or False. If false, replace the underlined term with the correct term.

anxiety **depression**

6. Depression is a prolonged feeling of helplessness.
7. Some symptoms of depression are rapid heart rate and shortness of breath.

Lesson 4 Fill the blanks with the correct term.

resiliency
protective factor

A condition that shields a person from the negative consequences of exposure to risk is a (_8_). If you are able to recover from difficulty, disappointment, and crisis, you are said to have (_9_).

> ## RECALLING THE FACTS
Use complete sentences to answer the following questions.

1. What occurs in your body during the alarm stage of the stress response?
2. Which type of fatigue is the effect of the stress of illness?
3. What is the effect of prolonged stress on the immune system?
4. How does planning help you manage stress?
5. How does physical activity help reduce the effects of stress?
6. How is nutrition related to stress?
7. How might perfectionism lead to anxiety?
8. What are three strategies for coping with mild depression?
9. What are three symptoms of depression?
10. Over which category of the factors that affect resiliency does a person have the most control?
11. What does "commitment to learning" mean?
12. List three things you can do to build your protective factors and strengthen your resiliency.

For more review questions for Chapter 8, go to **health.glencoe.com**.

➤ WRITING CRITICALLY

1. Narrative. Write a one-page story about a teen who reacts to a stressor in a positive way. In your story, identify what is causing the stress and what signs of stress the teen displays. Show how the teen handles the stress in a healthy way.

2. Descriptive. Write a one-page script describing a teen who is feeling anxious about an upcoming test. Have that teen confide in a friend or trusted adult about his or her feelings. Then, show the teen managing those feelings in a positive way.

Standardized Test Practice

Read the letter below and then answer the questions.

Dear Maya,

Things have really changed since you moved away. I've heard that more than 3,000 people are unemployed now that the factory has closed. I'm sure that more people will be leaving town the way you and your family did. Manuel and his family moved too, so now both of my best friends have left.

My parents don't want to talk about what's going on, but I can tell that things are not good. I overhear them talking a lot, but they just clam up when I ask anything. At least Dad has a job, even though he is making less money than he used to make at the factory.

Please write back and let me know how things are going for you. Do your parents have jobs? Have you made new friends? I miss you!

Love,
Isabel

1. Which phrase BEST describes the tone of this letter?

A angry
B worried
C bitter
D resigned

2. What does this letter reveal about Isabel?

F how hard it is for her to make new friends
G her understanding of life outside her town
H how the factory closing meant lost jobs and wages
I the stress she feels due to all the changes around her

3. Write a reply to this letter as Maya. Explain what life is like for her and her family, and how she is dealing with the stresses of moving.

Mental and Emotional Problems

Eye ON THE Media — Creating Positive Media Influences

Media campaigns can generate awareness and positive support for health issues. Awareness campaigns can focus on

► **improving current health systems.**

► **developing new health services.**

► **encouraging health research.**

Visit the Eye on the Media section at health.glencoe.com to learn more about the influence of the media on mental health issues.

FOLDABLES™ Study Organizer

Before You Read

Make this Foldable study guide to help you learn about six types of mental disorders. Begin with a sheet of 8½" x 11" paper.

► **Step 1**

Fold a sheet of paper in half along the long axis.

► **Step 3**

Unfold and cut the top layer along both folds. Then cut each tab in half to make six tabs.

► **Step 4**

Label the tabs as shown.

Anxiety Disorders
Mood Disorders
Eating Disorders
Conduct Disorders
Mental Disorders
Personal Disorders

► **Step 2**

Turn the paper, and fold into thirds.

As You Read

As you read and discuss the material in the chapter, use your Foldable to take notes, define terms, and write personal comments about what you learn.

SPOTLIGHT ON HEALTH

Using Visuals. Sometimes, feelings such as anger, loneliness, fear, or sadness can seem overwhelming. How do you manage these strong emotions?

Mental Disorders

Guide to Reading

Building Vocabulary

As you read this lesson, write each new highlighted term and its definition in your notebook.

▶ mental disorder (p. 224)

▶ anxiety disorder (p. 225)

▶ post-traumatic stress disorder (p. 226)

▶ mood disorder (p. 226)

▶ conduct disorder (p. 228)

Focusing on the Main Ideas

In this lesson, you will learn how to:

▶ **Name** the different types of mental disorders.

▶ **Identify** situations requiring professional mental health services.

▶ **Discuss** the types of mental disorders that affect our society.

Reading Strategy

Classify

▶ Divide your paper into three sections labeled Anxiety Disorders, Mood Disorders, and Personality Disorders. As you read, list the facts about each in the appropriate categories.

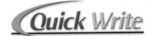 *Quick Write*

Write a brief paragraph describing how you think people with mental disorders are perceived by others.

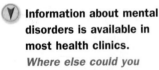 Information about mental disorders is available in most health clinics. *Where else could you find reliable information on a mental disorder?*

Almost everyone experiences periods of sadness, anxiety, and anger. For most people, these feelings are short-lived. For millions of others, however, these feelings persist. If such situations affect a person's behavior or daily activities, he or she may be suffering from a mental disorder. Health-literate individuals know how to analyze situations requiring professional health services.

What Are Mental Disorders?

A **mental disorder** is *an illness of the mind that can affect the thoughts, feelings, and behaviors of a person, preventing him or her from leading a happy, healthful, and productive life*. People who suffer from some form of mental disorder are often identified by their inability to cope in healthy ways with life's changes, demands, problems, or traumas. Each year, about 20 percent of the U.S. population—54 million people—are affected by some form of mental disorder. Of the 20 percent of children and adolescents who suffer from mental health problems, only one-third receive the help they need.

Take the Health Inventory for Chapter 9 at **health.glencoe.com**.

Some people are reluctant to seek treatment for mental/emotional problems because they feel embarrassed or ashamed. Another reason is the stigma associated with mental disorders. A *stigma* is a negative label or a mark of shame. Misconceptions and stereotypes may prevent some people from seeing mental disorders as medical conditions. However, mental disorders require medical attention just as physical illnesses do. In fact, many mental and emotional disturbances involve imbalances in brain chemistry. The sooner a person seeks treatment, the sooner he or she will be on the road to recovery.

Types of Mental Disorders

Mental disorders are classified as either organic or functional. An *organic disorder* is caused by a physical illness or an injury that affects the brain. Brain tumors, infections, chemical imbalances, exposure to drugs and toxins, or injuries resulting in brain damage may lead to organic mental disorders.

A *functional disorder* has a psychological cause and does not involve brain damage. These disorders may result from heredity, stress, emotional conflict, fear, ineffective coping skills, or other conditions. Often, functional disorders are tied to disturbing events in childhood, such as abuse, serious illness, or the traumatic death of a close relative. These disorders may also be tied to recent events, such as divorce, economic hardships, or natural disasters.

Anxiety Disorders

About 4 million Americans suffer from **anxiety disorder**, *a condition in which real or imagined fears are difficult to control.* An anxiety disorder is characterized by chronic fear. People with anxiety disorders often arrange their lives to avoid situations that make them feel anxious or fearful. Anxiety disorders can be classified according to four main types: phobias, obsessive-compulsive disorders, panic disorders, and post-traumatic stress disorders.

PHOBIA

A phobia is a strong and irrational fear of something specific, such as high places or dogs. People with phobias do everything they can to avoid the object of their fear. As a result, a person with a phobia may be unable to live a normal life. For example, people with *agoraphobia* have a fear of open or public places. Their phobia may make them prisoners in their own homes. Some mental health professionals believe that certain phobias are caused by childhood experiences. The fear resulting from these experiences lasts far past the actual threat.

Why are mental disorders a critical health issue?
In the United States, half of the people suffering from mental disorders are untreated, 40 percent of the homeless have some form of mental/emotional problem, and about 20 percent of people in prison have a mental disorder. It is a national concern to get professional mental help for those who need it.

Source: National Alliance for the Mentally Ill

▼ Arachnophobia, a fear of spiders, is a common phobia. People with phobias can seek help from classes, support groups, and mental health professionals.

Post-traumatic stress disorder may occur in the aftermath of a crisis. *What can members of a community do to support one another during crises?*

CHARACTER ✓ CHECK

Caring. People who suffer from mental disorders are sometimes seen as different. Although some people think it's fun to tease someone who is "different," such teasing is cruel and hurtful. When you show your disapproval of such behavior, you demonstrate consideration and caring for the person being teased. **What are some other ways of showing caring and respect for someone who is seen as "different"?**

OBSESSIVE-COMPULSIVE DISORDER

A person with obsessive-compulsive disorder is trapped in a pattern of repeated thoughts or behaviors. The term *obsessive* refers to persistent, recurrent, and unwanted thoughts that prevent people from attending to normal daily activities. *Compulsive* refers to repeated, irresistible behaviors. A person with obsessive-compulsive disorder might, for example, feel the urge to wash his or her hands constantly throughout the day.

PANIC DISORDER

A person with a panic disorder has sudden, unexplained feelings of terror. These "panic attacks" are accompanied by symptoms such as trembling, a pounding heart, shortness of breath, or dizziness. Panic disorder is a condition in which fear and anxiety get in the way of a person's ability to function and enjoy life. Panic attacks may occur at any time or place, but most are triggered by a particular object, condition, or situation.

POST-TRAUMATIC STRESS DISORDER

Post-traumatic stress disorder is *a condition that may develop after exposure to a terrifying event that threatened or caused physical harm.* This disorder is common after a personal assault, such as rape; natural or human-made disasters, such as earthquakes or bombings; accidents, such as plane crashes; or military combat. Symptoms may include flashbacks (sudden recall of the terrifying event), nightmares, emotional numbness, sleeplessness, guilt, and problems with concentration. The disorder may arise weeks or months after the event that caused it.

Mood Disorders

A **mood disorder** is *an illness, often with an organic cause, that involves mood extremes that interfere with everyday living.* These extremes are not the highs and lows that everyone experiences, nor are they the mood swings sometimes experienced during adolescence. The emotional swings of mood disorders are extreme in both intensity and duration.

CLINICAL DEPRESSION

Most people who say they are depressed are suffering from a passing case of the blues. For some people, however, depression doesn't go away. Their feelings of sadness, hopelessness, or despair last for more than a few weeks and interfere with daily interests and activities. This type of depression, known as clinical depression, can affect a person's ability to concentrate, sleep, perform at school or work, or handle everyday decisions and challenges. Clinical depression results from a chemical imbalance that a person cannot overcome without professional help.

Approximately 19 million Americans are affected by clinical depression each year. Depression often runs in families and can be biologically based, but it can also be caused by life events. Sometimes it may be a symptom of substance abuse or addiction, because alcohol and other drugs can affect brain chemistry.

BIPOLAR DISORDER

This disorder, also known as manic-depressive disorder, is marked by extreme mood changes, energy levels, and behavior. Characteristics of the manic "highs" and depressive "lows" of this disorder are described in **Figure 9.1.** Although adults with bipolar disorder may behave normally between episodes of extreme emotion, teens with the disorder tend to alternate rapidly between the two extremes with few clear periods of wellness between episodes.

Eating Disorders

Psychological pressures, possible genetic factors, and an obsession with body image and thinness can lead to an **eating disorder.** People with eating disorders such as anorexia and bulimia suffer from life-threatening disturbances in eating behavior. Eating disorders are not a failure of will or behavior; they are real, treatable medical illnesses. A person who suffers from an eating disorder can experience a wide range of physical health complications, including serious heart conditions and kidney failure, which may lead to death. It is therefore critical that a person with an eating disorder get help immediately.

HEALTH *Online*

TOPIC Depression

Go to health.glencoe.com and click on Health Updates to learn more about teens and depression.

ACTIVITY Using the information you find at the site, write a short paragraph on the most recent research on depression in teens.

Reading Check

Explain Why are some people reluctant to seek treatment for a mental disorder?

FIGURE 9.1

MANIA AND DEPRESSION—FLIP SIDES OF MOOD DISORDERS FOR TEENS

Manic Symptoms	Depressive Symptoms
• **Extreme changes in mood**—is either excessively happy or silly, or very irritable, angry, agitated, or aggressive • **Grandiosity**—unrealistically high self-esteem, feeling all-powerful • **Very high energy level**—including the ability to go with little or no sleep for days without feeling tired • **Pressured speech**—talks too much, too fast, changes topics too quickly, and does not allow interruption • **Distractibility**—attention moves constantly from one thing to another • **Repeated high-risk behavior**—alcohol or drug use, reckless driving, or sexual activity	• **Irritability,** persistent sadness, frequent crying • **Preoccupation with death** or suicide • **Loss of enjoyment** in favorite activities • **Frequent physical complaints** such as headaches or stomachaches • **Low energy level,** fatigue, poor concentration, boredom • **Dramatic change in eating or sleeping patterns,** such as overeating or oversleeping

Source: American Academy of Child and Adolescent Psychiatry

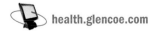

Compare and Contrast
What are some of the differences between a conduct disorder and schizophrenia?

▼ **Teens with a conduct disorder may act with aggression, but they often have low self-esteem.** *How might an untreated conduct disorder affect a teen's future?*

Conduct Disorders

Children and adolescents who act out their impulses toward others in destructive ways may have a **conduct disorder**, *a pattern of behavior in which the rights of others or basic social rules are violated.* Examples include lying, theft, aggression, violence, truancy, arson, and vandalism. The condition is more common among males than females. Although they may project an image of toughness, people with this disorder usually have low self-esteem. They may also have symptoms of other mental disorders including anxiety, depression, and substance abuse. Without treatment, many teens with this disorder will be unable to adapt to the demands of adulthood and will continue to have problems relating to others, holding a job, and behaving in appropriate ways. Health-literate teens are able to identify appropriate community resources providing information for mental health.

Schizophrenia

Schizophrenia (skit-suh-FREE-nee-uh) is a severe mental disorder in which a person loses contact with reality. Symptoms of schizophrenia include delusions, hallucinations, and thought disorders. Causes of this condition may be a combination of genetic factors and chemical and structural changes in the brain. The disease affects about 1 percent of the population. Schizophrenia affects both men and women and usually first appears between the ages of 15 and 35.

People who suffer from schizophrenia have difficulty understanding the difference between real and imaginary events. This inability leads to unpredictable behavior, difficulty functioning, and lack of good health habits. A common misconception about people who suffer from this disorder is that all of them are violent, or have multiple or split personalities. However, schizophrenic people are usually not a threat to others. Professional help and medication are necessary to successfully treat schizophrenia.

Personality Disorders

The term *personality* refers to an individual's unique traits and behavior patterns. People with healthy personalities can cope with the day-to-day challenges of life. However, people afflicted with personality disorders think and behave in ways that make it difficult for them to get along with others. Over the course of their lives, usually beginning in adolescence, they are in constant conflict with others—family, friends, teachers, coworkers, or supervisors. About 10 percent of the population has one of the several types of personality disorder. Counseling, and sometimes medication, are recommended as treatment.

▶ **Antisocial personality disorder.** People with this disorder tend to be irritable, aggressive, impulsive, and violent. In many cases, they are unable to show remorse for their behavior.

▶ **Borderline personality disorder.** People with this disorder frequently experience a series of troubled relationships. They tend to engage in high-risk activities, and many have poor self-esteem. Although they fear abandonment, they frequently lash out violently at the people they need most.

▶ **Passive-aggressive personality disorder.** People with this disorder are often uncooperative. They resent being told what to do, yet they rely on others' direction. Angry over issues of control, they show their anger, but only indirectly. For example, a passive-aggressive person who doesn't want to take part in an activity either may forget to show up or may arrive late and leave early.

As with all mental and emotional problems, it is important to know how to identify symptoms of mental disorders and know where to seek professional assistance.

Health Minute

Improving Attitudes About Mental Disorders

To help defeat the social stigma of mental disorders:

▶ Use respectful language when referring to a person with a mental disorder.

▶ Emphasize abilities over limitations.

▶ Express disapproval if someone shows disrespect or inconsideration toward people with mental disorders.

▶ Encourage people who have emotional problems to seek help.

LESSON 1 REVIEW

Reviewing Facts and Vocabulary

1. Define the term *mental disorder*, and explain how organic and functional disorders differ.

2. What do clinical depression and bipolar disorder have in common?

3. Compare and contrast the characteristics of schizophrenia and antisocial personality disorder.

Thinking Critically

4. **Synthesizing.** Although scientific evidence shows that mental disorders are medical conditions, the stigma attached to these illnesses persists. Why do you think this is so?

5. **Analyzing.** Describe how the causes, symptoms, and treatment of eating disorders differ from those of other types of mental disorders.

Applying Health Skills

Advocacy. Teens suffering from mental disorders often feel confused, isolated, scared, or ashamed. Create a Bill of Rights for people with mental disorders; your list should advocate demonstrating empathy. Focus on specific ways for students to be supportive, patient, and understanding.

After You Read

Analyze a Graph. After reviewing Figure 9.1, write a summary describing the differences between manic and depressive symptoms.

 Visit **health.glencoe.com** for the Interactive Study Guide for Lesson 1.

Lesson 1 Mental Disorders **229**

Suicide Prevention

Guide to Reading

Building Vocabulary

As you read this lesson, write each new highlighted term and its definition in your notebook.

▶ alienation (p. 230)

▶ suicide (p. 230)

▶ cluster suicides (p. 233)

Focusing on the Main Ideas

In this lesson, you will learn how to:

▶ List the warning signs of suicide.

▶ Determine strategies to prevent suicides and strategies for coping with depression.

Reading Strategy

Cause and Effect

▶ Make a T chart. List the risk factors of suicide on one side. List some of the strategies to prevent suicide on the other.

Quick Write

Write a brief paragraph describing what you would do if you thought someone was thinking about suicide.

Recognizing signs of depression and seeking help is critical to suicide prevention.

Life can be difficult for everyone at times. Challenges, responsibilities, and pressures can pile up and seem overwhelming. These feelings can be further complicated by troubling life events, such as the divorce of parents or the death of a friend or family member. For some people, this emotional overload can lead to depression or **alienation**, *feeling isolated and separated from everyone else*. When such painful feelings become unbearable, some people may try drastic, self-destructive measures to escape their pain. **Suicide**, the most drastic of all measures, is *the act of intentionally taking one's own life*. Suicide is preventable. By recognizing the signs of a potential suicide, you know when to seek help.

Suicide Risk Factors

Most suicidal thoughts, behaviors, and actions are expressions of extreme distress, not bids for attention. More than 90 percent of the people who kill themselves are suffering from depression or another mental disorder, or are abusing alcohol or drugs. Other suicidal risk factors include a history of physical or sexual abuse, a history of previous suicide attempts, or a family history of emotional disorders or suicides.

FIGURE 9.2

TEEN SUICIDE: RECOGNIZING THE WARNING SIGNS

The warning signs of suicide should be taken seriously. The more signs a person exhibits, the more likely it is that he or she is thinking about suicide.

Verbal Signs	Nonverbal or Behavioral Signs
• Direct statements such as these: "I want to die." "I don't want to live anymore." "I wish I were dead." • Indirect statements such as these: "I won't have to put up with this much longer." "I just want to go to sleep and never wake up." "They'll be sorry when I'm gone." "Soon this pain will be over." "I can't take it anymore." "Nothing matters." "I won't be a problem for you much longer." "What's the use?" • Writing poems, song lyrics, or diary entries that deal with death. • Suicide threats or insinuations that are either direct or indirect.	• An unusual obsession with death • Withdrawal from friends • Dramatic changes in personality, hygiene, or appearance • Impulsive, irrational, or bizarre behavior • An overwhelming sense of guilt, shame, or rejection; negative self-evaluation • Significant deterioration in schoolwork or recreational performance • Preoccupation with giving away personal belongings • Substance abuse • Frequent complaints about physical symptoms such as stomachaches, headaches, fatigue • Persistent boredom and indifference • Violent actions, rebellious behavior, or running away • Intolerance for praise or rewards

Sources: National Mental Health Association; American Academy of Child and Adolescent Psychiatry

Strategies to Prevent Suicide

Although most thoughts about committing suicide are impulsive and temporary, the unfortunate consequences—death or debilitating injury—are permanent. The warning signs of suicide are described in **Figure 9.2.** When a teen talks about committing suicide—whether it's done in a serious, casual, or even humorous way—*he or she must be taken seriously.* Never bargain with someone who is thinking about suicide. Any discussion or suggestion about suicide requires immediate intervention. Seek adult assistance without delay.

Despite the fact that depression is very treatable, untreated depression is the leading cause of suicide. People who appear to have mental health problems need to be encouraged repeatedly to seek help—especially if they seem suicidal. Knowing methods for effectively expressing feelings and opinions can help people suffering from depression, extreme stress, or other mental and emotional problems find new purpose and happiness.

Describe What are some of the behaviors that might tell you a person is thinking about suicide?

Decision Making: When a Friend Seems Troubled

When Ian started exhibiting signs of depression, his friend Jordan tried to persuade him to get help. Ian admitted that he was unhappy. However, he told Jordan, "I appreciate your trying to help me, but it's okay; I'm handling my problems by myself."

Jordan knows that Ian is a private person, but Jordan has never seen his friend this "down" before. Jordan wants to tell someone about his concerns, but he is hesitant about betraying a confidence.

What Would You Do?

Apply the six steps of the decision-making model to Jordan's concerns.

1. State the situation.
2. List the options.
3. Weigh the possible outcomes.
4. Consider values.
5. Make a decision and act.
6. Evaluate the decision.

Did You Know ?

You can use *CLUES* to remember how to communicate effectively with a friend who is suffering emotionally.
Connect (Make contact.)
Listen (Take time and pay attention.)
Understand (Let the person know that you empathize with his or her feelings.)
Express Concern (Say that you care, and stay with the person.)
Seek Help (Encourage the person to talk to an adult, and tell an adult yourself.)

Source: University of Minnesota Extension Service

Helping Others

Suicidal people often believe that their death will not matter to anyone. For this reason, it is critical to show concern and empathy for someone who is talking about suicide. All talk of suicide must be taken seriously. Remember, the suicidal person needs professional help—immediately. When you are with someone who appears to be suicidal, show you care by following these steps.

▶ **Initiate a meaningful conversation.** Showing interest and compassion for a person is an important first step. Listen closely to what that person says; be patient and understanding.

▶ **Show support and ask questions.** Remind the person that most problems have solutions. Make it clear that you understand that the person wants to end his or her pain, but emphasize that suicide is *not* the answer. Share the fact that most suicide survivors later express gratitude that they did not die.

▶ **Try to persuade the person to seek help.** Encourage the person to talk with a parent, counselor, therapist, or other trusted adult. Offer to go with the person to get help.

Multiple Suicides

Sometimes within a teen population, **cluster suicides** occur. These are *a series of suicides occurring within a short period of time and involving several people in the same school or community.* Studies have shown that cluster suicides in the United States occur mainly among teens and young adults and may account for as much as 5 percent of all suicides in any given year. Some cluster suicides are the result of pacts or agreements between two or more people to take part in suicide. Others result when individuals commit suicide in response to the suicide of a friend or a suicide that has been sensationalized in the media.

The Centers for Disease Control and Prevention (CDC) has developed guidelines for preventing cluster suicides. Among their recommendations is the evaluation and counseling of close friends and relatives of suicide victims because these people may themselves be at high risk for suicide. The CDC also recommends that the media report on suicide in a way that does not glorify the victim, oversimplify the victim's motivation, or portray the suicide as an understandable response to pressure or emotional pain.

Suicide can affect people beyond the victim's immediate family and friends. *Why might a teen be affected by the suicide of someone who is a stranger?*

LESSON 2 REVIEW

Reviewing Facts and Vocabulary

1. Name five warning signs of suicide.
2. List three risk factors of suicide.
3. Describe some of the strategies for suicide prevention.

Thinking Critically

4. **Analyzing.** How might support from family, friends, and mental health professionals help an individual cope with stress, depression, and anxiety? What strategies might each of these groups offer to help prevent suicides?
5. **Synthesizing.** Why is empathy important when talking with a suicidal person?

Applying Health Skills

Accessing Information. Compile a list of local resources for suicide prevention. This list should include mental health professionals, school counselors, hospital emergency rooms, suicide hot lines, and local authorities (including representatives of the police and fire departments).

After You Read

Identify Problems and Solutions. After reading the lesson, list some signs of suicide. Then describe ways that you can convince someone that suicide is not the answer to his or her problems.

Visit **health.glencoe.com** for the Interactive Study Guide for Lesson 2.

Getting Help

Guide to Reading

Building Vocabulary

As you read this lesson, write each new highlighted term and its definition in your notebook.

▶ psychotherapy (p. 237)

▶ behavior therapy (p. 237)

▶ cognitive therapy (p. 237)

▶ group therapy (p. 237)

▶ biomedical therapy (p. 237)

Focusing on the Main Ideas

In this lesson, you will learn how to:

▶ Tell early detection and warning signs that prompt individuals of all ages to seek mental health care.

▶ Describe methods for addressing critical mental health issues.

▶ Select available mental health services in the community.

Reading Strategy

Problems and Solutions

▶ Make a T chart. On one side, list some of the behaviors and signs that indicate a mental or emotional problem that needs help. On the other side, list the types of therapy methods that may help.

Write a brief paragraph describing why some people may find it difficult to seek help for a mental problem.

Counselors-Licensed Professional (Cont'd)

ABC COUNSELING CENTER

ADULTS • INDIVIDUAL • MARITAL • TEENS • COUPLES
Health Psychology
Promote Lifestyle Change And Wellness
PSYCHIATRIC SERVICES
EVALUATION • MEDICATION
TEEN PSYCHIATRIST ON BOARD
DR. J. HIGGINS Licensed Psychologist
756 Main St **555-6897**

ACKERLEY, JACK C. PHD
6800 Tall Oaks Rd **555-6589**

ADKINS, PAMELA & ASSOC
692 Kenwood St **555-6985**

ALL ABOUT ATTITUDES

FAMILY AND TEEN
COUNSELING
DEPRESSION • ANXIETY • STRESS
Licensed Professional Clinical
Counselor
1859 River Rd **555-6897**

BAKER, /
3300 Wir

BANNER, F
746 Gar

BEGINING
TEE
4460 C

BURKE, W/
715 Wils

CARTER,
111 Rollin

COUNSE
Ind
"Givin
810 Lc

CROWE &
8855 Lone

CROWN,
2158 Re

DANNER (

TEENS
LIC

Ⓐ Many sources of help are available to people who have mental health concerns. *How would you identify available sources of help and evaluate their appropriateness?*

The early detection of mental and emotional problems is critically important to getting help. Knowing how to analyze situations requiring professional health services can help a person determine if he or she should seek help.

Knowing When to Get Help

It can be difficult to ask for help in coping with mental or emotional problems. Our thoughts are private, and we tend to hide those that embarrass us or those we can't control. However, it is important to seek help if any of the feelings or behaviors listed below persist.

▶ You feel trapped with no way out, or you worry all the time.

▶ Your feelings affect your sleep, eating habits, school work, job performance, or relationships.

▶ Your family or friends express concern about your behavior.

▶ You are becoming involved with alcohol or other drugs.

▶ You are becoming increasingly aggressive, violent, or reckless.

Signs That Professional Help Is Needed

Some symptoms that are severe enough to require intervention by a mental health professional include: prolonged sadness for no specific reason; frequent outbursts of anger; overwhelming fear, anxiety, or anger at the world; unexplained change in sleeping or eating habits; and social withdrawal. Of course, if you have any doubt about your mental health, you should always get assistance. Like most forms of sickness, mental disorders may get worse if left untreated.

Real-Life Application

Evaluating Sources of Self-Help

Thousands of self-help materials are available in print, on tapes and CDs, and online. Health-literate consumers know how to evaluate factors that influence the personal selection of health products and services. Use these questions to evaluate self-help materials.

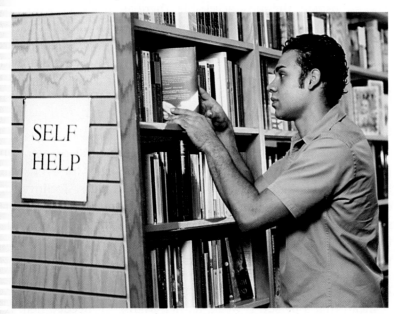

SELF HELP

Are you being advised to try medication or some other remedy?
Check first with a health professional. Certain herbs, for example, can be life-threatening.

What are the qualifications of the authors?
Do they have university-based training in mental health? Have they published in professional journals? In books, check the reference section for citations from professional journals.

Is the material backed by a nationally known and respected mental health organization?
Look for recommendations from organizations such as the American Psychological Association.

Is a cost involved?
If you are asked online for a credit card number or personal information, check with a parent or guardian.

ACTIVITY

Choose a self-help book, magazine article, CD, or Web site and evaluate the information using the criteria listed here. Share your findings with the class, and recommend any useful and appropriate sources to the school librarian.

FIGURE 9.3

MENTAL HEALTH PROFESSIONALS

- **Psychiatrist**—a physician who specializes in diagnosing and treating mental disorders and can prescribe medications
- **Neurologist**—a physician who specializes in organic disorders of the brain and nervous system
- **Clinical Psychologist**—a professional who diagnoses and treats emotional and behavioral disorders by means of counseling but cannot prescribe medications
- **Counselor**—a professional who works to help people with personal and educational matters
- **Psychiatric Social Worker**—a professional who provides guidance and treatment for clients with emotional problems, usually in the setting of a mental hospital, mental health clinic, or family service agency
- **School Psychologist**—a professional who specializes in the assessment of learning, emotional, and behavioral problems of schoolchildren

Reading Check

Explain What are some of the symptoms that might indicate a person needs professional help?

Methods for Seeking Help

Most people tend to wait too long to address critical mental health issues, even though there are many people in their lives who are willing and eager to assist them. Besides parents and guardians, who are usually the most accessible, there are teachers, school psychologists, counselors, coaches, clergy members, and crisis hot lines. According to the Surgeon General, school is the place where children and teens are most likely to receive treatment. **Figure 9.3** provides a list of mental health professionals to whom a person might be referred for help.

STUMBLING BLOCKS TO SEEKING HELP

Some people are afraid to seek help for mental or emotional problems. It is important that you know strategies for overcoming barriers when communicating information, ideas, feelings, and opinions. If someone you know needs treatment from a professional mental health expert, it is important that you respond to that person with empathy. If you or someone you know is reluctant to seek help, remember these facts.

▶ Asking for help from a mental health professional does not mean that a person is weak. Rather, asking for needed help is a sign of strength. It shows responsibility for one's own wellness.

▶ People who have mental disorders often cannot get better on their own. Serious disorders, compulsions, and addictions are complex and require professional intervention.

▶ Sharing your deepest thoughts with a "stranger" is not painful or embarrassing. In fact, most people are surprised and happy to find that unloading problems is a great relief.

Therapy Methods

A mental health professional may use any of several treatment methods, depending on his or her area of expertise and the needs of the patient. The following are the most commonly used therapy methods.

▶ **Psychotherapy** is *an ongoing dialogue between a patient and a mental health professional.* The dialogue is designed to find the root cause of a problem and devise a solution.

▶ **Behavior therapy** is *a treatment process that focuses on changing unwanted behaviors through rewards and reinforcements.*

▶ **Cognitive therapy** is *a treatment method designed to identify and correct distorted thinking patterns that can lead to feelings and behaviors that may be troublesome, self-defeating, or self-destructive.*

▶ **Group therapy** involves *treating a group of people who have similar problems and who meet regularly with a trained counselor.*

▶ **Biomedical therapy** is *the use of certain medications to treat or reduce the symptoms of a mental disorder.* It is sometimes used alone, but is often combined with other treatment methods, such as those listed above.

Most forms of therapy involve counseling. *What are some short-term and long-term benefits of receiving help for a mental health problem?*

LESSON 3 REVIEW

Reviewing Facts and Vocabulary

1. Identify three warning signs that may help a person detect a mental or an emotional problem early in its development.

2. Why do some people delay seeking help for mental or emotional problems?

3. Define *group therapy*, and use the term in a sentence.

Thinking Critically

4. **Synthesizing.** Identify at least three personal qualities one would need to fill a position at a mental health clinic.

5. **Demonstrating.** What criteria might you utilize to evaluate whether information about a mental health problem was appropriate?

Applying Health Skills

Decision Making. Imagine that you have a friend who is always making negative comments and seems to be withdrawing from his or her normal activities. Use the six steps of decision making to determine what actions to take.

After You Read

Organize Information. Create a wallet card listing what you can do to help someone who is mentally or emotionally distressed. Include a list of self-help and professional resources.

Visit **health.glencoe.com** for the Interactive Study Guide for Lesson 3.

Lesson 3 Getting Help **237**

Understanding Death and Grief

Guide to Reading

Building Vocabulary

As you read this lesson, write each new highlighted term and its definition in your notebook.

▶ coping (p. 239)

▶ grief response (p. 239)

▶ mourning (p. 240)

Focusing on the Main Ideas

In this lesson, you will learn how to:

▶ Describe the different kinds of emotional loss.

▶ Compare the stages of the grieving process and ways in which people cope with emotional loss.

▶ Discuss issues related to death and grieving.

▶ Connect the importance of using community mental health services to help cope with grief.

Reading Strategy

Predict

▶ After reviewing the headings, subheadings, and pictures, write a few sentences describing what information you believe you'll learn in this lesson.

Quick Write

Make a list of the words you associate with grieving.

Flowers and cards are appropriate expressions of sympathy for someone who has suffered a loss.
In what other ways can you show support?

L oss is a part of life. Although it is always difficult and painful to lose someone you love or care for, learning to cope with losses appropriately is an important part of human development. The strong bonds we form with others can help us deal with loss in appropriate ways and accept it as a part of the entire life experience.

Different Kinds of Loss

Y ou have probably experienced losses that resulted in emotional distress. Perhaps you missed a chance to play in a championship game because of an injury or failed to get the grade you needed on an important exam. You may have experienced rejection; the breakup of a relationship; or the death of a pet, friend, or family member. Maybe you have had to move or change schools and have felt the loss of whatever—or whomever—you left behind. A strong emotional attachment can make loss deeply painful. Understanding the grieving process will help you cope with loss and manage your feelings appropriately.

Expressions of Grief

Coping is *dealing successfully with difficult changes in your life.* When a loss occurs, it's common and natural to experience a **grief response**, *an individual's total response to a major loss.* The way a person responds to loss is unique to the situation and to the individual. If a death is sudden or traumatic, for example, the response is likely to be somewhat different from the response to a death that results from a long-term illness. A person's perspective on the lost relationship and his or her ability to remain open to interaction in other relationships might also affect the response to loss.

The Grieving Process

Mental health professionals have recognized a common phenomenon, called the *grieving process,* that occurs during the grief response. The purpose of this process is to reach closure, or acceptance of a loss. There is no correct way of experiencing loss, but the stages of grief reflect a variety of reactions that may occur as people work through the process. The reactions, which were identified in part by the noted Swiss American doctor Elisabeth Kübler-Ross, include the following:

- ▶ **Denial or Numbness.** In this stage, the person cannot believe the loss has occurred. This part of the process protects the person from being overwhelmed by his or her emotions.

- ▶ **Emotional Releases.** These reactions come with recognition of the loss and often involve periods of crying, which is important to the healing process.

- ▶ **Anger.** Feeling powerless and unfairly deprived, the person may lash out at whatever is perceived to be responsible for the loss. Sometimes a general resentment toward life sets in.

- ▶ **Bargaining.** As the reality of the loss becomes clear, the person may promise to change if only what was lost can be returned, even for a little while.

- ▶ **Depression.** Beyond the natural feelings of sadness, feelings of isolation, alienation, and hopelessness occur as the person recognizes the extent of the loss.

- ▶ **Remorse.** The person may become preoccupied with thoughts about what he or she could have done to prevent the loss or make things better.

- ▶ **Acceptance.** This stage can involve a sense of power, allowing the person to face reality in constructive ways and make significant and meaningful gestures surrounding the idea of loss.

- ▶ **Hope.** Eventually the person reaches a point when remembering becomes less painful and he or she begins to look ahead to the future.

Health Minute

Breaking Up

The breakup of a relationship can cause a person to experience many of the stages of grief. These feelings are a natural part of the healing process.

Overcoming a breakup:

- ▶ Allow yourself to feel the pain associated with the breakup. Denying your feelings only prolongs the grief process.

- ▶ Recognize that self-blame and guilt are defenses against feeling out of control. Remember that you can't control another person's decisions or behaviors.

- ▶ Be thankful for the good times you've had and the contributions the relationship has made to your life.

- ▶ Give yourself time to heal. Allow yourself to have new experiences and to make new friends, but avoid comparing new relationships with the one that has ended.

Reading Check

Describe What are the steps in the grieving process?

An Encouraging Word

Much of the day-to-day comforting of terminally ill persons is carried out by dedicated volunteers. These volunteers often experience a profound sense of loss when the patient passes away. A word of support in the form of a card will encourage these volunteers to continue their important work.

What You'll Need

- card stock paper
- felt-tip pens in different colors
- computer with clip art software (optional)

What You'll Do

1. On 8½″ x 11″ notebook paper, compose several versions of a message. Many volunteers report that inspirational messages are helpful.

2. Sketch the artwork you will include in your card. The artwork should emphasize serenity, peace, or hope. You may want to examine clip art options from a computer program for ideas.

3. Decide what "goodies," such as a flower or candy, to include with your card.

4. Create your card, using card stock paper and felt-tip pens or computer clip art.

Apply and Conclude

Send your card to a hospital, hospice, or other facility in which volunteers provide support for terminally ill people. Then compose a reflective essay describing what you have learned about dealing with loss and grieving by empathizing with those who work with terminally ill patients.

Coping with Death

To help cope with death, allow some time to reflect on who you were before the loss and who you will be after grieving. Focus on what you were able to do in the relationship, not what you could or should have done. Remember the wonderful things about the person and the good times you've shared. Another way to reach closure is by seeking support from others or writing a letter to say good-bye.

Helping Others Through the Grieving Process

Support from family and friends is important during **mourning**, or *the act of showing sorrow or grief.* To help others grieve, it helps to understand various ways in which different families handle grief. You can help by showing empathy or just being there to listen. Share your memories and appreciation of the person who is gone. Sharing memories can help survivors bridge the transition. By helping others, you are exploring the increased responsibility in the transition from adolescence to adulthood.

Did You Know ?

Unresolved grief tends to affect the grieving process at the next occurrence of a loss—causing a person to express some emotions and responses that have been held back. The surfacing of unresolved grief reactions can slow and complicate the healing process.

Grief Counseling

Seeing a counselor or therapist who specializes in grief can help people through the grieving process. These specialists often can be found through community mental health services, such as hospices.

▼ Memorial services are times for remembering and showing respect. *What are some other ways to remember a loved one?*

Coping with Disasters and Crises

Traumatic or sudden events, such as natural disasters, can leave people feeling a range of emotions from numb and helpless to horrified and afraid. Using effective coping mechanisms can ease the process of recovery.

▶ Spend time with other people, and discuss your feelings.

▶ Get back to daily routines as quickly as possible.

▶ Eat nutritious foods, exercise, and get enough rest and sleep.

▶ Do something positive to help your community through the event, such as assisting with cleanup or raising money for aid.

LESSON 4 REVIEW

Reviewing Facts and Vocabulary

1. Name the stages that may be involved in the grieving process.
2. Define the term *grief response.*
3. List three strategies for coping with disasters and crises.

Thinking Critically

4. **Analyzing.** How might coping with a death resulting from a long-term illness differ from coping with a sudden death caused by an accident?
5. **Applying.** Recall a story of personal loss, such as death, that you read about in a book. Write a paragraph that describes the process the grieving character went through. Be sure to examine issues of death and grieving that the book addressed.

Applying Health Skills

Communication Skills. How could you express support to a friend who is suffering from a loss? Make a list of things you could say to comfort someone in such a situation. Your statements should demonstrate consideration, respect, and empathy for others.

> **After You Read**

Explain. Draw a stairway with eight steps. On each step, write the name of one of the stages of the grieving process. Explain each stage.

Science is beginning to understand how phobias form—and how to treat them.

Fear NOT

For Martin, a high-school student from Minneapolis, Minnesota, his fear of snakes is so overwhelming that he stapled together pages in a textbook to avoid flipping to a photo of a snake. He often wakes with nightmares that he sees a snake slithering toward him. "It's odd," he says, "because I'm not in situations where I would ever see snakes."

His brain, however—or at least the parts of it that operate below the conscious level—may have been. One thing that helped early humans survive was an instinctive urge to flee from potentially dangerous situations. For today's humans, those early lessons are hard to unlearn.

The Big Four Phobias

Researchers believe that specific phobias usually fall into one of four subcategories, all of which would have had meaning for our ancient ancestors: fear of animals, such as spiders and snakes; fear of environments, like heights and the dark; fear of blood or injury; and fear of dangerous situations, like being trapped in a tight space. Michelle Craske, psychologist at UCLA's Anxiety and Behavioral Disorders Program, says, "We tend to fear anything that threatens our survival as a species."

Phobias may have originated with our distant ancestors, but we modern humans get phobias from our immediate ancestors—our parents. As many as 40 percent of all people suffering from a specific phobia have at least one phobic parent. This suggests that phobias could be influenced by genetics. However, genes don't have to be involved as long as learning is. An upsetting childhood event—a house fire, say, or a dog bite—may be more than enough to get the brain's attention and serve as a focus for uncontrollable fears.

Fortunately, doctors are successfully treating patients with phobias. They do it by gradually exposing them to what they fear. Psychologist Steven Phillipson, clinical director of the Center for Cognitive-Behavioral Psychotherapy in New York City, says, "Just as people get used to background chatter, so too can phobics stop responding to the thing that once frightened them." ◢

TIME to THINK...
About Phobias

As a class, brainstorm different types of phobias (you may need to consult your school's media center or the Internet). Determine which subcategory— fear of animals, fear of environments, fear of injury, and fear of dangerous situations—each phobia falls into. Be prepared to discuss your choice.

1. Analyzing Influences. Briefly describe some movies or television shows that have portrayed characters with mental disorders. Do you think that these depictions are realistic, accurate, and sensitive? How do you think media representations of mental disorders affect how the public views mental problems? *(LESSON 1)*

 2. Advocacy. Write a letter to your school newspaper to raise awareness of teen suicide as a serious problem. Include information on what everyone can do to help prevent teen suicide. *(LESSON 2)*

 3. Accessing Information. Evaluate the availability of mental health professionals in your community. *(LESSON 3)*

 4. Practicing Healthful Behaviors. Develop a strategy for coping with loss. Think about what would make you feel better if you were grieving a loss. Make a list of actions you could take to cope with the situation and with your feelings. *(LESSON 4)*

CAREER Corner

Psychologist

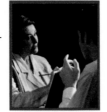

Are you interested in human behavior and the mental processes related to behavior? Do you enjoy talking with people and helping them with their problems? If so, a career as a psychologist might be for you. Psychologists counsel individuals to help them resolve mental and emotional problems.

If you want to be an advocate for children, you might consider specializing in school psychology. A school psychologist specializes in educational assessment, childhood development, behavioral management, individual and group counseling, and consultation.

To become a psychologist, you will need at least a master's degree. A doctoral degree is required for clinical counseling. Find out more about this and other health careers by clicking on Career Corner at **health.glencoe.com.**

BEYOND the Classroom

Parent Involvement

Accessing Information. Learn more about family counseling centers that are available in your community. With your parents, create a pamphlet that highlights the services offered through the centers, the costs of these services, and where financial assistance for counseling can be found. Provide the pamphlet to your school counselor.

School and Community

Crisis Centers. Identify local crisis centers that help teens deal with mental health problems. Contact the centers to determine how a person could become a volunteer either in the centers or on their associated hotlines.

After You Read

Use your Foldable to review what you have learned about the six types of mental disorders. On the back of your Foldable, explain how each type of disorder is classified.

FOLDABLES™
Study Organizer

► EXPLORING HEALTH TERMS
Answer the following questions on a sheet of paper.

Lesson 1 *Match each definition with the correct term.*

anxiety disorder	conduct disorder
eating disorder	mental disorder
post-traumatic stress disorder	mood disorder

1. An illness of the mind that can affect the thoughts, feelings, and behaviors of a person, preventing him or her from leading a happy, healthy, productive life.

2. An illness, often with an organic cause, that relates to emotions and may involve mood extremes that interfere with everyday living.

3. A pattern of behavior in which the rights of others or basic social rules are violated.

Lesson 2 *Fill in the blanks with the correct term.*

suicide	cluster suicides
alienation	

(__4__) can occur in a community when a local (__5__) is sensationalized in the media. These behaviors often result from feelings of depression and (__6__).

Lesson 3 *Replace the underlined words with the correct term.*

behavior therapy	biomedical therapy
cognitive therapy	group therapy
psychotherapy	

7. <u>Psychotherapy</u> usually involves several people.

8. A psychiatrist may use <u>behavior therapy</u> if medication is needed in the treatment.

9. A distorted thinking pattern requires <u>group therapy</u>.

10. The therapy that uses rewards and reinforcements is called <u>cognitive therapy</u>.

11. <u>Biomedical therapy</u> involves an ongoing dialogue between a patient and a mental health professional.

Lesson 4 *Match each definition with the correct term.*

mourning	grief response
coping	

12. Dealing successfully with difficult changes in your life.

13. An individual's total response to a major loss.

14. The act of showing sorrow or grief.

► RECALLING THE FACTS
Use complete sentences to answer the following questions.

1. What types of events are associated with post-traumatic stress disorder?

2. Name two eating disorders.

3. Describe antisocial personality disorder.

4. What should you do if you recognize the warning signs of suicide in yourself or others?

5. List three actions a person can take if he or she is with someone who appears to be suicidal.

6. What are the CDC's guidelines for preventing cluster suicides?

7. Where are teens and children most likely to receive treatment for mental health problems?

8. Name six types of mental health professionals.

9. List three therapy methods for treating mental disorders.

10. List three examples of loss.

11. What is one way of reaching closure after the death of a loved one?

12. How can you help someone who is mourning?

For more review questions for Chapter 9, go to **health.glencoe.com**.

➤ WRITING CRITICALLY

1. **Narrative.** Write a one-page story about a teen who suspects that his or her friend is suffering from depression and is contemplating suicide. In your story, identify ways in which the teen expresses his or her concern and offers help.

2. **Expository.** Conduct additional research about one of the mental health careers described in Figure 9.3. Write a one-page job description providing a detailed account of the job requirements needed for one of these careers.

Standardized Test Practice

MATH **Read the paragraph below, and then answer the questions.**

Recent research indicates that more people suffering from depression are seeking help compared to the number reported 20 years ago. Researchers aren't sure whether the increase means that more people have depression or that people are now better able to recognize the symptoms. Nearly everyone is mildly depressed at some time, but 16 percent of the U. S. population will suffer from major depression in a lifetime. A study was conducted on more than 9,000 people ages 18 and older. Fifty-seven percent of those who had major depression sought help. This rate is almost 40 percent higher than the rate reported 20 years before the study. Even though the number of patients treated is increasing, it is estimated that only 21 percent are receiving adequate care.

1. If the size of the general population is 200 million people, how many people will experience major depression at some time during their lives?

   A 32 million
   B 42 million
   C 75 million
   D 92.8 million

2. What function can be used to find the number of people who are seeking help for depression if you know the size of the population with depression? (Hint: The variable N is the number of people seeking help, and P is the size of the population.)

   F $N = P$
   G $N = (0.57)(0.16)P$
   H $N = 0.57P$
   I $P = 0.16N$

3. Examine the percentages reflecting how many people have major depression, how many of these people seek help, and how many who seek help receive adequate care. Of 20,000 people, how many people would you expect to be receiving adequate care for major depression? Justify your answer.

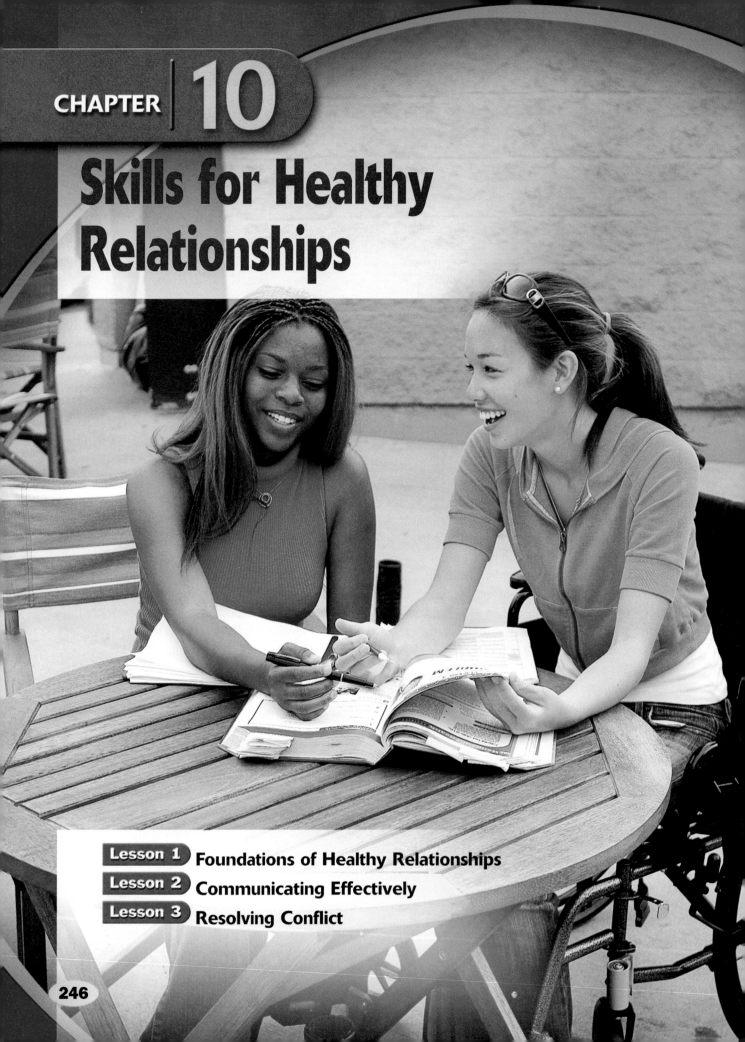

Skills for Healthy Relationships

HEALTH Online

Eye ON THE Media

Internet Etiquette and Relationships

The Internet has made it easier to keep in touch with family and friends. Strengthening your relationships requires good Internet etiquette. When sending emails, avoid

► including private or sensitive information.

► forwarding chain emails.

Visit the Eye on the Media section at **health.glencoe.com** to learn more about how the Internet can promote healthy communication.

FOLDABLES™ Study Organizer

Before You Read

Use this Foldable to organize what you learn about building and maintaining healthy relationships. Begin with two sheets of 8½" x 11" paper.

▶ **Step 1**

Stack two sheets of paper, with the top edges 1" apart. Keep the side edges straight.

▶ **Step 2**

Fold up the bottom half of the stack of papers 1" from the top half. All tabs should be the same size.

▶ **Step 3**

Crease the stack of papers to hold the tabs in place. Staple together along the fold and label the tabs as shown.

As You Read

As you read and discuss the material in the chapter, use your Foldable to record supporting facts under the appropriate tabs.

Foundations of a Healthy Relationship
Family, Friends, and Community
Building Healthy Relationships
Character and Healthy Relationships

SPOTLIGHT ON HEALTH

Using Visuals. Friendships are an important part of our lives. What kinds of skills do you think help friendships remain healthy and strong?

Foundations of Healthy Relationships

Guide to Reading

Building Vocabulary

As you read this lesson, write each new highlighted term and its definition in your notebook.

- relationship (p. 248)
- friendship (p. 249)
- citizenship (p. 249)
- role (p. 250)
- communication (p. 250)
- cooperation (p. 250)
- compromise (p. 251)

Focusing on the Main Ideas

In this lesson, you will learn how to:

- **Compare** and contrast the positive and negative effects of relationships with peers, family, and friends on physical, mental/emotional, and social health.
- **Demonstrate** how to communicate needs, wants, and emotions in healthy ways.
- **Point** out character traits that promote healthy relationships with peers, family, and friends.

Reading Strategy

Predict

- Review the headings, subheadings, and captions. Make a three-column chart. In the first, list what you know about relationships. In the next, predict the kinds of information you might learn from this lesson. After you read, list what you learned in the last column.

Quick Write

Make a list of the skills that you think help friendships remain healthy and strong.

Shared values and mutual respect are essential in healthy relationships.

As you learned in Chapter 7, human beings are social creatures with a need to belong and be loved. We also need to feel safe, secure, valued, and recognized. These needs are met when we form healthy relationships with others. A **relationship** is *a bond or connection you have with other people.*

Healthy Relationships

All your relationships can have positive and negative effects on your physical, mental/emotional, and social health. Healthy relationships are based on shared values and interests and mutual respect. You are naturally drawn to those who encourage and support your own best qualities. People in healthy relationships know skills for communicating effectively with family, friends, and others.

Take the Health Inventory for Chapter 10 at **health.glencoe.com.**

The roles you play in relationships with family, with friends, and in the community are part of your everyday life. *Name several different relationships and roles that you experience each day.*

Family Relationships

Family relationships, which involve both immediate family (parents or guardians and siblings) and extended family (grandparents, aunts, uncles, and cousins), last your entire life. Healthy family relationships enhance all sides of your health triangle. For example, your parents or guardians provide for your physical health with food, clothing, and shelter. They build your social health by teaching you the values that will guide you throughout your life. The love, care, and encouragement you receive from family members also contribute to your mental/emotional health.

Friendships

A **friendship** is *a significant relationship between two people that is based on caring, trust, and consideration.* Your friends can be of any age, and you can choose them for different reasons. Good friends share similar values. They can positively influence your self-concept and behavior and help you resist negative influences. Maintaining a good friendship can sometimes be hard work, but it is well worth the effort.

Community Relationships

Citizenship is *the way you conduct yourself as a member of the community.* Members of a community work together to promote the safety and well-being of the entire community. Citizens may volunteer at hospitals or work to provide food, clothing, or shelter to the homeless. You can demonstrate that you know how the social environment influences the health of the community by obeying laws and rules, by being a friendly and helpful neighbor, and by contributing to efforts to improve your school and community.

Did You Know ?

Your choice of friends can promote a positive self-image. When choosing a friend, ask yourself these questions:

- Does this person have the qualities I admire most?
- Is this someone I can trust with my thoughts and confidences?
- How does this person affect my health triangle?
- What interests and values do we have in common?
- What can I offer in this friendship? What can the other person offer?

This teen has a working relationship with her employer. *What other relationship roles might be part of this teen's life?*

Roles with Peers, Family, and Friends

What roles do you play as you interact with others? A **role** is *a part you play in a relationship.* You may be a daughter or son; a sister or brother; a granddaughter or grandson; a member of the school band or volleyball team; a volunteer at a homeless shelter; an employee; a member of a church, synagogue, or mosque; a best friend; and a girlfriend or boyfriend. You probably play many of these roles—all at the same time!

The role you play in a relationship may be obvious. For example, you know that when you baby-sit a neighbor's child, you are an employee. Sometimes your roles are less clear, and they may change gradually or even suddenly. For example, your relationship with a fellow choir member may change if you begin dating. Such role changes can be confusing and can make it difficult to know how to act.

Building Healthy Relationships

For a relationship to succeed, it is important to implement skills that develop positive relationships. For that to happen, the people involved need certain skills. Three of these skills are communication, cooperation, and compromise—the three Cs of healthy relationships.

Communication

Communication refers to *your ways of sending and receiving messages.* These messages may be exchanged in words or through gestures, facial expressions, and behaviors. You communicate to let others know your feelings, thoughts, and expectations. Communication also lets you discover the feelings, needs, wants, and knowledge of others. You will learn more about skills for effective communication in the next lesson.

Cooperation

Have you ever helped someone move a heavy object, such as a large piece of furniture? Such activities are almost impossible without **cooperation**, *working together for the good of all.* Working together through cooperation helps build strong relationships. For example, Susan helps prepare dinner each evening because her parents don't get home from work until 6 p.m. Because of her help, Susan's family is able to eat together and enjoy one another's company. Her contribution benefits the entire family.

Compromise

Three friends can't agree on how they'll spend the afternoon: Thomas and Elise want to go biking, but Serena wants to play miniature golf. Have you ever been in a similar situation? If so, you probably used compromise to solve the problem. **Compromise** is *a problem-solving method that involves each participant's giving up something to reach a solution that satisfies everyone.* It can be used to create a win-win situation for everyone involved.

The "give and take" of effective compromise strengthens relationships. By your willingness to give up something in order to reach a solution, you practice socially acceptable ways of resolving interpersonal conflict by practicing non-abusive behavior. Remember, however, that compromise involves seeking a solution that is acceptable to *all* persons involved. Therefore, it should not lead to a decision that goes against your values or beliefs. Learning when—and when *not*—to compromise is a vital relationship skill.

Characteristics of Healthy Relationships

By practicing the three Cs, you make positive contributions to healthy relationships. In addition, all good relationships—whether with family members, friends, or other members of your community—have certain recognizable characteristics. Some of these characteristics are described below.

▶ **Mutual Respect and Consideration.** In healthy relationships, people show mutual respect even when they disagree. This involves accepting one another's tastes and opinions and being tolerant of different viewpoints. Furthermore, each person shows consideration by being thoughtful about the rights and feelings of others.

▶ **Honesty.** Because of their mutual respect and consideration, participants in a healthy relationship have the confidence to be open and honest about their actions, thoughts, and feelings. Dishonesty can seriously weaken or even destroy a relationship.

▶ **Dependability.** Participants in a healthy relationship are dependable. They are trustworthy and reliable. Each is there for the others when needed.

▶ **Commitment.** Healthy relationships require commitment. The participants are willing to work together and make sacrifices that benefit everyone involved. They are loyal to each other, and they are committed to strengthening the relationship.

Isn't compromise really a matter of one person giving in or losing?
If two people can't agree on a compromise between two choices, they should look for a third choice that both can agree on. If there really are only two choices, the compromise might be for one person to "win" this time with the understanding that the next time it will be the other person's turn to "win." If only one person is always giving up something, there is no compromise.

Reading Check

Describe What are the characteristics of a healthy relationship?

Character and Healthy Relationships

Your **character**—the way you think, feel, and act—has the greatest influence on your relationships with others. Think about the people with whom you enjoy spending time. These people probably have values similar to yours. Your values are the beliefs and ideals that guide the way you live.

You can build a foundation for healthy relationships by demonstrating the six main traits of good character. It is also important to learn to identify positive aspects of a relationship. These traits are described in **Figure 10.1.** Think about ways you can demonstrate each character trait.

FIGURE **10.1**

DEMONSTRATING CHARACTER IN RELATIONSHIPS

Trustworthiness	Fairness
You show trustworthiness when you are honest, reliable, and loyal. Trustworthy people don't cheat, steal, or deceive; they have the courage to do what's right. • *Example:* Hector finds a wallet containing $300. He uses the name on the driver's license and the phone book to call the owner so that he can return the wallet.	You show fairness when you play by the rules, take turns, and share. You also don't blame or take advantage of others. A fair person listens to others and is open-minded. • *Example:* Maria shows fairness by telling the referee that the volleyball was on the line and the opposing team won the point.
Respect	**Caring**
You show respect by using good manners, being considerate of others, and being tolerant of differences. You are also respectful when you deal with anger and disagreements in a peaceful way and treat other people and property with care. • *Example:* Sid knows that his dad brought a lot of work home from the office. Sid turns down the volume of his music so he won't disturb his father.	You show that you are caring when you are kind and compassionate. Caring means putting in time and energy to help others. • *Example:* Juanita is entering a store. She holds the door open for a man whose arms are filled with packages.
Responsibility	**Citizenship**
You show that you are responsible when you do what is expected of you and are accountable for your choices. Being responsible also means that you use self-control, think before you act, and always try your best. • *Example:* Sarah's drama rehearsal runs late. She calls her parents to let them know she is going to be late.	You show good citizenship by cooperating and doing your share to improve your school and community. You obey laws and rules and respect authority. Staying informed about issues that affect you and your neighbors, voting when you are of age, and doing your part to protect the environment are other ways to demonstrate good citizenship. • *Example:* Brad sees that someone has left an empty juice bottle on a table in the school cafeteria. He picks up the bottle and puts it in a recycling bin.

Real-Life Application

The Importance of Good Character to Friendships

Discuss how the e-mail below demonstrates good character traits.

> **Dear Lola,**
>
> I'm sorry I didn't invite you to go with me to the grand opening of the new music store. I didn't think you were interested, so I was surprised when I found out that you were angry about not being invited. I'm not making excuses—I should have thought of you before we left. I don't blame you for feeling hurt and angry.
>
> I care about our friendship and I hope you'll forgive me. I'll try to be more considerate next time.
>
> **Your friend (I hope),**
>
> **Mieko**

Trustworthiness: apologizing, being honest, not making excuses

Fairness: not blaming Lola

Caring: saying that she is grateful for the friendship

Responsibility: realizing that she should have thought before she acted

ACTIVITY

Write a reply to the e-mail above. Show at least four traits of good character. Next, write a paragraph explaining how the character traits demonstrated in your message can strengthen the friendship.

LESSON 1 REVIEW

Reviewing Facts and Vocabulary

1. Define *relationship,* and evaluate the positive effects of family relationships on your emotional health.

2. What are the three Cs of healthy relationships?

3. List the six traits of good character.

Thinking Critically

4. **Evaluating.** Identify specific examples of how the roles you play with family and friends differ from those you play in other social groups.

5. **Applying.** Give an example of how you demonstrate consideration, respect, commitment, honesty, and dependability in your relationships with family members.

Applying Health Skills

Advocacy. Design a flip book for children about the six traits of good character. The book should demonstrate the importance of good character and persuade children to develop these traits.

After You Read

Explain. Draw four boxes on a sheet of paper. In each box, write one of the following terms: *mutual respect and consideration, honesty, dependability*, and *commitment*. In each box, provide a definition and one or two examples of each behavior.

 Visit **health.glencoe.com** for the Interactive Study Guide for Lesson 1.

Lesson 1 Foundations of Healthy Relationships **253**

Communicating Effectively

Guide to Reading

Building Vocabulary

As you read this lesson, write each new highlighted term and its definition in your notebook.

- ▶ "I" message (p. 256)
- ▶ active listening (p. 256)
- ▶ body language (p. 258)
- ▶ prejudice (p. 260)
- ▶ tolerance (p. 260)
- ▶ constructive criticism (p. 260)

Focusing on the Main Ideas

In this lesson, you will learn how to:

- ▶ **Compare** the forms of communication, including passive, aggressive, or assertive communication.
- ▶ **Develop** the communication skills you need to build healthy relationships with family, friends, peers, and others.
- ▶ **Demonstrate** communication skills that show respect for self, family, friends, and others.

Reading Strategy

Organize Information

- ▶ Make a word web with "effective communication" in the center, surrounded by circles labeled Communication Styles, Speaking Skills, Listening Skills, Body Language, Communication Barriers, Constructive Criticism, and Compliments. As you read, fill in the circles with facts.

Quick Write

Write a brief paragraph describing some of the different ways you use to communicate with others.

▲ Writing a note or letter can be an effective way to communicate your feelings.

In what other ways do you communicate with your family, friends, and peers?

How often have you given or received a shrug, a raised eyebrow, or a grin in reply to a comment or question? These responses are all forms of communication. Sometimes you may convey your feelings by writing notes or letters. There are many ways to exchange ideas with others. All of the ways in which you send and receive messages are forms of communication. Knowing positive strategies for expressing needs, wants, and feelings is a foundation of effective communication.

Effective Communication

Demonstrating effective communication skills and resistance skills is critical in building and maintaining healthy relationships. When you communicate effectively, you understand the relationship between verbal and nonverbal communication.

Three basic skills are needed for effective communication: speaking, listening, and body language. Effective communication helps you form and maintain healthy relationships and demonstrate consideration and respect for oneself, one's family, and others.

Communication Styles

Do you have any friends who always just "go along" with what others decide to do? Perhaps you know someone who is "pushy," always insisting on getting his or her own way. These examples reflect two of the three styles of communication.

▶ **Passive.** Passive communication involves the inability or unwillingness to express thoughts and feelings. Passive communicators do not stand up for themselves or defend their attitudes or beliefs.

▶ **Aggressive.** Aggressive communicators often try to get their way through bullying and intimidation. They do not consider the rights of others. In disagreements, they attack the other person, not the problem.

▶ **Assertive.** Assertive communication involves expressing thoughts and feelings clearly and directly but without hurting others. Assertive communicators defend their attitudes and beliefs, but they also respect the rights of others. In disagreements, they attack the problem, not the other person.

Using assertive communication—which involves effective speaking and listening skills as well as appropriate body language—rather than passive or aggressive communication is important in all communication situations.

Speaking Skills

Having good communication skills means that you do not assume that others can read your mind or know your needs and expectations. When you interact with others, you are responsible for making your thoughts and feelings known. For example, you need to say when your feelings have been hurt or when you've been disappointed. You demonstrate good speaking skills when you clearly say what you mean.

Changes in the tone, pitch, or loudness of your voice can affect communication. Kind words spoken in a sarcastic tone, for example, may not be interpreted as kind. Speaking loudly may make you seem bossy or arrogant. Saying "no" too softly can make you sound insincere or uncertain. These examples show that *how* you say something is as important as *what* you say.

Reading Check

Explain What are the three basic skills for effective communication?

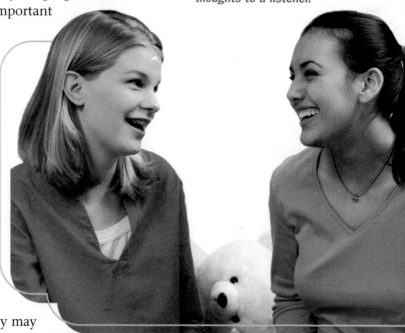

Good communication skills demonstrate consideration and respect for self, family, and others. *List some strategies for effectively communicating your thoughts to a listener.*

FIGURE 10.2

STATING YOUR FEELINGS EFFECTIVELY

Compare the messages and the probable results of these scenes.

Aggressive Messages	Assertive "I" Messages
(What *not* to say)	**(What to say)**
"You idiot! You took my favorite jacket and got paint all over it! You ruined it, and you'll have to pay for it."	"I'm upset that my favorite jacket was borrowed without my knowledge."
"Why are you always late? It's really annoying."	"I worry about you when you don't show up."
"Why do you always have to get what you want? You never do what I suggest."	"I'll agree to have Mexican food today if I can pick the restaurant the next time we go out."

When you want to deliver messages that have strong emotional content, consider using "I" messages. An **"I" message** is *a statement in which a person describes how he or she feels by using the pronoun "I."* As shown in **Figure 10.2,** using "I" messages can help you communicate your feelings positively, without blame or name-calling. Blaming and name-calling always put people on the defensive because they feel that they are being attacked.

Listening Skills

Speaking is an important communication skill, but listening is equally important. You can make use of **active listening**, *paying close attention to what someone is saying and communicating,* to improve your communication skills. Active listening involves giving your full attention to whatever the speaker is saying without interrupting or making judgments. **Figure 10.3** illustrates some ways of becoming a more active listener.

TECHNIQUES FOR ACTIVE LISTENING

Being a good listener is important to healthy relationships. When you listen to others, you show them that you care about what they have to say and how they feel. Active listeners use several techniques to show others that they are listening. These techniques include:

▶ **Reflective listening.** In reflective listening, you rephrase or summarize what the other person has said. This allows you to be sure you have understood what was intended.

▶ **Clarifying.** Clarifying involves asking the speaker what he or she thinks or how he or she feels about the situation being discussed. It also involves asking questions to help you understand more fully what is being said.

▶ **Encouraging.** You encourage the speaker when you signal that you are interested and involved. You can show your interest by nodding your head or saying "I see," "Uh-huh," or "I understand."

▶ **Empathizing.** When you have **empathy,** you are able to imagine and understand how someone else feels. Empathizing is feeling what the other person feels as you listen. For example, if a friend tells you how disappointed he was when he didn't make the baseball team, you are likely to share his disappointment. Keep in mind that sometimes empathy is not appropriate, such as when what the person is saying goes against your values.

Reading Check

Describe What are the techniques for active listening?

FIGURE **10.3**

TIPS FOR ACTIVE LISTENING

Practicing active listening skills can improve your relationships.

- Make direct eye contact.

- Use body language, such as leaning in toward the speaker, that shows you are listening and giving your full attention.

- Use signals, such as nodding, to show that you are involved and interested.

- Don't interrupt the speaker.

- Put away prejudices, images, or assumptions that you have of the other person so you can focus on what he or she is saying.

Hands-On Health ACTIVITY

Demonstrating Empathy

One way to be a good friend is to express empathy. Here are some tips:

- Maintain eye contact as you listen.
- Rephrase or summarize what the person has said.
- Avoid judging or offering advice.
- If a loss has been experienced, avoid trying to minimize the sense of loss by stating that it is not that bad.

In this activity you will role-play situations in which friends express empathy for each other.

What You'll Need

- index cards
- pen or pencil

What You'll Do

1. In groups of six, brainstorm three situations that could cause teens to feel sad. Write each one on a separate index card.
2. Your teacher will assign one situation to you and a partner in your group.
3. Practice and then role-play the situation for the class, demonstrating several different ways a friend can show empathy.

Apply and Conclude

Demonstrating empathy during happy moments is just as important as being empathetic during sad times. Make a list of situations in which you might share in a friend's joy or excitement. Explain how demonstrating empathy during these situations can strengthen your friendship.

Nonverbal Communication

Many of the messages you send to others do not involve words. Such messages involve **body language**, *nonverbal communication through gestures, facial expressions, behaviors, and posture.* You use body language when you nod or shake your head to show that you agree or disagree with something that is said. When you hold yourself in a tense posture, you silently communicate that you're feeling nervous or worried.

Nonverbal communication can be subtle, taking place at an unconscious level. For example, if you feel embarrassed or ashamed, you may look at the ground instead of at the person to whom you are speaking. If you are greatly interested in what someone is saying, you may find yourself leaning toward the speaker.

You can help send clearer messages by being aware of your body language. If your words and your body language seem to contradict each other, the person you are speaking to may be confused or unsure of what to believe.

Reading Check

Explain Why is it important to pay attention to nonverbal communication?

Eliminating Communication Barriers

Have you ever heard the saying, "A chain is only as strong as its weakest link"? The same is true of communication. If one person in a relationship has good communication skills but the other person does not, the entire communication process suffers. Sometimes a person's beliefs or attitudes can make communication difficult. Examples of obstacles to clear communication include:

▶ **Image and identity issues.** Many teens spend at least part of their teen years searching for an **identity**—a sense of who they are and their place in the world. If someone is unsure of his or her values, the uncertainty can complicate the communication process.

Health Skills Activity

Communication: Expressing Disapproval of Bullying

Walking in the school hallway, Marya and Ramone witness Matt intentionally bump into a boy walking the other way. The boy drops his books and papers.

"Hey!" Matt says rudely, "Watch where you're going!"

"Sorry," the boy apologizes, scrambling to pick up his things.

Matt places his foot on one of the boy's papers. "Looking for this?"

Ramone starts to laugh, but Marya frowns. "Matt is just having a little fun," Ramone says.

Marya shakes her head. She wonders how to let Matt know that she disapproves of his bullying.

What Would You Do?

Marya uses body language to communicate to Ramone that she disapproves of Matt's bullying behavior. Now it is important to verbally communicate this message to Matt. Use the following communication skills to role-play a dialogue between Marya and Matt that shows disapproval of his disrespectful behavior.

1. Present a clear, organized statement.
2. Use "I" statements.
3. Show appropriate body language.
4. Listen carefully.
5. Be firm and direct, but avoid being rude or insulting.

▶ **Unrealistic expectations.** Avoid imposing unrealistic expectations on your listener; this may cause the individual to become frustrated or defensive.

▶ **Lack of trust.** Good communication is built on trust between two people. If you don't trust a person—if you believe that you can't count on him or her to tell you the truth or to keep a confidence—communication is very difficult.

▶ **Prejudice.** Some individuals have a **prejudice** or *an unfair opinion or judgment of a particular group of people*. Prejudice prevents a person from having an open mind and listening to new information. To avoid developing prejudices, you can demonstrate **tolerance**, or *the ability to accept others' differences and allow them to be who they are without expressing disapproval*. Being tolerant helps you understand the differences among people and recognize the value of diversity.

▶ **Gender stereotyping.** Gender stereotyping is a type of prejudice that involves having an exaggerated or oversimplified belief about people of a certain gender. Assuming that all males like sports and that all females enjoy cooking are examples of gender stereotyping. Such assumptions make it difficult to communicate effectively.

Accept constructive feedback positively. This is one way you can learn from others and improve yourself. *Give an example of how a critical statement can be turned into constructive feedback.*

Constructive Feedback

No one, not even your best friend or your teacher, is perfect. It's only realistic to be disappointed in a relationship occasionally. Imagine that you are meeting a friend to see a movie. Your friend is late, causing you to miss the beginning of the show. How would you react in this situation? Some people might resort to name-calling or placing blame. However, when someone lets you down, you may find that giving the person feedback in a more positive manner helps him or her *and* your relationship. The feedback you provide should take the form of **constructive criticism**, *nonhostile comments that point out problems and encourage improvement.*

Constructive criticism is intended to bring about positive changes. Consequently, it should not be given in an aggressive way. Verbally attacking the other person will only make things worse. It is very important to begin your discussion by using an "I" message to explain how you feel. Identifying resources for managing relationship problems can help you avoid an angry confrontation. Point out what the person is doing or has done, and suggest a better way to do it. For example, you might deal with your friend's lateness by saying in a neutral voice, "I really don't like missing the opening scene of a movie. Let's try to get here a few minutes early next time, okay?"

Acknowledgments and Compliments

How do you feel when someone thanks you for being a good friend or tells you how much he or she admires your honesty? Hearing such acknowledgments and compliments probably makes you feel good about yourself and your relationship with the person who made the comments. Expressing and receiving respect, admiration, and appreciation with grace and sincerity can help you build and maintain healthy relationships.

Acknowledgments and compliments take many forms. For example, you might tell a parent how much you enjoyed a meal that he or she prepared. You might also tell a friend that she is a good artist. Gestures such as these can strengthen relationships and help you develop and maintain a positive self-concept and high self-esteem. It shows that you do not take the relationship for granted, and it demonstrates good sportsmanship and good character.

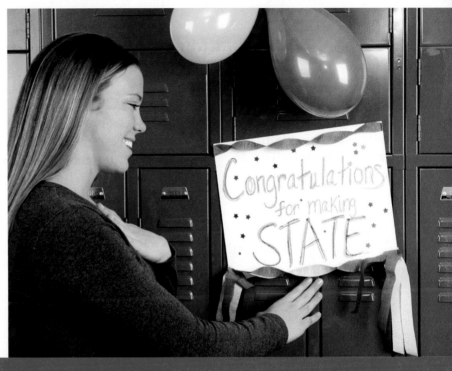

Acknowledging accomplishments is a way to show others that you care about them. *What are some other benefits of giving acknowledgments and compliments?*

LESSON 2 | REVIEW

Reviewing Facts and Vocabulary

1. Classify the three forms of communication.

2. List four ways to show that you are actively listening to another person.

3. Define the term *body language,* and give three examples of it.

Thinking Critically

4. **Evaluating.** What criteria would you apply to determine whether to use passive, aggressive, or assertive communication to resolve a conflict?

5. **Applying.** List three ways to demonstrate consideration and respect for self, family, and others through communication skills.

Applying Health Skills

Refusal Skills. In a group, develop a skit that includes both dialogue and body language. In the skit, show how teens can use refusal strategies to resist pressure to take part in an unhealthful activity.

After You Read

Compare and Contrast. Create a two-column chart listing at least three ineffective ways of stating your feelings. In the second column, list effective ways of stating your feelings.

Visit **health.glencoe.com** for the Interactive Study Guide for Lesson 2.

Lesson 2 Communicating Effectively **261**

Resolving Conflict

Guide to Reading

Building Vocabulary

As you read this lesson, write each new highlighted term and its definition in your notebook.

▶ conflict (p. 262)

▶ interpersonal conflicts (p. 262)

▶ conflict resolution (p. 264)

▶ negotiation (p. 266)

▶ mediation (p. 267)

▶ confidentiality (p. 267)

▶ peer mediators (p. 267)

Focusing on the Main Ideas

In this lesson, you will learn how to:

▶ Identify the causes of conflict.

▶ Compare the relationship between the use of refusal skills and the avoidance of unsafe situations.

▶ Explain healthful strategies for resolving conflicts and the effectiveness of conflict resolution techniques in various situations.

Reading Strategy

Explain

▶ Write each of the vocabulary terms on a sheet of paper. After each term, write a definition based on your current knowledge. After reading the lesson, review your definitions.

Quick Write

It is important to be able to resolve conflicts. What are some of the things you can do to avoid conflict?

ⓥ **Unresolved conflicts can interfere with healthy relationships.** *What communication skills can help teens deal with everyday conflicts?*

Two drivers argue over a parking space; fans of opposing soccer teams brawl in the stadium parking lot; a shoving match occurs as students wait in line in the cafeteria. All of these events have something in common—they involve conflict. **Conflict** is *any disagreement, struggle, or fight*. They often occur when one person's wants, needs, wishes, demands, expectations, or beliefs clash with those of another person.

Understanding Conflict

The types of conflicts that impact relationships are **interpersonal conflicts**. These are *disagreements between groups of any size, from two people to entire nations*. Interpersonal conflicts can begin over minor problems, such as when siblings argue over what to watch on television. They can also affect large groups of people, such as a dispute over how to spend community funds.

As you learn more about conflict, you'll understand the possible causes of conflict among youth in schools and communities. You'll also learn how you can demonstrate conflict resolution skills. A beneficial result of some conflicts is that they require people to come together to work out problems. Learning to recognize how conflict builds and knowing how to deal with conflict effectively demonstrates characteristics of a healthy decision-maker.

What Causes Conflicts?

Conflicts can begin in many ways and for many reasons. Some conflicts begin innocently, such as when one person accidentally bumps another's lunch tray. Other conflicts are the result of deliberate acts or remarks that provoke another person—for example, purposely tripping someone or making a derogatory comment. In personal relationships, conflicts can occur when one person wants to control the actions, opinions, or decisions of another person. Such conflicts may be *chronic*, or ongoing. **Figure 10.4** identifies other common causes of conflicts.

Understanding the causes of conflict in relationships may help you keep conflict from developing. If you see that a conflict is building, it is often wise to walk away. Doing so may prevent the conflict from escalating, or growing, into a situation that is unhealthful or unsafe for everyone involved.

How are internal conflicts different from interpersonal conflicts?
Internal conflicts take place within an individual. For example, if a friend's birthday party and a sibling's championship soccer game occurred on the same day, you might feel conflicted about which event to attend. Using an effective decision-making model and seeking advice from parents or other trusted adults will often help you resolve these struggles in a positive, healthful way.

FIGURE **10.4**

COMMON CAUSES OF CONFLICT

Situations such as these often lead to conflict.

Power struggles
Now that he is a teen, Terrence thinks that he, rather than his parents, should decide what time he will come home at night.

Loyalty
Manuel and Fred have always been best friends. When Fred takes Julio's side in an argument with Manuel, Manuel feels betrayed.

Jealousy/Envy
Keiko feels a little envious when she does not make the softball team but her best friend Meagan does.

Property disputes
Jan gets angry when Lisa borrows her clothes without asking permission.

Territory and space
Troy gets annoyed when his brother Sam uses Troy's room to watch television and play video games.

 Conflict often occurs over power, property, loyalty, territory, or issues of envy or jealousy. *What are some sources of conflict that you have observed?*

To communicate effectively:

▶ Talk about what is *really* troubling you.

▶ Practice being assertive. Learn to speak up for yourself and tell others how you feel.

▶ When you feel hurt or offended, use "I" messages to state your feelings clearly.

▶ Avoid keeping your feelings bottled up. Not stating your feelings can worsen the conflict.

Responding to Conflict

When a conflict arises, you have a choice: face the conflict or ignore it. As you decide which action to take, remember:

▶ Your primary concern should be your health and safety.

▶ Walking away from a potentially dangerous situation is a mature, healthful choice. It does not make you a coward. It is the smart and safe thing to do.

Minor conflicts can often be resolved by a simple compromise. If you and a sibling want to watch different television programs at the same time, for example, you might compromise by watching one program while taping the other. A compromise may be difficult to reach if the differences of opinion are strong or concern serious matters. Sometimes it can be inappropriate to compromise, such as when the compromise would go against your values or lead to harmful consequences. You must evaluate each conflict to decide whether a safe, agreeable solution can be reached or whether you should use refusal skills to avoid unsafe situations. It is often helpful to seek the advice of a parent, guardian, teacher, or other trusted adult.

Conflict Resolution

Learning strategies for solving interpersonal conflicts without harming yourself and others will prepare you for various situations. Part of conflict resolution is learning to analyze problems stemming from unhealthy relationships. **Conflict resolution** is *the process of solving a disagreement in a manner that satisfies everyone involved.* **Figure 10.5** shows some strategies for resolving conflicts peacefully.

Reading Check

Explain How should you respond to a conflict?

FIGURE 10.5

STRATEGIES FOR RESOLVING CONFLICTS

1. Take time to calm down and think over the situation.

2. When discussing the conflict, take turns explaining each person's side of the conflict without interruption. Use "I" messages.

3. Ask for clarification so that each person understands the other's position.

4. Brainstorm solutions.

5. Agree on a solution that benefits both sides.

6. Follow up to see whether the correct solution was chosen and whether that solution worked for each person.

Respect for Oneself and Others

To resolve a conflict fairly and effectively, you must show respect for yourself and others. Having respect for yourself means that you recognize that you have a right to your own opinions and values. When you respect yourself, you can stand up for your beliefs. When you respect others, you can listen to them with an open mind, consider their thoughts and feelings, and honor their values.

The views and ideals of others may be different from your own. Even though you may not agree, you can demonstrate respect and tolerance. When you are tolerant of different viewpoints or ideas, fewer conflicts arise. Therefore, tolerance is crucial to preventing conflict and promoting peace.

Resilient TEENS

After his parents divorced, Zach Adair and his mother moved to another state. Zach fell in with what he calls "a bunch of deadbeats." "Fortunately, Mom realized what was happening and made me talk to a counselor," he says.

Zach's situation was made even more difficult by the bullying he was facing at his new school. "They would wait at the bus stop after school and jump me," he says. "I felt like a loner then, like no one was on my side."

Since then, Zach has not only made friends but also learned to enjoy sports like golf and basketball. He has also begun working for his family's publishing firm, handling orders and dealing with customers. "I know some kids deal with stress by joining clubs and trying to help others," he says. "But I'm not the joining or advice-giving type. Mostly, I try to focus on school and being the best that I can be."

"Mostly, I try to focus on school and being the best that I can be."

Reading Check

Explain What feeling caused the greatest problem for Zach after his parents' divorce?

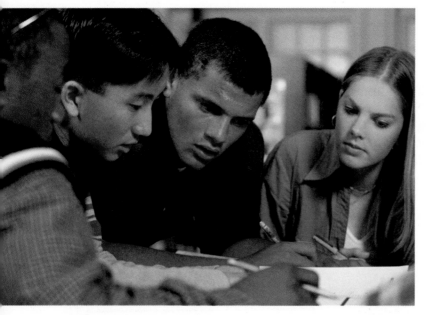

Negotiating During Conflict Resolution

Even if people demonstrate respect and tolerance, they may find it difficult to resolve their conflict. It is then necessary to try **negotiation**, *the use of communication and often compromise to settle a disagreement.* The negotiation process involves talking, listening, considering the other person's point of view, compromising if necessary, and devising a plan for working jointly to resolve the conflict.

PREPARING FOR NEGOTIATION

To prepare yourself for a successful negotiation process, keep the following points in mind:

▶ Make sure the issue is important to you.

▶ Check your facts. Make sure the disagreement is not based on incorrect information.

▶ Remind yourself that your goal is to find a solution, not to fight or prove who is "in control."

▶ Rehearse what you will say, even if you have to script it out in advance.

STEPS TO TAKE WHEN NEGOTIATING

You can become a better negotiator through practice. Follow these steps to negotiate effectively.

▶ **Select a time and place suited to working out problems.** Arrange to meet when you are calm, not impatient or rushed. Choose a quiet meeting place.

▶ **Work together toward a solution.** Do not approach the other person as an enemy. Instead, work together to reach a solution.

▶ **Keep an open mind.** Remember that there are two sides to every story. Listen carefully to what the other person has to say.

▶ **Be flexible.** Be willing to meet the other person halfway.

▶ **Take responsibility for your role in the conflict.** Apologize if you know that you have hurt the other person.

▶ **Give the other person an "out."** If the other person seems embarrassed or uncomfortable, suggest continuing the conversation at a later time.

Ⓐ **Successful negotiation requires the two parties involved to work together to find a satisfactory solution.** *How did you use negotiation to resolve a recent conflict?*

Describe What are the conflict negotiation steps?

The Mediation Process

Even with negotiation, it's not always possible for two parties in conflict to reach an agreement. When this happens, it may be time for **mediation**, *a process in which specially trained people help others resolve their conflicts peacefully.*

Mediation sessions take place in a neutral location. During the mediation process, the mediator maintains strict **confidentiality**. This involves *respecting the privacy of both parties and keeping details secret*. The process has well-defined ground rules that are set by the mediator and explained to both sides. The mediator begins by asking each person to describe the disagreement. The mediator then summarizes each side, asking for clarification of any points that are inaccurate. Each side is then given the opportunity to talk to the other under the supervision of the mediator. The mediator may then ask the parties to sign an agreement to work out the problem within a certain time frame.

Today, many schools offer peer mediation programs for settling conflicts that take place at school. These programs have **peer mediators**, *students trained to help other students find fair resolutions to conflicts and disagreements*. You will learn more about peer mediation programs in Chapter 13.

Peer mediation is often effective in settling disputes and resolving conflicts. *What qualities would an effective peer mediator have?*

LESSON 3 REVIEW

Reviewing Facts and Vocabulary

1. What is an *interpersonal conflict?* What are some causes of interpersonal conflicts?

2. What are the benefits of walking away from a situation when a conflict is building?

3. What are some healthful ways of resolving conflicts?

Thinking Critically

4. **Synthesizing.** Conflicts are not always negative. Describe a situation in which a conflict can be positive. Explain why the conflict is positive.

5. **Analyzing.** Describe a conflict you have had with another person. Explain how you resolved the conflict, and evaluate the effectiveness of your conflict-resolution techniques.

Applying Health Skills

Conflict Resolution. Luke wants to go to a basketball game with his friends this Saturday, but his parents want him to attend the family picnic. Write a skit in which Luke and his parents use conflict resolution techniques to solve their problem.

After You Read

Problems and Solutions. Create a chart with four sections. In the two top sections, list the causes of conflict on the left and strategies for resolving conflicts on the right. In the bottom sections, list the steps of the negotiating process on the left and the mediation process on the right.

Visit **health.glencoe.com** for the Interactive Study Guide for Lesson 3.

Lesson 3 Resolving Conflict **267**

Friends Matter

What's the key to escaping each of these three confining labels? A friend.

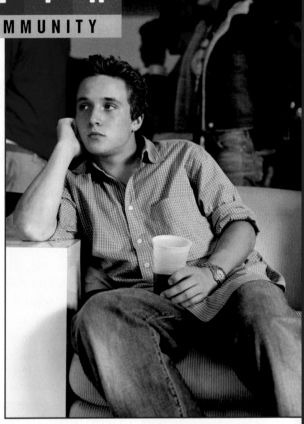

Wallflowers "If a teen is feeling shy or like a wallflower, making a connection with just one other person can help," says teen-education expert Nan Hunter. "Friendship can help bring people out of their shells."

How can a shy teen make these connections? Says Hunter, "If you're interested in science and you feel like everyone else is interested in sports, consider taking a class at the local museum or investigate your school's science clubs." The friend that you discover in a club or class can make the difference between feeling isolated and feeling connected to someone.

Bullies Teen bullies have an even tougher time making friends than do wallflowers. "Some kids have so much energy that they act without thinking," says Hunter. "Most don't actually want to hurt people."

Some teen bullies do want to hurt, however, because they have been hurt, or feel they have been. Many bullies misinterpret other people's behavior. They see aggression where none exists. Their response: revenge.

How can a bully reform? It takes time, warns Hunter: "Bullies hurt people, so naturally they don't have a lot of friends." Bullies must work on

dealing with conflicts when they occur and on strategies to calm inner feelings of anger. They have to learn to apologize and realize that bullying of any kind cannot be tolerated. Only then can bullies make true friendship connections.

Victims "Try to become part of a social network," advises SuEllen Fried, co-author of *Bullies & Victims*. "That way, friends will stand up for you." Victims should alert their parents, teachers, and counselors to what they're going through. ▪

TIME to THINK... | About Friends

Imagine that a new student at your school is looking for ways to meet people. Brainstorm with the class ten possible ways to make new friends. Create a pamphlet called "Top 10 Ways to Meet New Friends." Include any advice or ideas that you think would be helpful to the new student.

1. Analyzing Influences. Think about a relationship you have with a family member or a friend. Evaluate and describe the positive and negative effects of this relationship on each side of your health triangle. *(LESSON 1)*

2. Communication Skills. Imagine that you have a friend who frequently borrows things and returns them in poor condition. Explain how you could use constructive criticism to help the person change this pattern of behavior. *(LESSON 2)*

3. Advocacy. Write a persuasive letter to the principal of your school to advocate the use of peer mediators. In your letter, explain why peer mediation is important. Describe the steps involved in this process and the types of situations in which it might be used. *(LESSON 3)*

Professional Mediator

Are you a good listener? Are you the person in your group of friends who most often helps the others reach a compromise? These skills may indicate that you are suited to a career as a professional mediator. Professional mediators often work for corporations, schools, or government agencies. They help others work together to settle disputes peacefully.

To become a professional mediator, you'll need to attend a four-year college and receive training in mediation. You can find out more about this and other health-related careers by clicking on Career Corner at **health.glencoe.com.**

Parent Involvement

Advocacy. Learn more about community media- tion programs. With your parents, find out how your family can become involved in raising awareness about the existence and useful- ness of such programs in your community. If media- tion programs do not already exist in your community, learn how you can help create one.

School and Community

Overcoming Prejudice. Speak with a law enforcement official in your community who has helped victims of hate crimes—offenses against an individual or group that are a direct or indirect result of prejudice. Ask the official what communication skills a person would need to help victims of hate crimes. Report to your class what you have learned.

After You Read

Review the information you have recorded in your Foldable about building and maintaining healthy relationships. On the back of your Foldable, describe your character and explain how it influences your relationships with other students.

FOLDABLES™
Study Organizer

► EXPLORING HEALTH TERMS *Answer the following questions on a sheet of paper.*

Lesson 1 *Match each definition with the correct term.*

cooperation	citizenship
compromise	role
friendship	relationship
communication	

1. A significant relationship between two people based on caring, trust, and consideration.
2. A part you play in a relationship.
3. The ways in which you send and receive messages.
4. A process of working together for the good of all.

Lesson 2 *Fill in the blanks with the correct term.*

body language	constructive criticism
tolerance	"I" messages
active listening	prejudice

Tara is annoyed because Liz is late. To avoid placing blame, she uses (_5_) to let Liz know how she feels. Liz shows she is listening to Tara by using appropriate (_6_), such as nodding her head. Using (_7_) skills helps Liz understand why Tara is upset, and she apologizes for being late.

Lesson 3 *Replace the underlined words with the correct term.*

negotiation	peer mediators
conflict resolution	interpersonal conflict
mediation	confidentiality
conflict	

8. Any disagreement or struggle is a <u>negotiation</u>.
9. Negotiation and mediation are two processes used for <u>interpersonal conflict</u>.
10. Mediators must demonstrate <u>conflict</u>, respect for the rights and privacy of others.

► RECALLING THE FACTS *Use complete sentences to answer the following questions.*

1. Name three roles you play in your relationships with others. Explain when you play each role.
2. How can compromise help strengthen a relationship?
3. What are some ways you can demonstrate the character trait of responsibility?
4. How do you know when you are communicating effectively?
5. What is reflective listening?
6. How does prejudice set up a barrier to effective communication?
7. List the strategies for conflict resolution.
8. What two things should you consider when deciding how to respond to conflict?
9. Define negotiation.
10. When might it be necessary to have a mediator help settle a conflict?

270 **Chapter 10** Review

For more review questions for Chapter 10, go to **health.glencoe.com**.

➤ WRITING CRITICALLY

1. **Descriptive.** Write a one-page description of this friend who provides a positive influence. Describe his or her character traits that promote a healthy and positive relationship. What makes him or her a good friend? Remember to use specific examples to support your statements.

2. **Persuasive.** Tolerance involves keeping an open mind to new information, ideas, and other people's points of view. To gain an understanding for another point of view, write a debate, choosing the opposing side of the following question that you agree with:

   Which relationship has a greater influence on a teen's life, family or friendships?

   Make sure that your debate supports your answer with logical reasons and supporting examples.

Standardized Test Practice

 Read the passage below and then answer the questions.

Do Personalities Change?

According to most estimates, more adults and teenagers describe themselves as *extroverts,* people who are more interested in the world around them, than as reflective and quiet *introverts.* Do you consider yourself an extrovert or an introvert? Are you lively and outgoing? Do you find yourself the center of attention at most social events? Or, would you describe yourself as quiet and thoughtful?

Now that you've thought about your personality for a moment, consider whether your personality has changed as you've aged. Some researchers believe that the type of personality a person develops at a young age stays with that person for life. Others disagree, arguing that events or maturity may change one's personality or add to it in a significant way.

What do you think?

1. Which phrase in the first paragraph helps you understand the meaning of the word *extrovert*?

   A according to most estimates
   B not interested in personalities
   C more interested in the world around them
   D the center of attention at most social events

2. The author develops the first paragraph by

   F comparing two types of personalities.
   G making a judgment about personality types.
   H analyzing the consequences of personality types.
   I describing the two types of personalities at a party.

3. Write a paragraph describing your own personality as an extrovert, an introvert, or a combination of the two. Include specific examples of words and actions that support your description, and tell why you think events or maturity in general may or may not change people's personalities later in life.

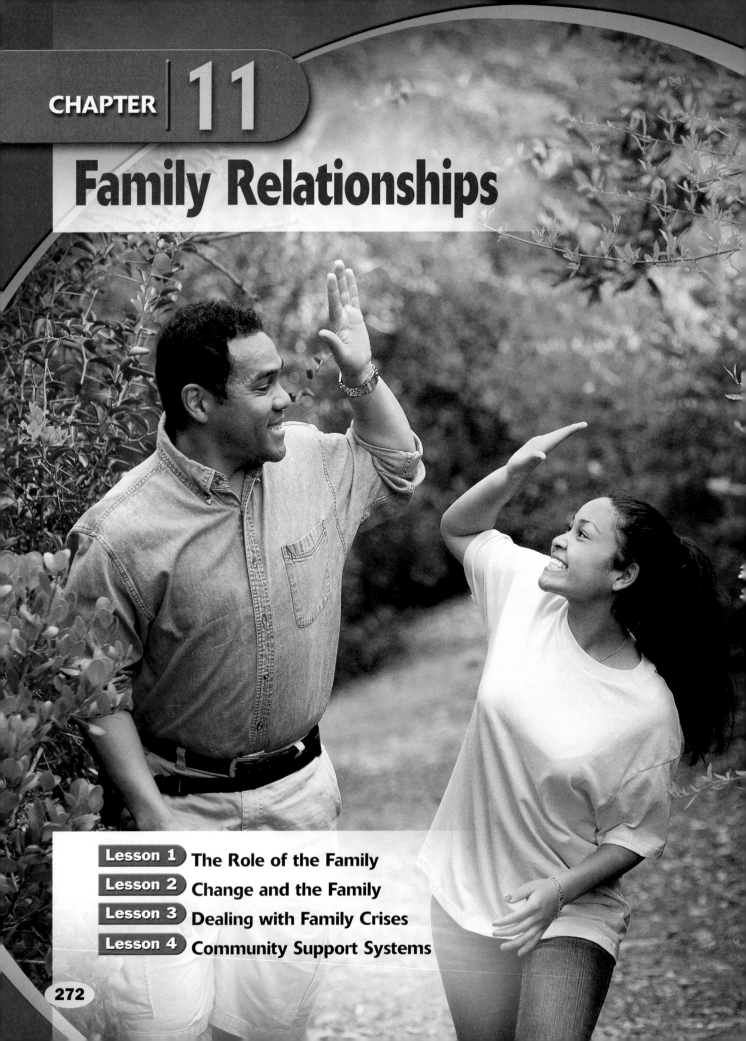

CHAPTER **11**

Family Relationships

Lesson 1 **The Role of the Family**
Lesson 2 **Change and the Family**
Lesson 3 **Dealing with Family Crises**
Lesson 4 **Community Support Systems**

Eye ON THE Media   Family Dramas

The media often explores the issue of family dynamics in film and on television. Some portrayals may show how families deal with

► **violence.**

► **loss.**

► **divorce.**

► **rebellious children.**

Visit the Eye on the Media section at **health.glencoe.com** to learn more about how to analyze how books and movies cover family issues.

FOLDABLES™
Study Organizer

Before You Read

Use this Foldable to help you record and organize the main ideas in this chapter on family relationships. Begin with a sheet of 8½″ x 11″ paper.

► **Step 1**

Line up one of the short edges of the sheet of paper with one of the long edges and fold. Cut off the leftover rectangle.

► **Step 2**

Fold the triangle in half. Unfold.

► **Step 3**

Cut up one fold line and stop at the middle. This will form two triangular flaps. Draw an X on one tab. Label the other tabs as shown.

As You Read

As you read and discuss the material in the chapter, use your Foldable to take notes, write definitions, and record main ideas on the back of each of the appropriate sides of the pyramid.

► **Step 4**

Fold the X flap under the other flap and glue together.

SPOTLIGHT ON HEALTH

Using Visuals. What do you and other family members do to promote the health and well-being of the entire family?

The Role of the Family

Guide to Reading

Building Vocabulary

As you read this lesson, write each new highlighted term and its definition in your notebook.

▶ family (p. 274)

▶ extended family (p. 277)

▶ sibling (p. 278)

▶ affirmation (p. 278)

Focusing on the Main Ideas

In this lesson, you will learn how to:

▶ Describe the effects of family relationships on physical, mental/emotional, and social health.

▶ Connect the roles of parents, grandparents, and other family members in promoting a healthy family.

▶ Relate family roles and responsibilities to healthy behavior.

Reading Strategy

Classify

▶ Draw a triangle. Label each side with one of the following Physical, Mental/Emotional, and Social Health. As you read, record the main ideas on the appropriate sides of the triangle.

Write a brief paragraph describing some of the ways you interact with, and support your family.

How would you describe your family? How has your family influenced your behaviors and goals? In what ways have family members contributed to your sense of security and belonging? Because the family plays an important part in all aspects of a person's health, it's important to learn about family dynamics and ways of promoting a healthy family.

Explain What is a healthy family?

What Is a Family?

The **family**, *the basic unit of society*, provides a safe and nurturing environment for its members. Because the health of society is directly related to the health of the family, promoting healthy families contributes to a healthy society.

A healthy family freely expresses mutual love and respect. Its members communicate effectively with one another, providing support and encouragement. Through caring family relationships, teens develop the values and self-confidence that help them make responsible decisions and work to achieve their goals. In addition, a strong family foundation can serve as an important **protective factor,** helping children and teens to avoid risky behaviors.

Take the Health Inventory for Chapter 11 at **health.glencoe.com**.

The Importance of Family

Although families differ in size and makeup, a healthy family strives to promote the physical, mental/emotional, and social health of its members. Some of the ways in which the family meets these needs are shown in **Figure 11.1.**

Meeting Physical and Other Basic Needs

Most parents and guardians work hard to provide for their family's basic physical needs, including food, clothing, and shelter. Adult family members also make certain that children get medical and dental checkups, receive immunizations, and learn to practice healthful behaviors. The family is responsible for teaching children the skills needed to live safely in their environment. For example, children need to be taught how to cross streets safely and not to get into a car with a stranger. As they grow and mature, children learn more life skills from older members of the family. These skills may include strategies for improving or maintaining personal, family, and community health.

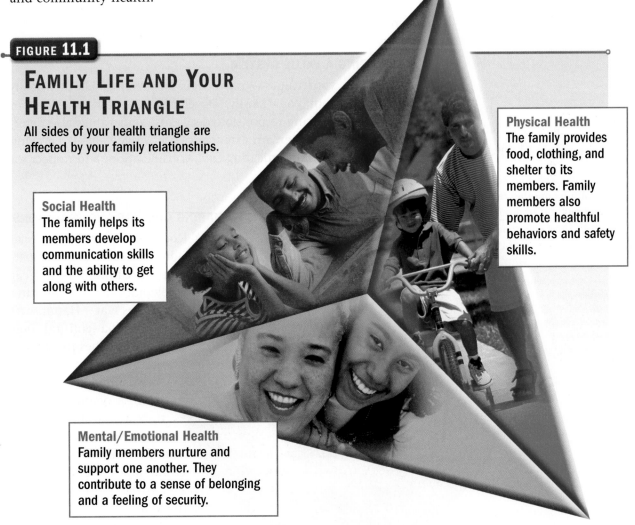

FIGURE 11.1

FAMILY LIFE AND YOUR HEALTH TRIANGLE

All sides of your health triangle are affected by your family relationships.

Social Health
The family helps its members develop communication skills and the ability to get along with others.

Physical Health
The family provides food, clothing, and shelter to its members. Family members also promote healthful behaviors and safety skills.

Mental/Emotional Health
Family members nurture and support one another. They contribute to a sense of belonging and a feeling of security.

Meeting Mental/Emotional Needs

The family provides a safe, comforting environment in which all members can express thoughts and emotions freely. For example, through your family, you will begin to understand the various ways in which different families handle grief. By providing emotional support and unconditional love, families promote positive self-concepts in their members. A positive self-concept, the view a person has of himself or herself, gives individuals a sense of confidence, helping them become healthy, happy adults.

Meeting Social Needs

In the first few years of life, children learn from family members how to communicate and get along with others. Families also play a major role in children's social growth by helping them develop a value system, by instilling religious beliefs, and by raising them with cultural and family traditions. A healthy family helps children become team players and teaches them to accept differences in others. Families prepare their members to survive and function independently in the world.

DEVELOPING A VALUE SYSTEM

You learn your values—your beliefs and feelings about what is important—from your family. Developing a good value system helps you in making responsible decisions. Your values also determine your **character.** An example of a positive value is knowing techniques for communicating care, consideration, and respect for yourself and others.

Reading Check

Describe How do healthy families help keep your health triangle in balance?

➤ **Families enhance social health by passing family and cultural traditions on to their children.**
What are some of your family's traditions?

SHARING CULTURE AND TRADITIONS

Does your family have special traditions, such as participating in Chinese New Year celebrations or lighting candles at Hanukkah? Sharing a cultural heritage enriches the lives of family members and helps individuals develop a sense of pride in who they are. By observing traditions such as these, adult family members show how ethnic and cultural diversity both enrich and challenge healthy living.

Dynamics of Family Roles and Responsibilities

Your family is more than just the people who live in your home. It also includes your **extended family**, that is, *your immediate family and other relatives such as grandparents, aunts, uncles, and cousins.* What are some of the benefits that you enjoy from your extended family? Have you learned about your family's history from a grandparent or vacationed with cousins who live in another part of the country? Perhaps an aunt or an uncle has helped you during times of need or has acted as your mentor. Each family member, including parents, grandparents, or other family members, has roles and responsibilities in promoting a healthy family. The adults are usually in charge of providing basic comforts and fulfilling basic needs such as food and shelter. They also set limits and make rules that protect the health and safety of their children.

A Family members can spend quality time together by sharing knowledge and interests. *What are some ways you spend time with your extended family?*

Hands-On Health ACTIVITY

Making Time for Family Fun

Busy schedules can make it difficult for family members to spend quality time together, but it is important to make time to strengthen family relationships. In this activity, you will develop a plan to spend more quality time with your family.

What You'll Need

- paper and markers
- ruler

What You'll Do

1. Brainstorm a list of activities you and your family enjoy doing together. Examples might include weekend outings or trips, recreational activities, family game night, and roundtable discussions.

2. Consider other ways you can strengthen family relationships. You might suggest projects such as putting together a memory album or starting a new family tradition like pizza night every Wednesday.

3. Using your ideas, create a chart of strategies that promote the physical, mental/emotional, and social health of family members.

Apply and Conclude

Show your chart to family members, and discuss how spending quality time together promotes healthy family relationships. Ask them for other suggestions, and then put your ideas into action.

Children and teens have roles and responsibilities in the household that relate to health behavior. They respect the authority of parents or guardians and may take on tasks such as washing dishes or cleaning. Teens may be asked to care for a younger **sibling**—*a brother or sister*—while a parent is at work. Sharing such tasks helps the family run smoothly. It also helps boost your self-esteem and gives you a greater sense of responsibility.

Strengthening Family Relationships

Good communication is one of the most important ways to build and maintain healthy family relationships. Sharing thoughts, feelings, experiences, and concerns helps strengthen family bonds. You can help strengthen your family in the following ways.

▶ **Demonstrate care and love.** Family members show that they care about and love one another through words and actions. You can give affirmation for a job well done, for example, through a compliment or a pat on the back. **Affirmation** is *positive feedback that helps others feel appreciated and supported.* You can also show empathy for a family member who is feeling down to remind that person that he or she is loved.

▶ **Show support, especially during difficult times.** Whether the difficulty is something minor (such as getting a low grade on a quiz) or a traumatic experience (such as a death in the family), talking about your feelings can help you feel better. Remember to be a good listener when others want to talk.

▶ **Demonstrate trust.** Members of a healthy family trust one another. Parents earn their children's trust by caring for them, being honest, and keeping promises. Children show that they can be trusted when they are honest, reliable, and loyal.

▶ **Express commitment.** Building a strong, healthy family requires commitment—the willingness to work together and make necessary sacrifices for the benefit of the entire family.

▶ **Be responsible.** Thinking before you act, avoiding risky behaviors, asking for permission, and being accountable for your actions demonstrate respect for yourself and family members.

Affirming family members' achievements demonstrates love and pride.
How do you show family members that they are appreciated and supported?

▶ **Spend time together.** Eating meals together, playing games or sports, and planning fun activities and trips all contribute to strong family relationships.

▶ **Respect individuality.** Strong families have respect for each other. They accept individual tastes, talents, and opinions.

▶ **Work together to solve problems.** Healthy families try to identify and work out problems before they become serious. If necessary, they seek outside help to resolve their conflicts. Working together can also mean planning events together, such as having a surprise party, choosing a pet, or going on vacation.

▶ **Be sensitive to others' needs.** Pay attention to how others feel. You can help relieve the stress of daily life by using good communication skills and helping with household tasks. Respecting the privacy of others is also a way to demonstrate sensitivity.

Spending time with family members strengthens your relationships. *What are some other ways to promote the health of your family?*

LESSON 1 REVIEW

Reviewing Facts and Vocabulary

1. List two ways that families help their members develop social health.
2. What is an *extended family*?
3. Why is it important for family members to give affirmation to one another?

Thinking Critically

4. **Analyzing.** Explain how family roles and responsibilities influence health behaviors.
5. **Synthesizing.** Identify three traits of a healthy family. Describe the roles your immediate and extended family members play in promoting the health of your family.

Applying Health Skills

Communication Skills. Work with classmates to list ways families can improve communication. Include the elements of effective communication, such as "I" messages, active listening, and appropriate body language. Write and perform a skit to demonstrate your ideas.

After You Read

Cause and Effect. List two or three ways that your family helps you meet your physical and/or emotional needs. Explain how your family helps you.

Visit **health.glencoe.com** for the Interactive Study Guide for Lesson 1.

Lesson 1 The Role of the Family **279**

Change and the Family

Guide to Reading

Building Vocabulary

As you read this lesson, write each new highlighted term and its definition in your notebook.

▶ separation (p. 281)

▶ divorce (p. 281)

▶ custody (p. 281)

▶ grief (p. 282)

▶ resiliency (p. 285)

Focusing on the Main Ideas

In this lesson, you will learn how to:

▶ Examine the effects of family relationships on physical and emotional health.

▶ Predict the ways family events can impact health.

▶ Describe issues related to death and grieving.

▶ Analyze the causes and effects of stress within families and ways to manage stress.

Reading Strategy

Predict

▶ After scanning the headings, subheadings, and pictures, write a summary describing what information you think you'll learn in this lesson.

 Quick Write

Make a list of some of situations that might cause stress in a family.

Some family events, such as moving to a new home, can be stressful. *What are some healthy ways to deal with the stress of moving?*

M inor problems and irritations are normal when people are living together. Usually, good communication and problem-solving skills can help family members work out such conflicts. Significant changes in family relationships, however, can have negative effects on the health of a family. It is important that all family members develop coping skills and know strategies for managing stress.

Families and Change

Change, a normal part of life, can be a major cause of stress within families. The sudden loss of a job, for example, may cause a financial hardship, making it difficult to provide food, clothing, and other basic physical needs. Serious or chronic illness in a family member can result in long-term stress for the whole family. Life events perceived as positive can also cause stress. For example, buying a new car, moving, or the marriage of an older sibling are positive events that may cause stress.

The changes that cause stress in families are of two main types. The first type involves changes in the structure, or makeup, of the family. The second involves changes in the family's circumstances.

Changes in Family Structure

Family structure changes when someone new joins the family or when a member of the family moves out of the home. A new family member brings a new personality that may change the character of the family. As a health-literate teen, you should learn to associate behaviors with personal, family, and cultural values. Some changes may be joyful, such as the birth or adoption of a child. Other changes may be sorrowful, such as the breakup of a marriage or the death of a family member. Losing a family member can mean losing the love and care he or she provided, as well as shared experiences. Whatever the nature, any change in the family requires that members know strategies for maintaining personal, family, and community health.

Separation and Divorce

Marriage is an agreement between two people to commit to sharing life's joys, struggles, and challenges. Usually, married couples find ways to work out their problems. However, if conflicts become too difficult to work out, the couple may decide to separate or divorce. A **separation** is *a decision between married individuals to live apart from each other.* A couple may separate until they resolve their differences and believe that they can live together again. If they can't work out their problems, the couple may decide to divorce. A **divorce** is *a legal end to a marriage contract.* Separation or divorce occurs because the two adults in the relationship are unable to resolve their problems. A separation or divorce is not the fault of the children.

MEETING THE NEEDS OF CHILDREN

When parents divorce, it must be decided where the children will live. **Custody** is *a legal decision about who has the right to make decisions affecting the children in a family and who has the responsibility of physically caring for them.* Custody may be granted to only one parent (sole custody) or divided so that both parents share in the child-rearing (joint custody).

FAMILY ADJUSTMENTS

Adapting to divorce requires emotional adjustments for the whole family. Teens and children often find it difficult to live apart from one parent and not see that parent for long periods of time. Some may experience some of the stages of grief, including denial or numbness; anger (at one or both parents); bargaining; depression; and finally, acceptance.

Did You Know ?

Family structure has become more diverse in past decades. Some teens live with only one parent, and others live with a grandparent or other family member. In blended families, teens live with stepparents, stepbrothers, and stepsisters. There are also many teens who live with adoptive families. In fact, more than 100,000 children are adopted in the United States each year. Belonging to different family structures may cause difficult feelings in some teens. In these situations, it is helpful to discuss feelings and concerns with family members.

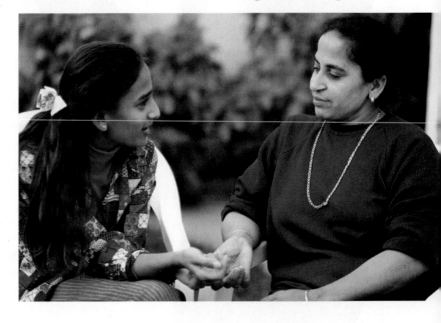

Separation and divorce can put a strain on the family unit. *What can family members do to support one another through such a change?*

Keep in mind that parents divorce each other, not their children. Although the feelings that divorced parents have for each other change, their love for their children can stay the same. Below are some suggestions for managing emotional stress when parents get divorced.

▶ Remind yourself that you did not cause the problem.

▶ Do not feel that you have to choose sides.

▶ Communicate your feelings about the divorce with your parents and other trusted, supportive adults.

▶ Take care of yourself by eating nutritious foods, getting physical activity, and managing your stress.

▶ Consider joining a support group for children of divorce. Doing so will help you realize that you are not alone.

Remarriage

The remarriage of a parent can also be stressful. Stepparents and children need time to adjust to one another. If the stepparent has children from a previous marriage, everyone in the blended family needs time to adjust to the change and to develop the communication skills and respect needed for healthful family relationships.

Death of a Family Member

A death in the family can cause intense feelings of **grief**, *the sorrow caused by the loss of a loved one*. When a death occurs, each family member needs time to grieve, but the length of time needed for grieving is different for each person. Here are some strategies for coping with the death of a loved one and related issues of grieving.

▶ **Focus on happy memories.** Remember good times and the qualities that made the person special.

▶ **Accept your feelings.** It's normal to feel hurt when you lose someone. Don't try to deny your pain.

▶ **Join a support group.** Grief support groups allow people who have suffered a loss to share their pain with others. Local religious institutions or other organizations may sponsor these groups.

▶ **Seek help from a grief counselor.** If feelings of grief interfere with a person's life for an extended period of time, it is necessary to seek professional help.

Ⓥ **Grief is a natural emotion when you lose someone you love.** *What might be a healthy way for this teen to deal with the loss of her loved one?*

Changes in Family Circumstances

Changes in circumstances can also cause difficulties for families. Often, honest and open communication can help families deal with such changes in healthful ways.

Moving

When a family moves, its members may miss their old friends and the familiar surroundings of their old home. Teens may be anxious about making new friends and adjusting to a new school. If a move follows the breakup of a marriage, children may miss the parent who no longer lives with them.

Financial Problems

Meeting a family's financial needs is not easy. Loss of a job, medical emergencies, and overdue bills can cause anxiety about how to support family needs. Impulse buying or poor planning may also cause financial problems. *Credit card abuse,* the overuse of credit cards, can be a serious problem for those who pay the bills, and it often leads to arguments about spending habits.

Illness and Disability

A serious illness or disability can disrupt a family's normal activities. One or more family members may need to change their schedules to care for the sick or disabled person. In addition to worry and concern for the person who is ill, family members may also experience the stress of making major medical decisions about types of care or treatments. Some of this stress can be relieved if all members of the family share in the responsibility of caring for the person who is sick or disabled.

Drug and Alcohol Abuse

Substance abuse within the family threatens the health of the entire family. Without intervention and outside help, this problem can cause the family system to break down. If a family member has a substance abuse problem, seek immediate help from trusted adults, school personnel, or organizations such as Alateen. These resources can help you understand the problem and guide you in getting additional assistance.

When a family member becomes ill or disabled, the rest of the family assumes responsibility for his or her care. *What are some ways that teens can help in the care of a family member who is ill or disabled?*

CHARACTER CHECK

Caring. When you seek help for a problem that affects the health of the family, you are demonstrating caring. **Make a list of people you think you could approach for assistance if a family member has a substance abuse problem.**

Health Skills Activity

Communication: That's What Friends Are For

"Are you okay?" Craig asked his friend Robert after school one day. "You seem down."

Robert hesitated before admitting, "My parents have decided to get a divorce. My dad's going to move across town soon. One of these days, I know that they're going to ask me who I want to live with. I feel close to both my mom and dad, and I don't want to have to choose sides. Everything is changing. I want to talk to my parents about my feelings and worries, but I'm afraid I'll add to their problems."

What Would You Do?

How would you respond if you were Craig? Finish the rest of this dialogue, incorporating effective communication skills to demonstrate how Craig shows support and empathy.

1. Listen attentively.
2. Use "I" statements.
3. Speak in a respectful tone of voice.
4. Display appropriate body language.

Reading Check

Explain What are some strategies for coping with family changes?

Coping with Family Changes

It is important to manage the stress caused by family changes. In some cases, this may be as simple as communicating your needs and wants to a family member. Talking with family members can often reduce the stress. If a parent is unavailable, find another adult who can help, such as a teacher, guidance counselor, member of the clergy, or a member of your extended family. Additional strategies for communicating effectively with family, friends, and others include the following:

▶ **Do what you can to help.** For example, if your parents are feeling stressed, you might be able to reduce their burden by taking on added chores and responsibilities.

▶ **Read books about the subject or talk to people who have faced a similar problem.** You may find strategies for managing the problem.

▶ **Use stress-management techniques.** Engage in physical activity, get adequate sleep, eat nutritious meals, and find a way to relax, such as listening to soothing music.

Resiliency Within the Family

Resiliency is an important trait of a healthy family. **Resiliency** is *the ability to adapt effectively and recover from disappointment, difficulty, or crisis.* Resilient people can call upon their own strengths to deal with changes. Resilient families pull together to cope with changing circumstances. Keeping a family healthy takes planning, compromise, and effort. When problems occur, family members must identify the problem, evaluate how the problem is affecting the entire family, discuss what can be done to handle the problem, and draw upon family unity and strength to resolve the problem together. If the family cannot resolve problems on their own in a healthful way, resources to which families can turn for help are available. You will learn more about these resources in Lesson 4.

 Resilient families work through problems and difficulties while maintaining strong, healthy relationships. *What are some ways you can cope with stress during times of family difficulties?*

LESSON 2 REVIEW

Reviewing Facts and Vocabulary

1. What are the two main types of stress that affect families?

2. What is *grief*?

3. What is *resiliency*?

Thinking Critically

4. **Applying.** Causes of stress may be positive or negative in nature. Give examples of a positive event and a negative event that have caused stress within your family. Explain how you handled this stress.

5. **Synthesizing.** Why might children whose parents have recently divorced experience the stages of grief? How might a young child express these feelings?

Applying Health Skills

Stress Management. All families face changes that result in stress. Imagine a change in your family that would cause you or other family members significant stress. Make a list of stress-management techniques you would employ in such a situation.

After You Read

Cause and Effect. Change can be a major cause of stress in a family. Create a T chart. On one side, list some ways that a family's structure may change. On the other side, list some of the ways families cope with these changes.

 Visit **health.glencoe.com** for the Interactive Study Guide for Lesson 2.

Lesson 2 Change and the Family **285**

Dealing with Family Crises

Guide to Reading

Building Vocabulary

As you read this lesson, write each new highlighted term and its definition in your notebook.

▶ domestic violence (p. 286)
▶ emotional abuse (p. 287)
▶ physical abuse (p. 287)
▶ sexual abuse (p. 287)
▶ spousal abuse (p. 287)
▶ child abuse (p. 288)
▶ neglect (p. 288)
▶ cycle of violence (p. 289)

Focusing on the Main Ideas

In this lesson, you will learn how to:

▶ Identify health strategies that prevent emotional, physical, and sexual abuse.
▶ Develop strategies for avoiding violence within the family.
▶ Outline ways to break the cycle of violence.

Reading Strategy

Explain

▶ List each of the vocabulary terms on a sheet of paper. After each term write a definition based on your current knowledge. After reading the lesson, review your definitions.

Make a list of what you think a family might do to deal with abuse or violence.

Striking out at others and destroying property are unhealthful ways to deal with conflict. *What are some healthful strategies for resolving conflict?*

Some families experience problems that can interfere with the normal, healthy conduct of family life. It may be a teen getting into trouble at school, a parent losing a job, or a disagreement over household rules. Most problems are resolved through effective communication and conflict resolution. However, sometimes negative and even dangerous situations may develop in families. It is critical to know strategies for solving interpersonal conflicts without harming yourself and others, and to deal with unhealthy cycles of family behavior.

Family Violence

When conflict occurs and family members react in out-of-control ways, violence may result. Violence can be emotional, physical, or sexual in nature. **Domestic violence**, *any act of violence involving family members,* is a criminal act that can be prosecuted by law.

All types of domestic violence involve abuse. Abuse includes any mistreatment of one person by another. The main forms of abuse in the home include the following:

Take the Health Inventory for Chapter 11 at **health.glencoe.com**.

► **Emotional abuse** is *a pattern of behavior that attacks the emotional development and sense of worth of an individual.* Yelling, bullying, name-calling, and threats of physical harm are examples of emotional abuse.

► **Physical abuse** is *the intentional infliction of bodily harm or injury on another person.* Slapping, punching, kicking, pinching, and throwing objects at another person are all forms of physical abuse.

► **Sexual abuse** involves *any sexual contact that is forced upon a person against his or her will.* Sexual abuse includes making unwelcome comments of a sexual nature to another person as well as actually touching the person in an unwelcome sexual way.

Spousal Abuse

Domestic violence directed at a spouse is called **spousal abuse**. Spousal abuse may occur in all kinds of families, regardless of education level, income, or ethnicity. Often, this mistreatment results when one partner uses physical strength to try to control the other. However, the abuse may also be emotional or sexual in nature.

Spousal abuse can seriously harm the victim's physical, social, and mental/emotional health. Physical abuse, for example, can result in serious injury or even death. A victim's social health suffers when he or she avoids friends and family to hide evidence of the abuse. Often, the mental/emotional trauma of spousal abuse, such as feelings of fear and shame, remains long after physical injuries have healed. Spousal abuse also harms the health of other family members. It is critical for victims of spousal abuse and their children to leave the dangerous situation and seek help.

What are the elements of a safety plan against abuse?
People in abusive situations should develop a safety plan that includes:

- **Places and situations to avoid.** Avoid locations that have only one exit. Try not to be around the abuser when he or she has been drinking or using drugs.
- **Possible escape routes.** Doors, first-floor windows, basement exits, elevators, and stairwells are options.
- **A place to go.** Go somewhere safe, such as a friend's or relative's home, a shelter, or a hotel.
- **Telephone numbers.** Know the number of the domestic violence hot line. Use it to get help or information.

◄ Police are often the first to respond to reports of domestic violence. *Learn what resources are available in your community to help victims of abuse.*

Resilient TEENS

Gerard Wheeler's early life was tough. "Violence was all I knew, and I bullied others to protect myself," says Gerard.

Then in his freshman year of high school Gerard was encouraged to apply to and was accepted by Highland School of Technology (HST). At HST, he found himself in a completely different environment. Suddenly it was "cool" not to be tough. Gerard began to make friends with students who shared his interests and believed in his abilities.

Gerard quickly found his niche. Today he's looking forward to studying psychology at North Carolina State University, and continues to spread the message about nonviolence. "Whether I'm helping kids learn to deal with bullies, or sharing information on dating violence, I know I'm making a difference," says Gerard, "and that feels good."

"I know I'm making a difference, and that feels good."

Reading ✓ Check Explain How was Gerard affected by domestic violence?

Child Abuse

Child abuse is *domestic abuse directed at a child*. Like spousal abuse, the abuse of a child can be emotional, physical, or sexual. Child abuse may also include **neglect**, the *failure to provide for a child's physical or emotional needs*. Physical needs include adequate food, clothing, shelter, and medical care. Emotional neglect may take the form of indifference or withholding love and support.

A child who lives in an abusive home may try to escape the abuse by running away. Runaways often become victims of exploitation because they do not have the money, job skills, or means to support themselves. In fact, they are prime targets for people dealing in pornography and prostitution. Children suffering abuse should ask for help from trusted adults, such as a parent or another family member, a teacher, a church leader, or a member of the medical profession.

Effects of Abuse

Victims of domestic abuse experience feelings of shame, fear, humiliation, and guilt. They often feel powerless to change their circumstances. Long-term effects of domestic abuse may include

▶ an inability to trust or establish healthy personal relationships.

▶ chronic physical pain.

▶ neglect of or injury to oneself, including suicide attempts.

▶ depression, anxiety, sleep disorders, and eating disorders.

▶ abuse of alcohol and other drugs.

It is critical that victims of domestic violence get outside help to deal with this extremely dangerous situation. Getting to a safe place is the first priority.

Breaking the Cycle of Violence

Involvement in domestic violence is often a learned behavior. A child who suffers or who witnesses abuse may view violence in the home as a normal way of life. As a result, the child may be more likely to become an adult who abuses others. In this way, domestic violence can cycle from one generation to the next. This *pattern of repeating violent or abusive behaviors from one generation to the next* is called the **cycle of violence**. The only way to break this cycle is to stop all forms of violence and abuse. **Figure 11.2** provides suggestions for breaking the cycle of violence.

Health Minute

Preventing Domestic Violence

To encourage an atmosphere of nonviolence at home:

▶ Don't provide violence-oriented toys to small children, such as toy guns or knives.

▶ Don't provide children with video games that focus on violence, such as attacks on property, people, or animals.

Reading Check

Problems and Solutions
What can you do to break the cycle of violence?

FIGURE 11.2

BREAKING THE CYCLE OF VIOLENCE

You can help break the cycle of abuse. If you or someone you know is being abused . . .

• Tell a trusted adult (parent, other family member, teacher, school nurse or counselor, doctor). Ask this person to help you find a way to resolve the problem.

• Contact an abuse hot line or crisis center that can assist you in finding counselors or other forms of help.

• Report the abuse to the police. It may also be appropriate to contact child welfare or youth services.

Source: Office of Justice Programs, U.S. Department of Justice

Avoiding Domestic Violence

There are several strategies that can help you avoid and prevent domestic violence. You can recall these strategies by remembering the three Rs.

▶ **Recognize.** Become aware of acts that are abusive. Remember that abuse takes many forms, including physical abuse, verbal and emotional abuse, sexual abuse, and neglect.

▶ **Resist.** If anyone tries to harm you physically or abuse you in a sexual way, resist in any way you can. Run away from the abuser, and seek help from a trusted adult.

▶ **Report.** If someone treats you in an abusive manner, tell someone about the incident as soon as you can. If you witness someone else being abused, report the abuse to the authorities or tell an adult who can help you.

Victims of domestic abuse need help. Their abusers also need help. Abusers can break the cycle of violence by getting help and learning new ways to manage their feelings. Domestic abuse is unacceptable, and most of these acts are illegal. In the next lesson, you will learn more about sources of help for victims of abuse.

▲ Seeking help is the first step to take when dealing with domestic violence issues. *What strategies might help individuals avoid violence within the family?*

LESSON 3 REVIEW

Reviewing Facts and Vocabulary

1. What are the effects of spousal abuse?
2. What is *neglect?* Explain how neglect affects each part of a child's health triangle.
3. What is the *cycle of violence?* What are some ways of breaking this cycle?

Thinking Critically

4. **Synthesizing.** One of the effects of abuse is the victim's feeling of worthlessness. How could you help a victim of abuse to feel better about herself or himself?
5. **Evaluating.** Some say that the long-term effects of abuse are worse than the short-term effects. Explain why this statement might be true for many victims.

Applying Health Skills

Advocacy. Write an article discussing the serious problem of domestic abuse. Describe the effects of abuse, and urge victims of any form of domestic violence to seek help immediately. Ask the school newspaper to print your article.

After You Read

Cause and Effect. Create a chart with two columns. On one side, list the types of domestic violence and abuse. On the other, list the effects of abuse.

Visit **health.glencoe.com** for the Interactive Study Guide for Lesson 3.

Community Support Systems

Guide to Reading

Building Vocabulary

As you read this lesson, write each new highlighted term and its definition in your notebook.

▶ crisis center (p. 291)

▶ foster care (p. 292)

▶ family counseling (p. 294)

▶ mediator (p. 294)

Focusing on the Main Ideas

In this lesson, you will learn how to:

▶ List situations that require professional health services and how to access those services.

▶ Develop conflict resolution techniques for various family situations.

Reading Strategy

Identify Problems and Solutions

▶ Prior to reading the lesson, identify some problems that you might encounter while dating, and list what you think might be solutions.

Name some community resources you think might help a family in crisis.

You've learned how the health of the entire family depends on the health of its individual members. It is important to manage stress and conflict to prevent problems from escalating. Sometimes, families need outside help to solve conflicts. For this reason, it's important to know resources from home, school, and community that provide valid health information.

Help for Families

The most appropriate resource for a family in crisis depends on the seriousness of the problem. Some problems, such as domestic violence, may require the intervention of law enforcement agencies. Problems such as substance abuse may require medical help. Members of a troubled family can call a **crisis center**, *a facility that handles emergencies and provides referrals to an individual needing help.* Many communities also have crisis hot lines, special telephone numbers people can call to receive help 24 hours a day. People who work at crisis centers and hot lines are often able to guide individuals toward solutions to their problems. The solution may include a referral to one of the resources described in **Figure 11.3** on the next page.

ⓐ Crisis centers can provide help and support for families facing difficult situations. *What other resources offer help for families in crisis?*

FIGURE **11.3**

SOURCES OF HELP FOR FAMILIES

Many agencies offer help to families in need.

Faith Communities

Community Services

Police

Hospitals/Clinics

Source of Help for Families

Hospitals/Clinics

Shelters

Support Groups

Family Counseling

Mediation

Health Minute

Calling a Hot Line for Help

Before you call:

▶ **State the problem to yourself.** Write out the problem and what you will say.

▶ **List all of the questions you have.** Don't dismiss a topic because you think it's trivial.

▶ **Practice.** Rehearse what you will say.

When you make the call:

▶ **Have paper and a pencil handy.** Record the names and numbers of people the counselor suggests you call.

▶ **Consider the counselor's suggestions.** Decide on the best course of action.

Community Services

Most communities offer a variety of services to families who need help. Health literate individuals know effective techniques for supporting community, state, and federal agencies that advocate healthier communities. Parenting and conflict resolution classes may be offered by both public and private agencies. Many services can help families get food, clothing, and shelter. Some agencies provide financial aid, medical care, job training, and help in finding employment.

HELP FOR CHILDREN

Children whose basic needs are not being met or who live in abusive situations may be placed in **foster care**, *a temporary arrangement in which a child is placed under the guidance and supervision of a family or an adult who is not related to the child by birth.* Foster families provide havens for abused or neglected children by giving care and support. Sometimes, foster families adopt the children they have been caring for.

HELP FOR VICTIMS OF SPOUSAL ABUSE

Victims of spousal abuse can seek help by contacting an organization dealing with domestic violence. Many communities provide shelters and a network with other safe houses throughout the United States. These organizations offer shelter, food, clothing, and counseling for women in crisis and their children. Some also help victims strengthen their employment skills by teaching them interviewing techniques and providing them with job training.

Support Groups

Some people find help through **support groups,** meetings in which individuals share their problems and get advice from others facing similar issues. Participants discuss their concerns and often take comfort in knowing that they are not alone. Support groups help many people cope on a day-to-day basis.

The purpose of support groups is to deal with various types of personal or family health concerns. For example, there are groups for personal health issues such as substance abuse, eating disorders, domestic violence, dealing with grief, and coping with a family member's long-term illness.

Reading Check

Explain Where can families in crisis turn for help in dealing with problems?

Real-Life Application

Family Support Services

There are many community resources that provide help for families facing difficulties.

 Al-Anon 555-2666
Support for family members of people addicted to substances such as alcohol and other drugs

 Alateen 555-8336
A support group for teens who live with someone addicted to alcohol or other drugs

 Conflict Resolution Center 555-1234
Offers counseling, mediation, and training to help resolve conflicts

 Family Resource Center 555-9876
Provides support for families, including counseling services

Family Services 555-5671
Provides counseling for individuals, couples, and families

 Teens in Transition 555-8485
Offers resources for teens seeking help for difficult life problems, such as coping with divorce or death

Using the above flyer as a guide, search your telephone directory to identify similar health-related services in your community. In small groups, compile a Community Family Support Directory that describes each agency. Include the services, hours, and locations. Target the directory toward teens. Use clip art to make it visually appealing.

Counseling

Family counseling, *therapy to restore healthy relationships in a family,* is another source of help for families facing problems. Family members meet regularly with counselors to discuss issues and to try to find solutions. Such counseling often provides families with the skills they need to resolve future conflicts on their own.

In some cases, a family member may benefit from individual counseling. When dealing with issues of domestic violence, one-on-one sessions with a counselor, a psychologist, or a psychiatrist may help an abuser see that he or she learned abusive family patterns in childhood. The cycle of violence may then be broken as the individual learns to recognize the abusive patterns and replace them with healthful behaviors.

Mediation

Families often have difficulty working out problems that involve divorce, including custody of children or disbursement of property. In such cases, mediation may help. A **mediator** is *a person who helps others resolve issues to the satisfaction of both parties.* The mediator sets ground rules and aids in effective communication that permits each party to speak and be heard. The mediation process encourages family members to communicate, cooperate, and compromise. Mediators often help both parties find the resources and make the emotional connections that will result in mutual agreement.

Maintaining Healthy Families

Each family member can do his or her part to keep the family healthy. Through communication and awareness, people can become knowledgeable about family health concerns. Spend time with other members of your family, and find out what's going on in their lives. Show an interest, ask questions, and offer help if you think it's needed. Healthy family members know how to analyze situations requiring professional health services or other interventions.

Because a family lives together in a household, it is important to respect one another's personal space and feelings. Be considerate of other people in the family. Keeping the noise level down, for example, may prevent you from invading a family member's space. Here are some additional ways to strengthen family relationships:

Reading Check

Explain What strategies are used in family counseling to restore healthy relationships?

Family counselors can help teens and their parents learn to communicate their feelings and find ways to resolve differences. *What strategies might counselors use to help improve communication in a family?*

▶ **Cooperate.** Respond politely to requests or questions. Meet your responsibilities without being asked or reminded.

▶ **Show appreciation.** Avoid taking family members for granted, and remember to say "Thank you" when appropriate. Be supportive and encouraging.

▶ **Be a good communicator.** Avoid interrupting, daydreaming, or jumping to conclusions when someone is speaking. Try not to raise your voice if you disagree with something.

▶ **Offer help.** Show concern, and offer support and help.

▶ **Be empathetic.** Try to see the situation from the family member's point of view.

▶ **Work to resolve conflicts.** Remember the Three Cs: communication, cooperation, and compromise. If appropriate, use **conflict-resolution** strategies.

▶ **Know when to get outside help.** Be able to identify situations that require professional help, and know how to access these services.

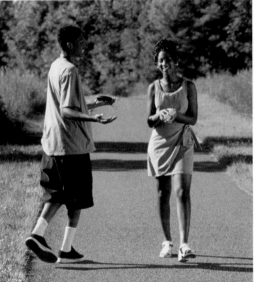

You can often help family members feel better by simply listening to what they have to say.

Reviewing Facts and Vocabulary

1. Identify some family situations that require help from professional health services.

2. When might a child be placed in foster care?

3. What are three things you can do to help maintain the health of your family?

Thinking Critically

4. **Applying.** Look at the resources for families in Figure 11.3. Give an example of a personal or family health concern that might be addressed by each resource.

5. **Synthesizing.** Explain how crisis centers and crisis hot lines are similar. How are the two health services different?

Applying Health Skills

Accessing Information. Research to find out what resources in your community help families in crisis. Make a list of the professional health services you identify, and learn how to access each resource. Create a handbook of the information you gather.

After You Read

Analyze a Graph. Using Figure 11.3 on page 292, make a wallet card listing information about community and family support services. Include phone numbers and other contact information you can use in an emergency.

Visit **health.glencoe.com** for the Interactive Study Guide for Lesson 4.

Lesson 4 Community Support Systems **295**

It's All Relative

Got questions about family relationships? Here are a few answers.

My parents don't say they love me. I know they do, but I want to hear it. Can this change? — *Mara, 12, Birmingham, Michigan*
Melt their ice by warming up yourself. Give your parents hugs, tell them you love them, leave them sweet notes. If they don't pick up on the shift in your behavior, ask them outright for more verbal reassurance, and be specific about what you want to hear.

My brother and I rarely talk about any-thing deep. How can we get closer?
— *Alex, 16, Martinez, California*
What's on your mind now? Go ask for your brother's opinion about it. You may be surprised by how flattered he is. Also, ask deeper ques-tions: How is he feeling about leaving for col-lege? About his relationships? It just takes one brave soul to break the silence.

My sister bad-mouths me to our father. How can I get her to talk to me and not about me? — *Esteban, 15, Wichita, Kansas*
This calls for a face-to-face talk with your sister, because that's the courtesy you're hoping she'll start paying you. Tell her you'd prefer she handle her gripes directly with you, and promise you'll do the same. As insurance, give your dad a heads-up about your plan. That way, your sister can't misrepresent it to him afterward.

How can I help my mom stop worrying about me whenever I go out? — *Liane, 17, Greenville, Texas*
The more specific information you can give her about where you're going (and when, and with whom, and at what time), the less she'll worry. Write up a mini-itinerary before you head out, complete with destinations and phone numbers for where you'll be. That way she'll know you're being responsible, which makes it easier for her to relax. Feel like really easing her mind? Offer to call to check in at a prearranged time. ◢

TIME to THINK... About Family Relationships

Take a moment to think about a relative or family friend you admire. Brainstorm a list of words that describe that person. Write a poem about the person you admire using the words from your list.

1. **Practicing Healthful Behaviors.** Make a list of specific actions that family members can take to strengthen their relationships with each other. Describe the roles of parents, grandparents, and other family members in promoting a healthy family. *(LESSON 1)*

2. **Communication Skills.** Write a skit in which one teen demonstrates active listening skills and empathy when a friend reveals that his or her parent is suffering from an illness or a disability. *(LESSON 2)*

3. **Advocacy.** Develop a poster or a PSA that can be used to make others aware of what they can do to break the cycle of abuse. *(LESSON 3)*

4. **Decision Making.** Carol thinks that her older sister has a drug problem. Use the steps of decision making to help Carol decide how to get help for her sister. *(LESSON 4)*

CAREER Corner

Family Therapist

Depression, marital problems, and parent-child conflicts can strain family relationships. A family therapist can help families find ways to work out their problems and communicate more openly and honestly. To become a family therapist, you'll need a master's degree in couples and family therapy. Learn more about this and other health careers by clicking on Career Corner at **health.glencoe.com.**

BEYOND the Classroom

Parent Involvement

Advocacy. With your parents, learn about shelters in your area that provide victims with a safe place to recover from abuse. Determine what needs the shelter has and what your family can do to help support the shelter's efforts. You might collect materials such as clothing, books, toys, and blankets for the shelter.

School and Community

Community Events. Identify events and programs in your community that are geared toward students and their families. Contact the organizations sponsoring the activities to find out how you, your classmates, and your family members can get involved.

After You Read

Use your Foldable to review what you have learned about family relationships and their effects on your physical, mental/emotional, and social health.

FOLDABLES
Study Organizer

► EXPLORING HEALTH TERMS *Answer the following questions on a sheet of paper.*

Lesson 1 *Match each definition with the correct term.*

affirmation   family
extended family   sibling

1. A brother or sister.
2. Positive feedback that helps individuals feel appreciated and supported.
3. The basic unit of society.

Lesson 2 *Fill in the blanks with the correct term.*

custody   resiliency
divorce   separation
grief

Dan's parents fight a lot. They have considered ending their marriage through (_4_) but decided instead on a (_5_), a period in which they will live apart from each other, to see whether they can resolve their differences. During this time, Dan's mom and dad have joint (_6_), so they care for and make decisions about Dan together.

Lesson 3 *Replace the underlined words with the correct term.*

sexual abuse   emotional abuse
cycle of violence   physical abuse
domestic violence   child abuse

7. Three forms of <u>exploitation</u> are emotional, physical, and sexual abuse in the home.
8. Calling someone names or attacking his or her self-worth is <u>physical abuse</u>.
9. Neglect of a baby is a form of <u>spousal abuse</u>.

Lesson 4 *Match each definition with the correct term.*

crisis center   foster care
mediator   family counseling

10. A temporary arrangement in which a child is placed under the guidance or supervision of a family or adult not related by birth.
11. Therapy to restore healthy relationships in a family.
12. A facility that handles emergencies and provides referrals to persons who need help.

► RECALLING THE FACTS *Use complete sentences to answer the following questions.*

1. List three ways that parents promote the physical health of their children.
2. Why is the family considered the basic unit of society?
3. List five traits of a healthy family.
4. Identify three situations that may result in a change in the family structure.
5. What events may lead to a change in a family's financial situation?
6. List three ways to cope with stress within the family.
7. What constitutes sexual abuse?
8. Why is a child who runs away from home often at risk of exploitation?
9. What are the three Rs for preventing and avoiding domestic violence?
10. Besides crisis centers and hot lines, list three resources to which families in crisis can turn for help.
11. What is the main difference between a support group and counseling?
12. What are three skills that mediators use to help families solve problems?

For more review questions for Chapter 11, go to **health.glencoe.com**.

➤ WRITING CRITICALLY

1. **Narrative.** Write a one-page story about a teen whose parents are getting divorced. In your story, show how the teen manages the stress and emotions involved with the divorce in healthy and positive ways. Also show how the teen communicates his or her feelings in positive ways to his or her parents and seeks support from friends and others.

2. **Personal.** Showing appreciation can strengthen family relationships. Write a one-page letter of appreciation to a family member. Let the family member know how he or she has positively influenced your life. Describe some of the ways in which he or she has positively influenced you and how your relationship with that person has helped you learn about positive character traits.

Standardized Test Practice

 The purpose of expository writing is to explain, define, or tell how to do something by giving information. The *Writing Situation* presents the topic: the effect of family crises on the family. The *Directions for Writing* suggests that you think about ways that families can rise to the challenge and keep the family strong through a difficult time.

PROMPT

Writing Situation: In the course of our lives, most families experience crises of one kind or another. Think about the types of family changes and crises that create stress in all families and family members, regardless of culture or gender.

Directions for Writing: Identify one type of family crisis. Explain how a family might accept the challenge in the situation and work together to keep the family strong through the hard time.

In your writing, give specific examples to show how families can meet such challenges and the ways that a caring community can help.

CHAPTER 12

Peer Relationships

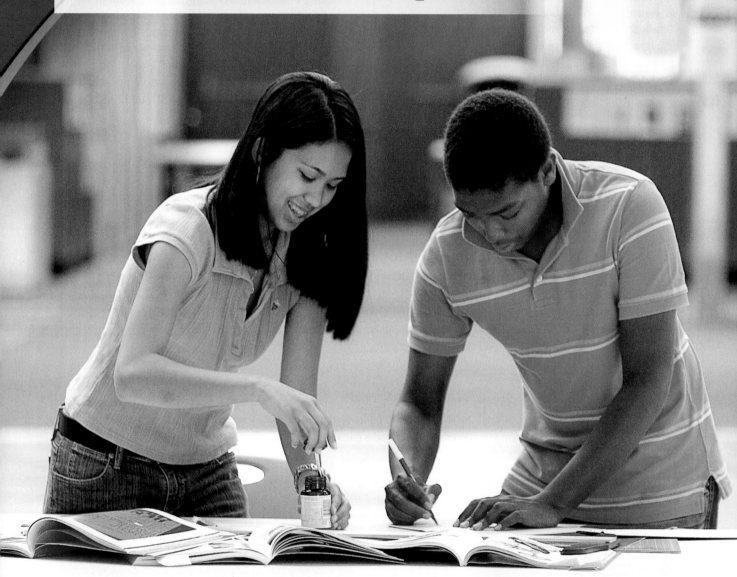

Lesson 1 **Safe and Healthy Friendships**

Lesson 2 **Peer Pressure and Refusal Skills**

Lesson 3 **Dating and Setting Limits**

Lesson 4 **Abstinence: A Responsible Decision**

Screenplays for Healthy Peer Relationships

What would you do if a peer encouraged you to do something against your values? Sometimes it helps to practice how you would react to peer pressure. Writing screenplays showing healthy relationships or engaging in role-playing activities can help you recognize and respond positively to peer pressure.

Visit the Eye on the Media section at health.glencoe.com to learn more about how writing a screenplay can support a healthy peer relationship.

Study Organizer

Before You Read

Use this Foldable to help you record and organize information about safe and healthy friendships. Begin with five sheets of notebook paper.

Step 1

Cut off the right margin of one sheet of notebook paper.

Step 2

Cut the header and 4 lines of space off another sheet of paper.

Step 3

Cut the header and 12 lines of space off another sheet of paper.

Step 4

Cut the header and 20 lines of space from the right margin off another sheet of paper.

Step 5

Stack the four cut sheets on top of another sheet of paper. Staple along the left margin and label as shown.

As You Read

As you read and discuss the material in the chapter, record main ideas, new terms, and personal experiences on the appropriate pages of your Foldable.

SPOTLIGHT ON HEALTH

Using Visuals. Write five sentences, each one beginning with the words: *A true friend is someone who . . . .* Discuss your descriptions with your classmates.

Safe and Healthy Friendships

Guide to Reading

Building Vocabulary

As you read this lesson, write each new highlighted term and its definition in your notebook.

- ▶ peers (p. 302)
- ▶ friendship (p. 303)
- ▶ platonic friendship (p.303)
- ▶ clique (p. 304)
- ▶ stereotype (p. 305)

Focusing on the Main Ideas

In this lesson, you will learn how to:

- ▶ Compare the effects of peer relationships and friends on physical and emotional health.
- ▶ List ways to form and strengthen healthy friendships.

Reading Strategy

Organize Information

- ▶ Use the Foldable at the beginning of the chapter to organize and record information and notes on building relationships, choosing friends, cliques, and safe and healthy relationships.

Quick Write

Write a paragraph describing what being a true friend means to you.

 You may know many class-mates and peers, but only a few may be your good friends. *What qualities set a friend apart from other peers?*

During your teen years, you begin a search for a personal identity. This identity will be shaped, at least in part, by your **peers**—*people of similar age who share similar interests*. Your relationships with friends and peers contribute to your personal identity. Knowing skills for communicating effectively with family, friends, and others can positively affect your health and well-being.

Types of Peer Relationships

As you get older, the dynamics of your social groups change. Perhaps you have a part-time job or a volunteer position in which you and your peers have a work-based relationship. Such situations can benefit your social health by giving you opportunities to meet people of all ages, races, religions, and backgrounds. Interacting with diverse peers can enrich your life and contribute to personal growth. Some of the friendships you form in high school may last throughout your life.

Take the Health Inventory for Chapter 12 at **health.glencoe.com**.

Friendships

A **friendship** is *a significant relationship between two people.* Healthy friendships are based on caring, respect, trust, and consideration. Friends are people with whom you share hobbies, interests, and other friends. They may also become people with whom you are comfortable sharing your needs, wants, emotions, and confidences. The people you choose as friends have a big impact in your life. Friends can help you by promoting a positive self-image. Healthy friendships can give you a sense of belonging and help you define and reinforce your values.

Your friends probably include both males and females. A **platonic friendship** is *a friendship with a member of the opposite gender in which there is affection but the two people are not considered a couple.* Such relationships can help you understand and become comfortable with individuals of the opposite gender. In addition, such friends can be a valuable source of advice concerning dating issues. Platonic friendships help you realize that all people, regardless of gender, have similar feelings, needs, and concerns.

Friendships vary in importance and commitment. If you have a best friend, you already know that not all friendships are the same. In fact, there are several kinds of friendships.

These teens have a casual friendship based on a common interest. *What interests do you share with the peers you think of as casual friends?*

CASUAL FRIENDSHIPS

A casual friendship is a relationship between peers who share something in common. You may form a casual friendship with a classmate, a teammate, or someone who attends your place of worship. You may sit with casual friends in the cafeteria or at school events. Casual friends are usually people with whom you share some interests but are not necessarily people with whom you form deep emotional bonds. You might not feel comfortable sharing your thoughts, feelings, and experiences with casual friends.

CLOSE FRIENDSHIPS

Some casual friendships may develop into close friendships. Close friends have strong emotional ties and feel comfortable sharing their thoughts, experiences, and feelings. They trust and support each other, acting with kindness, courtesy, and loyalty. When problems arise in the relationship, close friends will try to work them out together.

True friends have several common attributes:

▶ Similar interests, beliefs, and attitudes on basic issues

▶ Open and honest communication

▶ Sharing of joys, disappointments, dreams, and concerns

▶ Mutual respect, caring, and support

▶ Concern about each other's safety and well-being

Reading Check

Explain What are some of the types of peer relationships?

Cliques

Does your school have cliques? A **clique** is *a small circle of friends, usually with similar backgrounds or tastes, who exclude people viewed as outsiders.* Clique members may share the same attitudes, wear similar clothing, meet regularly in an area identified as their "turf," or engage in other behaviors that identify them as a clique.

Health Skills Activity

Conflict Resolution: When Best Friends Disagree

"Guess what?" Marissa asked excitedly when she saw her best friend, Julia. "Nicole and Dave asked us to join their group!"

"But I like the friends we have right now," Julia frowned. "Why do you want to be part of their group?"

"Because they're the most popular people in school!" Marissa answered. "It'll be great!"

"I've heard that they make fun of people who are different from them," Julia said.

"If we're part of their group, they won't make fun of us," Marissa insisted.

Julia doesn't want to lose Marissa as a best friend, but she also doesn't feel comfortable joining Nicole and Dave's group. She wonders how to respond.

What Would You Do?

Write an ending to the scenario in which Julia and Marissa resolve their conflict in a healthful way. Use the following tips as a guideline.

1. Take turns explaining each side of the conflict without interruption.
2. Use "I" messages.
3. Listen carefully, and ask appropriate questions.
4. Brainstorm solutions.
5. Agree on a solution that benefits both sides.

Cliques can have both positive and negative influences on peers. Being part of a clique, for example, may provide members with a sense of belonging. However, a clique is a negative influence if members are discouraged from thinking for themselves or acting as individuals.

Clique membership is often limited—not everyone who wants to belong is welcome. The beliefs and actions clique members use to exclude others may be prejudicial and based on stereotypes. **Prejudice** is making assumptions or judgments about an individual without really knowing him or her. A **stereotype** is *an exaggerated and oversimplified belief about an entire group of people, such as an ethnic or religious group or a gender.*

Forming Healthy Friendships

Relationships with friends may become more complex as you begin sharing thoughts and feelings that are more serious in nature than those you experienced in childhood. Learning positive strategies to express yourself is essential in building and maintaining healthy friendships.

Choosing Friends

Throughout your life you have many opportunities to choose friends. Positive people with healthy attitudes can support you emotionally and motivate you. For example, if your friends think education is important, you're likely to take education seriously and do well in school. Often, friends encourage each other to make healthy, responsible decisions. They might inspire each other to engage in more physical activity or participate in community service. They can also serve as mutual protectors, helping each other avoid unsafe or unhealthy situations. For example, a friend may encourage you to walk away from a fight. It's important that you learn to identify positive aspects of a relationship, and to evaluate friendships that may not be positive.

Some friends, however, may try to influence you to participate in risky activities or behaviors. If a friendship isn't contributing to your life in a positive way, it may be an unhealthy relationship. Healthy relationships are based on mutual respect and caring.

Reading Check

Describe What are some negative influences of cliques?

Group outings with friends can provide you with a sense of belonging. *Evaluate other positive effects of friends on mental/emotional health.*

▼ Mutual respect helps friends feel comfortable sharing their needs, wants, and emotions.

Building and Strengthening Friendships

Positive friendships are built on common values and interests. Having common values means friends won't pressure you to do things you believe are wrong. Having common interests gives friends something to talk about and do together. There are many ways to strengthen a healthy friendship.

▶ **Be loyal.** Friends can trust and depend on each other. They don't purposely do anything to hurt each other, and they always speak respectfully of each other.

▶ **Encourage each other.** A good friend is supportive and makes you feel good about yourself. Friends acknowledge each other's accomplishments and help each other through difficult times.

▶ **Respect each other.** Common courtesy helps keep friendships strong. Avoid taking friends for granted. Being on time and keeping your promises will let your friends know that you care about and respect them.

LESSON 1 | REVIEW

Reviewing Facts and Vocabulary

1. What are *peers*?
2. Define *friendship*. Identify four character traits on which friendships are based.
3. List two ways to strengthen a friendship.

Thinking Critically

4. **Evaluating.** Interactions with friends and peers can have both positive and negative effects on all sides of your health triangle. Evaluate and provide examples of the positive and negative effects of peer relationships and friends on physical, mental/emotional, and social health.

5. **Comparing and Contrasting.** Evaluate the dynamics of social groups consisting of casual friends, close friends, and platonic friends. What qualities do these groups share? How do they differ?

Applying Health Skills

Communication Skills. With a classmate, role-play two scenarios. In the first, demonstrate skills that close friends would use to communicate needs, wants, and emotions. In the second, show how peers might express disagreement about an issue while still showing respect for themselves and each other.

After You Read

Cause and Effect. Write a paragraph describing how cliques can be good for friendships and what barriers they may create to forming new friendships.

Visit **health.glencoe.com** for the Interactive Study Guide for Lesson 1.

Peer Pressure and Refusal Skills

Guide to Reading

Building Vocabulary

As you read this lesson, write each new highlighted term and its definition in your notebook.

- ▶ peer pressure (p. 307)
- ▶ harassment (p. 308)
- ▶ manipulation (p. 308)
- ▶ assertive (p. 310)
- ▶ refusal skills (p. 310)
- ▶ passive (p. 312)
- ▶ aggressive (p. 312)

Focusing on the Main Ideas

In this lesson, you will learn how to:

- ▶ **Develop** the skills you need for making responsible decisions under pressure.
- ▶ **Demonstrate** the use of refusal skills and the avoidance of unsafe situations.

Reading Strategy

Predict

- ▶ After scanning the headings, subheadings, and pictures, write a summary describing what information you think you'll learn in this lesson.

Quick Write

Your friends can apply positive or negative peer pressure. Write a paragraph describing how your friends might influence the way you feel and act.

Imagine that you are out with friends and someone suggests going to a party a few miles away. Most of your friends agree, but you aren't sure because you don't know the person who's throwing the party. Your friends spend the next few minutes trying to persuade you to join them. What will you do? Knowing positive ways to influence others to make positive choices will help you handle this type of situation.

Peer Pressure

Your peers can sometimes influence how you think, feel, and act. *The influence that people your age may have on you* is called **peer pressure**.

Peer pressure can have a positive or negative influence on your actions and behaviors. It is useful to learn to evaluate forms of peer pressure and develop healthful strategies for responding to it.

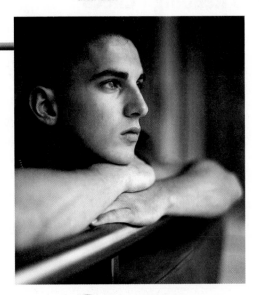

Peer pressure may make some decisions more difficult. *What strategies can help you make healthful, responsible decisions when faced with peer pressure?*

> Positive peer pressure can motivate you to try new activities that can benefit all sides of your health triangle. *What are some examples of positive peer pressure that you have experienced?*

Reading Check

Describe Name some ways that positive peer pressure can influence you.

Positive Peer Pressure

Peers can influence you in many positive ways. For example, they might encourage you to participate in a cleanup campaign to clear away trash from a roadside. Agreeing to work with your peers in this campaign benefits your social health because you have the opportunity to interact with others in positive ways. It also benefits the community by providing a cleaner environment. Volunteering to serve food at a homeless shelter or working at a Special Olympics event because a friend does so are other examples of positive peer pressure.

Positive peer pressure may also involve *not* participating in risky behaviors or activities. For instance, having friends who do not use tobacco, alcohol, or other drugs may positively influence you to avoid these harmful substances.

You can also use positive peer pressure to influence others in healthful ways. You can be a **role model** by inspiring peers to take part in a positive act or a worthwhile cause.

Negative Peer Pressure

Peers sometimes pressure others to take part in behaviors or accept beliefs that have negative consequences. The members of a clique, for example, may be disrespectful toward people they do not consider acceptable to their group. Such behavior may involve **harassment**, or *persistently annoying others*. Harassment may include name-calling, teasing, or bullying. Negative peer pressure may also lead some teens to engage in behaviors that go against their values. For instance, a peer might pressure a classmate to help him or her cheat on a test.

Manipulation is another way of exerting negative peer pressure on others. **Manipulation** is *an indirect, dishonest way to control or influence others*. Some examples of the ways people manipulate one another are listed in **Figure 12.1.** It's important to discourage this kind of hurtful behavior and encourage the victim to report the problem to a trusted adult.

FIGURE **12.1**

COMMON METHODS OF MANIPULATION

- Mocking or teasing another person in mean or hurtful ways
- Using "guilt trips" to get desired results
- Bargaining—offering to make a deal to get what one wants
- Using flattery or praise to influence another person
- Bribing—promising money or favors if the person will do what is asked
- Making threats—promising violence or some other negative consequence if the person does not do what is asked
- Using blackmail—threatening to reveal some embarrassing or damaging information if the person does not do what is asked

Resisting Negative Peer Pressure

Peer pressure doesn't stop at the end of the teen years. Throughout your life, you may experience many instances in which peers, including friends and coworkers, make requests or demands of you. In some cases, your responses to these requests or demands will directly affect your health. For example, refusing to use tobacco, alcohol, or other drugs shows that you understand the role of individual responsibility regarding personal risk behaviors. At times there may be instances in which your response to peer pressure could seriously impact your life leading to serious injury, or even death. For example, agreeing to get into a car with friends who have been drinking can place your life in danger.

One way to resist negative peer pressure is to develop friendships with people who share your values and interests. Friends who have respect for your health and well-being will be less likely to pressure you into doing something that goes against your values. You will find that it's much easier to resist negative peer pressure from someone else when you have supportive friends who stand by you and respect your decision.

Sometimes, however, the pressure to participate in unsafe or potentially harmful activities can be difficult to resist. When pressured by a friend, many teens worry about hurting the person's feelings or jeopardizing the relationship. Refusing to go along with a group may make some people concerned about appearing "uncool." Even though these situations may be difficult, it is important to remain firm and stay true to yourself. Remember, you have the responsibility to make decisions that have the best possible effect on your well-being. When making decisions that involve potentially risky consequences, your health and safety come first.

Resisting Peer Pressure

To resist negative peer pressure:

▶ Stand your ground by stating your values and beliefs.

▶ Consider the consequences of unsafe behavior.

▶ Decide whether the source of pressure is yourself or others.

▶ Be assertive, and use refusal skills to say no to risky activities.

▶ Leave the scene if necessary.

Assertive Refusal

Being **assertive** means *standing up for your rights in a firm but positive way.* When you practice assertive communication, you state your position and stand your ground while acknowledging the rights of others. This is the most effective approach when facing negative peer influences. Being assertive shows that you understand the possible causes of conflict among youth in schools and communities.

REFUSAL SKILLS

An important aspect of being assertive is the ability to demonstrate appropriate refusal skills. **Refusal skills** are *communication strategies that can help you say no when you are urged to take part in behaviors that are unsafe, unhealthy, or that go against your values.* Effective refusal skills involve a three-step process. Learning and practicing these steps will help you deal with high-pressure situations.

▶ **Step 1: State Your Position.** The first step in resisting negative peer pressure is to say no. You need to state your position simply and firmly. Make sure your "no" sounds as though you really mean it. Combining your words with nonverbal messages, such as those shown in **Figure 12.2**, will make your statement more effective. Having said no, give an honest reason for your response. Your reason may be as simple as, "It goes against my values." Offering a legitimate reason will help strengthen your refusal.

FIGURE 12.2

BODY LANGUAGE AND ASSERTIVE REFUSAL

Reinforce the meaning of your words with appropriate body language.

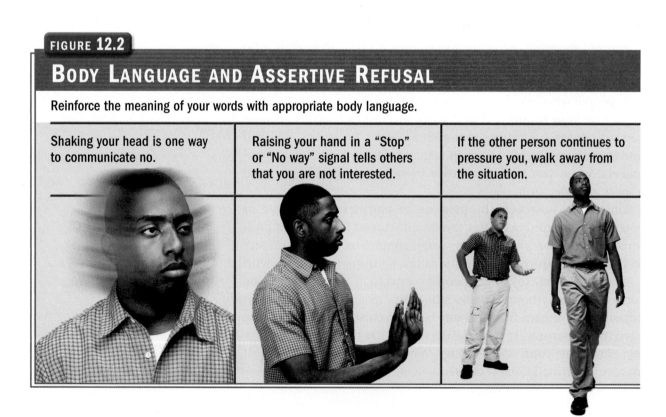

Shaking your head is one way to communicate no.

Raising your hand in a "Stop" or "No way" signal tells others that you are not interested.

If the other person continues to pressure you, walk away from the situation.

Hands-On Health ACTIVITY

Assert Yourself

Learning to be assertive can help you maintain your commitment to a healthful lifestyle. By practicing assertiveness, you will find it easier to live by your values. In this activity, you will role-play assertive communication skills.

What You'll Need

- large index cards
- pen or pencil and paper

What You'll Do

1. With a partner, think of a realistic scenario in which you are being pressured by one or more peers to do something against your values.

2. Write your scenario on an index card, and swap cards with another pair of partners.

3. Role-play the scenario you've received, using the checklist shown here to make sure you have included the elements of assertive communication.

Apply and Conclude

Write a short reflective paper describing how being assertive can help protect your physical, mental/emotional, and social health.

Checklist: Assertive Communication Skills

- ✓ "I" messages
- ✓ Respectful but firm tone of voice
- ✓ Alternatives to the action
- ✓ Clear, simple statements
- ✓ Appropriate body language

▶ **Step 2: Suggest Alternatives.** When a peer asks you to take part in an activity with which you are uncomfortable, try suggesting another activity. For example, if a friend wants to go to a party where there is no adult supervision, you might say, "No, let's go to the movies instead." By offering an alternative, you create an opportunity for your friend to be with you in a way that makes you comfortable. Keep in mind that your suggestion is most effective if it takes you away from the dangerous or unpleasant situation.

▶ **Step 3: Stand Your Ground.** Even after you've refused, peers may continue trying to persuade you to join in. Make it clear that you mean what you've said. Use strong body language and maintain eye contact. If this doesn't work, remove yourself from the situation. Simply say, "I'm going home."

When you're faced with negative peer pressure, refusal skills can lead to the avoidance of unsafe situations. Knowing that you made the decision to protect your safety and uphold your values will make you feel good about resisting the pressure.

Reading Check

Explain What are the three steps you can take when using refusal skills?

Practicing refusal skills will help you deal with negative peer pressure. *Give examples of passive, aggressive, and assertive communication in response to peer pressure. Which method is most effective? Why?*

Passive and Aggressive Responses

Being assertive may take some practice. To some people, a passive response to negative peer pressure seems more natural and therefore easier. People who are **passive** have *a tendency to give up, give in, or back down without standing up for their own rights and needs.* Teens who respond passively to peer pressure may believe they are making friends by going along. However, being passive may cause others to view them as pushovers who aren't worthy of respect.

Some people may feel more comfortable with an aggressive response. **Aggressive** people are *overly forceful, pushy, hostile, or otherwise attacking in their approach.* An aggressive way of resisting peer pressure may involve yelling, shouting, shoving, or insulting others or the use of other kinds of verbal or physical force. Aggressive people may get their way, but most people react to aggressive behavior by avoiding the individual or by fighting back. Either reaction can result in emotional or physical harm to both parties.

Learning and practicing assertive communication is the most effective way to deal with peer pressure. Being assertive shows that you know strategies for solving interpersonal conflict without harming yourself and others.

LESSON 2 | REVIEW

Reviewing Facts and Vocabulary

1. What is *peer pressure?*
2. Identify two examples of manipulation.
3. How might a friend help you resist negative peer pressure?

Thinking Critically

4. **Analyzing.** Suppose a group of friends constantly teases a student in your school. In what ways can you show disapproval of this inconsiderate and disrespectful behavior?
5. **Comparing and Contrasting.** Classify passive, aggressive, and assertive forms of communication, and explain the similarities and differences among them.

Applying Health Skills

Refusal Skills. With a classmate, develop a scenario in which peers use pressure to try to get you to use tobacco or alcohol. Demonstrate refusal strategies for resisting the negative peer pressure.

After You Read

Compare and Contrast. Create a two-column chart. In the left column, list examples of positive peer pressure. In the right column, list examples of negative peer pressure.

Visit **health.glencoe.com** for the Interactive Study Guide for Lesson 2.

Dating and Setting Limits

Guide to Reading

Building Vocabulary

As you read this lesson, write each new highlighted term and its definition in your notebook.

▶ infatuation (p. 313)

▶ affection (p. 313)

▶ curfew (p. 317)

Focusing on the Main Ideas

In this lesson, you will learn how to:

▶ **Identify** behavior in a dating relationship that will enhance the dignity relating to marriage.

▶ **Establish** strategies for maintaining safe and healthy dating relationships.

Reading Strategy

Explain

▶ Write down each of the Building Vocabulary terms on a sheet of paper. After each, write a definition based on your current knowledge.

Write a paragraph describing how teens can set limits for dating.

During adolescence it's natural to experience a change in attitude toward others. Teens may find themselves feeling attracted to people they'd thought of only as classmates or friends before. This is a good time to learn to formulate principles for healthy dating relationships.

Dating

Dating provides opportunities to develop social skills, such as communicating and interacting with another person. Dating also allows people to learn more about themselves. Through dating, some people discover new interests, reaffirm their values, and even start thinking about the type of person with whom they might like to build a future.

Sometimes when a teen is attracted to someone, an **infatuation**, or *exaggerated feelings of passion for another person,* develops. Although such feelings are natural, it is important not to mistake them for genuine affection. **Affection**, *a feeling of fondness for someone,* comes when you know another person well. Teens who are dating can express affection by communicating with and listening to each other, and spending quality time together.

▼ Dating teens can express their affection in healthy, respectful ways. *List three positive ways for teens to show affection for a dating partner.*

Deciding to Date

Not everyone dates. Some teens choose not to date because they're shy around people they like. Others may choose not to date because they have other interests or time commitments. Still others may not date because of family, religious, or ethnic traditions.

As a way of easing into dating, many teens go out with groups of friends of both genders. Being part of a group allows teens to develop and practice their social skills without having the pressure of focusing on only one person. It also gives you the opportunity to identify ways of resisting persuasive tactics regarding sexual involvement. Going out in a group takes some of the attention away from the individual, helping him or her relax and feel less self-conscious. Group dates or double dates can also relieve the pressure of being alone with someone new.

Reading Check

Compare and Contrast
What are the differences and similarities between infatuation and affection?

Resilient TEENS

Susanna Thomas has one piece of advice for her peers. "Don't let people get to you. When you graduate high school you'll never have to see those people again."

Back in junior high school Susanna was unpopular with what she calls the "snobs." "I struggled a great deal with teasing and many vicious rumors were spread about me," she says.

Susanna eventually transferred from the public junior high she'd been attending to a private school where she began healing her damaged ego.

"Don't let people get to you."

Today she's become very passionate about helping other teens understand the consequences of their actions. "Just because who you are doesn't fit some snob's personal criteria doesn't give him or her the right to try to make you feel like you're worse than anyone else," she says.

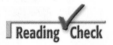

Reading Check

Explain What do you think Susanna means by saying, "Don't let people get to you."?

What to Do on a Date

What you decide to do on a date depends on the person you are with and your common interests. If you don't know the person well, a movie might be a good choice. Going out to dinner or to a school dance are also good options. You might also try attending a sports event such as a baseball or basketball game. When you get to know each other and have a better idea of your interests, you will probably find activities that both you and your date enjoy.

SPORTS OR ATHLETIC ACTIVITIES

If you and your date like sports, you might want to consider a date that includes athletic activities. In-line or ice skating, tennis, miniature golf, cycling, hiking, bowling, skiing, and horseback riding are all fun activities you can try on a date. Athletic activities such as these promote health and provide a way for dates to share and develop common interests. They also allow dates to get to know each other better in a friendly, relaxed atmosphere.

COMMUNITY ACTIVITIES

Consider going to the zoo or a local museum. If you and your date enjoy music or theater, you can attend concerts or plays being held in your community. You may also sign up for a painting, dancing, or photography class together at a local community center. Find out whether your community has any tourist attractions that you have overlooked. Learn what's available by asking friends and family, reading the local newspaper, and looking through the telephone book. Then, choose an event or activity that interests both you and your date, and go explore together. For example, you might attend a community festival or a stargazing party hosted by a local astronomy club.

CHARITABLE ACTIVITIES

Volunteering together can help build strong friendships and dating relationships. You can help build a house for Habitat for Humanity, participate in a charity walk-a-thon, volunteer to maintain a local park or beach, or attend a fund-raising event. Such activities allow you and your date to contribute to the community in positive ways. Volunteering is also a great option for group dates!

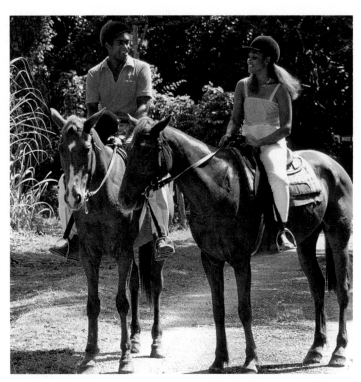

▲ **Many teens enjoy athletic activities during dates.** *Why are athletic activities a good option for dating?*

What can I do to make a good impression on a first date?

- **Relax and be yourself.** You want your date to like you for who you are, not who you're pretending to be.
- **Be honest.** There are no "rules" about who calls whom or about telling someone how you feel.
- **Plan your date.** Come up with something you'll both enjoy doing.
- **Be courteous.** Be on time, and treat your date with kindness and respect.

CHARACTER CHECK

Trustworthiness. When parents permit their teens to date, they show that they trust their children to make responsible decisions. A teen who has the self-control and self-discipline to resist peer pressure and avoid high-risk behaviors demonstrates trustworthiness. **What are some other ways you can demonstrate trustworthiness?**

A curfew is a limit that many parents set for their teens. *What are some other examples of limits that help keep you safe?*

Avoiding Risk Situations

Some dating situations may increase the chance of being pressured to participate in sexual activity or some other high-risk behaviors. Before you go on a date, know where you're going and what you will be doing. Find out who else will be there, and discuss with your parents what time they expect you home. If you're going to a party, for example, know where the party is being held and whether there will be adult supervision. Before you begin dating, it's important that you understand the role of individual responsibility regarding personal risk behaviors.

Below are more tips for avoiding high-risk dating situations:

▶ **Avoid places where alcohol and other drugs are present.** Learn to identify risk behaviors. The use of alcohol or other drugs interferes with judgment. People under the influence of these substances are more likely to engage in unsafe or high-risk behaviors. Prevent such situations by not using alcohol or other drugs and avoiding those who are using these substances.

▶ **Avoid being alone with a date at home or in an isolated place.** You may find it more difficult to maintain self-control when you are home alone or in an isolated place with a date. Being isolated from others also increases your risk of being forced into a sexual act against your will.

Dating Relationships

Some teens choose to have an ongoing dating relationship with only one person. This type of relationship may help you develop skills and behaviors that will someday prepare you for marriage. However, keep in mind that dating only one person during adolescence may limit your chances for socializing with others. This may prevent you from developing other positive relationships.

Your teen years are a time for trying many different roles and relationships. Although beginning and ending dating relationships can be difficult, such experiences help you mature emotionally. The teen years are also a time for refining skills and strategies for remaining or becoming abstinent from sexual intercourse, and avoiding sexually transmitted diseases, including HIV/AIDS. Staying in a relationship because you don't know how to leave it gracefully or clinging to a person who wishes to end the relationship are common dating problems. Honesty and open communication will help resolve such difficulties. Healthful behaviors help you mature into a thoughtful caring adult who can commit to a relationship.

Setting Limits

Your parents or guardians may set limits regarding your dating relationships. Such limits are intended to protect your health and safety. For example, your parent or guardian might insist on a **curfew**, *a set time at which you must be home at night.* A curfew is a limit that many parents establish for their teens. Limits should be established ahead of time and agreed upon by both teens and their families before the date.

As you mature, you'll need to know how to set your own limits. Remember, your parents or guardians can guide and support you through this process. For example, it's a good idea to set a limit on the age of the people you date. You also need to set limits with your date regarding places you'll go, how you'll get there, and what you will do. Setting such limits and making them clear before a date helps you avoid potentially risky situations.

When you communicate your limit on sexual activity, you need to be clear and firm about your decision to practice abstinence. You can make this task easier by developing and rehearsing avoidance techniques and refusal skills—including specific actions and phrases. You will learn more about these skills in the next lesson.

Health Minute

Healthful Dating Expectations

When in a dating relationship, remember:

► You deserve to be treated with consideration and respect.

► Your partner should recognize and respect your values.

► If pressured by your date, you can say no to drugs or other high-risk activities without apologizing or offering an explanation.

► No one has the right to force or pressure you into doing anything that goes against your values or your family's values.

LESSON 3 REVIEW

Reviewing Facts and Vocabulary

1. What is *affection?* How can teens show affection in a dating relationship in a way that enhances the dignity, respect, and responsibility relating to marriage?

2. What are some ways to avoid high-risk dating situations?

3. Why is it important to set limits in a dating relationship?

Thinking Critically

4. **Synthesizing.** List the personal benefits that establishing a curfew can have for your health.

5. **Analyzing.** Explain the role that substance abuse plays in increasing the risk of unsafe behaviors such as sexual activity.

Applying Health Skills

Analyzing Influences. Watch several television programs that portray characters involved in dating relationships. Observe the interactions among the characters, and identify what message the program communicates to teens about peer pressure and sexual activity. Summarize your observations in a written report.

After You Read

Problems and Solutions. Dating can be fun, but it can also increase the chance of being pressured into high-risk activities. Make a two-column chart. On the left side, list some of the activities to do on a date. On the right side, list tips for avoiding risk situations and ways to set limits such as a curfew.

 Visit **health.glencoe.com** for the Interactive Study Guide for Lesson 3.

Lesson 3 Dating and Setting Limits **317**

Abstinence: A Responsible Decision

Guide to Reading

Building Vocabulary

As you read this lesson, write each new highlighted term and its definition in your notebook.

- ▶ abstinence (p. 318)
- ▶ sexually transmitted diseases (STDs) (p. 318)
- ▶ priorities (p. 319)
- ▶ self-control (p. 319)

Focusing on the Main Ideas

In this lesson, you will learn how to:

- ▶ Define abstinence from sexual activity as the preferred choice of behavior for unmarried persons of school age.
- ▶ Summarize legal implications regarding sexual activity and prevention of pregnancy and sexually transmitted diseases.
- ▶ Apply using avoidance techniques and refusal skills to reduce the risk of being pressured into sexual activity.

Reading Strategy

Identify Problems and Solutions

- ▶ Prior to reading, identify some problems you think you might encounter while dating. List some ways that you can prevent those problems from occurring.

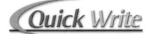

Quick Write

There are consequences to being sexually active. Write a paragraph describing how these consequences might affect the health of a teen and his or her family.

Ⓐ These teens recognize the importance and benefits of abstinence in preventing pregnancy and STDs. *Why is abstinence the preferred choice for unmarried persons of school age?*

Many of the sexual feelings teens experience are brought on by the body's release of chemicals. You don't have control over the feelings caused by your hormones, but you do have complete control over how you respond to them.

Abstinence Until Marriage

Each year, more and more teens make the choice of abstinence from sexual activity until marriage. **Abstinence** is *a deliberate decision to avoid high-risk behaviors, including sexual activity before marriage and the use of tobacco, alcohol, and other drugs.* Many teens choose to practice abstinence because it is the only 100 percent sure way to eliminate health risks associated with sexual activity. These risks include unplanned pregnancy and **sexually transmitted diseases (STDs)**—*infections spread from person to person through sexual contact.*

Committing to Abstinence

The teen years are a time for physical, mental/emotional, and social growth. Part of this growth process involves setting goals for the future and establishing priorities. **Priorities** are *those goals, tasks, and activities that you judge to be more important than others.* A priority for many teens, for example, is to get good grades and succeed in school. Think about your plans for the future. How might an unplanned pregnancy or a **sexually transmitted disease (STD)** affect your plans? Making abstinence from sexual activity a priority can eliminate these risks and help you achieve your goals.

Practicing abstinence requires planning and self-control. **Self-control** is *a person's ability to use responsibility to override emotions.* Use the following tips as a guide to commit to abstinence.

Reading Check

Explain What does it mean to commit to abstinence?

▶ **Establish your priorities.** Think about your goals, and set priorities that will help you reach them. Consider your values and those of your family.

▶ **Set personal limits on how you express affection.** Base your limits on your priorities. Set your limits before you are in a situation where sexual feelings may build.

▶ **Share your thoughts with your partner.** One sign of a mature, responsible relationship is being able to communicate with your partner openly and honestly. Discuss your priorities, and clearly define your limits.

▶ **Talk with a trusted adult.** Parents and other trusted adults are often able to suggest safe and healthful ways for you to manage your feelings.

▶ **Avoid high-pressure situations.** When possible, go out on dates in a group. Stay away from unsupervised parties and dark rooms. Avoid parking in secluded spots.

▶ **Do not use alcohol or other drugs.** Using alcohol or other drugs interferes with the ability to think clearly. It is also wise to avoid people who are using these substances.

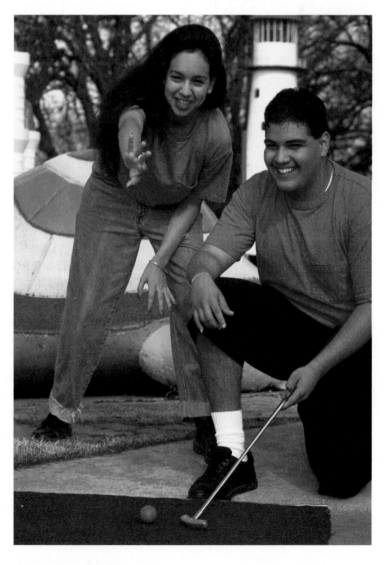

▼ Choosing a safe, supervised area for a date helps you uphold your values. *What other strategies can help you maintain your commitment to abstinence?*

Reasons to Practice Abstinence

Sexual activity has many short-term and long-term consequences. In addition to having legal consequences, teen sexual activity can seriously harm an individual's physical, mental/emotional, and social health. Practicing abstinence shows that you know strategies for health enhancement and risk reduction, and that you recognize abstinence from sexual activity as a positive choice.

Legal Implications

It is illegal for an adult to have sexual contact with anyone under the age of consent, which varies from state to state. In many states, it is illegal for unmarried minor persons to engage in sexual activity. For example, if the age of consent in a state is 18, two seventeen-year-old teens who engage in sexual activity are breaking the law. People who are arrested for and convicted of breaking sexual laws can go to jail. Depending on the situation, they may be identified as sex offenders—a label that will follow them for the rest of their lives.

Effects on Physical Health

Teen sexual activity can affect the physical health of both females and males in significant ways.

UNPLANNED PREGNANCY

Unplanned pregnancy is one possible consequence of sexual activity. While the rate of teen pregnancy has decreased in the United States during the last decade, it continues to risk the health of both the teen mother and her child. Often, the body of a teen is not sufficiently mature to sustain a healthy pregnancy. This can lead to complications that threaten the lives of mother and baby.

SEXUALLY TRANSMITTED DISEASES (STDS)

Teens from 15 to 19 years of age are at the greatest risk of contracting STDs. Each year, almost 4 million teens in the United States contract some form of STD. If diagnosed early, many STDs can be treated and cured. However, some of these diseases have no cure and can have lifelong consequences. For example, chlamydia can cause sterility if left untreated, making it impossible for a person ever to have a child. Other STDs, such as **acquired immune deficiency syndrome (AIDS),** can be fatal.

Careful consideration of the negative consequences associated with sexual activity will reinforce the decision to practice abstinence until marriage. *What are your reasons for practicing abstinence?*

Real-Life Application

Respecting Limits

Healthful dating relationships require teens to set limits on where they will go and what they will do. Good dating relationships also require teens to respect their date's decisions regarding these limits.

It's All About RESPECT

I can show someone that I respect them by...
- setting limits on how we show affection.
- sharing my feelings.
- not using alcohol and drugs.

ACTIVITY

In small groups, create posters or public service announcements that promote the importance of respecting the sexual limits of one's date. Poster should include reasons to respect another person's limits and should persuade others to do so.

Effects on Emotional Health

The teen years are a time of heightened emotions. This is primarily due to changing hormone levels as teens mature into adulthood. Events and incidents that have not seemed important in the past may now become increasingly important to some teens. One of the ways that teens express their heightened emotions is through their relationships with others. Some teens may recognize that their feelings for others are beginning to change and grow. They may begin thinking about engaging in sexual activity as a way to express those feelings. While sexual activity between adults may deepen a relationship, teens are generally not prepared for the emotional commitment of a sexual relationship. Some of the feelings that may result from beginning a sexual relationship during your teen years include:

▶ Hurt if your partner is not as committed to the relationship as you are.

▶ Guilt associated with lying to your parents or others about your sexual activity.

▶ Regret if the relationship results in an unplanned pregnancy or a sexually transmitted disease.

Abstinence of sexual activity enables you to develop deeper relationships with others and to avoid the risks to your emotional health.

Teens who choose sexual abstinence safeguard their health. *What are some other benefits of abstinence?*

Effects on Social Health

The teen years are a time for exploring a variety of interests, meeting new people, and deciding what career you may want to pursue. During this time, you'll develop a greater understanding of your interests. You'll identify the type of people you enjoy spending time with and will find friends who share your interests and beliefs. Teens who engage in sexual activity may feel that they need to make a commitment to only one person. This may cause them to avoid forming new friendships. By abstaining from sexual activity, teens allow themselves the opportunity to pursue new friendships without feeling that their partner has other expectations.

Some teens may begin to think about their sexual orientation during adolescence. Sexual orientation develops over a lifetime, and refers to the emotional and sexual attraction that you have for another person. The American Psychological Association says that sexual orientation results from an interaction of environmental, cognitive, and biological factors. Concerns related to sexual orientation may be difficult for some teens to talk about. Find a trusted adult with whom you can discuss topics that make you uncomfortable.

Engaging in sexual activity may also harm a teen's relationship with parents and other family members. When teens become sexually active, they may go beyond the limits that their parents and others have set for them. Parents who discover that their teen is sexually active may feel disappointment that their child did not wait longer to become sexually active. These feelings can cause tension among family members.

One result of teen sexual activity is unplanned pregnancy. Teen parents face many challenges, such as providing financial and emotional support for their child. Teens who become parents may have to put their own plans for college or job training on hold.

Abstinent teens protect their health by eliminating the risk of an unplanned pregnancy or the consequences of STDs.

Using Avoidance Techniques and Refusal Skills

To reduce the risk of being pressured into sexual activity, learn avoidance techniques—actions or phrases you can use to avoid risky situations. For example, if your date wants to go to a party that will not be supervised by adults, you might suggest going to a restaurant instead. Using avoidance techniques shows that you know methods for effectively expressing feelings and opinions on health and other issues.

FIGURE 12.3

SAYING NO TO SEXUAL ACTIVITY

If someone uses pressure lines to persuade you to break your commitment to abstinence, use refusal statements to communicate your stance firmly.

Pressure Line	Refusal Statement
• If you love me, you will. • Everyone's doing it. • Don't be such a baby. • My feelings won't change. I'll still respect you.	• If you care about me, you won't pressure me. • I'm not. • I'm not being a baby. I'm being smart. • Maybe I won't respect myself.

Share your commitment to abstinence with your girlfriend or boyfriend, stating your position simply but firmly. After you have discussed your decision to practice abstinence, you will find it easier to exercise self-control. If a situation seems to be getting out of control, insist on stopping. Then, back away and explain why you want to stop. If your girlfriend or boyfriend tries to pressure you, become more assertive. You might use refusal statements similar to those in **Figure 12.3.** You may just want to say, "No, I don't want to." Make sure your body language supports your verbal message. Don't be afraid of hurting the other person's feelings. It's possible to say no and still remain friends.

Reading Check

Predict What are some of the possible consequences of teen sexual activity?

LESSON 4 REVIEW

Reviewing Facts and Vocabulary

1. What is *abstinence*?
2. Discuss the legal implications of sexual activity as it relates to minor persons.
3. What are effective ways to avoid being pressured into sexual activity?

Thinking Critically

4. **Evaluating.** Write a paragraph describing the importance and benefits of abstinence as it relates to emotional and social health.
5. **Analyzing.** How can practicing abstinence benefit a teen's self-image? Explain your answer.

Applying Health Skills

Refusal Skills. With a classmate, role-play situations in which teens use refusal skills to avoid the unsafe situation of participating in sexual activity. Have classmates analyze the relationship between refusal skills and sexual abstinence.

After You Read

Cause and Effect. Sexual activity has many consequences. Make a two-column chart. On the left side, list some of the ways to commit to abstinence. On the right side, list the reasons to practice abstinence and the consequences of sexual activity.

CULTURE & COMMUNITY

Just Friends

Meet two sets of pals who prove that being platonic is a plus.

Jamie and David: Friends for five years

For David, 16, and Jamie, 16, friendship means having the best of both worlds—and the inside scoop on what the other gender thinks. "Since I'm a guy," says David, "I'll give her my honest opinion of what other guys will think." In turn, Jamie does her best to clear up the confusion in the way he communicates with girls. "Jamie helped me write a poem for a girl I liked," says David. "She tells me where to take a date and how to treat her."

Of course, the now-solid friendship has had its shaky moments. "I think she wanted to date me at first," says David, "but I didn't think it would work out." In retrospect, Jamie is glad that they stayed just friends. "It wouldn't have been worth risking our friendship," she says.

Michelle and Darren: Friends for six years

Michelle, 16, and Darren, 17, started out as "sweethearts." "We had a little puppy love going on in third grade," says Michelle. However, by the time the pair hit junior high, romance had given way to friendship. It's been that way ever since. "Romantic relationships usually end," Michelle says, "but friendships go on forever."

So do their nightly marathon phone conversations, in which no topic is off-limits. Darren finds he can really open up to Michelle about girls, school, and parents. "It's okay to express yourself to a girl, whereas a guy might think you sound corny," says Darren. "When I talk to Michelle, time passes really quickly." As for Michelle, she finds it easier to confide in Darren than in some of her girlfriends. Summing up their friendship, Michelle says, "What we have right now is the best it's ever been." ◼

TIME to THINK... About Platonic Relationships

The teens in the article mention ways their friends help them. Brainstorm ways friends are important to you. Then with your classmates create a list of the values of friendships. Are any of those values unique to boy/girl friendships?

1. **Practicing Healthful Behavior.** Develop a plan for demonstrating to your friends each of the traits that characterize a healthy friendship. Over the span of a week, keep a log to describe how you demonstrated each trait. *(LESSON 1)*

PRACTICING HEALTHFUL BEHAVIORS

2. **Analyzing Influences.** Locate a magazine or newspaper article about a teen who has set a positive example in the community. Write a brief summary of the article, and identify how the actions of that teen might be a positive influence on other teens. *(LESSON 2)*

ANALYZING INFLUENCES

3. **Communication Skills.** Write a skit that depicts a responsible, healthful dating relationship between two teens. The teens should demonstrate effective communication skills to show their respect for each other and their commitment to practicing abstinence. *(LESSON 3)*

COMMUNICATION SKILLS

4. **Advocacy.** Write a letter to the editor of your school newspaper discussing abstinence as the only method that is 100 percent effective in preventing pregnancy, STDs, the sexual transmission of HIV/AIDS, and the emotional trauma associated with adolescent sexual activity. *(LESSON 4)*

ADVOCACY

CAREER Corner

School Social Worker

School social workers deal with a wide range of social, emotional, cultural, and economic concerns among students. They help students overcome problems that may be interfering with their education. School social workers also help improve students' decision-making skills, motivation, attendance, and self-concept.

To become a school social worker, you need a bachelor's or a master's degree in social work and a license or certificate from your state. Learn more about this and other health careers by clicking on Career Corner at **health.glencoe.com.**

BEYOND *the* Classroom

Parent Involvement

Practicing Healthful Behaviors. Many communities have programs that provide drug-free places where teens can socialize under adult supervision. Such programs help teens avoid pressure to participate in high-risk behaviors. With your parents, learn about the programs for teens in your area. If such programs do not exist in your community, find out how one might be created.

School and Community

Stopping Harassment. Speak with a law enforcement official in your community to learn the legal definition of harassment and what penalties exist for teens found guilty of harassment. Share your findings with the class. Discuss actions that students, faculty, and community members can take to help stop harassment.

After You Read

Use your Foldable to review what you have learned about safe and healthy friendships. On the back of your Foldable, write a description of your best friend and the common values and interests that you share.

FOLDABLES™
Study Organizer

► EXPLORING HEALTH TERMS *Answer the following questions on a sheet of paper.*

Lesson 1 *Match each definition with the correct term.*

clique   friendship
peers   platonic friendship
stereotype

1. A relationship with a member of the opposite gender in which there is affection but the people are not considered a couple.

2. A small circle of friends that excludes people viewed as outsiders.

3. An exaggerated or oversimplified belief about an entire group of people.

Lesson 2 *Replace the underlined words with the correct term.*

aggressive   assertive
harassment   manipulation
passive   peer pressure
refusal skills

4. <u>Harassment</u> is an indirect and dishonest way to control someone.

5. An important aspect of being assertive is to use effective <u>manipulation</u>.

6. Being overly pushy and hostile is being <u>assertive</u>.

Lesson 3 *Fill in the blanks with the correct term.*

affection   curfew
infatuation

Shane's parents worry about his (_7_), or exaggerated feelings of passion, with his girlfriend. To help Shane avoid situations that could involve him in high-risk behaviors, his parents set guidelines for him, including an early (_8_), or time by which he must be at home.

Lesson 4 *Match each definition with the correct term.*

abstinence   self-control
sexually transmitted disease   priorities

9. A risk associated with not choosing abstinence.

10. Goals, tasks, and activities you judge as more important than others.

11. A person's ability to use responsibility to override emotions.

► RECALLING THE FACTS *Use complete sentences to answer the following questions.*

1. What is the relationship between peers and casual friendships?

2. What are the benefits of a platonic friendship?

3. Identify five attributes of a true friendship.

4. What is positive peer pressure?

5. How can body language be used to communicate refusal?

6. Describe an aggressive response to peer pressure.

7. What are some benefits of dating?

8. Why do some teens choose not to date?

9. What are some advantages of group dating over individual dating?

10. Identify three risks associated with sexual activity during the teen years.

11. Analyze the importance of abstinence from sexual activity as the preferred choice of behavior in relationship to all sexual activity for unmarried persons of school age.

12. Describe a problem that can result from an unplanned teen pregnancy.

For more review questions for Chapter 12, go to **health.glencoe.com**.

➤ WRITING CRITICALLY

1. **Narrative.** Write a one-page story about a teen who is being pressured to take part in an unsafe activity. In your story, identify the unsafe activity and how the teen uses refusal skills to resist peer pressure.

2. **Personal.** Write a letter to yourself outlining your personal reasons for practicing abstinence from sexual activity until marriage. Keep your letter with you as a reminder if you feel pressure to engage in sexual activity.

Standardized Test Practice

 Read the passage below and then answer the questions.

Tamara

I have been best friends with Tamara since her family moved to my town when I was in the first grade. Tamara is nice to me and to other people.

Tamara's kindness shows in many things that she does. Once she gave her circus tickets to some neighborhood kids who had never been to the circus. Tamara visits a nearby nursing home at least once a month. She worries about some of the people she has met there because they have no one else visiting them.

Tamara was a good friend to me when my parents divorced. She listened to me for hours as I talked about how angry I was. She also let me cry when I felt like crying. Tamara never told me that I was overreacting or that I would get over it. I knew that she couldn't do anything to change the situation, but she always made me feel better.

1. How does the author support the idea that Tamara is a good friend?

A by comparing Tamara's actions to those of her other friends

B by pointing out that Tamara once helped with a canned-food drive

C by citing examples of Tamara's kindness to her and to other people

D by saying that Tamara does not talk about people behind their backs

2. How would you summarize the subject of the third paragraph?

F Tamara probably knows about divorce firsthand.

G Tamara's listening skills have made me feel better.

H Tamara thinks she always knows what's best for me.

I Tamara likes to get involved in people's personal lives.

3. Describe the qualities that *you* think make someone a good friend. Give examples and details to back up your opinions.

Violence Prevention

Antiviolence Media Campaign

Communities and schools can create an environment promoting antiviolence. Media campaigns can help teens and others learn to

▶ promote peaceful solutions to conflict.

▶ avoid gang activities.

▶ prevent bullying.

Visit the Eye on the Media section at **health.glencoe.com** to learn more about how you can use media to create an antiviolence message.

FOLDABLES™
Study Organizer

Before You Read

Use this Foldable to help you record what you learn about personal safety. Begin with two sheets of notebook paper.

▶ **Step 1**

Fold two sheets of notebook paper in half along the short axis. Cut one sheet about 1" along the fold at both ends, stopping at the margin lines.

▶ **Step 2**

Cut or shave the other sheet along the fold between the margin lines.

▶ **Step 3**

Roll up the first sheet, slip it halfway through the cut in the second sheet, and open it up.

As You Read

As you read and discuss the material in the chapter, use your Foldable to take notes, define terms, and record examples and personal experiences.

▶ **Step 4**

Personal Safety Journal

Fold the pages in half and label as shown. Label the inside pages Protective Factors, Smart Precautions, Body Language and Self-Defense, Keeping Homes Safe, Safety in the Community, and Analyzing My Personal Safety Habits.

SPOTLIGHT ON HEALTH

Using Visuals. Community involvement and advocacy can contribute to safer environments for everyone. What can you do to help keep your neighborhood safe?

Personal Safety

Guide to Reading

Building Vocabulary

As you read this lesson, write each new highlighted term and its definition in your notebook.

▶ body language (p. 332)

▶ self-defense (p. 332)

▶ assertive (p. 332)

Focusing on the Main Ideas

In this lesson, you will learn how to:

▶ **Identify** behaviors and strategies that enhance personal safety.

▶ **Examine** ways to avoid and reduce threatening situations.

▶ **Discover** strategies for safety at home and in the community.

Reading Strategy

Predict

▶ Scan the headings, subheadings, and pictures. List three things you think might be included in this lesson.

Write a brief paragraph describing how you can keep yourself safe from violence.

Being confident and not looking like a victim can help keep you safe. *How can you project self-confidence?*

The key to personal safety is to be able to recognize potentially dangerous situations and learn strategies to avoid them. Simple safety habits that you practice every day can decrease your exposure to risk. Being aware of your surroundings, not walking alone, staying away from dark or isolated areas, and looking alert and confident are all behaviors that can protect you. A relatively new issue that has impacted all of our lives is the raised awareness of terrorism. In response to this threat to personal safety, the Department of Homeland Security was created.

Your Protective Factors

Although you may not be conscious of them, you already have many assets that increase your chances of staying safe. A list of personal traits and environmental conditions that reduce teens' risk of violence is shown in **Figure 13.1** on the next page. These traits and conditions are specific protective factors that can help shield you from harm. Everyone can work to strengthen those protective factors that he or she can control, and help to reduce the risk of violence. Doing so will contribute to personal safety.

330 **Chapter 13** Violence Prevention

Take the Health Inventory for Chapter 13 at **health.glencoe.com**.

FIGURE 13.1

INDIVIDUAL AND SOCIAL PROTECTIVE FACTORS AGAINST VIOLENCE

These protective factors decrease the likelihood of teen violence.

Individual	Family	Peer/School	Community
• No history of aggressive behavior • Positive social skills; gets along with others • Intelligent • Antiviolence attitude • Being female	• Parents monitor child's behavior • Parents positively evaluate peers • Warm, supportive relationship with parents or other adults	• Peers and friends avoid high-risk behaviors • Commitment to school • Good attitude	• Strong economic opportunity • Involvement in community activities

Source: Youth Violence: A Report of the Surgeon General

Strategies for Staying Safe

In addition to strengthening your **protective factors,** there are behaviors you can practice to stay safe. These actions include taking precautions against risky situations and developing safety habits.

Smart Precautions

The first step in taking responsibility for your personal safety is to consider preventive behaviors that will help protect you. Identify local support systems concerning safety, such as the police, your family, teachers and other school personnel, friends, and even religious advisors. Many safety precautions that can prevent your becoming a victim are commonsense actions. Here are some preventive measures to follow.

► Avoid unsafe areas, including places with high crime rates.

► Don't carry your wallet or purse in a conspicuous, easy-to-grab place.

► Walk briskly and confidently. *Always* look as though you know where you are going and what you are doing.

► Avoid walking alone at night, in wooded areas, or in dark alleys. If you must walk at night, avoid doorways and walk under lights near the curb.

► If you drive, park your car in a well-lit area. Have your keys out and ready as you approach your parked car. Before getting into your car, look to make sure that no one is inside. Lock the doors as soon as you get in.

Reading Check

Evaluate How do protective factors decrease the likelihood of teen violence?

Taking safety precautions is particularly important when you are out at night. *What behaviors demonstrated by these teens help keep them safe?*

► Let your family know where you're going and when you'll return.

► Do not get into an elevator alone with a stranger.

► Get on and off buses in well-lit areas.

► If someone you know gives you a ride, ask the person to wait until you have safely entered a building.

► Do not hitchhike or give rides to hitchhikers.

► Avoid the use of alcohol or other drugs. These substances impair your judgment and reduce your ability to protect yourself.

Body Language and Self-Defense

You can protect yourself from harm by communicating to others that you are worthy of being treated with respect and that you have a right to be safe and secure. You can project this information through the use of **body language**, *nonverbal communication through gestures, facial expressions, behaviors, and posture.* Making direct eye contact, using a strong voice, holding your head high, and walking with a deliberate stride demonstrate that you are in charge of your safety. A health-literate individual understands the relationship between verbal and nonverbal communication.

Key self-defense strategies can also protect you from becoming a victim of violence. **Self-defense** includes *any strategy for protecting oneself from harm.* A range of self-defense classes is available, including various martial arts courses. Signing up for such a class is an effective way to enhance your confidence and sense of preparedness. Although physical strategies can be a useful part of self-defense, mental strategies are also important. In some communities, law enforcement officials teach personal safety classes on awareness and preparedness. Often, they stress the importance of projecting self-confidence and assertiveness. Being **assertive** means *standing up for your rights and beliefs in firm but positive ways.* Through words and actions, such as walking purposefully, assertive people show that they are not easy targets. They are proactive in protecting their health and safety.

ⓥ **Taking a self-defense class can increase your sense of personal safety.** *What other strategies can help protect your health and safety?*

Hands-On Health ACTIVITY

Practicing Safety Strategies

Staying safe doesn't mean living in fear. It means analyzing and applying strategies that will reduce your risk of becoming a victim of violence. In this activity, you will role-play some strategies for avoiding violence.

What You'll Need

• pencil and notebook paper

What You'll Do

1. With a partner or in a small group, brainstorm several unsafe situations that teens may face. For example, a stranger in a car tells you that he is lost and asks you to approach the window to look at his map. Record your scenarios on a sheet of paper.

2. For each situation, discuss safe ways for teens to respond. If necessary, refer to the tips given in this lesson.

3. Role-play a situation from your list.

4. As a class, discuss the situations that were role-played. Which did you think were the most realistic? Why? What safety strategies might be effective?

Apply and Conclude

Using what you learned from the role-plays you observed, compose a short essay for the school paper informing teens how to stay safe in various situations. The article should include three or four safety tips and be relevant to teens in high school.

Keeping Homes Safe

A home should be a nurturing haven in which family members feel secure. Here are some tips for you to follow to help maintain the safety of your home environment.

▶ Lock doors with a bolt. All family members should make an effort to keep all doors, including sliding doors and French doors, secure and in good repair.

▶ Make sure windows have locks. Keep windows locked at night and when no one is home. Repair broken windows immediately.

▶ Install a peephole in your front door.

▶ Never open the door to someone you don't know or trust. Don't let strangers use your phone.

▶ Do not tell unknown callers that you are home alone.

▶ Do not give out personal information over the telephone or computer.

▶ Ask for identification before allowing repair or utility personnel into your home.

 Keeping your doors and windows locked can help keep you and your family safe. *What are some other strategies for keeping your home secure?*

Explain How does body language help protect you from harm?

Safety in the Community

How safe a community is has a significant impact on personal safety. Many communities have taken steps to make neighborhoods safer. Some of the strategies include:

▶ **Increased police patrol.** Some communities have increased the number of law enforcement officers on street patrol.

▶ **Neighborhood Watch programs.** Residents have joined the crime prevention effort by looking for signs of suspicious activity and reporting such incidents to the police.

▶ **After-school programs.** Academic, cultural, or recreational programs after school provide safe environments where teens can use their time productively. These programs also give teens an opportunity to participate in physical activity programs.

▶ **Improved lighting in parks and playgrounds.** Better lighting can discourage crime by making it more difficult to commit crimes without being seen.

By supporting and participating in efforts such as these, residents can contribute to making communities safer for everyone. A health advocate participates in and knows the health concerns that require collaborative decision making.

LESSON 1 REVIEW

Reviewing Facts and Vocabulary

1. What is *body language*? Give three examples.
2. Define the term *assertive*, and use it in a sentence.
3. List two ways to keep your home safe.

Thinking Critically

4. **Evaluating.** Assess the value of avoiding potentially dangerous situations, even if you know how to defend yourself.
5. **Analyzing.** How can involvement in community activities serve as a protective factor against violent behavior?

Applying Health Skills

Practicing Healthful Behaviors. Develop a list of strategies that you and other members of your family can use to promote individual and family safety. Discuss these safety behaviors with your family, and put your plan into action.

After You Read

Explain. Write a short skit featuring two people. Show how body language can lead to misunderstandings.

Keeping Schools Safe

Guide to Reading

Building Vocabulary

As you read this lesson, write each new highlighted term and its definition in your notebook.

- violence (p. 335)
- bullying (p. 336)
- sexual harassment (p. 336)
- gang (p. 337)
- peer mediation (p. 339)

Focusing on the Main Ideas

In this lesson, you will learn how to:

- Describe factors that play a role in school violence.
- Determine actions that individuals, schools, and communities can take to reduce violence.

Reading Strategy

Organize Information

- On a sheet of paper, list each of the vocabulary terms. As you read, write down the definition for each term.

Quick Write

What are some of the causes of conflict that lead to violence among high school students? Write a paragraph summarizing your views.

In recent years, the media has focused attention on acts of violence in schools, including gang activities, physical attacks, and shootings. However, despite the publicity given to violent incidents, schools are generally safe places. According to the Centers for Disease Control and Prevention (CDC), the trend has been toward *less* violence in schools since 1991. For example, the number of students who participated in physical fights at school has dropped nine percentage points. During that same time, the number of students who carried weapons decreased from 26.1 to 17.1 percent.

Issues of School Safety

Although schools are generally safe, some violence may occur on or near school grounds. **Violence** is *the threatened or actual use of physical force or power to harm another person or to damage property.* The 2003 Youth Risk Behaviors Surveillance Survey found that 33 percent of teens in grades 9–12 had been in at least one physical fight at school in the previous year. In the same year, 9.2 percent of students were threatened or injured with a weapon at school.

School should be a safe place for students to learn and engage in fun, healthy activities. *How does your school help ensure the safety of students and school personnel?*

Because any violence threatens the safety of everyone in the school community, national health goals have been set to reduce physical fighting and the carrying of weapons by adolescents on school property. In order to meet these goals, it's important to look at factors that play a role in school violence.

Bullying and Hazing

Bullying is *the act of seeking power or attention through the psychological, emotional, verbal, or physical abuse of another person.* Cyber bullying is a new type of bullying where someone is attacked through hurtful emails or cell phone messages.

While bullying is often meant to exclude someone from a group, hazing is an attempt to include someone through an initiation process that can be physically, emotionally, and psychologically abusive. For more information on hazing, see the Health Skills Activity on page 339.

Bullies come in all ages and genders. Bullying is harmful behavior. Bullies tend to select teens who they perceive as being emotionally weak, different, or who don't have many friends. Teens who are bullied may become depressed, withdrawn, fearful, and angry. If you are experiencing bullying, there are actions you can take:

▶ Hold your head high, look the bully straight in the eye, then turn around and walk away. This confident action shows that you are not afraid.

▶ Tell a trusted adult that you are being bullied, especially if the bullying is physical or violent. If you are not being heard, tell another adult. Keep talking until something is done to put a stop to the bully.

▶ If it gets physical, stay calm and get help.

Sexual Harassment

Sexual harassment is *uninvited and unwelcome sexual conduct directed at another person.* Words, jokes, gestures, or touching of a sexual nature are all forms of sexual harassment. Harassment is unethical and causes embarrassment, discomfort, and emotional pain for the victim. Federal law states that sexual harassment is illegal. Incidents of sexual harassment should be reported to school personnel at once. After a complaint has been made, school officials will investigate and take action to solve the problem.

A Bullies use words and physical force to seek power or attention. *What are some ways you can let bullies know that you don't approve of their actions?*

Did You Know ?

Bullies often target others who are different or who they believe have low self-esteem. People become bullies for the following reasons:

- Bullies may be responding to a difficult situation in their life. Perhaps their parents are divorcing, and they're having a difficult time coping with the situation.
- Bullies might be treating others the way they're treated at home. It may be normal in a bully's family to behave aggressively.
- Bullies might not know how their behavior hurts others.

Gangs

A **gang** is *a group of people who associate with one another to take part in criminal activity.* Common gang activities include vandalism, robbery, defacing public property with graffiti, and selling drugs. Some gang activities are unpredictable and place innocent people in harm's way. Random shootings, for example, can injure or kill non–gang members. Gang members may bring weapons or drugs to school, endangering the safety of other students.

Reducing the Risk of Violence

Students and faculty have the right to feel safe at school. Being worried about personal safety in the school environment hinders the teaching and learning process. Keeping schools safe is a priority shared by communities across the nation.

Recognizing Warning Signs

Being able to recognize the warning signs of violence can help members of a school community address potentially threatening situations before they occur. **Figure 13.2** lists some common warning signs of violence. Evidence of these signs may indicate that a person is near to acting in a dangerous manner. If you observe any of these signs in a student and suspect that he or she may become violent, inform a teacher, counselor, or other faculty member immediately. An informed teen knows strategies for dealing with individuals who are exhibiting dangerous behaviors.

 You can help keep your school safe by reporting any behaviors that may lead to violence. *What other actions can you take to contribute to school safety?*

FIGURE 13.2

WARNING SIGNS OF VIOLENCE

- Has difficulty controlling anger
- Disobeys school rules
- Frequently engages in risk behaviors
- Creates violent artwork or writing
- Constantly talks about weapons or violence
- Vandalizes and destroys property
- Uses alcohol or other drugs
- Harms animals
- Makes threats or detailed plans to hurt others
- Brings or talks about bringing a weapon to school

Explain What are three warning signs of violence?

What You Can Do

Making your school safe begins with building a culture of respect among all students and faculty members. You are empowered to contribute to a safe and healthy school environment. Nationwide, teens are pledging to avoid violence and are encouraging their peers to do the same. A health-literate individual knows strategies for solving interpersonal conflicts without harming self and others. To take a stand and help keep schools safe, you can apply these strategies:

▶ refuse to carry weapons and report people who do carry them.

▶ report any violent acts or threats of violence to school authorities or police.

▶ practice **conflict-resolution** skills and help others settle disputes peacefully.

▶ use refusal skills to resist negative peer pressure and avoid unsafe situations and behaviors.

▶ choose your friends carefully. Having friends who share similar values can help protect you from violence.

▶ avoid spending time with people who show warning signs of violent behavior.

▶ tell a parent, teacher, or other adult about your fears if you suspect that your safety is in danger. Avoid being alone.

▶ join or develop a S.A.V.E. chapter (Students Against Violence Everywhere).

Reading Check

Infer What can you do to help make your school safe?

Some schools use metal detectors to reduce the threat of violence. *What other measures might schools adopt to promote safety?*

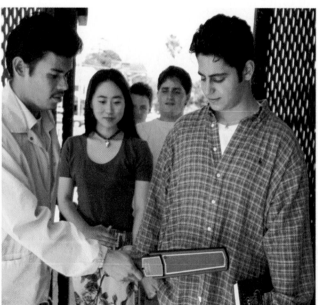

What Schools Are Doing

Schools have procedures and policies to ensure the safety of students. For example, some schools have adopted a *zero-tolerance policy,* which can require expulsion of students who participate in violence or who are found with drugs or weapons. Other efforts to reduce school violence include using metal detectors, examining students' backpacks, or searching lockers for weapons or drugs. Some schools have "closed" campuses, keeping all doors except the main entrance locked. This helps prevent unauthorized persons from coming into the school. Security guards may also be hired to patrol hallways and grounds while classes are in session.

Health Skills Activity

Decision Making: When Joining a Group Becomes Dangerous

Angie has belonged to a swim team since she was five years old. She just tried out for the junior varsity team and now anxiously waits to hear if she made the cut.

"I hope I make the team," the girl next to her confides, "but I'm a little scared of the hazing. I heard that last year the varsity girls dunked the new members and wouldn't let them out of the pool for over an hour. If they refused to participate, the varsity girls told them they weren't 'really' members of the group."

The results have now been posted, and Angie sees her name on the list. She has made the team, but now she doesn't know what to do. She can't imagine giving up swimming, but she doesn't want to risk getting hurt just to be part of a team.

What Would You Do?
Apply the six steps of the decision-making model to Angie's situation.

1. State the situation.
2. List the options.
3. Weigh the possible outcomes.
4. Consider values.
5. Make a decision and act.
6. Evaluate the decision.

PEER MEDIATION

Many schools use peer mediation to help reduce the risk of violence that may stem from unresolved conflicts. **Peer mediation** is *a process in which trained students help other students find fair ways to resolve conflict and settle their differences.* Such programs are successful because they are confidential and do not punish the students involved. Peer mediation sessions typically follow these steps:

▶ **Making introductions.** The mediator explains that he or she will remain neutral and that the session will be confidential.

▶ **Establishing ground rules.** The parties agree to the rules of the process, such as listening without interrupting, maintaining respect and honesty, and being willing to accept the adopted solutions. Then, the mediator decides who talks first.

▶ **Hearing each side.** The mediator allows each party to speak. He or she may ask questions and take notes.

▶ **Exploring solutions.** After all parties have spoken, the mediator asks for possible solutions. A list is made of the suggestions, and each one is discussed. The mediator helps the parties negotiate until a solution is agreed upon.

▶ **Closing the session.** The mediator summarizes the agreement and asks participants to discuss their feelings about the process. The parties are encouraged to use these skills to solve future conflicts.

V These teens are holding a rally to promote safe schools in their community. *What are some ways that communities can promote school safety?*

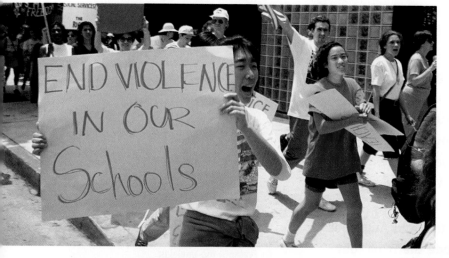

Parent and Community Involvement

Parents can work with police officers, social workers, and business leaders to promote safety in schools. Community members can help by taking part in school events and by volunteering to monitor hallways, rest rooms, cafeterias, and other areas where students gather. Developing and supporting programs and activities that provide teens a safe place to gather can also help reduce violence.

LESSON 2 REVIEW

Reviewing Facts and Vocabulary

1. Define *gangs*. How might gang members endanger the safety of other students?

2. List two warning signs that a person may be close to acting in a dangerous manner.

3. Identify three policies, procedures, or strategies that schools use to prevent and respond to deliberate injury.

Thinking Critically

4. **Analyzing.** Explain the similarities and differences between bullying and sexual harassment.

5. **Applying.** What are some strategies for avoiding unsafe situations or violence at school?

Applying Health Skills

Refusal Skills. Write a scenario in which a student applies refusal skills as a strategy to avoid participation in a potentially violent situation that may involve weapons.

After You Read

Problems and Solutions. Create a T chart. On one side, list issues of school safety and facts about violence on school grounds. On the other side, list ways to reduce the risk of violence.

Visit **health.glencoe.com** for the Interactive Study Guide for Lesson 2.

Protecting Yourself from Violence

Guide to Reading

Building Vocabulary

As you read this lesson, write each new highlighted term and its definition in your notebook.

▶ assailant (p. 341)

▶ prejudice (p. 342)

▶ assault (p. 344)

▶ random violence (p. 344)

▶ homicide (p. 344)

▶ sexual violence (p. 345)

▶ sexual assault (p. 346)

▶ rape (p. 346)

Focusing on the Main Ideas

In this lesson, you will learn how to:

▶ Compare the causes and effects of violence.

▶ Show influences on violence, such as the media and alcohol and other drugs.

▶ Identify different types of violence and strategies for avoiding violence.

▶ Develop strategies for avoiding gangs and weapons.

Reading Strategy

Predict

▶ After scanning the headings, subheadings, and pictures, write a summary describing what information you think you'll learn in this lesson.

Quick Write

Think about some of the things that might cause violent behavior. Write a paragraph describing ways you can avoid violence.

The nature of violence is complex. For years, psychologists have investigated why people commit violent acts but have not yet reached a conclusion. Your personal safety depends on your ability to recognize possible sources of violence in your environment. This will help you choose behaviors that minimize your chances of being a victim. An informed individual knows strategies for health enhancement and risk reduction and is able to identify threats to personal safety. Other ways to protect yourself from violence include identifying resources for managing relationships, and demonstrating conflict resolution skills.

Ⓐ Going out in groups and being aware of your surroundings are two ways of reducing your risk of violence. *What are some other strategies you can use to avoid unsafe situations?*

Why Violence Occurs

Violence may occur for many reasons. Some people use violence as a means of dealing with conflicts. In such cases, the victim may know his or her **assailant**—*a person who commits a violent act against another.* Violence may also result from anger or frustration.

Other common causes of violence and deliberate injury include the following:

▶ **Need to control others.** Some people use violence to control others or to get something they want.

▶ **Way of expressing anger.** People who are unable to manage their anger may strike out against others in a violent way.

▶ **Prejudice.** Some acts of violence are crimes of hate that stem from **prejudice**—*an unfair opinion or judgment of a particular group of people.*

▶ **Retaliation.** People sometimes use violence to retaliate against—or get back at—individuals or groups who have hurt them in some way.

Reading Check

Explain What are some of the reasons that violence occurs?

Influences on Violence

In addition to motives for violent behavior, several factors may also contribute to violence. These include weapons availability, media messages, substance abuse, and mental/emotional health issues such as a negative self-concept.

Weapons Availability

Most homicides that occur among 15- to 19-year-olds involve firearms. A recent survey sponsored by the CDC found that almost one-fifth of responding high-school students reported carrying a weapon in the month proceeding the survey. Most of these weapons are conventional weapons such as handguns, knives, and clubs. However, newer, more dangerous weapons, including assault rifles, are finding their way into teens' hands. Teens with gang affiliations are more likely than others to acquire these weapons.

Strategies exist to reduce accidents and intentional injuries caused by firearms, as well as to avoid weapons altogether. Efforts have been made to control gun ownership through stronger laws. People must now undergo background checks in order to purchase guns from licensed dealers. In some states, they must also register their handguns. People who own guns legally can install safety devices on their firearms. In addition, owners are encouraged to keep guns unloaded and securely stored when not in use and to store ammunition in a separate, secure location.

▼ Working together to stop prejudice can help reduce violence. *What strategies can individuals and communities use to prevent and respond to deliberate injury?*

The Media

By age 13, most American children have seen 100,000 acts of violence on television, including about 8,000 murders. Violence is also a common theme in movies, video games, song lyrics, and music videos. The role of the media in contributing to violent behavior is a matter of great debate. Some critics think that exposure to violence may provide a "recipe" for violence. They point to increased occurrences of violent acts following extensive media coverage of such events. Other experts think that young people become desensitized, or emotionally indifferent, to acts of violence when they see such images repeatedly. People who become desensitized are no longer bothered or upset when they witness violent acts. As a result, they may be less inclined to take action to prevent or stop violence.

Alcohol and Other Drugs

Use of alcohol and other drugs may contribute to incidents of violent crime. Drug users often turn to illegal activities, such as robbery, to obtain money to purchase drugs. Many drive-by shootings involve disputes between gangs or individuals who sell drugs.

People using alcohol or other drugs cannot think clearly and have difficulty making safe, healthful decisions. Accidents caused by people driving under the influence of drugs or alcohol result in thousands of injuries and deaths each year. Use of these substances also makes it difficult for an individual to control his or her emotions. This may cause a person to behave violently.

Mental/Emotional Issues

Some studies have found a direct correlation between engaging in violent behavior and having a negative self-concept. People who feel unvalued may use violence in an attempt to prove their self-worth. Some violent behaviors are acts of revenge by people who have never learned any other way of dealing with disagreements. Also, some people have a very low tolerance for frustration or inconvenience. These people may lash out at others, including those who are not the source of the frustration. **Anger management** workshops and counseling are available in most communities for people who have problems controlling their anger.

> ### Man held up in drive-by shooting
>
> **Green City** — Tuesday night there was a do' the new development in the case was ren the sheriff's office was going to iss·

> ### Violence breaks out at a Community Concert
>
> Thursday, June 16

> ### Three suspects sought in convenience store robbery

A Headlines focusing on violent acts are common in local and national newspapers. *Find three news stories that center on acts of violence. Analyze the health messages delivered by these media stories.*

Did You Know ?

→ Understanding statistics can help dispel misconceptions about incidents of violence.

- In about 75 percent of teen homicides, the victim and the person who committed the crime knew each other.
- Most homicides are not hate crimes based on race. In 90 percent of homicides, the victim and killer are of the same race.
- Among adolescents injured by guns, 35 percent report carrying a gun when they were shot.
- More than half of all violent acts involve someone who is under the influence of alcohol or another drug.

Types of Violence

Youth violence is violence directed toward or carried out by persons under the age of 19. Many violent acts today involve teens. In fact, teens are two and a half times more likely to be crime victims than adults are. According to a recent report of the Surgeon General, the proportion of young people involved in violent crimes has actually leveled off during the past decade. Nonetheless, about 100,000 teens are arrested each year for violent crimes. The crimes for which teens are often arrested include assault, homicide, and sexual violence.

Assault and Homicide

Each day in the United States, about 18,000 people survive an assault. An **assault** is *an unlawful attack on a person with the intent to harm or kill.* Some assaults involve people who do not know one another. For example, **random violence** is *violence committed for no particular reason.* Innocent bystanders can become victims of both intended and random violence. For instance, innocent bystanders are sometimes injured in store robberies.

Assault may sometimes result in **homicide**, *the willful killing of one human being by another.* After automobile accidents, homicide is the second leading cause of death among individuals ages 15 to 24. Most of these deaths involve firearms. To protect yourself from assault and homicide, follow the general safety tips outlined in Lesson 1 as well as the violence-avoidance strategies listed here.

▶ If an attacker wants your money or jewelry and you are in danger, throw your purse, wallet, or jewelry away from you. Then run in the opposite direction. It's better to lose possessions than risk injury or death.

▶ If you are being followed, go to a place where there are other people.

Police are among the first to arrive at a crime scene. *What can citizens do to help law enforcement officers keep the community safe?*

Real-Life Application

Stopping Sexual Harassment

Sexual harassment is illegal behavior that may result in violence. Use this graph to help you develop a campaign against sexual harassment.

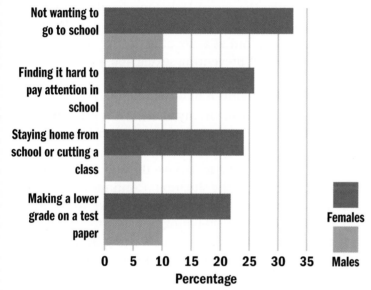

Effect of Sexual Harassment on Students

Source: based on American Association of University Women Educational Foundation study

- How is sexual harassment related to truancy and dropout rates?

- How can being sexually harassed affect a student's ability to graduate from high school? To get a college scholarship?

- How might being sexually harassed affect a teen's ability to form friendships?

ACTIVITY

In small groups, create a poster or a public service announcement (PSA) that informs students about the harmful effects of sexual harassment. Make a clear statement showing disapproval of these inconsiderate and disrespectful behaviors and encouraging healthful behaviors.

Sexual Violence

Sexual violence is *any form of unwelcome sexual conduct directed at an individual, including sexual harassment, sexual assault, and rape.* Sexual assault and rape differ from sexual harassment in that physical attacks are involved. These are acts of violence rather than acts of passion. The attacker is generally motivated not by sexual desire but by the desire to force another person to do something he or she does not want to do. All forms of sexual violence are illegal.

Did You Know?

➤ Sexual violence affects many children and teens. Data show that

- 51 percent of rape victims are under the age of 18, and 29 percent of victims are under the age of 12.
- friends or acquaintances are involved in nearly half of all rapes reported by women.

Reading Check

Explain What are some of the measures you can take to prevent sexual assaults?

Sexual assault is *any intentional sexual attack against another person*. Sexual assault is often accompanied by battery or the beating of the victim. **Rape** is *any form of sexual intercourse that takes place against a person's will*. It is also one of the least reported crimes. In fact, of the estimated 683,000 rapes taking place each year, only about 16 percent are reported to police.

Most sexual violence is directed at females, but males may also be victims. Often, sexual violence among teens occurs within a dating relationship. Currently, 8 percent of teens report being victims of sexual violence during dating by the time they reach the ninth grade. In some states, sexual intercourse between a male of any age and a female under the age of 18 is considered rape unless the two are married. Penalties for this crime may include going to prison as well as a life-long record as a sex offender. In the next lesson, you will learn more about preventing sexual abuse during dating.

ESCAPING AND SURVIVING A SEXUAL ATTACK

Sexual attacks can happen anywhere. They can happen in your home, the home of a friend or an acquaintance, or outside the home. If you are attacked, your main concern must always be your safety. Your goal should be to survive the attack. Whether you submit or resist depends on the situation. Continue assessing the situation as it is occurring. If one strategy doesn't work, try another. Possible options include negotiating or trying to form a connection with the attacker, stalling for time, distracting the attacker and fleeing, verbal assertiveness, screaming to attract attention, and physical resistance. Your safety may depend upon your ability to stay calm. Your best defense however, is to be prepared—know your options ahead of time. Avoid areas and situations that you know could put you at risk. As with any encounter with violence, it's important to keep in mind that your survival is of the utmost importance.

➤ Many law enforcement departments offer instructions in basic self-defense and techniques for escaping attackers. *What resources in your community provide self-defense instruction?*

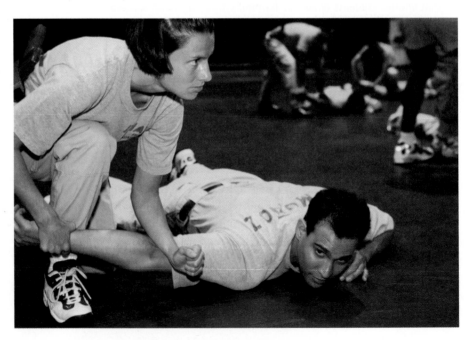

Gang-Related Violence

Many crimes committed by teens are gang-related, and often include the sale of drugs, physical assaults on rival gang members, and homicide. Teens may join gangs because of peer pressure or to gain a sense of identity or belonging. Others join gangs to gain protection from violence in their neighborhoods. A health-literate teen understands the possible causes of conflict among youth in schools and communitites.

Joining a gang increases one's risk of being arrested, hurt, or killed. The U.S. Department of Justice reports that in large cities, most acts of gang-related violence are committed against members of rival gangs. In smaller towns, most gang-related violence is directed at individuals not involved in a gang. Strategies for avoiding risks associated with gang membership include resisting pressure to join a gang and leaving when you see gang members.

People who feel a part of their community are less inclined to commit acts of violence, including vandalism. *How can you and your community work together to promote nonviolence?*

LESSON 3 REVIEW

Reviewing Facts and Vocabulary

1. Identify four common causes of violence.
2. Define *prejudice,* and explain how it can lead to violence.
3. Explain the role that alcohol and other drugs play in violent behaviors.

Thinking Critically

4. **Analyzing.** Explain how practicing tolerant attitudes is a strategy for reducing and avoiding violence.
5. **Evaluating.** How might messages from the media influence violent behavior?

Applying Health Skills

Analyzing Influences. Find three different media sources, such as movies, music, and video games, that contain messages involving violence. Analyze the health messages delivered through each media source you choose. How do you think these messages affect teens?

After You Read

Cause and Effect. Create a two-column chart. In the first column, list the causes of and influences on violence. In the other column, list the types and effects of violence.

Preventing and Overcoming Abuse

Guide to Reading

Building Vocabulary

As you read this lesson, write each new highlighted term and its definition in your notebook.

- abuse (p. 348)
- physical abuse (p. 349)
- verbal abuse (p. 349)
- stalking (p. 349)
- date rape (p. 350)

Focusing on the Main Ideas

In this lesson, you will learn how to:

- Describe types of abuse and responses to abusive situations.
- Develop healthy strategies that help prevent physical, sexual, and emotional abuse.
- Determine the legal and ethical ramifications of harassment, date rape, and sexual abuse.

Reading Strategy

Organize Information

- Create a graphic organizer listing each of the Building Vocabulary terms. As you read, fill in definitions.

There are many types of abuse. Write a brief paragraph describing behaviors you think might be abusive.

Some people abuse others by yelling or mistreating them with angry words. *What strategies can help a person manage his or her anger?*

A healthy relationship is one in which both parties feel valued. The health of some relationships can be threatened by violence in the form of abusive behavior. You can protect yourself from such relationships by becoming aware of what behaviors are abusive and learning how to protect yourself from abuse. You should also learn to analyze problems stemming from unhealthy relationships.

Types of Abuse

Abuse is *the physical, mental/emotional, or sexual mistreatment of one person by another.* Like other types of violence, abuse takes many forms and affects people of all economic, racial, and ethnic groups. Abuse also affects both males and females of all ages. Unlike many other forms of violence, abuse is most common between people involved in close relationships. Physical abuse, emotional abuse, and sexual abuse are unacceptable behaviors. All forms of abuse are unethical and illegal. One way to protect yourself is to learn strategies for dealing with individuals who are exhibiting dangerous behaviors.

Physical Abuse

Physical abuse is *the intentional infliction of bodily harm or injury on another person.* This form of abuse includes behaviors such as slapping, punching, kicking, biting, shaking, beating, or shoving another person. It may also involve inflicting injury by using items such as belts or weapons. Often, the person inflicting abuse tries to make the victim feel deserving of the mistreatment. However, abuse is not the victim's fault; no one deserves to be abused. Such behavior is not only physically harmful to the victim, but also harmful to the mental/emotional health of everyone involved.

Emotional Abuse

Have you ever witnessed one person screaming insults at another? This behavior is an example of **verbal abuse**, *using words to mistreat or injure another person.* Name-calling, hurling insults, and yelling in a threatening way are all forms of verbal abuse. Such abuse harms the victim's mental/emotional health by making the person feel stupid, worthless, or helpless. Anger caused by such behavior may eventually result in physical violence.

Verbal abuse is a type of *emotional abuse,* a pattern of behavior that attacks an individual's emotional development and sense of worth. Emotional abuse may be used to gain a sense of power over another person or to make victims feel that they deserve to be punished. Emotional abuse should not be ignored. Emotional abuse may serve as a warning of future physical abuse.

Stalking is *the repeated following, harassment, or threatening of an individual to frighten or cause him or her harm.* Following a person, standing outside his or her home, making repeated phone calls, and destroying property are common stalking behaviors. Stalking is a form of emotional abuse. Victims are often made to feel anxious, nervous, and unsafe. Stalking is a growing problem. Many times, the stalker wants a relationship with the victim. A stalker may not accept that the victim does not feel the same as he or she does. Each year in the United States, as many as 200,000 people are victims of stalking.

Is neglect a form of abuse? How is it related to violence?
Neglect is a form of abuse that involves the failure to meet a person's basic needs, such as adequate food, clothing, shelter, love, and support. Although neglect is not violent in nature, it can result in future violence. Children who are victims of neglect may be at an increased risk of violent behavior, gang membership, and criminal activities.

Teen victims of abuse should seek help immediately from a trusted adult. *What other steps might help someone put a stop to abuse?*

Health Minute

Strategies for Preventing Date Rape

To protect yourself:

▶ Do not go out with a person whom you do not know well.

▶ Date people who are close to your own age.

▶ Set clear sexual boundaries, and communicate them assertively.

▶ Avoid being completely alone with your date—for example, at home or in a car.

▶ Do not use alcohol or drugs or date anyone who does. Avoid places where alcohol or drugs may be present.

▶ Watch your food and drink. Do not allow an opportunity for someone to give you a date rape drug.

Dating Violence

Abuse in dating relationships, or *dating violence,* is on the rise. Dating violence includes all forms of abuse—physical, emotional, and sexual. Sometimes, teen victims may accept abuse as part of a relationship. Some teens, for example, mistake dominant treatment by a girlfriend or boyfriend as an expression of caring. These teens may see jealousy as an expression of love. However, true caring involves kindness, gentleness, and respect, *not* control and abuse.

Signs indicating that an unhealthy dating relationship may be headed toward abusive behavior include

▶ expressions of jealousy.

▶ attempts to control a partner's behavior.

▶ use of insults or put-downs to manipulate a partner.

▶ use of guilt to manipulate a partner.

Anyone in such a relationship should seek advice from parents or other trusted adults about ending the relationship. Remember that in healthy relationships, people respect and care about each other. They hold each other in high esteem, acting with consideration and kindness. A health-literate teen knows techniques for communicating care, consideration, and respect of self and others.

Date and Acquaintance Rape

Rape occurs whenever one person is forced into participating in any form of sexual intercourse. Often, a victim of rape knows the attacker. For example, **date rape** occurs *when one person in a dating relationship forces the other person to participate in sexual intercourse.* Although most reported cases of date rape are committed against young women, both males and females may be victims. Another form of rape, called *acquaintance rape,* occurs when someone known casually or considered a friend forces a person to have sexual intercourse. All forms of rape may traumatize victims and leave lasting emotional scars.

▶ **Issues of jealousy or control may lead to an unhealthy relationship.** *What are healthful ways to resolve such issues before they become violent?*

Communication: Helping a Victim of Dating Violence

Dyann became concerned when her friend Raye began dating an older boy from another school. Dyann thought he was possessive and controlling. It seemed that whenever Dyann and Raye had a chance to talk, Raye's boyfriend would call her cell phone, demanding to know where she was and what she was doing.

Now, Dyann feels as if Raye is avoiding her. Today, she notices that one of Raye's eyes is swollen and discolored. When Dyann tries to speak to her, Raye barely nods and rushes off in the opposite direction. Dyann suspects that Raye's boyfriend has been hitting her. Dyann would like to help her friend, but she's not sure how.

What Would You Do?

Apply the following communication skills to Dyann's situation. Write a dialogue that Dyann could use to persuade Raye to seek help.

1. Use "I" messages to show concern.
2. Use appropriate listening skills to encourage the other person to talk.
3. Provide facts or data about why it is important to get help.
4. Demonstrate conviction about the urgency of getting help.

ALCOHOL, DRUGS, AND DATE RAPE

Research shows that alcohol use is involved in as many as two-thirds of date-rape cases involving teens and college students. In recent years, the **drugs** GHB and Rohypnol, sometimes called "date rape drugs," have also become common in such cases. These drugs are sometimes placed in a victim's food or drink without that person's knowledge. The victim who consumes the substance may black out, becoming an easy target for rape. You can help protect yourself from rape by avoiding the use of alcohol or other drugs and situations in which these substances are present. When at a party or another social situation, get your own beverage, keep the beverage container covered, and never leave your beverage unattended. Pairing with a trustworthy friend to keep tabs on each other is also a good strategy for staying safe in such social situations. It is important that teens formulate principles for healthful dating relationships before they begin dating.

Reading Check

Explain What four behaviors may indicate that a dating relationship may become violent?

Overcoming Abuse

It is important for people who have suffered abuse or rape to remember that they are victims and have not done anything wrong. All forms of abuse, including rape, are illegal and should be reported to authorities. Reporting such incidents may help prevent future abuse. Today, all states have laws that require health care professionals to report child abuse.

Reading ✓ Check

Explain Why is it important to report all forms of abuse to authorities?

Help for Victims

If you or someone you know is raped, call law enforcement officials immediately. Next, seek medical attention and be sure to get tests for pregnancy, **STDs,** and **HIV** infection. These actions may help prevent further illness or injury and may provide physical evidence that will be useful in the conviction of the rapist.

A teen victim of abuse or rape should speak with a caring, trusted, and knowledgeable adult, such as a parent. The trusted adult can provide emotional support and aid the teen in getting help. **Figure 13.3** identifies resources that can provide help, including support and counseling, for abuse and rape victims.

In cases of child abuse, counseling is available and recommended for both the abused child and his or her parents or guardians. With help, most people can recover from the trauma of abuse, violence, or rape. However, the recovery requires patience and time. An informed individual knows how to access school and community health services for self and others.

FIGURE 13.3

SOURCES OF HELP FOR VICTIMS OF ABUSE OR RAPE

Many sources of help are available for people in abusive situations.
- Parents or guardians
- Teacher, coach, guidance counselor
- Clergy member
- Police
- Private physician, hospital emergency room
- Battered women's shelter
- Rape crisis center
- Private therapist/counselor
- Support groups

WomanLine CRISIS CENTER

Let our caring and supportive staff of counselors help you. Call our 24-Hour **HELPLINE**

1-800-555-1234

Help for Abusers

In cases of abuse, both the victim and the abuser need help. Abusive behavior is learned. Often, individuals who abuse others were themselves victims of abuse. Thus, abusers may see violence and abuse as a normal way of life. This is one reason why the **cycle of violence** may continue from one generation to the next. Abusers need intense counseling to succeed at breaking this harmful cycle.

Counseling can help break the cycle of violence. *Why is it important for both abusers and their victims to seek counseling?*

To break the cycle of violence, long-range prevention of abuse is needed in society as a whole. One solution may be to provide parents and prospective parents with opportunities to learn about family life, child development, and parent-child relationships. Another is to provide counseling for all victims of abuse and violence. Support and counseling can help victims recover from abuse and learn prevention strategies. People convicted of abuse are required to participate in treatment programs conducted by mental health professionals. To prevent and overcome abuse, all individuals need to learn skills for developing and maintaining healthy relationships.

LESSON 4 REVIEW

Reviewing Facts and Vocabulary

1. What is *verbal abuse*, and how does it harm the victim?

2. List two signs that may indicate an unhealthy dating relationship.

3. What is *date rape?*

Thinking Critically

4. **Applying.** What healthy strategies can help a person prevent the physical, sexual, and emotional violence of date rape? Analyze the importance of such strategies.

5. **Evaluating.** Why might victims of rape be reluctant to tell others what has happened to them? What should these victims keep in mind to help them overcome their fears and report the crime?

Applying Health Skills

Advocacy. Design a pamphlet that informs teens how to recognize the signs of an abusive situation. Provide strategies for avoiding or dealing with such situations, stressing the importance of seeking help.

After You Read

Problems and Solutions. Create a chart with two columns. On the left side, list the types of abuse, including dating violence. On the other side, list some of the ways to overcome abuse and find help for victims and abusers.

When Dating Is Dangerous

One in five teenage girls reports being a victim of violence by her date.

According to a study by the Harvard School of Public Health, dating during adolescence can be dangerous, especially for girls. The study of 1,977 high-school girls shows that 1 in 5 reports being a victim of physical or sexual violence in a dating relationship. Girls reported being hit, slapped, shoved, or forced into sexual activity by dates. Because this is the first study of its kind, it's not clear whether such abuse is on the rise, but Dr. Jay Silverman, author of the report, called the numbers "extremely high."

Pressure to Date

Laura Sessions Stepp, author of *Our Last Best Shot*, isn't surprised by statistics that show a high incidence of violence during dates. "Girls in high school talk a lot about the pressure to have a physical relationship," she says, "and I wonder if 'girl power' makes them think they can handle situations they're not ready for." Sara Stillman, 17, wrote *Soul Searching*, a book for high-school girls. She thinks the pressure of having a boyfriend early can push girls into unhealthy relationships.

Many girls won't tell their parents or friends about dating violence. Warning signs include symptoms of depression, such as changes in eating and sleeping habits, or an increase in violent outbursts. Teens who suspect their friends might be victims of dating violence should talk to their parents or counselors. Experts in youth violence prevention say kids need to enter the dating stage of their lives with their eyes wide open, to realize that all violence is unacceptable, and to demand respect in their friendships. ◼

TIME to THINK... | About Dating Safety

With a small group, develop an ad campaign that promotes safe dating. What easy-to-remember slogan can you create to help teens remember the importance of dating safety? Each group should design one poster with this slogan. With your school's permission, put up the posters around the school.

1. **Analyzing Influences.** Using Figure 13.1 as a reference, write a short story describing how peer and school protective factors help protect a teen from violence. *(LESSON 1)*

 2. **Accessing Information.** Find out what policies your school has for protecting students from sexual harassment. Develop a presentation to make others in your school aware of these policies. *(LESSON 2)*

 3. **Practicing Healthful Behaviors.** Analyze strategies you might apply to your selection of friends as a means of avoiding violence, gangs, weapons, and drugs. *(LESSON 3)*

 4. **Accessing Information.** Research the resources available to victims of abuse and violence in your community. Make a flyer that includes these resources, their contact information, and details about the services they provide. *(LESSON 4)*

CAREER Corner

Social Worker

Helping people in need—including victims of abuse—can be rewarding. Social workers are among the many resources to which victims of abuse can turn for help. Social workers can be found in hospitals, nursing homes, governmental agencies, and community service agencies. Social workers can help people find alternative housing or other resources that will help them escape abusive situations.

To obtain a job as a social worker, you'll need to complete a four-year college program followed by a master's degree program in social work. Find out more about this and other health careers by clicking on Career Corner at **health.glencoe.com.**

BEYOND *the* Classroom

Parent Involvement

Accessing Information. With a parent, contact your local police department to determine whether there is a Neighborhood Watch program in your community. If there is such a program, obtain information on how the program works and how your family can become involved. If no program exists, discuss with local law enforcement officials how you might start such a program.

School and Community

Crisis Centers and Shelters. Contact a local rape crisis center or battered women's shelter. Arrange for an interview with a worker at the facility to discuss the services the agency provides, how the services are accessed, and how the agency is funded. Share this information with your class.

After You Read

Use your Foldable to review what you have learned about personal safety. On another sheet of paper, list ways that you might use what you have learned in your everyday life.

FOLDABLES™
Study Organizer

➤ **EXPLORING HEALTH TERMS** *Answer the following questions on a sheet of paper.*

Lesson 1 *Fill in the blanks with the correct term.*

assertive   **body language**
self-defense

1. Any physical or mental strategies used to protect oneself from harm are forms of _____.

2. When you protect yourself by clearly stating your intentions and displaying confidence, you are being _____.

3. Making direct eye contact or walking with a deliberate and confident stride are examples of _____.

Lesson 2 *Match each definition with the correct term.*

bullying   **gang**
peer mediation   **sexual harassment**
violence

4. Threatened or actual use of physical force or power to harm another person or to damage property.

5. Seeking power or attention through the psychological or physical abuse of another person.

6. Process in which trained students help other students find fair ways of resolving conflict and settling differences.

Lesson 3 *Fill in the blanks with the correct term.*

assailant   **assault**
homicide   **prejudice**
random violence   **rape**
sexual assault   **sexual violence**

(_7_) is an unlawful attack on a person with the intent to harm or kill. Rape, sexual harassment, and sexual assault are all forms of (_8_). The person who commits any of these acts against another person is known as the (_9_). If a person is killed during an assault, the crime is known as (_10_).

Lesson 4 *Replace the underlined words with the correct term.*

date rape   **abuse**
physical abuse   **stalking**
verbal abuse

11. Any physical, mental, or emotional mistreatment of one person by another is <u>physical abuse</u>.

12. The repeated following, harassment, or threatening of an individual to frighten or cause harm to him or her is known as <u>verbal abuse</u>.

13. <u>Stalking</u> occurs when one person in a dating relationship forces the other to have sexual intercourse.

➤ **RECALLING THE FACTS** *Use complete sentences to answer the following questions.*

1. List two individual protective factors that can help keep you from harm.

2. List and analyze five strategies that you might use to avoid violence.

3. What are three strategies that communities use to increase safety in their neighborhoods?

4. What are two ways of dealing with a bully?

5. Identify three strategies you can apply to avoid school violence. Analyze how applying these strategies can help keep you safe.

6. What are the steps used in peer mediation?

7. Identify two safety tips that can help protect an individual from assault.

8. Define *sexual violence.*

9. How can teens avoid the risks associated with gang membership?

10. Why is verbal abuse considered a form of emotional abuse?

11. Explain the role that the use of alcohol and other drugs plays in abusive situations such as date rape.

12. Name two strategies to break the violence cycle.

► WRITING CRITICALLY

1. **Narrative.** Write a one-page story from the perspective of a teen who volunteers for a community project and encourages another teen to get involved in a volunteer activity. Include quotes from the teen telling why he or she feels it is important to volunteer and what benefits the teen gains from participating in community projects.

2. **Expository.** Write a one-page article for a crisis center newsletter encouraging teens to report abuse and seek help. Describe the steps that an abuse victim should take and include sources of help that are available.

Standardized Test Practice

MATH **Read the paragraph below, study the diagram, and then answer the questions.**

Bullying occurs more frequently among middle school students, but it also happens in high school. At some time during your life, you may have either been bullied or have bullied another student. This diagram shows the estimated number of students who are affected by bullying.

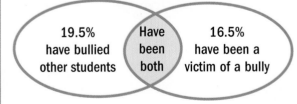

19.5% have bullied other students | Have been both | 16.5% have been a victim of a bully

1. About 6% of all students have both bullied other students and have been the victim of a bully. From this information and the diagram, what percentage of students have either been bullied or have bullied another student, but not both?

A 3.5% **C** 30%
B 6% **D** 36%

2. Suppose there are 842 students in your school. Use a proportion to find the number of students in your school who have bullied another student.

F 51 **H** 164
G 139 **I** 303

3. Using the proportions given above, explain how you would determine the number of students in your school who have neither bullied another student nor been bullied.

Personal Care and Healthy Behaviors

Eye ON THE Media

Media Technologies for People with Disabilities

Adaptive technologies assist people with hearing or vision impairments to

▶ communicate.

▶ work.

▶ read.

▶ learn.

Visit the Eye on the Media section at health.glencoe.com to learn more about how media technology can assist people with disabilities.

FOLDABLES™ Study Organizer

Before You Read

Use this Foldable to help you record what you learn about healthy skin, hair, and nails. Begin with two sheets of 8½" x 11" paper.

Step 1
Stack two sheets of paper, with the top edges 1" apart. Keep the side edges straight.

Step 2
Fold up the bottom half of the stack of papers 1" from the top half. All tabs should be the same size.

Step 3
Crease the stack of papers to hold the tabs in place. Staple together along the fold and label the tabs as shown.

Epidermis
Dermis
Subcutaneous
Skin

As You Read

As you read and discuss the material in the chapter, use your Foldable to record supporting facts under the appropriate tabs.

SPOTLIGHT ON HEALTH

Using Visuals. What are some simple behaviors you can practice each day to protect your health?

Healthy Skin, Hair, and Nails

Guide to Reading

Building Vocabulary

As you read this lesson, write each new highlighted term and its definition in your notebook.

▶ epidermis (p. 360)
▶ dermis (p. 360)
▶ melanin (p. 361)
▶ sebaceous glands (p. 361)
▶ sweat glands (p. 361)
▶ melanoma (p. 364)
▶ hair follicle (p. 365)
▶ dandruff (p. 365)

Focusing on the Main Ideas

In this lesson, you will learn how to:

▶ Describe the structure and functions of the skin.
▶ Identify warning signs that lead to early detection of skin diseases.
▶ Examine the effects of health behaviors on skin, hair, and nails.

Reading Strategy

Predict

▶ Scan the headings, subheadings, and photo captions. Write a short summary detailing what you know about keeping your skin, hair, and nails healthy.

Quick Write

Make a list of some simple behaviors you can practice each day to protect your health.

Washing your face regularly keeps skin free of dirt, bacteria, and perspiration. *How does keeping your face and hands clean affect your overall health?*

Beads of perspiration form on your forehead while you are exercising or when you are outside on a hot day. Your skin, the largest organ of your body, produces perspiration in order to help keep your body cool. Skin is the main organ of the integumentary system, which also includes hair, nails, and glands found in your skin. Your skin serves as a physical barrier between the outside world and your internal organs. It shields them from injury, and it is the first line of defense against pathogens entering your body.

Structure and Function of the Skin

The skin consists of two main layers, as shown in **Figure 14.1.** The **epidermis** is *the outer, thinner layer of the skin that is composed of living and dead cells.* The **dermis** is *the thicker layer of the skin beneath the epidermis that is made up of connective tissue and contains blood vessels and nerves.*

The epidermis is composed of several layers. The top layer consists of dead cells that are constantly being shed and replaced. In the deeper layers of the epidermis, living cells continually divide and replace dying cells, which are pushed toward the surface layer.

Take the Health Inventory for Chapter 14 at **health.glencoe.com.**

FIGURE 14.1

STRUCTURE OF THE SKIN

The two main layers of skin, the epidermis and the dermis, are attached to bones and muscles by the subcutaneous layer, a layer of fat and connective tissue located beneath the dermis.

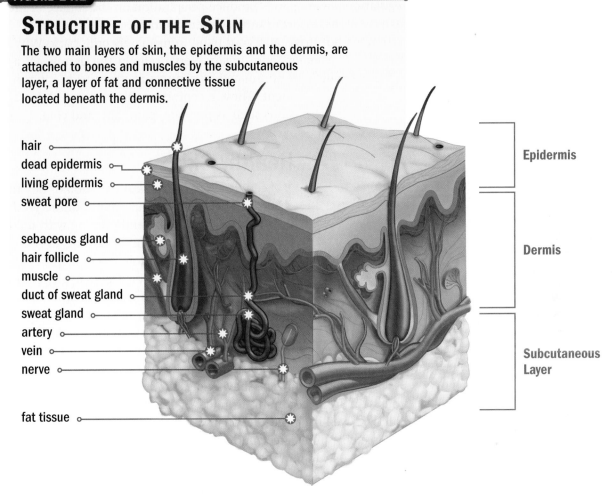

hair
dead epidermis
living epidermis
sweat pore

sebaceous gland
hair follicle
muscle
duct of sweat gland
sweat gland
artery
vein
nerve

fat tissue

Epidermis

Dermis

Subcutaneous Layer

Certain cells in the epidermis make a substance called *keratin*, a protein that toughens nails. These same cells also produce substances called lipids, which make your skin waterproof. This waterproofing helps the body maintain a proper balance of water and electrolytes. Other cells produce **melanin**, *a pigment that gives the skin, hair, and iris of the eyes their color*—the more melanin, the darker the skin. People with fair skin have less melanin and are at risk of damage from harmful ultraviolet (UV) radiation.

The dermis is a single thick layer composed of connective tissue, which gives the skin its elastic qualities. **Sebaceous glands**, *structures within the skin that produce an oily secretion called sebum*, are also found in the dermis. Sebum helps keep skin and hair from drying out.

Blood vessels in the dermis supply cells with oxygenated blood and nutrients and facilitate the removal of cellular wastes. These blood vessels also function in temperature regulation. When body temperature begins to rise, the blood vessels in the skin dilate. This allows heat to escape through the skin's surface. If body temperature begins to drop, the blood vessels in the skin constrict, decreasing the amount of blood and heat loss at the skin's surface. **Sweat glands**, *structures within the dermis that secrete perspiration through*

Reading Check

Describe What are the dermis and the epidermis?

A diet rich in vitamin A will contribute to healthy skin. *Which foods do you enjoy that are a good source of vitamin A?*

ducts to pores on the skin's surface, also are involved in temperature regulation. Sweat glands produce perspiration on the surface of the skin. Body heat is lost as the sweat evaporates.

Touch a hot stove, and your hand immediately pulls back. Why? The skin is a major sense organ. Nerve cells in the dermis act as receptors, which are stimulated by changes in the outside environment. These receptors enable you to feel sensations such as pressure, pain, hot, and cold.

Healthy Skin

Keeping your skin healthy should be an important part of your daily routine. Wash your face every morning and evening with mild soap and water. Daily washing, bathing, or showering helps remove and slow the growth of bacteria that cause body odor. Good hygiene and grooming habits also help you gain employment opportunities and build relationships. Avoid touching your face with your hands. This can introduce new bacteria to the skin's surface. Carefully choose personal skin care products, such as moisturizers, shaving cream, or cosmetics, to help keep your skin from becoming irritated or having an allergic reaction. Follow a well-balanced diet that is rich in vitamins and minerals. Foods such as milk, green and yellow vegetables, and liver are rich in vitamin A—a vitamin that is particularly important for healthy skin.

Skin and the Sun

Understanding the effects of UV radiation on the skin and knowing some preventive behaviors can help you protect your skin now. It also shows that you understand how to delay the onset of and reduce the risk for potential health problems during adulthood. When skin is exposed to UV rays, whether from the sun, a tanning booth, or another source, melanin production is increased. This self-protective mechanism is the skin's attempt to protect its cells from UV rays. Fair-skinned people whose skin has little melanin, and thus little natural protection from UV radiation, burn in the sun.

Prolonged exposure to UV rays damages the genetic material in skin cells and causes it to undergo changes. These changes can eventually result in the formation and growth of cancerous cells. Exposure to UV radiation is the leading cause of certain types of skin cancer. UV radiation also breaks down the elastic fibers that support your skin and allows it to be flexible yet retain its shape. The skin will become wrinkled or hard and leathery with repeated exposure to UV radiation.

Q&A

What are UVA and UVB radiation?

Ultraviolet rays come in different wavelengths—UVA and UVB. UVB rays cause most sunburn; thus, most sunscreens block these rays. However, UVA rays penetrate the skin more deeply than UVB, causing more damage. Now that dermatologists know about UVA, they recommend sunscreens that block both UVA and UVB rays.

PROTECTING YOUR SKIN FROM UV RAYS

Protecting your skin from the damaging rays of the sun can be accomplished by adopting a few simple health behaviors. It also shows that you understand the potential impact of common risk behaviors on the quality of life.

▶ **Always wear sunscreen on exposed areas of skin.** Use an SPF 15 or higher sunscreen that blocks both UVA and UVB rays. Apply it 15 to 30 minutes before going outside. Use it even on cloudy days and while participating in winter sports.

▶ **Wear protective clothing.** Hats, long-sleeved shirts, and long pants can help prevent sun exposure. Don't forget your sunglasses. Exposure to UV rays can damage the eyes, causing burns, cataracts, and even blindness. Avoid outdoor activities when sunlight is most intense, between 10:00 a.m. and 4:00 p.m.

Body Piercing and Tattooing

Ear piercing and tattooing are practices that have been around for thousands of years. Unlike decorating the body with makeup or changing hair color, however, these changes to the body are permanent, and both carry potential health risks.

Both procedures result in the physical barrier of the skin being broken, so the possibility of bacteria or viruses entering the body increases. Bacteria that are normally found on the surface of the skin can cause a localized infection if they enter deeper layers of tissue. New bacteria can be introduced through nonsterile needles. Of special concern is the transfer of bloodborne pathogens such as the viruses **hepatitis B, hepatitis C,** and **HIV** through nonsterile needles used during tattooing.

Tattooing and piercings can threaten your social health as well. Imagine dating someone who is tattooed with the name of a past boyfriend or girlfriend. Body piercings may make a poor impression on a future employer or in-law.

A tattoo can be removed by using a laser procedure. However, the procedure can cause skin discoloration and infection and can leave scars. Consider the long-term consequences when you think about tattooing and piercing.

Health and Beauty
SUNSCREEN

SPF 30

SPF 30 provides UVA and UVB Protection.
It is water and perspiration resistant and PABA Free.
Weightless, nongreasy lotion provides 30 times the skin's natural protection against sunburn.

 A broad-spectrum sunscreen protects against both UVA and UVB radiation. *Why is it important to protect against both forms of ultraviolet radiation?*

Reading Check

Describe Name two ways that you can avoid sunburn.

Skin Problems

Many problems of the skin are not life threatening. They can, however, affect a person's self-image. Teens with skin problems should check with a health care professional before purchasing skincare products. This shows that you can distinguish between fact and fallacy as related to health products. Some common skin problems include:

▶ **Acne,** a common skin problem among teens, is caused when pores in the skin get clogged and the sebum produced by sebaceous glands cannot reach the skin's surface. One type of bacteria normally found on the skin thrives in the trapped sebum. The surrounding area becomes inflamed, and pus may form. Washing your face gently twice a day, applying over-the-counter treatment creams, and avoiding the use of oily products can help control breakouts. Touching and picking at acne only aggravates the condition and may cause scarring.

▶ **Warts** are caused by a virus that infects the surface layers of the skin. They are usually noncancerous growths that can appear anywhere on the body, but they are most commonly found on the hands, feet, and face. The virus that causes warts can be acquired through contact with infected skin.

▶ **Vitiligo** is a skin condition in which patches of skin have lost all pigment. For reasons not yet known, the melanin-producing cells in the affected areas of the skin are destroyed. With no melanin, these patches of skin are extremely susceptible to burning when exposed to UV light. Sunscreen should be applied or protective clothing should be worn over these areas to avoid severe sunburn. Although treatments involving repigmentation are available, there is no known cure for vitiligo.

▶ **Boils** form when hair follicles become infected with bacteria that are normally found on the surface of the skin. The tissues around a boil become inflamed, and pus forms. Treatment can include draining the pus and taking a course of antibiotics. Never squeeze or burst a boil because this can spread the infection. Keeping skin clean can help prevent boils.

▶ **Moles** are spots that contain extra melanin. Most moles are harmless. Certain types of moles may develop into **melanoma,** *the most serious form of skin cancer,* which can be deadly. Early detection of warning signs and treatment are critical to controlling the spread of **skin cancer** throughout the body. Monitoring the appearance of moles, as described in **Figure 14.2,** and seeking health care by reporting any changes to a dermatologist are essential to the early detection of melanoma.

Reading Check

Explain What can teens do to treat acne?

FIGURE 14.2

THE ABCDs OF MELANOMA

Regularly checking the appearance of your moles for warning signs is important for the early detection of melanoma.

A = Asymmetry
An imaginary line drawn through the center of the mole does not produce matching halves.

B = Border irregularity
Noncancerous moles have smooth edges. Suspect moles often have irregular edges.

C = Color
Look for moles that are intensely black, possibly with a bluish tint, or that have an uneven color.

D = Diameter
Check for moles that are wider across than a pea.

Your Hair

Except for the palms of your hands and the soles of your feet, you have hair on almost every skin surface. You have between 100,000 to 200,000 hairs on your head alone! Although hair itself is composed of dead cells that contain keratin, living cells in the epidermis make new hairs and cause hair growth. A **hair follicle** is *a structure that surrounds the root of a hair.* Hair helps protect the skin, especially the scalp, from exposure to UV radiation. The eyes are protected from dust or other particles by the eyebrows and eyelashes. Hair also reduces the amount of heat lost through the skin of the scalp.

The foundation of healthy hair is a well-balanced diet. Hair can become thin and dry without proper nutrients. Regular shampooing is a must to keep your hair healthy. Daily brushing keeps dirt from building up and helps distribute the natural hair oils evenly. Limit the use of treatments such as permanents, dyes, or bleach. Overexposure to these harsh chemicals can cause hair to become dry and brittle.

Hair Problems

Normally, oil produced by sebaceous glands protects the skin from drying out and keeps hair soft and shiny. **Dandruff** is *a condition that can occur if the scalp becomes too dry and dead skin cells are shed as sticky, white*

Give your hair daily attention to keep it clean and healthy. *How do you choose hair care products that are right for your hair?*

Keeping nails neatly clipped and filed improves your overall appearance. *List three other grooming habits that contribute to a healthy appearance.*

flakes. Dandruff can usually be treated by washing hair with an over-the-counter dandruff shampoo. If itching or scaling persists, consult a health care professional.

Head lice are tiny parasitic insects that live in the scalp hair of humans. They feed on blood by biting through the skin of the scalp. Lice are transmitted mainly by head-to-head contact and can infect anyone. They can also be acquired by using objects such as combs or hats that have been used by an infected person. These insects can be eliminated by washing hair with a medicated shampoo that kills the organisms. Washing sheets, pillowcases, combs, and hats in hot water with soap can help prevent the spread of head lice or a repeat infection.

Your Nails

Your fingernails and toenails are made of closely packed dead cells that contain keratin. Nails function to protect and support the tissues of the fingers and toes. Keeping your nails healthy should be part of your daily routine. Good care includes keeping nails clean and evenly trimmed. Use a nail file to shape and smooth nails, and keep cuticles pushed back. Trim toenails straight across and just slightly above skin level to reduce the risk of infection and ingrown nails.

LESSON 1 | **REVIEW**

Reviewing Facts and Vocabulary

1. Define the terms *epidermis* and *dermis*.
2. Why is early detection of skin cancer important to your overall health?
3. What is a *hair follicle*?

Thinking Critically

4. **Applying.** Consider your daily activities in the sun. Compose a list of ways you can protect your skin from the sun for each activity.
5. **Synthesizing.** Explain how your overall appearance makes a statement about how you care for your skin, hair, and nails.

Applying Health Skills

Decision Making. With a partner, role-play deciding whether to get a tattoo. Include the steps of the decision-making model in a discussion on why someone might want a tattoo and discuss the consequences to physical health. Include some dialogue on tattoo removal.

After You Read

Problems and Solutions. Create a two-column chart. In one column list some of the effects of sun exposure. In the second column, list ways that you can reduce the risk of sun exposure.

Visit **health.glencoe.com** for the Interactive Study Guide for Lesson 1.

Caring for the Teeth and Mouth

Guide to Reading

Building Vocabulary

As you read this lesson, write each new highlighted term and its definition in your notebook.

▶ periodontium (p. 367)
▶ pulp (p. 368)
▶ plaque (p. 368)
▶ periodontal disease (p. 370)
▶ tartar (p. 370)

Focusing on the Main Ideas

In this lesson, you will learn how to:

▶ Label the parts of a tooth.
▶ Describe the effects of health behaviors on prevention of diseases of the teeth and mouth.
▶ Identify warning signs that prompt individuals to seek dental care.

Reading Strategy

Organize Information

▶ Draw a two-column chart. On one side, list the parts of a tooth. On the other side, list problems of the teeth and mouth.

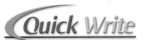

Write a paragraph explaining why it is important to brush your teeth after meals.

Maintaining healthy teeth is important not only for your appearance but also for your overall health. Your teeth allow you to chew foods properly and help form the shape and structure of your mouth. In this lesson you will learn about the structure and function of the teeth and how to prevent tooth decay.

 Healthy teeth are a result of good oral hygiene.
Explain why it is important to brush and floss after meals.

Your Teeth

You may remember losing your teeth when you were younger, only to have new, permanent teeth grow in their place. Although your permanent teeth have different shapes, depending on their exact role in chewing food, they all have the same structure.

Parts of a Tooth

The **periodontium** (per-ee-oh-DAHN-tee-uhm) is *the area immediately around the teeth.* It is made up of the gums, periodontal ligament, and the jawbone. The structures of the periodontium support the teeth and hold them in place.

A tooth is made up of three main parts: the crown, neck, and root, as shown in **Figure 14.3** on page 368. The crown is the visible portion of the tooth. It is covered with enamel, a hard substance made of calcium that protects the teeth.

Beneath the enamel is dentin, a layer of connective tissue that contributes to the shape and hardness of a tooth and acts as a barrier to protect the pulp. The **pulp** is *the tissue that contains the blood vessels and nerves of a tooth.* Pulp extends into the root canal and provides nourishment to the tooth.

Healthy Teeth and Mouth

Thorough, regular oral hygiene is necessary for healthy, clean teeth. One of the main threats to the health of your teeth is the bacteria that inhabit your mouth and live on the sugar found in foods you eat.

Plaque is *a sticky, colorless film that acts on sugar to form acids that destroy tooth enamel and irritate gums.* As plaque coats a tooth, it prevents your saliva, which has substances that protect teeth from bacteria, from reaching the tooth surface. In areas where plaque accumulates, bacteria thrive and the acids from the bacteria break down enamel. If the breakdown of enamel continues, a hole, or cavity, is formed in a tooth. The tooth can continue to decay to the pulp and may have to be removed if left untreated.

Tooth decay and other diseases can be easily prevented by practicing good oral hygiene. Brushing teeth after eating removes plaque from the surface of the teeth, before bacteria can produce the acid that harms teeth. Flossing between teeth removes plaque in areas that cannot be reached with the bristles of a toothbrush.

FIGURE 14.3

CROSS-SECTION OF A TOOTH

A protective layer of enamel covers the crown of a tooth. Inside the tooth, blood vessels supply the living tissue with oxygen and nutrients.

enamel

dentin

pulp cavity with nerves and vessels

gum

gingiva

cementum

periodontal ligaments

periodontal membrane

root canal

bone

Crown

Neck

Root

Examining Product Claims

Tooth whitening products work either by removing surface stains or by bleaching the natural tooth color. The FDA does not regulate these products, but the American Dental Association (ADA) approves products that meet certain standards for safety and effectiveness.

Whiter Teeth in Just 24 Hours! ✳

✳ **Unique Formula!**

WHITE TEETH

Manufacturers may make exaggerated or misleading claims about a product or fail to explain the way the product works.

Some products use peroxide-based whiteners, others contain mild abrasives and polishing agents. Gum irritation, tooth sensitivity, and possible tooth damage can occur if products are not used correctly.

ACTIVITY

Identify at least two types of over-the-counter tooth whitening products. Compare marketing claims with facts from the American Dental Association. How can you determine which products are safe and which ones may cause damaging side effects? Report your findings to the class. Cite your sources and explain how you know that they are reliable.

Regular visits to a dental care professional are the next most important part of maintaining dental health and ensuring early detection of dental problems. These professionals will clean your teeth and examine them for warning signs of decay.

Following a well-balanced diet that includes foods containing phosphorus, calcium, and vitamin C helps keep your teeth strong and your gums healthy. Reducing the number of sugary snacks eaten between meals also helps delay the onset of and reduce the risk for potential health problems during adulthood.

Reading Check

Describe What substance covers the teeth and can cause tooth decay?

Problems of the Teeth and Mouth

Many oral problems are caused by poor hygiene. Others result from poorly aligned teeth.

▶ **Halitosis,** or bad breath, can be caused by eating certain foods, poor oral hygiene, smoking, bacteria on the tongue, decayed teeth, or gum disease. If halitosis is caused by tooth decay or disease, treatment by a dental professional is needed.

▶ **Periodontal disease**, *an inflammation of the periodontal structures,* is caused by bacterial infection. Often called gum disease, periodontal disease begins with the buildup of plaque. *The hard, crustlike substance formed when plaque hardens is* **tartar**. Plaque and tartar cause the gums to become irritated and swollen. In this early stage, called gingivitis, the disease is reversible through regular, thorough brushing and flossing. Early detection is important since, left untreated, periodontal disease can destroy the bone and tissue that support the teeth.

▶ **Malocclusion** means "bad bite." Sources of a malocclusion include extra teeth, crowded teeth, and the misalignment of the upper and lower jaws. Malocclusion can lead to decay and disease, and it can affect a person's speech and ability to chew. Some malocclusions can be corrected by wearing braces, which reposition teeth by exerting pressure on them.

LESSON 2 REVIEW

Reviewing Facts and Vocabulary

1. Define the terms *periodontium* and *pulp.*
2. How does plaque affect the teeth?
3. Examine the effects of health behaviors and list three that help prevent tooth decay and periodontal disease.

Thinking Critically

4. **Evaluating.** How can early detection of gum disease affect your long-term health?
5. **Synthesizing.** How might you be able to distinguish between a person who practices good oral hygiene and one who does not?

Applying Health Skills

Accessing Information. Research library or Internet resources to learn more about how braces can help a person with misalignment of the jaw or malocclusion. Collect brochures to share with the class.

After You Read

Explain. Write a paragraph describing how dental plaque is formed. What can you do to reduce the risk of periodontal disease from a build-up of dental plaque?

Eye Care

Guide to Reading

Building Vocabulary

As you read this lesson, write each new highlighted term and its definition in your notebook.

- ▶ lacrimal gland (p. 371)
- ▶ sclera (p. 372)
- ▶ cornea (p. 372)
- ▶ choroid (p. 372)
- ▶ retina (p. 372)

Focusing on the Main Ideas

In this lesson, you will learn how to:

- ▶ Label the parts of the eye.
- ▶ Explain how the eye forms visual images.
- ▶ Examine the effects of health behaviors on the eye.
- ▶ List different types of eye problems.

Reading Strategy

Organize Information

- ▶ Create a four-column chart labeled *Your Eyes*. Label columns Parts of the Eye, Vision, Health Behaviors, and Eye Problems. As you read, write facts in the appropriate columns.

Quick Write

After scanning the headings and subheadings, write a brief paragraph describing what information you believe will be included in this lesson.

More than 70 percent of the sensory information your brain receives comes to it by way of your eyes. The function of the eye is to gather light. The images formed in the eye are sent to the brain, which interprets those images. The amount of light that enters the eye is controlled by the size of the pupil. When light hits the retina, light-sensitive cells are stimulated and an image is formed.

Your Eyes

Your eyes sit in bony sockets, called orbits, in the front of your skull. A layer of fat surrounds each eyeball and cushions it inside its socket. The eyebrows, eyelashes, and eyelids protect the eyes from foreign particles and bright light. Each eye has a group of structures that make and allow drainage of tears. One of these structures is the **lacrimal gland**, *the gland that secretes tears into ducts that empty into the eye.* As you blink, tears are moved across the surface of the eye. On average, most humans blink about 6,205,000 times a year! Tears keep the surface of the eyeball moist and clear of foreign particles. Tears consist of water, salts, and mucus that protect the eye against infection.

(A) Like the click of a camera lens, in the blink of an eye images are formed in the process of vision.
What structures help protect the eye?

FIGURE **14.4**

THE EYE

The optic nerve connects the eye with the brain to produce images.

sclera
choroid
vitreous humor
optic nerve
retina

cornea
iris
pupil
lens
aqueous humor

Parts of the Eye

The eye is made up of two main parts, shown in **Figure 14.4,** the optic nerve and three layers of the eyeball wall.

▶ The outermost layer of the eye is made up of the sclera and the cornea. The **sclera** (SKLEHR-uh), *the tough, white part of the eye,* is composed of tough, fibrous tissue that protects the inner layers of the eye and supports and shapes the eyeball. At the front of the eye is the cornea. The **cornea** is *a transparent tissue that bends and focuses light before it enters the lens.*

▶ Within the middle layer of the eyewall is the **choroid,** (KOHR-oid), *a thin structure that lines the inside of the sclera.* Also within the middle layer of the eye is the iris, the colored portion of the eye that contains the pupil. The pupil is the hole through which light reaches the inner eye. The muscles of the iris control the size of the pupil. In bright light the pupil constricts; in dim light it enlarges to let in more light.

▶ The **retina** is *the light-sensitive membrane on which images are cast by the cornea.* The light-sensitive cells in the retina are called rods and cones, each named for its basic shape. Rods are very sensitive to light and allow us to see in dim light. Cones function in bright light and allow us to see color. When light stimulates these cells, a nerve impulse travels to the brain via the optic nerve, which is located at the back of the eye.

Reading Check

Name What are the parts of the eye?

Behind the iris and the pupil is the lens of the eye. Like the cornea, the lens is transparent and functions to refine the focus of images on the retina. The area between the cornea and the lens is filled with a watery fluid called *aqueous humor*. Aqueous humor provides nutrients to the structures of the eye. Between the lens and retina is a cavity that is filled with a gelatin-like substance called *vitreous humor*. Vitreous humor helps the eyeball stay firm.

Vision

Image formation begins as light passes through the cornea, pupil, and lens and reaches the retina. Light rays are first focused by the curved cornea, and then the focus is refined by the lens. Muscles attached to the lens contract or relax to change its shape. The lens becomes more curved to focus the eye on a near object; it becomes flatter to focus the eye on a distant object. Light stimulates rods and cones in the retina, and a **nerve impulse** is transmitted to the brain through the optic nerve. In humans both eyes focus on the same set of objects. This allows our brains to interpret depth and judge distances.

If your vision is normal, a sharp image will be produced on the retina. The sharpness of vision can be measured by reading an eye chart. If you have 20/20 vision, you can stand 20 feet away from an eye chart and read the top eight lines. If you have 20/60 vision, you can see the chart from 20 feet the way a person with normal vision would see it from 60 feet. In other words, a person with 20/60 vision is "nearsighted." Other components of vision include eye coordination, peripheral or side vision, and depth perception.

Healthy Eyes

Practicing health behaviors to keep your eyes healthy shows that you understand the impact of personal health behaviors on body systems.

▶ **Follow a well-balanced diet.** Include foods that contain vitamin A. Deficiency in vitamin A could result in night blindness, reducing a person's ability to see well in dim light.

▶ **Protect your eyes.** Wear safety goggles or a mask when participating in activities in which the eyes could be damaged. Keep dirty hands or other objects away from your eyes to reduce the risk of eye infections and injury. Wear sunglasses that block UV light, and never look directly into the sun or bright lights.

▶ **Have regular eye exams.** Routine eye exams allow certain eye diseases to be detected and treated in their early stages.

HEALTH Online

TOPIC Virtual Eye

Go to **health.glencoe.com** for links to more information about the eye.

ACTIVITY Click on the Web Links to experience a virtual view of the eye.

Having vision problems diagnosed and treated reduces the risk of future eye problems. *What are some signs that you may need corrective lenses?*

► **Rest your eyes regularly.** Take regular breaks while working on the computer or when reading. Looking up and away from close work every 10 minutes or so reduces eyestrain.

Eye Problems

Eye problems can occur, despite good health practices. These problems can be classified as vision problems or diseases of the eye.

Vision Problems

Two common vision problems reflect the inability of the eye to properly focus light on the retina. *Myopia,* or nearsightedness, results in a person not being able to see distant objects clearly. For a person diagnosed with *hyperopia,* or farsightedness, distant objects can be seen clearly; however, near objects appear blurry. These conditions can be corrected with glasses or contact lenses. In recent years, laser surgery has become an option for correcting vision problems. In this procedure, a laser is used to reshape the cornea in order to change its focusing power. Other vision problems include:

► **Astigmatism.** Because of an irregularly curved cornea or lens, the eye is not able to focus properly, resulting in images that appear blurry. This condition can usually be corrected with glasses, contact lenses, or laser surgery.

► **Strabismus.** If the muscles of the eyes are weak or don't function properly, strabismus may result. One or both eyes may appear to be off-center, turned inward, or turned outward. Treatment includes corrective lenses, vision therapy, or surgery.

Diseases of the Eye

Diseases of the eye range from easily treated infections such as sties and pinkeye to conditions that can threaten sight. A sty is an inflamed swelling of a sebaceous gland near the eyelash. *Conjunctivitis,* also known as pinkeye, is an inflammation of the conjunctiva, a thin membrane that covers the sclera lining of the eyelids.

A serious threat to vision results from a detached retina. This occurs if a portion of the retina is separated from the choroid as a result of natural aging or from an injury. Warning signs include blurred vision or seeing bright flashes of light. Treatment includes using a laser to repair a tear or surgery to reattach the retina. Three other serious eye diseases are described on the next page.

Reading Check

Describe What are two common vision problems?

▶ **Glaucoma.** The pressure inside the eye is normally maintained by the aqueous and vitreous humor. In glaucoma, abnormally high pressure leads to irreversible damage of the retina and the optic nerve and can result in loss of sight. Glaucoma can only be diagnosed by a health care professional. Regular eye checkups can lead to early detection and treatment to control the condition.

▶ **Cataracts.** In this condition the normally transparent lens becomes cloudy. The formation of a cataract interferes with the lens' ability to focus light rays, making images appear blurry or vision seem foggy. Treatment of a cataract is typically the surgical removal of the old lens and replacement of it with a new, artificial lens.

▶ **Macular Degeneration.** This condition occurs when the light-sensing cells of the macula, the portion of the retina directly opposite the lens, begin to malfunction. Macular degeneration is the leading cause of vision loss for individuals over 60. There is no cure, and treatment is limited.

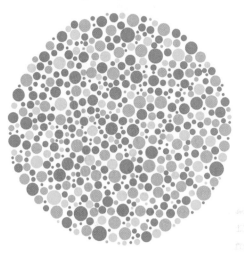

This simple test is used to identify people with color blindness. *What other types of vision problems can be identified through regular eye exams?*

LESSON 3 REVIEW

Reviewing Facts and Vocabulary

1. List the structures that make up the three layers of the eyeball wall.
2. Give three examples of health behaviors you can practice to care for your eyes.
3. Explain the difference between myopia and hyperopia.

Thinking Critically

4. **Analyzing.** How might having night blindness affect a person's activities?
5. **Applying.** How could you demonstrate the effect of cataracts on vision?

Applying Health Skills

Accessing Information. Research various community health services that provide vision screenings for all ages, such as Unite for Sight. Make a pamphlet that can be used as a reference on the availability and costs of these community services.

After You Read

Infer. Make a list of activities during which you should wear some type of eye protection.

Visit **health.glencoe.com** for the Interactive Study Guide for Lesson 3.

Lesson 3 Eye Care **375**

Ears and Hearing Protection

Guide to Reading

Building Vocabulary

As you read this lesson, write each new highlighted term and its definition in your notebook.

▶ external auditory canal (p. 376)

▶ auditory ossicles (p. 377)

▶ labyrinth (p. 377)

▶ tinnitus (p. 379)

Focusing on the Main Ideas

In this lesson, you will learn how to:

▶ Label the parts of the ear.

▶ Examine the effects of health behaviors on the ears and hearing.

▶ List some problems of the ear.

Quick Write

Write a paragraph describing situations that might cause hearing damage and how you can protect your hearing.

Reading Strategy

Organize Information

▶ Make a three-column chart. As you read, list the parts of the ear in the first column. In the next, list effects of health behaviors on hearing. In the last column, list some problems of the ear.

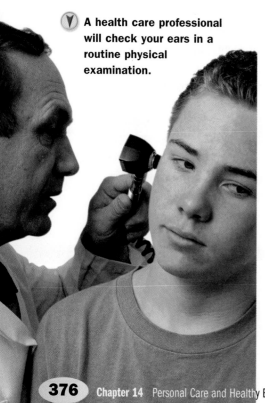

Ⓨ A health care professional will check your ears in a routine physical examination.

When you attend a sporting event, you can hear the crowd cheering, whistles blowing, athletes yelling, and music playing. All of these stimuli add to the excitement and perhaps to your enjoyment of the game. Your ears and brain, working together, allow you to hear and interpret sounds and form a response, such as turning your head when you hear a friend calling your name.

Parts of the Ear

The ear has three main sections, each with its own unique structures. The parts of the ear are shown in **Figure 14.5.**

▶ **The Outer Ear.** The outer ear begins with the visible part of the ear, the auricle. The auricle helps channel sound waves into the **external auditory canal**, *a passageway about one inch long that leads to the remaining portion of the outer ear, the eardrum.* The external auditory canal is lined with tiny hairs and glands that produce wax to protect the ear from dust and foreign objects. The eardrum, also called the *tympanic membrane,* is a thin membrane that acts as a barrier between the outer and middle ear.

FIGURE 14.5

INNER, MIDDLE, AND OUTER EAR

The ear has two functions: hearing and balance. Identify the parts of the ear involved in hearing.

Inner Ear (Labyrinth)
- semicircular canals
- cochlear nerve
- vestibule
- cochlea
- round window
- eustachian tube

Middle Ear

Outer Ear
- auricle
- oval window
- eardrum
- temporal bone
- mastoid process
- external auditory canal
- malleus ⎤
- incus ⎥ **Auditory Ossicles**
- stapes ⎦

▶ **The Middle Ear.** Directly behind the eardrum are the **auditory ossicles**, *three small bones linked together that connect the eardrum to the inner ear.* The auditory ossicles are the smallest bones in the body. The middle ear is connected to the throat by the eustachian tube. This tube allows pressure to be equalized on either side of the eardrum when you swallow or yawn.

▶ **The Inner Ear.** *The inner ear,* or **labyrinth**, consists of a network of curved and spiral passages with three main parts. The cochlea is the area of hearing in the inner ear. The vestibule and semicircular canals are where balance is controlled.

Hearing and Balance

When receptors in your inner ear are stimulated by a sound wave, a nerve impulse is sent to your brain. Your brain interprets the impulse as a sound. Sound waves enter the external auditory canal and cause the eardrum to vibrate. The vibrations cause fluid in the cochlea to move, which stimulates receptor cells to send a nerve impulse to the brain where sounds are interpreted. Receptor cells in the vestibule and the semicircular canals send messages to the brain about your sense of balance. Tiny hairs located in the ear sense movement and send nerve impulses to the brain. The brain then signals muscles to make adjustments to maintain balance.

How does the brain know where the source of a sound is located?
The ear that is closer to the sound hears it louder and a little sooner than the other ear. The brain picks out this difference and uses it to figure out where the sound is coming from. This is known as *binaural hearing.*

Yolanda Urbina speaks with the speed and enthusiasm of an engine in overdrive. She just learned she been accepted into the Coast Guard Academy in Connecticut.

Yolanda is the first to admit that she's had a tough time keeping her dream alive. When she was 14 her parents split up and she became depressed.

Eventually Yolanda was prescribed anti-depressants and sleep medication. Instead of making things better, the drugs themselves became a problem.

Fortunately a caring aunt and uncle helped Yolanda overcome her addiction. "They helped me set goals," says Yolanda.

Today Yolanda is studying to take the AP calculus exam. "I always tell my friends, 'Never give up. Things will turn around.' Just look at me," she adds with a big smile.

> "I always tell my friends, 'Never give up. Things will turn around.' Just look at me."

Reading Check

Explain How did setting goals help Yolanda through difficult times?

Reading Check

Describe What are the three main sections of the ear? What do they do?

Health Behaviors for Healthy Ears

To keep your ears healthy, clean them regularly and always protect the outer ear from injury and extreme cold. Wear protective gear such as batting helmets when playing sports. A hat that covers both the auricles and the earlobes should be worn in cold weather. Keep foreign objects, including cotton-tipped swabs, out of the ear. Ear infections can damage ear structures and should be treated immediately by a health care professional. Have your ears examined and your hearing tested to detect any problems.

An important step you can take to protect your hearing is to avoid loud noise. Exposure to loud noise over time can lead to temporary, and sometimes permanent, hearing loss or **deafness.**

Problems of the Ear

Reducing your exposure to loud noises is one way you can show that you understand the potential impact of common risk behaviors on the quality of life. Hearing loss can be divided into two categories: conductive and sensorineural.

Conductive Hearing Loss

In conductive hearing loss, sound waves are not passed from the outer to the inner ear, usually because of a blockage or injury to the inner ear. For example, middle-ear infections may lead to rupture of the eardrum. Persistent buildup of fluid within the middle ear, often caused by infection, is most common in children.

Sensorineural Hearing Loss

Sensorineural hearing loss results from damage to the cochlea, the auditory nerve, or the brain. **Tinnitus** is *a condition in which a ringing, buzzing, whistling, roaring, hissing, or other sound is heard in the ear in the absence of external sound.* Tinnitus can occur as a result of natural aging, health conditions such as high blood pressure, or overexposure to loud noise. To protect your ears from this condition, lower the volume of the source of noise. Wear earplugs in noisy environments, when operating machinery, and at loud concerts or sporting events. Limit the length of time you are exposed to loud noise to reduce the chance of permanent damage.

LESSON 4 REVIEW

Reviewing Facts and Vocabulary

1. Identify the three main parts of the ear and the structures that can be found in each part.

2. Define the term *tinnitus.*

3. Examine the effects of health behaviors on hearing: What effect can loud noises have on hearing?

Thinking Critically

4. **Analyzing.** What activities might cause the inner ear to send mixed messages to the brain and result in dizziness and nausea?

5. **Synthesizing.** Under what circumstances might you need to protect yourself from sensorineural hearing loss? How might you do so?

Applying Health Skills

Advocacy. Work with classmates to create a campaign that raises awareness about hearing loss. Brainstorm ways teens can reduce exposure to damaging noise levels and protect their hearing. Use effective strategies to promote hearing protection.

After You Read

Explain. Do you think hearing problems affect only the elderly? List some hearing problems that you think may affect younger people.

Visit **health.glencoe.com** for the Interactive Study Guide for Lesson 4.

Lesson 4 Ears and Hearing Protection **379**

Sunscreen 101: The **Basics**

To decode the information on a sunscreen bottle, just look for a few key words.

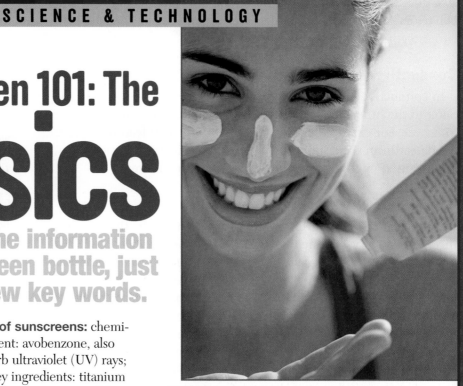

• **There are two types of sunscreens:** chemical blockers (key ingredient: avobenzone, also called Parsol 1789) absorb ultraviolet (UV) rays; and physical blockers (key ingredients: titanium dioxide, zinc oxide) create a layer on top of the skin that deflects UV rays. Dermatologists recommend using either type.

• **There are two kinds of UV rays:** UVB (which causes sunburn and cancer) and UVA (which causes wrinkles). "A high sun protection factor (SPF) is good, but SPF only measures the UVB coverage," says Yohini Appa, Ph.D., an executive at a major cosmetics company. "The most important thing to look for on the label is 'broad spectrum protection,' which means protection against both UVA and UVB rays."

• **"Anything under an SPF 15 is like wearing sunglasses with no lenses.** It's not adequate protection," says dermatologist Patricia Wexler, M.D., who recommends at least an SPF 30 for extensive outdoor activity.

• **To cover your entire body,** use one ounce of sunscreen (so a 4-ounce bottle equals four applications). "If you don't use enough, you're not getting the level of SPF protection on the label," explains Appa, who recommends increasing the SPF level and applying two coats to ensure complete coverage.

• **"Waterproof" doesn't mean you don't need to reapply at all.** Do so every two hours or after an hour in the water.

• **Sunscreens can't guard against every problem**—dehydration, for example. "The sun's heat depletes the natural moisture of the skin," says Wexler. To replenish what you've lost, drink lots of water. When you get out of the sun, apply a lightweight oil or moisturizer that contains nourishing, skin-soothing ingredients like arnica, shea butter, or aloe vera. If you have a severe sunburn accompanied by swelling or blistering, consult a doctor immediately. ◢

TIME to THINK... About Sunscreen

Imagine you're at the beach. Over the course of six hours, you cover yourself adequately three separate times from an 8-ounce tube of sunscreen. (Check back to the article for guidelines on adequate coverage.) How many total ounces of sunscreen must you use over those six hours? What percentage of the tube's contents will you use?

1. **Communicating.** A young child refuses to have a bath or wash his or her hair. How can you encourage him or her to change this behavior? *(LESSON 1)*

2. **Goal Setting.** Set a goal to brush and floss your teeth every morning and every evening. Use the goal-setting steps to help you identify behaviors that will help you meet this goal. *(LESSON 2)*

3. **Accessing Information.** Imagine that you have just been told that you need corrective lenses. Research the advantages and disadvantages of glasses and contact lenses. Make a chart that lists the pros and cons of each. Use this information along with the decision-making steps to determine which you would prefer. *(LESSON 3)*

4. **Communicating.** You suspect that a close family member is experiencing hearing loss, but he or she is not asking for help. What clues might make you think this is the case? How can you talk to this person about what is happening? *(LESSON 4)*

CAREER Corner

Dental Hygienist

Regular dental care includes more than just seeing the dentist. Most dental offices rely on dental hygienists to provide some routine dental care. A dental hygienist can take your dental and medical history, clean your teeth, and teach you how to achieve and maintain good oral health.

To become a dental hygienist, you will need a high school diploma or its equivalent. After high school, hygienists complete a two-year training program in which they earn an associate's degree. You can find out more about this and other health careers by clicking on Career Corner at **health.glencoe.com.**

BEYOND the Classroom

Parent Involvement

Advocacy. With a parent or guardian, learn more about the services available for hearing-impaired individuals in your community. Are there any services that are unavailable in your community? Discuss with family members the possible reasons for this lack. What can you do to raise awareness about services for the hearing impaired?

School and Community

Volunteering. Locate an agency that works with individuals with hearing or sight impairments. Ask whether there are any opportunities for volunteer work within the agency. Report to your class on what you have learned.

After You Read

On the back of your Foldable, collect information on the structure and function of hair and nails. Compare their structure and function to those of skin.

FOLDABLES™
Study Organizer

➤ EXPLORING HEALTH TERMS *Answer the following questions on a sheet of paper.*

Lesson 1 *Match each definition with the correct term.*

dermis	epidermis
dandruff	hair follicle
melanin	sebaceous glands
sweat glands	melanoma

1. A pigment that gives skin, hair, and eyes their color.
2. Structures within the skin that produce perspiration through ducts to pores on the skin's surface.
3. Structures within the skin that produce sebum.
4. A condition that can occur if the scalp becomes too dry and dead skin cells are shed as sticky, white flakes.

Lesson 2 *Replace the underlined words with the correct term.*

periodontium	pulp
tartar	plaque
periodontal disease	

5. <u>Tartar</u> is a sticky, colorless film that acts on sugar to form acids that destroy tooth enamel and irritate gums.
6. <u>Periodontium</u> is completely preventable.

Lesson 3 *Fill in the blanks with the correct term.*

choroid	cornea
lacrimal gland	retina
sclera	

The outer layer of the eyewall consists of the (_7_), the white part of the eye, and the (_8_), the transparent tissue in the front of the eye. The (_9_) is the inner layer of the eyewall.

Lesson 4 *Match each definition with the correct term.*

auditory ossicles	labyrinth
external auditory canal	tinnitus

10. A passageway in the outer ear that leads to the eardrum.
11. Three small bones in the middle ear.
12. Another name for the inner ear.

➤ RECALLING THE FACTS *Use complete sentences to answer the following questions.*

1. Explain how the skin protects your body.
2. List three steps you can take to keep your skin healthy.
3. Why may getting a tattoo be hazardous to your health?
4. Name two functions of the teeth.
5. How do the foods you eat and your eating habits affect the health of your teeth?
6. List three strategies for reducing bad breath.
7. How do the lacrimal glands contribute to the health of your eye?
8. Explain how the iris and pupil regulate the amount of light entering the inner eye.
9. Describe what 20/60 vision means.
10. What is the function of the eustachian tube?
11. List two actions you can take to keep your ears healthy.
12. What are three causes of hearing loss?

For more review questions for Chapter 14, go to **health.glencoe.com**.

➤ WRITING CRITICALLY

1. **Persuasive.** Write a public service announcement encouraging teens to protect their skin from sun damage. In your public service announcement, state facts about the possible consequences of exposure to UV rays, and give advice on how teens can protect their skin from exposure. Make sure to use supporting evidence giving logical reasons, give examples, and quote experts.

2. **Expository.** Write a health bulletin that could be placed on the bulletin board in the office of your school nurse that informs others about behaviors they can practice to keep their eyes healthy. Explain why these behaviors are important for both short-term and long-term health.

Standardized Test Practice

 Read the passage below and then answer the questions.

Let's Get Fit!

(1) People start exercise programs for many reasons. (2) Some hope to lose weight, while others want to look better. (3) Many people are simply following doctor's orders. (4) But people often find that exercising helps them feel good as well as look good. (5) Here are two simple steps to help you get fit.

(6) Schedule your workout in the same way you schedule any important activity or part of your daily life. (7) Morning works best for most people. (8) Some people however, prefer to exercise later in the afternoon. (9) The important thing is to find the best time for you and stick to it.

(10) Second, discover which exercises you enjoy, which ones you are best at, and which ones challenge you. (11) Then keep up with them. (12) Learn your limitations: avoid exercise that is beyond your strength.

1. Read the sentence below from the essay:

   (6) Schedule your workout in the same way you schedule any important activity or part of your daily life.

   Which revision of the sentence best supports the organization of the piece?

   A There are three important things to remember in scheduling a workout.

   B First, schedule your workout in the same way you schedule any important activity or part of your daily life.

   C Second, schedule your workout in the same way you schedule any important activity or part of your daily life.

   D First, it's hard to know where to begin to discuss scheduling workouts as part of your daily life.

2. What change in **punctuation** should be made to sentence 8?

   F Insert a colon after *people*.

   G Insert a comma after *people*.

   H Delete the comma after *however*.

   I Delete the period after *afternoon*.

3. Write a column for a magazine or newspaper that asks and answers three questions from different age readers about exercise programs and problems. Use good reflective listening skills to gear your answers to each reader's question.

CHAPTER 15

Skeletal, Muscular, and Nervous Systems

Eye ON THE Media

Soft Drink Versus Milk Advertisements

Advertisers have influenced the rise in soft drink sales. Ads for soft drinks are now seen in

▶ video games.

▶ billboards and posters.

▶ movies and TV shows.

▶ sport and amusement venues.

Visit the Eye on the Media section at health.glencoe.com to learn more.

FOLDABLES™
Study Organizer

Before You Read

Use this Foldable to help you organize your notes on the structure and function of the skeletal system, muscular system, and nervous system. Begin with three sheets of 8½" x 11" paper.

▶ **Step 1**

Fold the sheets of paper along the long axis so that one edge is about 1" from the other.

▶ **Step 2**

Fold the paper in half. Unfold and cut along the inside fold line.

▶ **Step 3**

Repeat with the other two sheets of paper. Label as shown. Staple the sheets together.

Muscular System	
Structure	Function

Skeletal System	
Structure	Function

Nervous System	
Structure	Function

As You Read

As you read and discuss the material in the chapter, use your Foldable to record what you learn.

SPOTLIGHT ON HEALTH

Using Visuals. What steps do you take in your day-to-day activities to keep the skeletal, muscular, and nervous systems functioning and to protect them from injury?

The Skeletal System

Guide to Reading

Building Vocabulary

As you read this lesson, write each new highlighted term and its definition in your notebook.

▶ axial skeleton (p. 387)
▶ appendicular skeleton (p. 387)
▶ cartilage (p. 387)
▶ ossification (p. 387)
▶ ligament (p. 389)
▶ tendon (p. 389)

Focusing on the Main Ideas

In this lesson, you will learn how to:

▶ Describe the functions of the skeletal system.
▶ Identify the main divisions and types of bones of the skeletal system.

Reading Strategy

Predict

▶ Scan the headings, subheadings, and photo captions. Write a brief summary describing three ways you can protect your skeletal system.

Write a paragraph describing behaviors you think will keep your skeletal system healthy.

The interaction of bones and muscles allows you to perform all kinds of motions. *List three functions of the skeletal system.*

It's 6:00 a.m.—time to rise and shine. As you roll out of bed, you reach your arms above your head, stretching your arms and back and rolling your shoulders. You are able to start your day thanks to the interrelationships of your skeletal, muscular, and nervous systems. In this lesson you'll learn about the system that provides the basic framework for your body, your skeletal system. You'll also learn how to make positive decisions related to injury.

Functions of the Skeletal System

Your skeletal system provides a living structure for your body. Strong bones, including the vertebrae of your spine, support your upper body and head. The skeleton plays a crucial role in movement by providing a strong, stable, and mobile framework on which muscles can act. Your skeletal system also protects your internal tissues and organs from trauma. The skull, vertebrae, and ribs create protective cavities for the brain, the spinal cord, and the heart and lungs, respectively. Bones store minerals such as calcium and phosphorus, which are important to the health and strength of the skeleton and to various essential processes in your body. Bone marrow, a connective tissue within bones, produces new red blood cells and white blood cells.

Structure of the Skeleton

Your skeletal system consists of 206 bones that can be classified in two main groups. The **axial skeleton** consists of *the 80 bones of the skull, spine, ribs, vertebrae, and sternum, or breastbone*. The **appendicular skeleton** is composed of the remaining *126 bones of the upper and lower limbs, shoulders, and hips*. The bones of these two groups are shown in **Figure 15.1** on page 388.

Types of Bones

All bones are covered with an outer layer of hard, densely packed, compact bone. Beneath the compact bone is spongy bone, a less dense bone with a network of cavities filled with red bone marrow. Almost every bone in the body can be placed in the following categories by shape, as shown in the illustration:

▶ **Long Bones.** Examples of long bones include the bones in your legs and arms. The *humerus* is the bone in your upper arm. The *diaphysis,* or main column of a long bone, is composed of compact bone. Within the diaphysis is a narrow cavity that contains yellow bone marrow, a type of connective tissue that stores fat. The end of a long bone is called the *epiphysis.* The epiphyses form joints with other bones and contain red bone marrow, where new blood cells are produced.

▶ **Short Bones.** Short bones are almost equal in length and width. Examples include the small bones in the wrists and ankles.

▶ **Flat Bones.** Flat bones are somewhat thinner and much flatter than other bones. Flat bones, such as those in the skull, protect organs. The scapula, or shoulder blade, is another example of a flat bone.

▶ **Irregular Bones.** Irregularly shaped bones, such as some facial bones or the vertebrae, have unusual shapes and do not fit into the other categories.

Cartilage

Cartilage, *a strong, flexible connective tissue,* is another component of your skeletal system. Cartilage can be found in many areas of the body: at the ends of long bones, at the end of the nose, and within the outer ear. In some joints, such as the knee, cartilage acts as a cushion, reducing friction and allowing smooth motion.

An embryo's skeleton consists mostly of cartilage that serves as a template from which bones will form. Early in embryonic development, the cartilage hardens. This **ossification** (ah-suh-fuh-CAY-shun) is *the process by which bone is formed, renewed, and repaired.*

Bone tissue consists of living cells embedded in a hard matrix of calcium, phosphate, and other calcium minerals.

cartilage
marrow
cavity
compact bone
spongy bone

Bones are shaped according to their function: long, short, flat, or irregular. *Give an example of each of these types of bones.*

Long bone
(humerus)

Short bone
(wrist)

Flat bone
(rib)

FIGURE 15.1

THE SKELETAL SYSTEM

Your bones continue to grow both in length and in thickness until you are about 25 years old. At this age bones usually stop growing, but may continue to thicken.

Axial Skeleton

atlas (1st vertebra)
axis (2nd vertebra)

cervical vertebrae (neck)

Appendicular Skeleton
(shoulders, arms,
hips, legs)

thoracic vertebrae
(upper back)

lumbar vertebrae
(lower back)

Pelvis
illium
sacrum
coccyx
pubis
ischium

occipital bone
parietal bone
frontal bone
nasal bone
cheek bones
temporal bones
mandible (jaw)

clavicle (collar bone)
scapula (shoulder blade)
sternum
ribs (flat bones)

humerus
radius
ulna

carpal bones (wrist)

metacarpal bones (hands)
phalanges (fingers)

femur (long bone)
patella (knee cap)

tibia (long bone)
fibula (long bone)

tarsal bones (ankle)
calcaneus (heel)
metatarsal bones (foot)
phalanges (toes)

Joints

Joints are points at which bones meet. Some joints, such as those between the bones of the skull, do not move. Others, including the joints between vertebrae, have limited movement.

More flexible joints are classified by type:

▶ **Ball-and-socket joints** are formed when the rounded head of one bone fits into the rounded cavity of an adjoining bone, as in a hip or shoulder joint. These joints allow the widest range of movement in all directions.

▶ **Hinge joints,** found at the elbow, knee, ankle, and fingers, allow a joint to bend and straighten, promoting rotation.

▶ **Pivot joints** allow limited rotation or turning of the head.

▶ **Ellipsoidal joints,** such as the one in your wrist, have an oval-shaped part that fits into a curved space. Gliding joints allow bones to slide over one another.

A **ligament** is *a band of fibrous, slightly elastic connective tissue that attaches bone to bone.* Ligaments help stabilize the movements of bones at a joint. A **tendon** is *a fibrous cord that attaches muscle to the bone.* Movement is produced because muscles are attached to bones by tendons and ligaments.

Joints allow a wide range of motions. *What is another example of a ball-and-socket joint?*

Hip (ball-and-socket joint)

Knee (hinge joint)

LESSON 1 | REVIEW

Reviewing Facts and Vocabulary

1. What are the functions of the skeletal system?
2. Define the terms *cartilage* and *ossification*.
3. Name and give examples of each type of joint.

Thinking Critically

4. **Analyzing.** The ligament that holds the bones in your forearm together and helps form the pivot joint there has been torn. How might this affect your ability to move your hand and arm? What movements might be affected?

5. **Comparing and Contrasting.** Recognize how knowledge of the skeletal system is important for maintaining personal health. How are the bones in the axial skeleton similar to those in the appendicular skeleton?

Applying Health Skills

Decision Making. Hector's friends have invited him to go mountain biking. He is hesitant because he thinks this activity would pose some risks to his bones or joints. Using the decision-making steps, role-play with a friend the process of Hector's decision.

After You Read

Compare and Contrast. Describe the difference between injuries affecting the tendons and ligaments. Is medical attention required for both types of injuries? What action should you take after injuring a tendon or ligament?

Visit **health.glencoe.com** for the Interactive Study Guide for Lesson 1.

Lesson 1 The Skeletal System   **389**

Caring for the Skeletal System

Guide to Reading

Building Vocabulary

As you read this lesson, write each new highlighted term and its definition in your notebook.

▶ osteoporosis (p. 391)

▶ scoliosis (p. 391)

▶ repetitive motion injury (p. 393)

Focusing on the Main Ideas

In this lesson, you will learn how to:

▶ Examine health promotion and prevention of bone disorders.

▶ Describe types of bone and joint injuries and strategies to prevent injuries that damage the skeletal system.

Reading Strategy

Make Inference

▶ What do you think the term *repetitive motion injury* means? What types of activities may cause repetitive motion injuries? Review your answer after reading the text.

Quick Write

Write a brief paragraph describing a type of bone injury and ways you might be able to prevent the injury.

▲ Getting enough calcium during your teen years is essential for a lifetime of healthy bones. *Name two foods you enjoy that provide calcium, phosphorus, and vitamin D.*

The overall health of your body very much depends on the health of your skeletal system. If your skeletal system cannot perform its functions properly, your freedom of movement may be limited and other areas of your health and lifestyle may also be affected.

Care of the Skeletal System

Caring for your skeletal system is something you can do every day. Eating foods that contain calcium, vitamin D, and phosphorus can help prevent the development of certain skeletal disorders. Phosphorus can be found in dairy products, beans, whole grains, and liver. Dark green, leafy vegetables are a source of calcium. Milk is fortified with vitamin D and also provides calcium. Eating foods that protect your skeletal system shows that you know methods for predicting immediate and long-term impact of health decisions.

Regular physical activity, including weight-bearing exercise, helps keep bones strong. Wearing protective gear such as a helmet and padding when you participate in sporting or recreational activities shows that you know and apply safe practices in physical activity settings.

Problems of the Skeletal System

Skeletal system disorders and bone injuries can be the result of many factors, including poor nutrition, infections, sports and recreational injuries, and poor posture. The skeletal system is also affected by degenerative disorders such as osteoporosis.

Fractures

A fracture is any type of break in a bone. Fractures can be either compound or simple. A compound fracture is one in which the broken end of the bone protrudes through the skin. A simple fracture is one in which the broken bone does not protrude. Fractures are also classified by the pattern of the break:

▶ **Hairline fracture.** The fracture is incomplete, and the two parts of the bone do not separate.

▶ **Transverse fracture.** The fracture is completely across the bone. A transverse fracture may result from a sharp, direct blow or from stress caused by prolonged running on an already damaged bone.

▶ **Comminuted fracture.** The bone shatters into more than two pieces, usually as a result of severe force.

Osteoporosis

You can build bone mass only during the time you are growing. Health behaviors that you practice now, during your teen years, can reduce your risk of developing osteoporosis later in life. **Osteoporosis** is *a condition in which progressive loss of bone tissue occurs.* It is a very serious bone disease that affects millions of older Americans and has no warning signs in its early stages. Bones are weakened and become brittle, causing them to break easily. Adequate amounts of calcium, vitamin D, and phosphorus help bones remain strong and healthy. Regular weight-bearing physical activities, such as walking and weight training, stimulate bone cells to increase bone mass, thereby reducing the risk of osteoporosis. Early detection is essential to treatment and to slowing loss of bone tissue. A bone scan (in which X rays measure bone density) can be performed at regular intervals later in life.

Scoliosis

Scoliosis is *a lateral, or side-to-side, curvature of the spine.* Scoliosis may exist at the time of birth, or it can develop during childhood. The curvature of the spine worsens as growth continues and may proceed even after growth stops. Early detection is important in the treatment of scoliosis. Treatment includes wearing a brace to help straighten the spine and, in more severe cases, surgery.

A break like the comminuted fracture shown here might be avoided by keeping bones strong through good nutrition and following safety precautions. *What health promotion steps do you take to prevent diseases of the bones and joints?*

Reading Check

Compare and Contrast What is the difference between a compound and a simple fracture?

Real-Life Application

Are You Getting Enough Calcium?

During the teen years it is very important to choose calcium-rich foods to build maximum bone density. Building strong bones during adolescence will help prevent osteoporosis and bone fractures later in life. You should have at least 3 servings of milk, cheese, or yogurt daily to meet your calcium needs. If you don't drink milk, then choose other foods high in calcium, such as yogurt, kale, or fortified fruit juices. The Recommended Dietary Allowance of calcium for teens between the ages of 11 and 18 is 1,300 milligrams (mg). The following table shows the approximate calcium content in a single serving of some common calcium-rich foods.

Food	Serving size	Mg of Calcium per Serving
Milk	1 cup	300
White beans	½ cup	113
Broccoli cooked	½ cup	35
Broccoli raw	1 cup	35
Cheddar cheese	1.5 oz	300
Low-fat yogurt	8 oz	300–415
Kale cooked	1 cup	67
Calcium-fortified orange juice	1 cup	300
Orange	1 medium	50
Sardines or salmon with bones	20 sardines	50
Sweet potatoes	½ cup	44

ACTIVITY

List all the calcium-rich foods you eat over the next 24 hours, and record the amount or serving size you eat. Compare your calcium intake to the amounts of calcium shown on the chart to see whether you are getting at least 1,300 mg of calcium daily. Create a written plan describing how you will maintain or increase your calcium intake. Include specific actions you will take.

Injuries to Joints

Injuries to joints can occur due to overuse, strain, or disease. The following are joint injuries that may require professional health services.

► **Dislocation** results when the ligaments that attach the bone at the joint are torn as the bone slips out of place. Never attempt to replace a dislocated joint; get immediate medical help. Treatment includes having the joint reset and immobilized while the ligaments heal.

► **Torn cartilage** can result from a sharp blow or the twisting of a joint. Injuries are treated with arthroscopic surgery.

▶ **Bursitis** results from the inflammation of a fluid-filled sac called the bursa. Certain joints, such as the elbow, have bursae that help reduce friction between their movable parts. When the bursa becomes inflamed, pain and swelling can occur at the joint.

▶ **A bunion** is a painful swelling of the bursa in the first joint of the big toe. Wearing ill-fitting shoes can make bunions worse. Large bunions may require surgery.

▶ **Arthritis** is the inflammation of a joint. The condition can result from an injury, natural wear and tear, or autoimmune disease. The most common form of arthritis, osteoarthritis, results from wear and tear on the joints.

Repetitive Motion Injury

A **repetitive motion injury** is *damage to tissues caused by prolonged, repeated movements* such as in computer work, sewing, or assembly line work. One of the most common repetitive motion injuries is carpal tunnel syndrome. This condition occurs when swollen ligaments and tendons in the wrist cause numbness, a burning or tingling sensation in the thumb and forefinger, pain, and weakness in the hand. Treatment includes wearing a splint to reduce wrist movements, medication to reduce swelling and, in a small percentage of cases, surgery.

Health Minute

Reduce the Risk of Carpal Tunnel Syndrome

Use these tips to reduce your risk of developing repetitive motion injuries.

While using a computer:

▶ Rest your hands and wrists from repetitive motion by taking frequent breaks.

▶ Use a keyboard or other equipment designed to reduce strain and pressure.

▶ Adjust chair height, so that your forearms are level with your wrists. This will reduce the angle of your bent wrists when you are typing.

LESSON 2 | **REVIEW**

Reviewing Facts and Vocabulary

1. Name three behaviors that help keep your bones and joints healthy.

2. What should you do if you think someone has a fractured bone or dislocated joint?

3. Define the term *repetitive motion injury.* Explain how to prevent this type of injury.

Thinking Critically

4. **Analyzing.** A dislocated or injured joint is often immobilized by putting a rigid cast around the affected area. How might this procedure affect the health of the surrounding muscle tissue?

5. **Evaluating.** Analyze the relationship between health promotion during your teen years and the prevention of osteoporosis later in life.

Applying Health Skills

Accessing Information. Research more about keeping the skeletal system healthy. Choose a category such as injury prevention, nutritional needs, or building bone mass to focus your research. Then prepare a pamphlet of step-by-step strategies you and your peers can use to promote the health of bones during the teen years.

After You Read

Problems and Solutions. Create a T chart. On one side, list the problems of the skeletal system. On the other, list ways to care for the skeletal system and to prevent problems and injuries.

The Muscular System

Guide to Reading

Building Vocabulary

As you read this lesson, write each new highlighted term and its definition in your notebook.

- smooth muscles (p. 395)
- skeletal muscles (p. 395)
- flexors (p. 395)
- extensors (p. 395)
- cardiac muscles (p. 395)
- muscle tone (p. 396)
- tendonitis (p. 398)
- hernia (p. 398)

Focusing on the Main Ideas

In this lesson, you will learn how to:

- Describe the functions of the muscular system.
- Examine the different types of muscles in the body and the effects of health behaviors on the muscular system.
- List problems of the muscular system.

Reading Strategy

Organize Information

- Create a two-column chart. As you read, list ways to care for the muscular system in the first column. In the next, list some of the problems of the muscular system.

Quick Write

Write a paragraph describing some of the benefits of having good muscle tone.

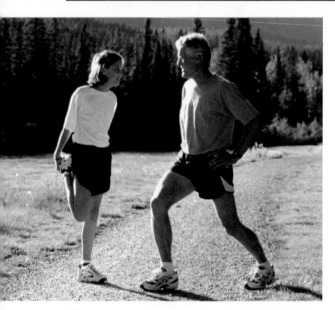

Proper warm-up and stretching before and cool-down after any physical activity keeps your muscles flexible and strong.

The action of a slingshot is the result of two interdependent parts—a forked stick and a rubber band or other elastic material. The same is true of the human body. The role of the stick is played by the skeleton. The role of the rubber band is played by the muscular system. Muscles are elastic; they stretch to allow a wide range of motion.

Functions of the Muscular System

Certain muscles in your body are always at work. Even when you sleep, muscles help you breathe, make your heart beat, and move food through your digestive system. These involuntary processes happen without your consciously controlling them. At other times, such as when you play the piano or a video game, make a dash toward first base, or throw a ball, you are using muscles that are under conscious, or voluntary, control. Without the use of both voluntary and involuntary muscles, you would be unable to perform any of these activities.

Structure of the Muscular System

Amuscle is made up of hundreds of long cells called fibers. Major muscles in the body are made up of hundreds of bundles of these fibers. Muscles work by means of two complementary, or opposing, actions. These are contraction, the shortening of a muscle, and extension, the stretching of a muscle. Muscle contraction is triggered by nerve impulses. Some nerves provide impulses for many muscle fibers, especially to large muscles such as the calf muscle or biceps. In other areas, such as your eyes, a single nerve may provide impulses to only two or three muscle fibers.

Reading Check

Explain What are the three types of muscles?

Types of Muscles

The body contains three types of muscle tissue: smooth muscle, skeletal muscle, and cardiac muscle.

▶ **Smooth muscles** *act on the lining of passageways and internal organs.* These muscles can be found in the lining of the blood vessels, the digestive tract, the passageways that lead into the lungs, and the bladder. Smooth muscles are under involuntary control.

▶ **Skeletal muscles** *are attached to bone and cause body movements.* Skeletal muscle tissue has a striated, or striped, appearance under a microscope. Most of your muscle tissue is made up of skeletal muscle, and almost all skeletal muscles are under voluntary control. Skeletal muscles often work together, undergoing opposing actions to produce movement. One muscle contracts while the other muscle extends. An example of this can be seen in the diagram at the right, which shows the biceps and triceps muscles of the upper arm. To bend and straighten your arm at the elbow, these muscles oppose each other's action. The **flexor** is *the muscle that closes a joint.* In this example the biceps is the flexor. The **extensor** is *the muscle that opens a joint.* In this case the triceps is the extensor. Identify other opposing skeletal muscles that appear in **Figure 15.2** on page 396.

▶ **Cardiac muscle** is *a type of striated muscle that forms the wall of the heart.* The involuntary cardiac muscles are responsible for the contraction of your heart, the most important part of the cardiovascular system. The heart contracts rhythmically about 100,000 times each day to pump blood throughout your body.

V Skeletal muscles produce movement by working in pairs. One muscle contracts while the other extends. *Try holding your thigh as you bend your leg at the knee. Identify the flexor and the extensor muscles as you perform this action.*

Muscle Movement

biceps muscle (flexor)

triceps muscle (extensor)

tendons

Care of the Muscular System

Regular physical activity is the best way to keep your muscles strong and healthy. Muscles that remain unused for long periods of time will *atrophy,* or decrease in size and strength. **Muscle tone** is *the natural tension in the fibers of a muscle.* Regular **physical activity** helps keeps muscles toned and healthy. Practicing good posture strengthens back muscles. Wearing safety equipment and appropriate clothing can protect muscles during physical activity.

FIGURE 15.2

THE SKELETAL MUSCLES

Major muscle groups include the arms, legs, back, abdomen, shoulders, and chest.

extensor muscles (dorsal surface)

teres
trapezius
rhomboid
triceps
biceps (of arm)
latissimus dorsi

gluteus maximus

abductor muscles (pull legs away from body)
biceps (of thigh)

semitendinosus
peroneus
gastrocnemius

Achilles tendon

adductor muscles (pull legs toward body)

gastrocnemius
soleus

Facial Muscles
frontalis
temporalis
orbicularis oculi
masseter
orbicularis oris

sternocleidomastoid

flexor muscles (inside of arm)
biceps
deltoid
pectoralis major
serratus oblique
external oblique (muscle of abdomen)

sartorius
adductor muscles (pull legs toward body)
quadriceps muscles

patella (kneecap)

peroneus
anterior tibial

Training Safety Checklist

Participating in weight-bearing exercise throughout life is important to maintain muscle tone and to keep bones strong and healthy. As with any physical activity, however, safety comes first. In this activity you will create safety checklists for teens doing weight or resistance training.

What You'll Need

- paper and pen or pencil
- textbook and other sources of information

What You'll Do

1. In your group, identify at least one weight-bearing exercise for every major muscle group.

2. Use a separate sheet of paper for each exercise. Describe the exercise, and then list the following: appropriate clothing, when and where to work out, safe exercise procedures, and how to use equipment properly. Refer to your textbook and other reliable sources to develop your checklist.

3. For each exercise, include at least five easy-to-remember tips for practicing safe weight training. Create an acronym that teens can recall easily.

4. Staple the pages together to make a guide. If your classroom has a computer, input the text and print copies. Place the guides in the gymnasium and in other areas around the school.

Apply and Conclude

Write a paragraph explaining what you have learned about the benefits of weight-bearing exercise. Note the importance of following safety procedures while keeping your muscles healthy.

Problems of the Muscular System

When you are exercising, your muscles are working very hard. They might be sore after strenuous activity, such as going for an all-day hike or bike ride. Although it can be painful, muscle soreness is usually temporary. However, other problems of the muscular system are far more serious and can affect a person's overall health and lifestyle. The recovery time for injury-related muscle problems varies with the type and severity of the injury.

By getting regular physical activity, you strengthen your muscles. This shows that you know how to delay the onset of and reduce the risk for potential health problems during adulthood.

Reading Check

Explain What are some of the ways to protect muscles during physical activity?

Muscles produce heat when they contract. Shivering is an involuntary contraction of skeletal muscles in an effort to warm the body.

• Smooth muscles located in the skin at the base of hairs contract involuntarily, raising the hair and producing "goose bumps" in response to cold or fear.

• A muscle spasm occurs when a single muscle involuntarily contracts. A tic is the twitching that results when muscles involuntarily contract in a repeated spasm.

▶ **Bruise.** A bruise is an area of discolored skin that appears after an injury causes the blood vessels beneath the skin to rupture and leak. Swelling can be reduced with an ice pack.

▶ **Muscle strain or sprain.** A strained muscle results when a muscle is stretched or partially torn as a result of overexertion. Strains are usually treated by using the P.R.I.C.E. (protection, rest, ice, compression, elevation) procedure. A sprain is an injury to the ligament in a joint, and it requires medical treatment.

▶ **Tendonitis. Tendonitis**, or *the inflammation of a tendon,* can be caused by injury, overuse, or aging. Signs of tendonitis include joint pain or swelling that worsens with activity. Treatment includes rest, anti-inflammatory medication, or ultrasound.

▶ **Hernia.** A **hernia** occurs *when an organ or tissue protrudes through an area of weak muscle.* This condition can result from straining to lift a heavy object. Hernia repair usually requires surgery.

▶ **Muscular dystrophy.** Muscular dystrophy is an inherited disorder in which skeletal muscle fibers are progressively destroyed. There is no cure, but with early detection muscle weakness can be delayed through exercise programs.

LESSON 3 REVIEW

Reviewing Facts and Vocabulary

1. Give examples of how muscles work together with other body systems.

2. Describe *cardiac muscle.*

3. What is *tendonitis?* Why does it occur?

Thinking Critically

4. **Applying.** Examine the effects of health behaviors on the muscular system. Which muscles are most involved in your favorite physical activities? What behaviors can help you protect the health of these and other muscles?

5. **Analyzing.** Describe two types of muscle injury, and suggest strategies that can prevent them.

Applying Health Skills

Goal Setting. Set a goal to begin a program of strengthening your muscles. Decide on a weight-training program or another physical activity that will increase muscle strength. On which muscle groups will you focus? Use the steps of goal setting to develop your plan.

After You Read

Explain. Write a brief paragraph describing each of the three types of muscles. What can you do to care for your muscular system?

The Nervous System

Your nervous system is a complex network that allows communication between the brain and all other areas of the body.

Function and Structure of the Nervous System

Your nervous system coordinates all of the activities in your body—from breathing or digesting food to sensing pain or feeling fear. The brain, spinal cord, and nerves work together. Nerves transmit messages back and forth to every organ, tissue, and cell. For this reason, it is important that you understand the impact of personal health behaviors on body systems.

The nervous system has two main divisions. The *central nervous system (CNS)* consists of the brain and spinal cord. The *peripheral nervous system (PNS)* gathers information from inside and outside your body. It includes nerves that extend from the brain, spinal cord, and sensory receptors, such as those in the skin that sense pressure, temperature, or pain. The central nervous system receives messages from the nerves in the peripheral nervous system, interprets them, and sends out a response. Impulses can be carried at speeds of up to 280 miles per hour, which means, for example, that you can let go of a hot pan before you are badly burned.

A computed tomography (CT) scan is used to diagnose problems that can affect the function of the nervous system. *Name a type of injury that can cause damage to the brain.*

Neurons

Messages are transmitted to and from the spinal cord and brain by **neurons**, or *nerve cells*. Neurons are classified by their function: sensory neurons, motor neurons, and interneurons. Interneurons communicate with and are found between other neurons. **Figure 15.3** illustrates the nerve impulse.

A neuron consists of three main parts:

Reading Check

Explain What are the three main parts of a neuron?

▶ **Cell body.** The cell body of a neuron contains the nucleus, the control center of the cell. The nucleus regulates the production of proteins within the cell. Unlike other cells in the body, neurons have limited ability to repair damage or replace destroyed cells.

▶ **Dendrites.** Dendrites are branched structures that extend from the cell body in most neurons. Dendrites receive information from other neurons or sensory receptors and transmit impulses toward the cell body.

▶ **Axons.** Axons transmit impulses away from the cell body and toward another neuron, muscle cell, or gland. Some axons are surrounded by a covering called a myelin sheath and can transmit impulses more quickly than axons without coverings.

FIGURE 15.3

THE NERVE IMPULSE

A nerve impulse begins when a sensory receptor is stimulated. The impulse travels to the CNS and is interpreted with the help of an interneuron. Then a motor neuron carries the message to a muscle cell or gland in response to the stimulus.

Sensory Neuron
interneuron dendrites (receptors)
interneuron cell body
skin
receptors
axon
cell body of sensory neuron
synapse

Motor Neuron
motor neuron dendrites
motor neuron cell body
axon
skeletal muscle

The Central Nervous System

Impulses in the body are carried to and from the spinal cord and the brain, the two organs that make up the central nervous system, as shown in **Figure 15.4.**

FIGURE 15.4

THE NERVOUS SYSTEM

Nerves extend to various parts of the body along the length of the spinal cord.

cerebrum

cerebellum

spinal cord

vertebra

12 pairs of cranial nerves

8 pairs of cervical nerves

12 pairs of thoracic nerves

5 pairs of lumbar nerves

5 pairs of sacral nerves

1 pair of coccygeal nerves

Spinal Cord Cross Section
white matter
spinal cord
gray matter

Spinal Meninges
spinal nerve
pia mater
arachnoid
dura mater
vertebra (bone)

The Spinal Cord

The spinal cord is a long column of nerve tissue about the thickness of your index finger, extending about 18 inches down your back. Vertebrae are the bones that make up your spine. Connective tissue called the spinal meninges, along with the vertebrae, help protect the spinal cord. The spinal cord is also bathed in cerebrospinal fluid that absorbs shock and nourishes nerve tissue.

Reading Check

Explain What two organs make up the central nervous system?

The Brain

The brain, shown in the illustration, integrates and controls the activities of the nervous system. Your brain helps you receive and process messages; think, remember, and reason; and coordinate muscle movements. Breathing, digesting food, learning math, running a race, and remembering a family vacation are all processes accomplished by the brain. It is involved in emotions and all of your senses.

An adult human brain weighs up to three pounds and sits in the protective cavity formed by the bones of the skull. Like the spinal cord, the brain is covered with layers of cranial meninges and surrounded by cerebrospinal fluid. Both help protect the tissues of the brain from injury. Although the brain makes up only about 2 percent of a person's total body weight, it uses more than 20 percent of the oxygen inhaled. Without oxygen, the brain can last for only four to five minutes before suffering serious and irreversible damage. It is important to use protective equipment when participating in activities that might result in brain injury. In this way, you show that you know how to make positive decisions related to injury-prevention.

The brain has three main divisions: the cerebrum, the cerebellum, and the brain stem.

THE CEREBRUM

The **cerebrum** is *the largest and most complex part of the brain.* It is covered with a thin layer of gray matter. The billions of neurons in the cerebrum are the center for conscious thought, learning, and memory. Learning how to use language, creating art and music, remembering the past, and dreaming about the future all take place in the cerebrum. The cerebrum is divided into two hemispheres that communicate with each other. The right hemisphere controls the left side of the body, and the left hemisphere controls the right side of the body. Both hemispheres contain centers for different processes that take place in the brain. The left hemisphere is the center for language, reasoning, and the ability to analyze and think critically about mathematical or scientific problems. The right hemisphere is the center for processing music and art and comprehending spatial relationships.

Each hemisphere has four lobes, and each lobe is named after the skull bone that protects it:

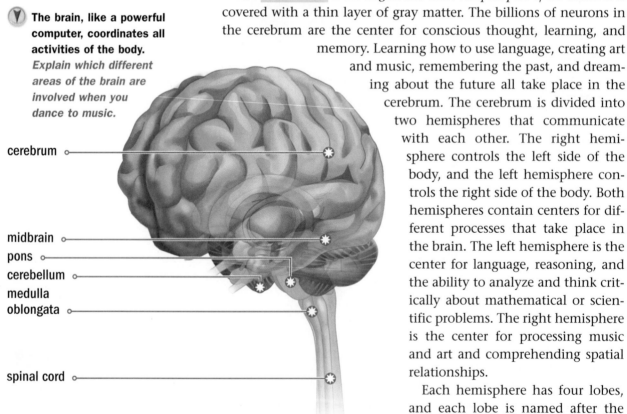

▼ The brain, like a powerful computer, coordinates all activities of the body. *Explain which different areas of the brain are involved when you dance to music.*

cerebrum

midbrain
pons
cerebellum
medulla
oblongata

spinal cord

- **The frontal lobe** controls voluntary movements and has a role in the use of language. The prefrontal areas are thought to be involved with intellect and personality.

- **The parietal lobe** is involved with sensory information such as heat, cold, pain, touch, and body position in space.

- **The occipital lobe** controls the sense of vision.

- **The temporal lobe** controls the senses of hearing and smell; it is also involved with memory, thought, and judgment.

THE CEREBELLUM

The **cerebellum** is *the second largest part of the brain*. Its principal function is to coordinate the movement of skeletal muscles. This area of the brain continually receives messages from sensory neurons in the inner ear and muscles, and it uses this information to maintain the body's posture and balance. Being able to complete a complex series of muscle movements, such as serving a volleyball, dancing, or playing the violin, is made possible by the cerebellum.

THE BRAIN STEM

The **brain stem** is *a three-inch stalk of nerve cells and fibers that connects the spinal cord to the rest of the brain*. Incoming sensory impulses and outgoing motor impulses pass through the brain stem. It consists of three main parts—the medulla oblongata, the pons, and the midbrain—and two smaller regions—the thalamus and the hypothalamus.

- **Medulla oblongata.** Rising from the top portion of the spinal cord, the medulla oblongata is the lowest part of the brain stem. Within the medulla are centers that regulate heartbeat and respiratory rates as well as reflexes such as coughing, sneezing, and vomiting. The medulla also receives input and sends motor impulses to the cochlea of the inner ear for hearing and to the tongue for movement during speech and swallowing.

- **Pons.** Approximately one inch in length, the pons is just above the medulla. The pons is the pathway connecting nerve impulses to other areas of the brain; it also helps regulate breathing. The pons controls the muscles of the eyes and face.

- **Midbrain.** The highest portion of the brain stem, the midbrain is involved in such functions as controlling eyeball movement and pupil size. The reflexive response of turning your head when you hear an unexpected loud noise is also initiated by the midbrain.

- **Thalamus.** The thalamus is an important relay center for incoming sensory impulses. Nerve cells within the thalamus

How do scientists learn about the brain?
Recent advances in technology have enabled scientists to "see" inside a living brain. Brain imaging techniques help scientists understand the functions of the brain, locate areas affected by neurological disorders, and develop new strategies to treat brain disorders. These techniques include:

- CT, or "CAT" scans, in which a series of X rays are beamed through the head, producing an image that shows the structure of the brain.

- PET scans, in which a machine detects and images radioactive material that is either injected into or inhaled by the patient. This type of scan provides information on brain function.

- MRI, which uses radio waves and magnetic fields to produce an anatomical view of the brain.

Reading Check

Explain What is the function of the peripheral nervous system?

receive information from different sense organs such as the eyes and ears. Through the spine the thalamus also receives information from touch and pressure receptors in the skin.

▶ **Hypothalamus.** The hypothalamus controls and balances various body processes to regulate body temperature, stimulate appetite for food and drink, and regulate sleep. The hypothalamus also controls secretions from the **pituitary gland** that control metabolism, sexual development, and emotional responses.

The Peripheral Nervous System

The peripheral nervous system (PNS) consists of all of the nerves that are not part of the CNS. The PNS carries messages between the CNS and the rest of the body. The PNS can be divided into two categories, the autonomic nervous system and the somatic nervous system.

The Autonomic Nervous System

The autonomic nervous system (ANS) controls such involuntary functions as digestion and heart rate. The ANS consists of a network of nerves divided into two smaller networks: the sympathetic nervous system and the parasympathetic nervous system.

THE SYMPATHETIC NERVOUS SYSTEM

You may have felt the effects of the sympathetic nervous system the last time you were startled. Messages from the sympathetic nervous system cause your heart rate to increase and the blood vessels leading to your muscles to dilate, allowing greater blood flow. This is the "fight or flight" response that prepares your body to react to what may be a dangerous situation. You also have experienced a **reflex**, *a spontaneous response of the body to a stimulus,* as when a doctor tests the knee-jerk reflex by tapping the ligament below the knee. **Figure 15.5** on page 405 shows the steps of a reflex action.

(Y) When you are nervous about taking a big test, increased heart rate and sweaty palms are signs that your sympathetic nervous system is at work. *Name another situation that will cause a response from your sympathetic nervous system.*

THE PARASYMPATHETIC NERVOUS SYSTEM

During periods of rest and relaxation, the parasympathetic system opposes the action of the sympathetic system by slowing body functions. It slows down the heartbeat, opens blood vessels, and lowers blood pressure.

Somatic Nervous System

The somatic nervous system consists of sensory neurons that relay messages from receptors in the eyes, ears, nose, tongue, and skin to the CNS and motor neurons that carry impulses from the CNS to skeletal muscles.

FIGURE 15.5

STEPS OF A REFLEX ACTION

Reflexes can prevent injuries. For example, when you touch something hot, your hand jerks away before you feel your finger being burned.

1. **Stimulus:** the hand touches a hot stove.

2. The **sensory neuron** makes contact with a **connecting neuron** in the spinal cord.

3. The **connecting neuron** contacts a **motor neuron** that sends an impulse to the muscles.

4. **Reflex:** The muscle responds by pulling the hand away from the stove.

LESSON 4 | **REVIEW**

Reviewing Facts and Vocabulary

1. What is the main function of the brain?

2. Define the term *neuron.* What are the parts of a neuron?

3. What is a *reflex?* How does having quick reflexes benefit your health?

Thinking Critically

4. **Analyzing.** After sustaining a head injury, a patient is having trouble understanding language and controlling movement on the right side of his or her body. What parts of the brain might be damaged?

5. **Evaluating.** Why is an injury to the brain stem considered critical?

Applying Health Skills

Advocacy. Research the benefits of wearing a helmet when biking, skating, or skate-boarding. Make an informative pamphlet that outlines helmet laws and explains the importance of protecting the brain from injury. Make your pamphlet available to your classmates to demonstrate your knowledge about this personal health concern.

> **After You Read**

Explain. Write a paragraph explaining how neurons send messages to and from the spinal cord and brain.

Visit **health.glencoe.com** for the Interactive Study Guide for Lesson 4.

Lesson 4 The Nervous System **405**

Caring for the Nervous System

Guide to Reading

Building Vocabulary

As you read this lesson, write each new highlighted term and its definition in your notebook.

▶ epilepsy (p. 409)

▶ cerebral palsy (p. 409)

Focusing on the Main Ideas

In this lesson, you will learn how to:

▶ Examine the effects of health behavior on the nervous system.

▶ List different types of head and spinal cord injuries.

▶ Define disease and disorders of the nervous system.

Reading Strategy

Problems and Solutions

▶ Create a T chart. On one side, list the problems of the nervous system. On the other, list the ways to care for the nervous system and prevent problems and injury.

Quick Write

Write a paragraph describing ways to prevent injury to your head and spine.

Take care of your nervous system by protecting your head. Wear an approved helmet when participating in outdoor activities and certain sports.

Proper use of helmets and safety belts protects the brain and spinal column from injury. Using safety equipment shows that you understand the potential impact of common risk behaviors on the quality of life. Your nervous system interacts and coordinates with all other body systems so that your body will remain internally balanced and functioning properly. Any injury to the nervous system affects the immediate tissues and may lead to dysfunction in other areas of the body.

Care of the Nervous System

Your health behaviors, such as eating a well-balanced diet, exercising regularly, and getting enough sleep, affect the health of your nervous system. Keep your nervous system healthy by protecting it from injury. To protect your head and spine, wear a helmet and protective gear while riding a bike, motorcycle, or other open vehicle or when playing a contact sport or engaging in activities such as skateboarding. Before diving, always check water depth and look along the bottom for protruding logs or rocks. Wear a safety belt when driving or riding in a motor vehicle.

Problems of the Nervous System

Problems of the nervous system can result from damage to nerve cells or injury to the head or spinal cord. Nerve tissue can also be damaged by degenerative diseases. Using **drugs** and **alcohol** can destroy brain cells and cause nervous system disorders.

Head and Spinal Cord Injuries

In the United States each year, over one million people sustain head injuries and an estimated 11,000 new cases of spinal cord injury occur. These injuries may result from falls, sports or recreational activities, motor vehicle crashes, physical assaults, or gunshot wounds.

HEAD INJURIES

Although the brain is protected by the bones of the skull, any direct blow to the head can cause injury. A concussion, the mildest

Reading ✓ Check

Compare and Contrast
What is the difference between quadriplegia and paraplegia?

Health Skills Activity

Decision Making: Riding Smart

When Alfonso's friend Noah wants to give him a ride home from school on his motorcycle, Alfonso hesitates. An avid dirt bike rider, Alfonso knows the importance of wearing a helmet. Unfortunately, Noah doesn't have a spare one.

"Hop on, Alfonso," Noah says, "there's a thunderstorm coming. The sooner we get home, the better."

"I'd really like to," Alfonso replies, "but you don't have an extra helmet. I never ride without one."

"Don't worry," Noah says. "We're going only a couple of miles and I know a short cut. Nothing can happen in that short distance."

As the thunderstorm nears, Alfonso wonders what he should do.

What Would You Do?

Apply the six steps of the decision-making process to help Alfonso make a health-enhancing decision.

1. State the situation.
2. List the options.
3. Weigh the possible outcomes.
4. Consider values.
5. Make a decision and act.
6. Evaluate the decision.

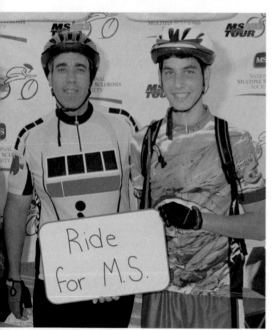

Bicycle tours and races are often held to fund research on degenerative diseases such as multiple sclerosis. *Participating in a fund-raising event can be a rewarding experience. Find out more about such opportunities in your community.*

and most common type of brain injury, results in a temporary loss of consciousness, sometimes lasting only a few seconds. A more serious brain injury is a contusion, a bruising of the brain tissues that can result in dangerous swelling. A major trauma to the brain can result in a coma, a state of unconsciousness from which a person cannot be roused.

SPINAL INJURIES

Any injury to the spine must be considered serious and should be evaluated by a health care professional. Swelling of the spinal cord or the tissue around it in response to trauma can result in temporary loss of nerve function. Without treatment, this can lead to permanent nerve damage. If the spinal cord has been severed or damaged beyond repair, paralysis usually results. An injury to the upper part of the spinal cord may result in *quadriplegia,* or paralysis of both upper and lower limbs. *Paraplegia,* paralysis of both lower limbs, can be caused by an injury that occurs at a lower point in the spinal column. By using safety equipment and avoiding dangerous activities, you show that you understand the impact of personal health behaviors on body systems.

Degenerative Diseases

Degenerative diseases cause affected cells and tissues to break down or deteriorate over time. Common degenerative ailments of the nervous system are listed below.

▶ **Parkinson's disease** results in the destruction of nerve cells in an area of the brain that helps coordinate skeletal muscle movement. Parkinson's is a progressive disorder, meaning that it gradually involves more and more nerves. As the cells are destroyed, muscle function is impaired. Symptoms include uncontrolled muscle tremors and increased muscle rigidity. There is no known cause or cure at present.

▶ **Multiple sclerosis** involves the destruction of the myelin sheath that surrounds the axons of neurons in the CNS. The scar tissue that remains on the neuron interferes with the conduction of nerve impulses, and voluntary control of muscles gradually decreases. With each attack, loss of nerve function increases. Multiple sclerosis is an autoimmune disease in which the body attacks its own tissues.

▶ **Alzheimer's disease** results when neurons in the brain are destroyed. If neurons become clogged with protein deposits, they are unable to transmit impulses. The result is confusion, loss of memory, and gradual mental deterioration. Currently, the cause of Alzheimer's disease is unknown, but the search to find prevention methods continues.

Other Disorders and Problems

Other disorders of the nervous system may not be progressive or degenerative. In some cases a cause may never be identified. These disorders include the following:

▶ **Epilepsy** is *a disorder of the nervous system that is characterized by recurrent seizures—sudden episodes of uncontrolled electrical activity in the brain.* Epilepsy can be caused by several different factors, including brain damage before or during birth, infections, head injury, withdrawal from drugs or alcohol, or exposure to toxins. Seizures may be small and brief, involving little body movement; or they may be quite severe, involving muscle contractions throughout the entire body. Medications can help control seizures so that a person with epilepsy can lead a normal, healthy life.

▶ **Cerebral palsy** refers to *a group of nonprogressive neurological disorders that are the result of damage to the brain before, during, or just after birth or in early childhood.* Causes of cerebral palsy may include infections such as encephalitis or meningitis, head injury, or exposure to radiation before birth. Physical therapy, braces to enable walking, and medication can help cerebral palsy patients be independent and participate in everyday activities.

Many people lead full, independent lives in spite of nervous system disorders. *How would you encourage a close friend or family member who is coping with a nervous system disorder?*

LESSON 5 | REVIEW

Reviewing Facts and Vocabulary

1. What precautions should you take before diving into water?
2. Explain the difference between a concussion and a coma.
3. How does multiple sclerosis affect the nervous system?

Thinking Critically

4. **Analyzing.** Examine the effects of health behaviors you can practice to prevent injury to the nervous system. Give a specific example.
5. **Evaluating.** Most states have enacted laws requiring that children under a certain age be restrained by car seats, booster seats, or safety belts. How do such laws benefit the health of small children?

Applying Health Skills

Accessing Information. Write a one-page report on research that is being done to treat spinal cord injuries. Which treatments have had the most success? Why is it so difficult to restore function to the spinal cord after it has been injured?

After You Read

Explain. What can you can do to protect your nervous system from injury? What else can you do to care for your nervous system?

Some Schooling on Backpacks

Doctors are concerned that looking cool could be hurting you. Here are some ways to avoid injury.

According to the U.S. Consumer Product Safety Commission, 5,900 kids were treated at hospital emergency rooms, clinics, and doctors' offices last year for sprains and strains caused by backpacks. Such injuries are so widespread that more than 70 percent of physicians surveyed by the American Academy of Orthopedic Surgeons listed backpacks as a potential clinical problem for children.

How do you avoid such problems? Choose bags that have wide, padded straps and a belt. That will help transfer some of the weight from the back and shoulders to the hips. You should also tighten both straps firmly, so the pack rests about 2 inches above your waist. Also, remember to pack your bag with the heaviest items closest to your back and to bend both knees when you pick it up.

Try to Lighten Your Load!

How much should you stuff into your pack? That depends on your size and strength, but a general rule is not to exceed 20 percent of your body weight. So if a child weighs 100 pounds, the backpack and its load should not be more than 20 pounds. One hint: Make frequent trips to your locker to exchange books between classes.

Trendy backpacks with wheels let you pull the weight along the ground, but they have problems too. Many are larger than the average shoulder bag, so students are tempted to carry more than they would in a conventional pack. Roller bags often don't fit into a locker. They can also lead to tripping and falls in crowded halls.

Whatever you use, 10 or 15 minutes of stretching and back strengthening (stomach crunches and holding the pushup position for 10 seconds, for example) is a good idea. ▰

TIME to THINK... About Backpacks

According to the article, the total weight of your backpack and its cargo shouldn't be more than 20 percent of your body weight. With the class, create an easy-to-use formula (where X = YOU and Y= BACKPACK AND ITS CARGO) to help your fellow students determine how much weight they should be carrying.

Health Skills Application

1. **Communicating.** Your younger brother loves to in-line skate. However, he never wears protective gear while skating. List some strategies you can use to teach him about the importance of preventing injury and encourage him to change his behavior. *(LESSON 1)*

2. **Advocacy.** Find out how often screening for scoliosis is offered in your community. To which age groups does it apply? Is there a cost? Raise community awareness by making and displaying a poster that advertises the next screening and demonstrates knowledge about this personal health concern. *(LESSON 2)*

3. **Analyzing Influences.** A healthy muscular system depends on physical activity. Even when people are aware of this connection, they may fail to get the physical activity they need. List factors that may positively influence someone's decision to engage in physical activity. *(LESSON 3)*

4. **Accessing Information.** Use the Internet to find brain images made with positron-emission tomography (PET) scanners. Compare images of drug users' brains to those of individuals who have never used drugs. How could you use these images to explain the effects of drug use on the nervous system? *(LESSON 4)*

5. **Refusal Skills.** Alicia and her friends are exploring a lake in which they have not swum before. Someone spots a rock beneath the water's surface but suggests that it is probably safe to dive anyway. Write a dialogue between Alicia and her friends, demonstrating how she refuses to take this unnecessary risk. *(LESSON 5)*

CAREER Corner

Physical Therapy Assistant

Do you enjoy seeing people make progress and reach goals? Physical therapy assistants work with people to help them recover mobility after an injury or reduce the impact of a progressive condition such as multiple sclerosis.

To become a physical therapy assistant, you need a high school diploma or its equivalent. After high school, physical therapy assistants complete a two-year program and receive an associate's degree. Find out more by clicking on Career Corner at **health.glencoe.com.**

After You Read

Use your Foldable to review what you have learned about the structure and function of the skeletal, muscular, and nervous systems.

FOLDABLES™
Study Organizer

▶ **EXPLORING HEALTH TERMS** *Answer the following questions on a sheet of paper.*

Lesson 1 *Match each definition with the correct term.*

appendicular skeleton	ligament
axial skeleton	ossification
cartilage	tendon

1. A division of the skeletal system that includes the bones of the skull and face, the vertebrae, and the ribs.

2. A division of the skeletal system that includes the bones of the upper and lower limbs and the shoulders and hips.

3. A band of fibrous, slightly elastic connective tissue that attaches bone to bone.

4. A fibrous cord that attaches muscle to bone.

Lesson 2 *Identify each statement as True or False. If false, replace the underlined term with the correct term.*

osteoporosis	scoliosis
repetitive motion injury	

5. A condition in which there is a progressive loss of bone tissue is called <u>scoliosis</u>.

6. <u>Osteoporosis</u> is a lateral or side-to-side curvature of the spine.

Lesson 3 *Match each definition with the correct term.*

smooth muscles	skeletal muscles
flexors	extensors
cardiac muscle	muscle tone
tendonitis	hernia

7. The muscles that act on the lining of passageways in the body and on internal organs.

8. A type of striated muscle that forms the wall of the heart.

9. The natural tension in the fibers of a muscle.

10. A condition created when an organ or tissue protrudes through an area of weak muscle.

Lesson 4 *Fill in the blanks with the correct term.*

brain stem	cerebrum	reflex
cerebellum	neurons	

The (**_11_**) is a stalk of nerve cells and fibers that connects the spinal cord to the rest of the brain. The second largest part of the brain is the (**_12_**). The (**_13_**) is the largest and most complex part of the brain.

Lesson 5 *Replace the underlined words with the correct term.*

epilepsy	cerebral palsy

14. A disorder of the nervous system that is characterized by recurrent seizures is <u>cerebral palsy</u>.

15. <u>Epilepsy</u> is a group of nonprogressive neurological disorders that are the result of damage to the brain before, during, or just after birth.

▶ **RECALLING THE FACTS** *Use complete sentences to answer the following questions.*

1. Compare and contrast the axial and appendicular skeletons.

2. Describe and give examples of each type of bone.

3. Explain how tendons are involved in movement.

4. Why is the early detection of scoliosis important?

5. Explain the association between dislocated joints and torn ligaments. Identify situations that may require professional health services.

6. Explain the difference between bursitis and arthritis.

7. Describe the functions of the muscular system.

8. Examine the effects of health behaviors on the muscular system. Why is good posture important to the health of your muscles?

For more review questions for Chapter 15, go to **health.glencoe.com**.

9. What is muscular dystrophy?

10. What natural protective mechanisms exist in the body for the brain and spinal cord?

11. Identify and describe the three parts of the brain stem.

12. Explain the difference between the autonomic nervous system and the somatic nervous system.

13. Examine the effects of health behaviors, and name three ways to prevent spinal cord injury.

14. What are some symptoms that result from neuron damage caused by Alzheimer's disease?

15. What is quadriplegia? What is paraplegia?

16. What is a degenerative disease?

17. Compare and contrast Parkinson's disease and Alzheimer's disease.

➤ WRITING CRITICALLY

1. **Descriptive.** Write a newspaper article describing a bone or joint injury suffered by an athlete. Describe how the injury occurred, and explain how it might have been prevented.

2. **Persuasive.** Write a newsletter article on behalf of a nonprofit health organization persuading others to participate in an upcoming fundraising event to fund research. Make sure to state facts about the organization and its mission. Use supporting evidence that gives logical reasons as to why further research is needed, and quote experts.

Standardized Test Practice

 The purpose of expository writing is to explain, define, or tell how to do something by giving information. The *Writing Situation* presents the topic: the skeletal system. The *Directions for Writing* suggests that you identify why the skeletal system is important and what the skeletal system and the framework of a building have in common.

PROMPT

Writing Situation: In this chapter you have learned that the skeletal system has specific and important jobs to do. Think about what a building framework and skeletal system have in common in terms of structure, function, and importance.

Directions for Writing: In your writing, explain why the skeletal system is so important in terms of structure, function, and importance, using the analogy of a building to make your points.

Cardiovascular and Respiratory Systems

Healthy Heart and Lungs Week

Nonprofit health associations such as the American Heart Association® and the American Lung Association® promote awareness of heart and lung disease. These groups sponsor national, local, and world events to raise funds for

► research.

► community education programs.

► advocacy.

Visit the Eye on the Media section at health.glencoe.com to learn more about this topic.

FOLDABLES™ Study Organizer

Before You Read

Use this Foldable to help you organize your notes on the structure and function of the cardiovascular system. Begin with three sheets of 8½″ x 11″ paper.

► **Step 1**

Fold a sheet of paper in half along the short axis.

► **Step 2**

Unfold. Fold the bottom 2″ of the paper up. Glue along the sides of the fold to form pockets.

► **Step 3**

Label as shown. Place 3″ x 5″ index cards or pieces of paper in the pockets.

| Structure | Function |

As You Read

As you read and discuss the material in the chapter, record and define terms, draw diagrams, and list main ideas and supporting facts on the index cards in the appropriate pockets of your Foldable.

SPOTLIGHT ON HEALTH

Using Visuals. How might a respiratory condition such as asthma affect a person's ability to participate?

The Cardiovascular System

Guide to Reading

Building Vocabulary

As you read this lesson, write each new highlighted term and its definition in your notebook.

▶ plasma (p. 418)
▶ hemoglobin (p. 418)
▶ arteries (p. 419)
▶ capillaries (p. 419)
▶ veins (p. 419)
▶ platelets (p. 420)
▶ lymph (p. 421)
▶ lymphocytes (p. 421)

Focusing on the Main Ideas

In this lesson, you will learn how to:

▶ Describe the functions and structures of the cardiovascular system.
▶ Show the circulation of blood throughout the heart and body.
▶ List the structures and functions of the lymphatic system.

Reading Strategy

Organize Information

▶ Create a two-column chart. On one side, list the functions and structures of the cardiovascular system. On the other side, list the functions and structures of the lymphatic system.

Write a brief paragraph describing what you think can cause your heart rate to increase or decrease.

Any physical activity that raises your heart rate will help strengthen your cardiovascular system.
What is the main function of the cardiovascular system?

When you look at a road map, you see a series of interconnected roads—some small, others large—that connect cities and towns. Vital goods are transported into and out of central areas on these roads. Similarly, your cardiovascular system consists of vessels, both large and small, that transport life-supporting materials to cells of your body. Your heart, one of the main organs of your cardiovascular system, is the central point from which these vessels branch.

Functions of the Cardiovascular System

The cardiovascular system is composed of the heart and all the blood vessels of the body. Its function is to circulate blood, thereby maintaining an internal environment in which all the cells of your body are nourished. As your heart pumps blood, blood vessels carry oxygen and nutrients to body cells. At the same time, carbon dioxide is carried, along with waste matter, from your cells. Carbon dioxide is delivered to your lungs and waste products to the kidneys for removal from the body.

Structure of the Cardiovascular System

The cardiovascular system consists of the heart; blood; and blood vessels, including arteries, capillaries, and veins, which transport blood throughout the body. Health-literate teens know methods for predicting the immediate and long-term impact of health decisions on the individuals who make them.

The Heart

The heart and the brain are perhaps the most important organs in your body. Your heart is the pump that makes the cardiovascular system work. It never rests. Most of the heart is made of muscle tissue called the myocardium, which contracts and relaxes constantly and rhythmically. Your heart rate adjusts automatically in response to an increase or decrease in physical activity. In an average life span, a person's heart beats more than 2.5 billion times.

CHAMBERS OF THE HEART

Inside the heart are four chambers. Each of the two smaller chambers is called an *atrium.* The two lower, larger chambers are called *ventricles.* A wall of tissue called the *septum* separates the right and left atria, as well as the right and left ventricles, from one another.

At the top of the right atrium is an area of muscle that acts as a natural pacemaker for the rest of the heart. Regular electrical impulses generated from this area stimulate the muscles of each atrium to contract, forcing blood into the ventricles. Within milliseconds each electrical impulse travels through the heart to an area between the two ventricles. There it stimulates the muscles of the ventricles to contract, pumping blood out of the heart.

Valves between the atria and ventricles allow blood to flow through the chambers of the heart. These valves are "one-way" valves, opening to allow blood to flow from the atria into the ventricles. When the ventricles contract, the valves close again to keep blood from flowing back into the atria. The sounds heard as the heart beats are produced by the closing of the valves.

CIRCULATION IN THE HEART

The circulation of blood through the heart and lungs is shown in **Figure 16.1** on page 418. Blood that has been depleted of oxygen but contains carbon dioxide and waste matter is carried to the heart by two large blood vessels called the *vena cava.* This deoxygenated blood enters the right atrium and is transferred to the right ventricle. The blood is then pumped to the lungs. In the lungs the blood releases carbon dioxide and picks up oxygen from inhaled air. This newly oxygenated blood is returned from the lungs to the left atrium of the heart. The left atrium pumps the oxygenated blood into the left ventricle, which then pumps the blood out of the heart to the rest of the body by way of a large artery called the aorta.

Health Minute

Get the Most from Your Physical Activity

Aerobic activities can reduce your risk of developing cardiovascular diseases later in life.

Exercising within your target heart range:

► Sit quietly for five minutes, and then take your pulse. This is your resting heart rate.

► Subtract your age from the number 220 to find your maximum heart rate.

► Subtract your resting heart rate from your maximum heart rate.

► Multiply the number you arrived at by 60 percent and again by 85 percent. Round off these numbers.

► Add your resting heart rate to the numbers you just calculated. These two new numbers represent your target heart range.

FIGURE 16.1

PULMONARY CIRCULATION

The circulation of the blood between the heart and lungs is called pulmonary circulation.

right lung

pulmonary artery

superior vena cava

capillaries

pulmonary veins

right atrium

right ventricle

inferior vena cava

left lung

pulmonary artery

aorta

left atrium

left ventricle

What is blood type?

There are four blood types: A, B, AB, and O. Blood type is determined by the presence or absence of certain substances, called antigens, that stimulate an immune response. Type A has antigen A, type B has antigen B, type AB has both those antigens, and type O has neither. Most blood also carries another substance called the Rh factor. Blood that doesn't have the Rh factor is called *Rh negative.*

Blood

Blood delivers oxygen, hormones, and nutrients to the cells and carries away wastes that the cells produce. About 55 percent of total blood volume consists of **plasma**, *the fluid in which other parts of the blood are suspended.* Plasma, which is mostly water, contains nutrients, proteins, salts, and hormones. Red blood cells make up about 40 percent of blood. White blood cells and platelets together make up the remaining 5 percent of blood. One milliliter of blood contains millions of each of these types of cells.

RED BLOOD CELLS AND WHITE BLOOD CELLS

Red blood cells transport oxygen to the cells and tissues of the body. Formed in bone marrow, red blood cells contain hemoglobin. **Hemoglobin** is *the oxygen-carrying protein in blood.* Hemoglobin contains iron that binds with oxygen in the lungs and releases the oxygen in the tissues. Hemoglobin also combines with carbon dioxide, which is carried from the cells to the lungs.

The main role of white blood cells is to protect the body against infection and fight infection when it occurs. White blood cells, which are part of the body's immune system, are also produced in bone marrow. Production of these cells increases when an infection is present. Some white blood cells surround and ingest disease-causing microbes. Others are involved in allergic reactions. Still another type of white blood cell forms antibodies that provide immunity.

Blood Vessels

The network of more than 60,000 miles of blood vessels that transports blood is shown in **Figure 16.2** on page 420. There are three main types of blood vessels: arteries, capillaries, and veins.

ARTERIES

The *blood vessels that carry blood away from the heart* are called **arteries**. Arteries have thick elastic walls that contain smooth muscle fibers. The elastic fibers in the walls of arteries allow them to withstand the pressure exerted by the blood as the heart beats.

Pulmonary arteries carry deoxygenated blood from the right ventricle to the lungs. Systemic arteries, such as the aorta, carry oxygenated blood from the left ventricle to all areas of the body. As arteries move away from the heart, they branch into progressively smaller vessels called *arterioles*. Arterioles deliver blood to capillaries.

CAPILLARIES

Capillaries are *small vessels that carry blood between arterioles and vessels called venules*. Capillaries form an extensive network throughout tissues and organs in the body, reaching almost all body cells. The exchange of gases, nutrients, and wastes between blood and cells takes place through the ultra-thin walls of capillaries. Capillaries also play a role in body temperature regulation. As body temperature rises, capillaries near the skin's surface dilate, allowing heat to escape the body through the skin. If body temperature begins to drop below normal, the capillaries constrict, reducing heat loss.

VEINS

The *blood vessels that return blood to the heart* are called **veins**. Although the walls of veins are thinner and less elastic than those of arteries, veins are still able to withstand the pressure exerted by blood as it flows through them. The large veins called the *vena cava* carry deoxygenated blood from the body to the right atrium of the heart. Pulmonary veins carry oxygenated blood from the lungs to the left atrium. Many veins throughout the body, especially those in the legs, have valves that help prevent the backflow of blood as it is pumped under lower pressure back to the heart. Pressure on the vessel walls from the contraction of surrounding muscles helps move blood through the veins. The venules collect blood from capillaries and empty it into larger veins.

Reading Check

Classify What are the three main types of blood vessels?

The blood regulates body temperature. *Explain how these swimmers' bodies adjust to cold water temperature.*

PLATELETS

Platelets are *cells that prevent the body's loss of blood*. Platelets gather at the site of an injury and release chemicals that make them sticky, causing them to clump together with other cells. The chemicals released by platelets also stimulate the blood to produce small thread-like fibers called *fibrin*. Fibrin threads trap platelets along with red and white blood cells. A mass of fibrin, platelets, and red and white blood cells continues to clump together until a clot is formed. This stops the loss of blood from the injury site. A scab is formed on a healing wound as the surface of the clot dries.

FIGURE 16.2

THE CARDIOVASCULAR SYSTEM

A network of arteries, veins, and capillaries moves blood throughout the body, providing cells with oxygen and nutrients and removing wastes.

right jugular vein

right common carotid artery

right subclavian artery

superior vena cava

right pulmonary vein

right pulmonary artery

hepatic veins

right brachial artery

inferior vena cava

right common iliac vein

right common iliac artery

femoral artery

femoral vein

great saphenous vein

anterior tibial artery

anterior tibial vein

left jugular vein

left common carotid artery

left subclavian artery

aortic arch

left pulmonary vein

left pulmonary artery

heart

left brachial artery

abdominal aorta

left common iliac vein

left common iliac artery

femoral artery

femoral vein

popliteal artery

popliteal vein

posterior tibial artery

posterior tibial vein

The Lymphatic System

The lymphatic system helps fight infection and plays an important role in the body's immunity to disease. This system, shown in **Figure 16.3,** is a network of vessels that helps maintain the balance of fluids in the spaces between the cells. The lymphatic system supports the cardiovascular system. All body tissues are bathed in a watery fluid that comes from the blood. Although much of this fluid returns to the blood through capillary walls, some excess remains and is carried to the heart through the lymphatic system. Health-literate teens understand the impact of personal health behaviors on body systems, and know how to delay the onset of and reduce the risk for potential health problems during adulthood.

Lymph

Lymph is *the clear fluid that fills the spaces around body cells.* It is transported by the lymphatic system to the heart and eventually returns to the blood. Lymph is similar to plasma in content, consisting of water and proteins along with fats and lymphocytes. **Lymphocytes** are *specialized white blood cells that provide the body with immunity* and protect the body against pathogens. A pathogen is an organism that causes disease. There are two types of lymphocytes, **B cells** and **T cells.**

B CELLS

B cells are lymphocytes that are stimulated to multiply when they come in contact with a pathogen. Some of the new B cells form plasma cells, which produce antibodies that attack the pathogen. Other B cells form memory cells that are activated if the body is exposed to the same pathogen a second time, creating immunity.

T CELLS

Like B cells, T cells are lymphocytes that are stimulated to enlarge and multiply when they encounter a pathogen. There are two main types of T cells, killer cells and helper cells. Killer T cells stop the spread of disease within the body by releasing toxins that destroy abnormal and infected cells. Helper T cells aid in the activation of B cells and killer T cells and control the body's immune system.

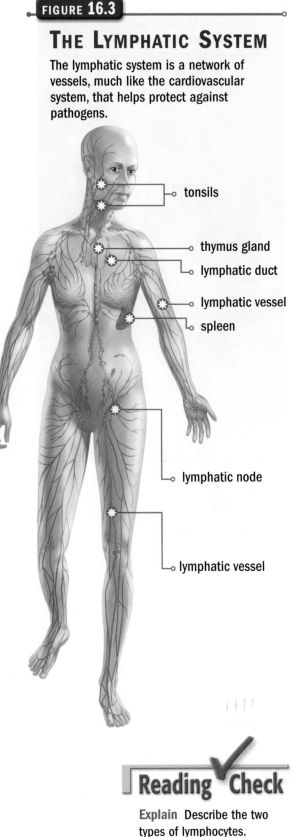

FIGURE 16.3

THE LYMPHATIC SYSTEM

The lymphatic system is a network of vessels, much like the cardiovascular system, that helps protect against pathogens.

- tonsils
- thymus gland
- lymphatic duct
- lymphatic vessel
- spleen
- lymphatic node
- lymphatic vessel

Reading Check

Explain Describe the two types of lymphocytes.

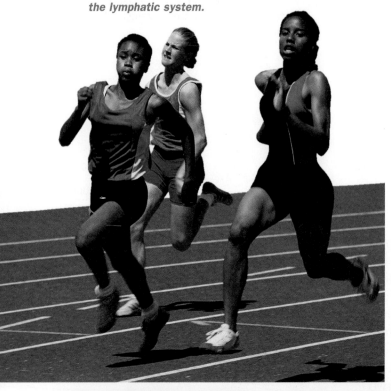

Lymph is moved through the body by the contraction of skeletal muscles during physical activity.
Name the structures of the lymphatic system.

Structure of the Lymphatic System

The lymphatic system consists of a network of vessels and tissues that are involved in the movement and filtering of lymph. Much like the capillaries and arterioles in the cardiovascular system, small lymph vessels collect lymph and combine to form larger vessels. Lymph is moved toward the heart both by the contraction of smooth muscles that line the walls of lymph vessels and by the contraction of surrounding skeletal muscles.

Two large lymphatic ducts empty lymph into veins close to the heart, where it is returned to the blood. As it is moved through the body, lymph is filtered by lymph nodes, small, bean-shaped organs that are found in lymph vessels. White blood cells within lymph nodes trap and destroy foreign organisms such as bacteria and viruses to keep them from spreading throughout the body. Other structures of the lymphatic system include the spleen, thymus gland, and tonsils, all of which play a role in immunity, protecting the body from infection.

LESSON 1 REVIEW

Reviewing Facts and Vocabulary

1. What are the functions of the cardiovascular system?
2. Describe the functions of arteries, capillaries, and veins.
3. Define *lymph* and *lymphocytes*.

Thinking Critically

4. **Comparing and Contrasting.** Compare and contrast the cardiovascular and lymphatic systems.
5. **Evaluating.** What might swollen lymph nodes indicate?

Applying Health Skills

Advocacy. Research and demonstrate knowledge about personal and family health related to the cardiovascular system. Examine the effects of sedentary behavior on cardiovascular health. Create an informative brochure about the relationship between an active lifestyle and a healthy heart. Share the brochure with your family.

After You Read

Explain. What are two types of lymphocytes? How does each protect your body from pathogens?

Caring for the Cardiovascular System

Guide to Reading

Building Vocabulary

As you read this lesson, write each new highlighted term and its definition in your notebook.

▶ blood pressure (p. 424)

▶ congenital (p. 425)

▶ anemia (p. 426)

▶ leukemia (p. 426)

▶ Hodgkin's disease (p. 427)

Quick Write

Write a short paragraph describing how a heart ailment might affect a person's ability to participate in sports or other activities.

Focusing on the Main Ideas

In this lesson, you will learn how to:

▶ Discuss health promotion and prevention of cardiovascular disease.

▶ Examine the effects of health behaviors on the cardiovascular and lymphatic systems.

▶ Identify warning signs that prompt individuals to seek health care.

Reading Strategy

Predict

▶ Prior to reading, list some of the problems of the cardiovascular system that you know about. After you read, compare your answers to the text.

These coronary arteries are partially blocked. Blood supply to the heart is reduced if blood cannot flow through arteries. *What health behaviors will help you avoid cardiovascular system problems?*

Most problems of the cardiovascular and lymphatic systems can be prevented with proper care. These involve physical activity, adequate rest, proper diet, and regular medical checkups. Some problems may be hereditary. If heart disease runs in your family or if you have other traits that may lead to heart disease, you need to make careful choices now to promote a lifetime of cardiovascular health. Making careful choices shows that you understand the potential impact of common risk behaviors on the quality of life.

Health Behaviors and the Cardiovascular and Lymphatic Systems

Practicing healthful habits shows that you understand the impact of personal health behaviors on body systems. Here are some healthful behaviors that should become part of your life.

Reading Check

Describe What are some of the healthful habits that can help reduce the risk of cardiovascular problems?

Medical professionals check your heart and blood pressure during regular medical examinations.

What measurements are taken during blood pressure readings?

▶ Follow a well-balanced diet that is low in saturated fats, **cholesterol,** and salt.

▶ Maintain a healthy weight to reduce stress on the heart, blood vessels, and lymph vessels.

▶ Participate in regular aerobic exercise for at least 30 minutes three to four times per week.

▶ Avoid the use of tobacco products and exposure to secondhand tobacco smoke.

▶ Avoid **illegal drugs,** including stimulants, marijuana, and ecstasy (MDMA).

Blood Pressure

Maintaining pressure in the cardiovascular system is important for proper blood circulation. Pressure in arteries is created as the ventricles contract. As blood is forced into the arteries that exit the heart, arterial walls stretch under the increased pressure. When the ventricles relax and refill with blood, arterial pressure decreases. **Blood pressure** is *a measure of the amount of force that the blood places on the walls of blood vessels, particularly large arteries, as it is pumped through the body.*

Blood pressure can be measured with an instrument called a sphygmomanometer (sfig-mo-muh-NAH-muh-ter) and a stethoscope. A cuff is placed around the upper arm and inflated until the pressure from the cuff blocks the flow of blood. As the cuff is deflated, the health care professional listens through the stethoscope for blood flow. As your heart contracts to push blood into your arteries, the maximum pressure, called *systolic* pressure, is measured. This is recorded as the upper number of the fraction representing your blood pressure. As the ventricles relax to refill, blood pressure is at its lowest point, called the *diastolic* pressure. This is the lower number of the fraction in a blood pressure reading.

Blood pressure is an indicator of cardiovascular health. Although a healthy person's blood pressure will vary with physical activity or emotional stress, it should remain within a normal range. Blood pressure above 140/90 is considered high, and if chronic, places a strain on the heart as it pumps. Chronic high blood pressure is an early indicator of several cardiovascular system problems and should prompt individuals of all ages to seek health care. Prevention of high blood pressure includes maintaining a healthy weight, staying physically active, managing stress, avoiding tobacco and drugs, and following a **healthful eating plan** that is low in salt.

Cardiovascular System Problems

Disorders of the cardiovascular system can interfere with blood flow through the heart and body, reduce the amount of oxygen that reaches the cells, and keep the blood from clotting properly. Some problems are inherited; others result from illness.

Congenital Heart Defects

A condition that is present at birth is said to be **congenital**. One common type of congenital heart defect is a septal defect, in which a hole in the septum allows oxygenated blood to mix with deoxygenated blood and affects the pumping efficiency of the heart. In other cases of congenital heart defects, valves may not function properly, or the aorta may be abnormally narrow, reducing the amount of blood flowing to the body.

Some congenital heart defects are less serious than others, but most require medication and possibly surgery to repair the affected portion of the heart. In many cases the cause of a congenital defect remains unknown. Use of alcohol and other drugs during pregnancy is associated with heart defects in newborns. Certain infections during pregnancy can also increase the risk of congenital heart defects. Some cases may be hereditary.

Cardiovascular Disease

Cardiovascular disease (CVD) is actually a group of diseases of the cardiovascular system that includes hypertension, heart disease, and stroke. CVD is the number one killer of both men and women among all racial and ethnic groups in the United States. According to the Centers for Disease Control and Prevention, about 930,000 Americans die of CVD each year. Many of these diseases are associated with lifestyle behaviors. Early detection is important for reducing the risk for CVD.

Heart Murmur

Heart murmurs are abnormal sounds that are made as blood flows through the heart. Some heart murmurs may be very slight and disappear without treatment. Other murmurs can be an indication of problems in the heart, such as the valve between the left atrium and ventricle not closing properly, and may require surgery.

Varicose Veins

Varicose veins form if valves in the veins do not close tightly enough to prevent backflow of blood. Varicose veins become enlarged and can be painful. They most commonly occur in veins in the legs. Weakened valves can be the result of a congenital defect or natural aging. Physical activity helps prevent varicose veins. Treatment includes reducing standing time, exercise, elevating legs when sleeping, and in severe cases, surgery to remove the affected vein.

Did You Know?

Substances taken into the body can have serious effects on the heart and cardiovascular system—including consequences that can result in death.

- Ephedra stimulates the cardiovascular system. As a result, its use has been linked to heart attacks and strokes.
- Stimulant drugs including cocaine and amphetamines can cause rapid heart rate, high blood pressure, and damage to blood vessels.
- Marijuana use has been linked to heart and lung damage.

➤ Individuals in good health who are from 17 to 70 years of age can donate blood. *Name one way donated blood can be used.*

Anemia

Anemia is *a condition in which the ability of the blood to carry oxygen is reduced.* Anemia can result from low numbers of red blood cells or from low concentrations of hemoglobin in the blood. Both of these conditions interfere with the blood's ability to carry oxygen. The most common cause of anemia is **iron deficiency,** which can be avoided by eating foods high in iron, such as dark green leafy vegetables, red meat, liver, egg yolks, and fortified cereals. Taking an iron supplement also may be recommended by a medical professional. Health-literate teens understand the impact of personal health behaviors on body systems.

Leukemia

Leukemia is *a form of cancer in which any one of the different types of white blood cells is produced excessively and abnormally.* The abnormal white blood cells cannot function properly, making the leukemia patient very susceptible to infection. Because all blood cells are produced in the bone marrow, the uncontrolled production of white blood cells can hinder the production of red blood cells and platelets. The result is infection, severe anemia, or uncontrolled bleeding. Childhood leukemia is often curable, and in adults leukemia can go into remission. Chemotherapy and radiation are among the treatment options. Also, some forms of leukemia have been successfully treated with bone marrow transplants.

Hemophilia

Hemophilia is an inherited disorder in which the blood does not clot properly. Certain proteins, called clotting factors, are absent. This may cause uncontrolled bleeding that can occur spontaneously or as a result of injury. Bleeding can take place internally in muscles, tissues of the digestive and urinary tract, and the joints. It may also occur externally as a result of injury or surgery. Treatment for hemophilia includes injections that introduce the missing clotting factors into the blood. These clotting factors can be extracted from blood donated by healthy individuals.

CHARACTER CHECK

Respect. Making healthful decisions about diet and incorporating physical activity into your daily routine are ways to demonstrate responsibility and respect for your body. **Determine what type of eating plan and physical activity program would be best suited for you. With the advice of a health care provider, make a plan to maintain your cardiovascular health.**

Lymphatic System Problems

Problems in the lymphatic system can be the result of infection or heredity and may range in severity from mild to life-threatening.

▶ **Immune Deficiency.** Immune deficiencies occur when the immune system can no longer protect against infection. Some immune deficiencies may be congenital, and others can be caused by **HIV,** the virus that causes AIDS. A weakened immune system may be the result of natural aging or a side effect of chemotherapy.

▶ **Hodgkin's Disease.** **Hodgkin's disease**, or Hodgkin's lymphoma, is *a type of cancer that affects the lymph tissue* found in lymph nodes and the spleen. Early detection and treatment, as in all types of **cancer,** is essential for recovery. Treatment may include removal of lymph nodes, radiation, and chemotherapy.

▶ **Tonsillitis.** Tonsils are part of the immune system and help reduce the number of pathogens entering the body through the respiratory system. Infected tonsils, or *tonsillitis,* can be common in children. The condition is most often treated with antibiotics. Chronic cases may call for surgical removal of the tonsils.

LESSON 2 REVIEW

Reviewing Facts and Vocabulary

1. Analyze the relationship between health behaviors and diseases of the cardiovascular system. List three health promotion behaviors you can practice to help prevent cardiovascular diseases.

2. What is *blood pressure?*

3. Name and describe two problems that can occur in the lymphatic system.

Thinking Critically

4. **Applying.** What symptoms might indicate that a person is suffering from anemia?

5. **Analyzing.** Relate the importance of early detection of cardiovascular disorders in prompting individuals of all ages to seek health care.

Applying Health Skills

Communication Skills. Imagine that you are worried about a close family member who has unhealthy eating and fitness habits. Write a dialogue in which you encourage this person to incorporate positive health behaviors into his or her lifestyle. Examine and include the positive effects such a change would have on his or her cardiovascular and lymphatic systems.

After You Read

Problems and Solutions. Create a T chart. List the problems of the cardiovascular and lymphatic systems on one side. List health behaviors that help reduce the risk factors of cardiovascular and lymphatic systems on the other side.

The Respiratory System

Guide to Reading

Building Vocabulary

As you read this lesson, write each new highlighted term and its definition in your notebook.

▶ respiration (p. 428)
▶ diaphragm (p. 429)
▶ pharynx (p. 431)
▶ trachea (p. 431)
▶ bronchi (p. 431)
▶ larynx (p. 431)

Focusing on the Main Ideas

In this lesson, you will learn how to:

▶ Describe the functions and structures of the respiratory system.
▶ Diagram the process of breathing.

Reading Strategy

Predict

▶ How can smoking affect your respiratory system? After you read, review your answers and revise them, if necessary.

List some of the situations or activities that cause your breathing rate to change.

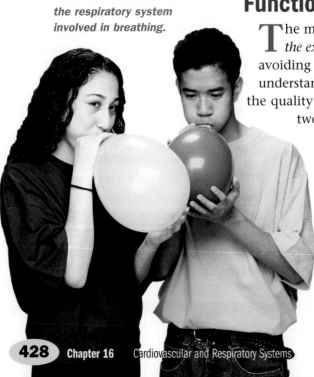

Your lungs and chest expand like a balloon as you inhale. As you exhale, your lungs deflate slightly. *Name the structures of the respiratory system involved in breathing.*

Without your conscious control, your lungs rhythmically fill with air and then empty. This rhythm varies with changes in your level of activity.

Functions of the Respiratory System

The main function of the respiratory system is **respiration**, *the exchange of gases between the body and the environment.* By avoiding certain behaviors, such as smoking, you show that you understand the potential impact of common risk behaviors on the quality of life. The process of respiration can be divided into two parts. *External respiration* is the exchange of oxygen and carbon dioxide that takes place between air and blood in the lungs. Oxygen moves from the lungs into the blood, and carbon dioxide moves from the blood into the lungs. *Internal respiration* is the exchange of gases between blood and body cells. Oxygen moves from the blood into the cells, and carbon dioxide moves from the cells into the blood. The continual exchange of gases in both external and internal respiration is essential for survival.

Structure of the Respiratory System

The respiratory system, shown in **Figure 16.4,** consists of the lungs and a series of passageways through which air travels. The nose and throat make up the upper respiratory system. The lower respiratory system contains the larynx, trachea, bronchi, and lungs.

The Lungs

The lungs are the principle organs of the respiratory system and the site of external respiration. They are found within the chest cavity and are protected by the ribs. The **diaphragm** is *the muscle that separates the chest from the abdominal cavity.*

The structure of the lungs can be compared to the structure of a branching tree. Air moves into the lungs through the trachea, or the windpipe. The trachea branches out into the bronchi, the main airways that reach into each lung. The airways that lead into the lungs divide and subdivide to form a network of tubes called *bronchioles.* At the end of each bronchiole are groups of microscopic structures called *alveoli,* thin-walled air sacs covered with capillaries. Gas exchange takes place as oxygen and carbon dioxide diffuse across capillary and alveolar walls.

Reading Check

Explain What is the main function of the respiratory system?

FIGURE 16.4

THE RESPIRATORY SYSTEM

The lungs are the principle organs of the respiratory system.

The **epiglottis** (e-puh-GLAH-tis) is a flap of tissue that closes over the trachea when you swallow.

The **larynx** (LA-ringks) is the voice box and contains the vocal cords.

The **trachea** (TRAY-kee-uh) is the windpipe.

The **bronchi** (BRAHN-ky) are the passages through which air spreads through the lungs.

The **diaphragm** (DY-uh-fram) is a dome-shaped muscle that causes the chest cavity to expand and contract.

The **alveoli** are tiny air sacs through which the gas exchange of external respiration takes place.

A **capillary** is a tiny blood vessel through which gas exchange takes place.

A **branch of the pulmonary artery** brings blood from the heart into the lung.

The **bronchioles** (BRAHN-kee-ohlz) are tubes that carry air closer to the site of external respiration.

A **branch of the pulmonary vein** takes oxygenated blood from the lung back to the heart.

Did You Know?

Hiccups occur as a result of the diaphragm contracting in a spasm, quickly followed by the closure of the vocal cords. This sudden closure produces the unmistakable sound of a hiccup.

THE BREATHING PROCESS

The breathing process is made possible by creating a pressure difference between the lungs and the outside of the body. When you inhale, the diaphragm and muscles between your ribs contract, expanding your chest cavity and your lungs. When your lungs expand, the pressure inside them becomes lower than the pressure outside your body. Air naturally flows into your lungs to equalize the pressure. When you exhale, the same muscles relax and the volume of your chest cavity decreases, making the pressure in your lungs higher than the pressure outside your body. Air naturally flows out of your lungs to the area of lower pressure.

Other Respiratory Structures

The upper respiratory system includes structures such as the nose and mouth. Air enters and exits your body through the nose and mouth. The membranes of the nose are lined with hairlike structures called *cilia* and with cells that produce mucus. Together, the cilia and mucus trap and remove foreign particles, such as dust, bacteria, and viruses, that would otherwise move farther into the respiratory system.

Hands-On Health ACTIVITY

Seeing the Effects of Smoking

What You'll Need

- glass jar with a lid
- one cup of dark brown corn syrup
- packaging tape
- poster board and markers

What You'll Do

1. Pour the cup of corn syrup into the jar, put on the lid, and secure it with packaging tape to prevent leaks.

2. Examine the contents of the jar. The liquid represents the amount of tar that gets into a smoker's lungs during a single year of smoking one pack of cigarettes each day.

3. Discuss your response to this activity with the class. Are you surprised by the amount of "tar" in the jar? How do you think this affects a smoker's health?

4. Create a poster that highlights the dangers of tar, a substance that can cause cancer. Write a convincing statement about why teens should avoid tobacco. Present your information in a clear, concise manner.

Apply and Conclude

Present this activity and your poster to a class of younger students. Is it effective in persuading others to avoid tobacco? Why or why not?

In addition to being filtered, air is warmed and moistened as it moves through the nasal passages. Air continues through the respiratory system to the **pharynx**, or *throat*, and into the **trachea**, or *windpipe*, which is located in front of the esophagus. Like the nasal passages, the tissue that lines the trachea is covered with mucus and cilia to trap particles and prevent them from going deeper into the respiratory system. As the trachea reaches the lungs, it branches into two tubes called **bronchi**, *the airways that connect the trachea and the lungs.*

The Larynx and the Epiglottis

Other structures that are not directly involved in respiration but have important functions in the respiratory system are the larynx and the epiglottis. The **larynx**, or *voice box*, connects the throat and the trachea. The larynx contains the vocal cords, two bands of tissue that produce sound when air forced between them causes them to vibrate.

The epiglottis is a flap of cartilage located above the larynx. It folds down to close off the entrance to the larynx and trachea when you swallow, keeping food or drink from entering the respiratory system. If you eat too quickly or laugh while eating, food may go down the "wrong pipe." The cough reflex is then stimulated in an attempt to expel the material from the respiratory system.

Ⓐ Your voice may be affected by health behaviors. For example, smoking irritates structures in the throat and can cause hoarseness. *What are some other factors that can affect your voice?*

LESSON 3 REVIEW

Reviewing Facts and Vocabulary

1. What is the function of the respiratory system?
2. Explain the relationships among the trachea, the pharynx, and the larynx.
3. What role does the diaphragm play in respiration?

Thinking Critically

4. **Evaluating.** Explain the relationship between oxygen and carbon dioxide in the respiration process.
5. **Analyzing.** Demonstrate knowledge about personal and family health concerns related to respiratory system functions. Explain why it is important that the lungs are elastic.

Applying Health Skills

Advocacy. Tobacco use is associated with several types of cancer that occur in the upper respiratory system, most notably the throat. Research the effects of tobacco use on the structures of the upper respiratory system. Use what you learn to produce an educational pamphlet.

After You Read

Analyze. Create a chart with two columns. In the first column, list the functions of the respiratory system. In the second column, list the organs that are part of the respiratory system.

Visit **health.glencoe.com** for the Interactive Study Guide for Lesson 3.

Lesson 3 The Respiratory System **431**

Caring for the Respiratory System

Guide to Reading

Building Vocabulary

As you read this lesson, write each new highlighted term and its definition in your notebook.

- bronchitis (p. 433)
- pneumonia (p. 433)
- pleurisy (p. 433)
- asthma (p. 434)
- sinusitis (p. 435)
- tuberculosis (p. 435)
- emphysema (p. 435)

Focusing on the Main Ideas

In this lesson, you will learn how to:

- Examine the effects of health behaviors on the respiratory system.
- Identify warning signs that prompt individuals to seek care for respiratory problems.

Reading Strategy

Predict

- What are some problems of the respiratory system? What health behaviors can lead to these problems? After reading, compare your answers to those in the book.

 Quick Write

Write a short paragraph describing how asthma might affect a person's ability to participate.

A Imagine not being able to perform so simple an act as climbing a single flight of stairs without having to stop to catch your breath. *What are some reasons for shortness of breath?*

For your body to function properly, all your body systems must be healthy and working together. Respiratory system problems can affect the functioning of other body systems.

Health Behaviors and the Respiratory System

Many respiratory system disorders can be prevented by practicing strategies for health enhancement and risk reduction. The single most important decision you can make for respiratory health is not to smoke. Tobacco use has also been connected with cancers of the mouth, pharynx, and larynx. It can cause bronchitis, emphysema, and an increase of asthma in children and adults. In teens, smoking reduces the rate of lung growth. Avoiding the use of tobacco and all secondhand smoke, including smoke from cigarettes, cigars, pipes, and marijuana, greatly reduces your risk of all these effects.

Regular physical activity is also important to the health of the respiratory system. Increased respiration during exercise improves the capacity of the lungs to diffuse oxygen into the blood. Exercise also increases the total amount of air moved into and out of the lungs per minute.

Although the mucus and cilia that line the nasal passages and trachea work to keep out foreign particles, the respiratory system is still vulnerable to infection from bacteria and viruses. Pathogens can be transmitted easily to the respiratory system by contaminated hands touching the nose or mouth. Washing your hands regularly helps prevent infection.

Air pollution contributes to lung diseases, including respiratory tract infections, **asthma,** and lung **cancer.** Limiting your exposure to pollutants in the air, including **environmental tobacco smoke,** can also reduce your risk of developing respiratory disorders. By working within your community to reduce environmental pollutants, you show that you know effective techniques for supporting community, state, and federal agencies that advocate for healthier communities.

Respiratory System Problems

Problems of the respiratory system range from mild infections to disorders that can damage lung tissue or interfere with respiration. Colds and influenza are common infections of the upper respiratory system. Other infections and disorders affect the lower respiratory tract.

Bronchitis

Bronchitis is *an inflammation of the bronchi caused by infection or exposure to irritants such as tobacco smoke and air pollution.* In this condition the membranes that line the bronchi produce excessive mucus in the airways. Decreased airway diameter leads to symptoms such as coughing, wheezing, and shortness of breath that worsens with physical activity. Treatment includes medication that dilates the bronchial passages. Chronic bronchitis, a more serious form of the disease, is often caused by smoking. Early detection and treatment is important because the disease can cause irreversible tissue damage. Treatment includes eliminating exposure to the irritant.

Pneumonia

Pneumonia, *an inflammation of the lungs commonly caused by a bacterial or viral infection,* actually includes several types of lung infections. In a common type of pneumonia, the alveoli swell and become clogged with mucus, decreasing the amount of gas exchange. Symptoms of pneumonia include cough, fever, chills, and chest pain. Bacterial pneumonia is treated with antibiotics. **Pleurisy** (PLUR-uh-see), *an inflammation of the lining of the lungs and chest cavity,* causes chest pain when breathing and coughing.

Reading Check

Explain Why is regular physical activity important to the health of the respiratory system?

Health Minute

Reduce Your Exposure to Air Pollution

Know the dangers:

▶ The Air Quality Index (AQI) is a daily measure of the air quality in an area. Information about the levels of pollutants such as carbon monoxide, fine particles, and ozone is usually included in the report.

▶ Check the AQI for your area in the newspaper, television or radio weather forecasts, or on the Internet.

Respond to alerts:

▶ If the AQI measurement for the day is very high or if you are sensitive to certain air pollutants, avoid participating in strenuous outdoor activities.

Health Skills Activity

Communication: Asthma and Physical Activity

Todd and Rohan are friends and are happy to be in the same gym class this semester. Todd is a captain and has to choose teammates for the next few weeks. He is aware that Rohan has recently been suffering from asthma attacks. Todd decides not to choose Rohan to be on his team, but he does not explain why.

Rohan is disappointed and a little hurt. He suspects that his asthma is Todd's reason for not choosing him. Rohan has talked to his doctor and knows that it's perfectly okay to participate in physical activity as long as he uses his medication. His performance should not be affected by his asthma.

Rohan sees Todd at lunch. He wants to explain how he feels and let his friend know what the doctor said.

"Hey, Todd," Rohan calls out. "Can we talk about gym class?" Todd looks a little embarrassed, but he comes over to sit with his friend.

What Would You Do?

Finish the dialogue showing how Rohan can let Todd know how he feels.

1. Use "I" messages.
2. Use appropriate body language.
3. Maintain a respectful tone of voice.
4. Use clear, simple statements.

Reading Check

Infer How can a person avoid an asthma attack?

Asthma

Asthma (AZ-muh) is *an inflammatory condition in which the trachea, bronchi, and bronchioles become narrowed, causing difficulty in breathing.* An asthma attack is characterized by the involuntary contraction of smooth airway muscles that leads to wheezing, chest tightness, and difficulty in breathing. Acute asthma attacks can be relieved by the use of an inhaler that contains a bronchodilator, a medicine that dilates, or widens, the airways. Long-term treatment of asthma includes using medication that reduces inflammation and avoiding substances that can trigger an attack, such as pollen, dust, animal dander, and tobacco smoke. Certain food preservatives, aspirin, and inhalation of cold air can also trigger asthma attacks.

Sinusitis

An inflammation of the tissues that line the sinuses, air-filled cavities above the nasal passages and throat, is called **sinusitis**. Symptoms include nasal congestion, headache, and fever. Treatment includes nasal decongestant drops or sprays and antibiotics.

Tuberculosis

Tuberculosis is *a contagious bacterial infection that usually affects the lungs.* When a person is infected with tuberculosis, the immune system surrounds the infected area and isolates it. In this inactive stage, symptoms do not appear. This stage can last for many years. If the immune system is weakened by illness or advancing age, the infection can become active. Symptoms of active tuberculosis include cough, fever, fatigue, and weight loss. Treatment involves antibiotics and hospitalization. Numbers of reported cases of tuberculosis have increased in the United States in recent years.

Emphysema

Emphysema is *a disease that progressively destroys the walls of the alveoli.* Symptoms include difficulty breathing and chronic cough. Although the symptoms of emphysema can be treated, tissue damage is irreversible. Eventually the lungs cease to function. Emphysema is almost always caused by smoking.

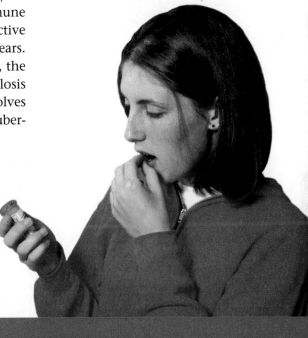

Anti-inflammatory medications keep bronchial tubes open and reduce swelling to help control asthma before an attack. *What other treatment can be used to relieve symptoms during an asthma attack?*

LESSON 4 REVIEW

Reviewing Facts and Vocabulary

1. Explain the effects of smoking on the health of the respiratory system.
2. Define *bronchitis* and describe its symptoms.
3. List three things you can do to help keep your respiratory system healthy.

Thinking Critically

4. **Applying.** Your friend is having trouble with shortness of breath during everyday activities. How can you encourage him or her to be examined by a health care professional?
5. **Analyzing.** Why is early detection important in prompting individuals of all ages to seek health care for respiratory disorders?

Applying Health Skills

Accessing Information. Analyze the relationship between health promotion and the prevention of respiratory system disorders. Draw a diagram of the respiratory system, and label each part with health behaviors that will help teens avoid respiratory problems.

After You Read

Explain. Create a plan to keep your respiratory system healthy. Include steps you can take to protect or improve your respiratory health.

A Heart to Last a Lifetime

Looking to avoid heart disease down the road? Check out these tips that will keep your heart healthy and strong far into the future.

1. Don't Smoke!

Smoking can more than triple a person's chances of having a heart attack. When a smoker quits, that risk is cut in half within 2 years. It takes more than 10 years for the odds to return to nearly normal—so unless you want to waste a decade of your life getting back your health, don't start smoking in the first place.

2. Watch Your Weight

Carrying excess fat, especially around the middle, increases the risk of a heart attack or stroke later on in life. Obesity can also lead to diabetes, a major risk factor in heart disease. Doctors recommend a reduced-calorie diet with lots of vegetables and whole grains, plus at least 30 minutes of moderate aerobic exercise a day.

3. Lower Your Bad Cholesterol

High levels of LDL (bad cholesterol) can tell doctors that heart problems are on the way. Although doctors have focused on levels of LDL, HDL (good cholesterol) may be a better predictor of heart-disease risk. Low levels of HDL might indicate that heart trouble is in the future.

4. Control Blood Pressure

Hypertension makes the heart work harder to move blood through the body and puts those who suffer from it at higher risk of both heart disease and stroke. Teens don't usually have to worry about hypertension. However, if you get short of breath when you exercise, tell a doctor. High blood pressure can be treated with proper diet, exercise, and medication if needed.

5. Reduce Stress

Stress can increase the risk of heart disease and lead to unhealthy habits such as drinking alcohol and eating junk food. Exercise and meditation can reduce stress; so can getting enough sleep every night. If you are feeling stressed out for an extended period of time, talk about it with your parents, teachers, or counselor. ▰

TIME to THINK... | About Cholesterol

The article mentions LDL and HDL. Research these two kinds of cholesterol and answer the following questions:
1. What do the letters LDL and HDL stand for?
2. What is the difference between LDL and HDL?
3. What are two examples of foods that contain high levels of each?

1. **Analyzing Influences.** Explain how technology has impacted the cardiovascular health of individuals. Evaluate both the positive and negative effects of technologies such as the automobile, elevators, and medical equipment. *(LESSON 1)*

2. **Decision Making.** You are sick with tonsillitis and your friends want you to go hiking. Your doctor has advised you to avoid physical activity and get plenty of rest. Using the steps in the decision-making process, role-play with a friend how you will make your decision. *(LESSON 2)*

3. **Accessing Information.** Find information about abdominal thrusts. Why is it important to properly perform this maneuver? What agencies in your community offer training in first aid for choking? *(LESSON 3)*

4. **Advocacy.** An antibiotic-resistant strain of tuberculosis is increasing in frequency in the United States. Find out how often testing for tuberculosis is offered in your community. For which age groups does it apply? Is there a cost? Raise community awareness by making a poster that encourages individuals to get tested. *(LESSON 4)*

Medical Laboratory Technician

If you are interested in biology, chemistry, math, and computer science, and if you enjoy working in the laboratory, consider a career as a medical laboratory technician (MLT). MLTs discover information about

a patient's health by analyzing tissue samples and using the latest laboratory technology and techniques.

To become an MLT, you need a high school diploma or its equivalent to enter a college-level course of study. Successful completion of an associate's degree program and a national certification exam are required for employment. You can find out more about this and other health careers by clicking on Career Corner at **health.glencoe.com.**

Parent Involvement

Practicing Healthful Behaviors. Brainstorm with parents or guardians ways your family can practice healthful behaviors to maintain the health of your cardiovascular and respiratory systems. Find ways to incorporate low-fat, low-cholesterol foods, including fresh fruits, into your family's daily eating plan.

School and Community

A Smoke-Free Community. Find information about the Great American Smoke Out. What does your community do to participate in this event? Share the information you learn with your classmates, and brainstorm ideas about how your school can become involved with this event.

After You Read

Use your Foldable to review what you have learned about the structure and function of the cardiovascular system. Make a similar Foldable to note what you have learned about the respiratory and lymphatic systems.

➤ **EXPLORING HEALTH TERMS** *Answer the following questions on a sheet of paper.*

Lesson 1 *Match each definition with the correct term.*

arteries	lymphocytes
capillaries	plasma
hemoglobin	platelets
lymph	veins

1. The fluid in which other parts of the blood are suspended.

2. The oxygen-carrying protein in blood.

3. Cells that prevent the body's loss of blood.

4. Blood vessels that carry blood to the heart.

Lesson 2 *Identify each statement as True or False. If false, replace the underlined term with the correct term.*

anemia	Hodgkin's disease
blood pressure	leukemia
congenital	

5. <u>Leukemia</u> is a condition in which the ability of the blood to carry oxygen is reduced.

6. A <u>congenital</u> condition is present at birth.

7. <u>Anemia</u> is a type of cancer that affects the lymphatic system.

Lesson 3 *Replace the underlined words with the correct term.*

bronchi	pharynx
diaphragm	respiration
larynx	trachea

8. The exchange of gases between the body and the environment is known as <u>bronchi</u>.

9. The <u>pharynx</u> is a muscle that separates the chest from the abdominal cavity.

10. The <u>diaphragm</u> are airways that connect the trachea and the lungs.

11. The windpipe is also referred to as the <u>pharynx</u>.

12. The voice box is the <u>trachea</u>.

Lesson 4 *Match each definition with the correct term.*

asthma	pneumonia
bronchitis	sinusitis
emphysema	tuberculosis
pleurisy	

13. An inflammation of the lungs commonly caused by a bacterial or viral infection.

14. An inflammatory condition in which the trachea, bronchi, and bronchioles become narrowed, causing difficulty breathing.

15. An inflammation of the lining of the lungs and chest cavity.

➤ **RECALLING THE FACTS** *Use complete sentences to answer the following questions.*

1. Compare and contrast red blood cells, white blood cells, and platelets.

2. Differentiate between B cells and T cells.

3. What is the purpose of the lymphatic system?

For more review questions for Chapter 16, go to **health.glencoe.com**.

4. What are some possible causes of congenital heart disease?

5. What causes anemia, and how can it be avoided?

6. What can cause a deficiency of the immune system?

7. What is the difference between external and internal respiration?

8. Explain how the process of breathing occurs.

9. What is the function of the epiglottis?

10. How is physical activity related to the health of your respiratory system?

11. What is pneumonia? What causes it?

12. What effects does emphysema have on the respiratory system?

▶ WRITING CRITICALLY

1. **Personal.** Write a journal entry describing your current level of physical activity and what types of foods you eat during a typical day. Then imagine yourself at age 40, and describe your fitness level, weight, and health of your cardiovascular system based on your behaviors and choices today. Devise a prevention strategy that incorporates physical activity and a healthful eating plan to reduce the risk of future cardiovascular disease.

2. **Persuasive.** Write a public service announcement persuading teens not to begin smoking. Include information on the negative health consequences of smoking. Persuade teens to abstain from tobacco use by stating facts, providing supporting evidence that gives logical reasons, and quoting experts.

Standardized Test Practice

Read the paragraphs below and then answer the questions.

Tackling Asthma

What is an asthma attack?

An asthma attack is a time of increased asthma symptoms. Anyone can have an asthma attack, even someone with mild asthma. An attack can start gradually or suddenly. Sometimes an attack will go away, but then come back in a few hours. This second attack might be worse than the first attack.

What should I do if I have an asthma attack?

· Stay calm. It isn't easy, but your breathing will worsen if you panic.

· Tell someone. Let whoever is nearby know what is happening to you so they can get help.

· Take your quick-relief medication. Be sure you know which medication is the quick-relief one before you need it an emergency!

· If the medication has not helped in five to ten minutes, dial 911.

· Continue to take your quick-relief medication every five to ten minutes until the ambulance arrives.

1. What is the writer's purpose?

(A) to compare which types of asthma medications work best

(B) to explain an asthma attack and offer ways to deal with one

(C) to help people understand what can trigger a severe asthma attack

(D) to persuade the reader to choose a particular type of asthma medication

2. Which phrase in the first paragraph helps the reader understand the meaning of the term *asthma attack*?

(F) An attack can start gradually

(G) Sometimes an attack will go away

(H) This second attack might be worse

(I) a time of increased asthma symptoms

3. Add a final paragraph to this brochure that explains how you could help someone during an asthma attack.

Digestive and Urinary Systems

Dietary Supplement Advertising

Dietary supplement ads may make false claims. Advertisers may claim that using their product will help you

► **lose weight.**

► **alleviate pain.**

► **cure disease.**

Visit the Eye on the Media section at health.glencoe.com to learn more about how to analyze the claims made by makers of dietary supplements.

FOLDABLES™
Study Organizer

Before You Read

Make this Foldable to help you organize your notes on the structure and function of the digestive system. Begin with one sheet of plain 11″ x 17″ paper.

► **Step 1**

Mark the midpoint of the long axis on a sheet of paper.

► **Step 2**

Fold the outside edges of the paper in to touch the middle mark. Label as shown.

Structure   Function

As You Read

As you read and discuss the material in the chapter, record what you learn about the structure and function of the digestive system under the appropriate side of your Foldable.

SPOTLIGHT ON HEALTH

Using Visuals. What choices can you and your family make to incorporate a variety of nutritious foods into your meal plans?

The Digestive System

Guide to Reading

Building Vocabulary

As you read this lesson, write each new highlighted term and its definition in your notebook.

▶ digestion (p. 442)

▶ absorption (p. 442)

▶ elimination (p. 442)

▶ mastication (p. 443)

▶ peristalsis (p. 443)

▶ gastric juices (p. 444)

▶ chyme (p. 444)

▶ bile (p. 445)

Focusing on the Main Ideas

In this lesson, you will learn how to:

▶ Describe the structures and functions of the digestive system.

▶ Show the pathway of food through the digestive system.

Reading Strategy

Predict

▶ Scan the headings, subheadings, and photo captions. List three questions you think will be answered in this lesson.

Quick Write

Describe how you can include a variety of nutritious foods in your meal plans.

▲ Digestion begins when you take your first bite of food. *What are three functions of the digestive system?*

You may not give much thought to the digestive process as you enjoy a meal with friends or family. Your body cannot receive nourishment directly from the foods you eat. Food and drink are digested into smaller nutrients before they can be absorbed into the blood and carried to the body's cells.

Functions of the Digestive System

The functions of the digestive system can be divided into three main processes:

▶ **Digestion**, *the mechanical and chemical breakdown of foods for use by the body's cells.*

▶ **Absorption**, *the passage of digested food from the digestive tract into the cardiovascular system.*

▶ **Elimination**, *the expulsion of undigested food or body wastes.*

Digestion includes both mechanical and chemical processes. The mechanical portion involves chewing, mashing, and breaking food into smaller pieces. The chemical process involves digestive juices

Take the Health Inventory for Chapter 17 at **health.glencoe.com**.

that change food into simpler substances. Digestive juices are secretions produced by various organs in the digestive system. These secretions contain chemicals that help break down the food.

The nervous system and the cardiovascular system also play major roles in digestion. The nervous system triggers the digestive process to begin at the sight or smell of food and controls the muscles that move food through the digestive system. After food has been broken down, nutrients, including carbohydrates, proteins, fats, vitamins, and minerals, are absorbed into the blood and delivered to all cells of the body by the cardiovascular system. Health-literate teens understand how body systems work, and know strategies for health enhancement and risk reduction.

Structures of the Digestive System

The digestive process begins in the mouth. Ingestion, the first stage of the process, is the taking of food into the body. Structures involved in ingestion include your teeth, salivary glands, and tongue. These structures are shown in **Figure 17.1** on page 444.

▶ **Teeth.** The primary function of the teeth is to break the food you eat into smaller pieces. **Mastication** (MAS-tuh-KAY-shuhn) is *the process of chewing,* which prepares food to be swallowed.

▶ **Salivary glands.** The salivary glands in the mouth produce the first digestive juices used in the digestive process. Saliva produced by these glands contains an enzyme that begins to break down the starches and sugars in food into smaller particles. Saliva also lubricates food, making it easier to swallow.

▶ **Tongue.** The tongue forms chewed food into a size and shape that can be swallowed. As you swallow, muscular contractions force food into the pharynx, or throat. The uvula, a small flap of muscular tissue at the back of the mouth, closes the opening to the nasal passages. The epiglottis, the flap of tissue covering the throat, closes the opening to the trachea, or windpipe, to prevent food from entering the respiratory system.

The Esophagus

When food is swallowed, it enters the esophagus, the muscular tube about 10 inches long that connects the pharynx with the stomach. Food is moved through the esophagus, stomach, and intestines by a process called **peristalsis** (PER-uh-STAWL-suhs), *a series of involuntary muscle contractions that move food through the digestive tract.* The action of peristalsis is like a wave moving through the muscle to push food and fluid through each hollow organ. The peristaltic action begins as soon as food is swallowed and enters the esophagus. A sphincter muscle at the entrance to the stomach allows food to move from the esophagus into the stomach.

Your salivary glands respond to the smell of foods before you begin to eat. *How does saliva help in the digestion process?*

FIGURE **17.1**

THE DIGESTIVE SYSTEM

The organs of the digestive system work together to break food down and move it through the body, providing nutrients that are absorbed into the blood and transferred to cells.

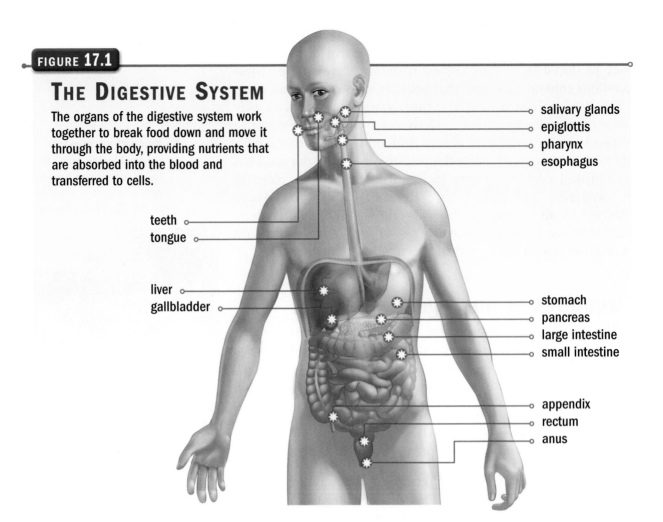

teeth
tongue

liver
gallbladder

salivary glands
epiglottis
pharynx
esophagus

stomach
pancreas
large intestine
small intestine

appendix
rectum
anus

Reading Check

Explain What are the three structures involved in ingestion?

The Stomach

The stomach is a hollow, saclike organ enclosed in a muscular wall. These flexible muscles allow the stomach to expand when you eat. The stomach, shown in **Figure 17.2,** has three tasks in digestion.

▶ **Mixing foods with gastric juices.** Gastric juices are *secretions from the stomach lining that contain hydrochloric acid and pepsin, an enzyme that digests protein.* Hydrochloric acid in the stomach kills bacteria taken in with food and creates an acidic environment for the pepsin to do its work. The hydrochloric acid is strong enough to dissolve metal. Mucus produced in the stomach forms a protective lining so that the strong gastric juices do not digest the stomach.

▶ **Storing swallowed food and liquid.** The stomach holds food and liquid for further digestion before they move into the small intestine.

▶ **Moving food into the small intestine.** As food is digested in the stomach, it is converted to **chyme** (kym), *a creamy, fluid mixture of food and gastric juices.* Peristalsis moves the chyme into the small intestine.

FIGURE 17.2

THE STOMACH

Digestion continues in the stomach. Each of the three layers of stomach muscles moves in a different direction. These movements aid both mechanical and chemical digestion.

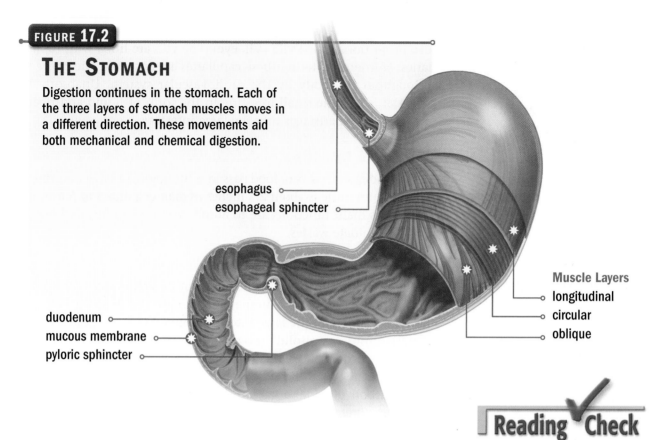

esophagus
esophageal sphincter

duodenum
mucous membrane
pyloric sphincter

Muscle Layers
longitudinal
circular
oblique

The Pancreas, Liver, and Gallbladder

In the small intestine, the juices of two other digestive organs mix with the food to continue the process of digestion. One of these organs is the pancreas. It produces enzymes that break down the carbohydrates, fats, and proteins in food. Other enzymes that are active in the process come from glands in the wall of the intestine.

The liver produces another digestive juice—**bile**, *a yellow-green, bitter fluid important in the breakdown and absorption of fats.* Between meals, the bile is stored in the gallbladder. At mealtime, it is secreted from the gallbladder into the bile duct to reach the intestine and mix with the fats in food. Bile acids dissolve the fats into the watery contents of the intestine. After the fat is dissolved, it is digested by enzymes from the pancreas and from the lining of the intestine.

The Small Intestine

The small intestine is 20 to 23 feet in length and 1 inch in diameter. It consists of three parts, the duodenum (doo-uh-DEE-nuhm), the jejunum (juh-JOO-nuhm), and the ileum (IL-lee-uhm). As chyme enters the duodenum from the stomach, it includes partially digested carbohydrates and proteins and undigested fats. This mixture is further dissolved by digestive juices secreted from glands in the lining of the small intestine, along with secretions from the liver and the pancreas.

Reading Check

Compare and Contrast
What are the differences between the small intestine and the large intestine?

Did You Know ?

The liver is the body's heaviest gland and largest organ after the skin. It produces bile and removes toxic substances such as alcohol from the blood.

The pancreas produces three digestive enzymes: *amylase,* which breaks down carbohydrates; *trypsin,* which breaks down proteins; and *lipase,* which breaks down fats. These enzymes are carried to the small intestine by a tube leading from the pancreas to the small intestine.

The small intestine is named for its diameter, not its length. It is about 1 inch wide and 20 to 23 feet long.

- It takes three to five hours for material to move through the small intestine.
- The small intestine is the main site of nutrient absorption. Ninety percent of all nutrients are absorbed through this organ.

The inner wall of the small intestine contains millions of finger-like projections called villi (VIL-eye). The villi are lined with capillaries. Nutrients entering these capillaries are absorbed and carried throughout the body by the cardiovascular system. Unabsorbed material leaves the small intestine in the form of liquid and fiber and moves by peristalsis into the large intestine.

The Large Intestine

The undigested parts of food pass into the colon, or large intestine. The large intestine is about 2.5 inches in diameter and 5 to 6 feet in length. Its main functions are to absorb water, vitamins, and salts, and to eliminate wastes.

REMOVING WASTES FROM THE BODY

The body produces wastes in the form of solids, gases, and liquids. Solid wastes are eliminated through the large intestine. Bacteria that live in the large intestine convert the undigested food materials into a semisolid mass called feces. Feces are excreted from the body through the anus during a bowel movement. The skin excretes some wastes through the pores by perspiration. The lungs expel carbon dioxide, a gaseous waste, when you exhale. Liquid wastes are filtered through the urinary system, described in Lesson 3.

LESSON 1 REVIEW

Reviewing Facts and Vocabulary

1. What are the functions of the digestive system?
2. Define *peristalsis.*
3. Describe the pathway of food and undigested wastes through the digestive system.

Thinking Critically

4. **Synthesizing.** Explain how the digestive system interacts with the cardiovascular system.
5. **Evaluating.** Assess the importance of the role of the pancreas in the digestive process.

Applying Health Skills

Advocacy. Prepare a booklet that demonstrates knowledge about personal health concerns related to the digestive system. Your booklet should outline the organs of the digestive system, describe the function of each organ, and list behaviors that contribute to the health of these organs. Share the booklet with your family.

After You Read

Describe. What are the three main processes of the digestive system? Write one or two sentences describing each.

Caring for the Digestive System

Guide to Reading

Building Vocabulary

As you read this lesson, write each new highlighted term and its definition in your notebook.

- ▶ indigestion (p. 448)
- ▶ heartburn (p. 448)
- ▶ hiatal hernia (p. 448)
- ▶ appendicitis (p. 450)
- ▶ peptic ulcer (p. 451)

Focusing on the Main Ideas

In this lesson, you will learn how to:

- ▶ Examine the effects of health behaviors on the digestive system.
- ▶ Identify the problems of the digestive system.

Reading Strategy

Predict

- ▶ After reviewing the headings, subheadings, and pictures, write a few sentences describing how you care for your digestive system.

Write a summary describing the benefits of eating a healthful diet.

D o you often rush through your day without giving much thought to your next meal? Part of having good digestive health includes taking the time to prepare and eat a variety of nutrient-rich foods. Practicing health behaviors that include healthy eating habits can reduce the risk of developing problems with digestion or with the organs of the digestive system.

Health Behaviors and the Digestive System

T aking care of your digestive system begins with the choices you make about which foods to eat and how you eat them. The reward for maintaining good eating habits may well be a lifetime free of digestive problems or habits that may lead to disease. An informed individual understands the impact of personal health behaviors on body systems. The following health behaviors will keep your digestive system healthy.

- ▶ Follow a well-balanced diet that includes a variety of foods that are low in fat and high in fiber.

Choose high-fiber foods such as whole grain breads and vegetables to help keep your digestive system healthy. *What are some other health behaviors that might affect your digestive system?*

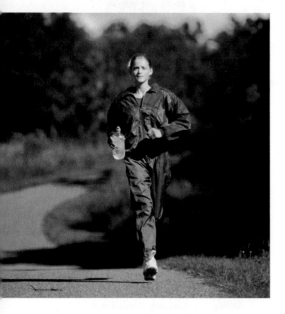

Incorporate physical activity into your day.

How does physical activity enhance the health of your digestive system?

▶ Wash your hands before preparing a meal and before eating to reduce the risk of introducing harmful bacteria into your digestive system.

▶ Eat slowly and chew your food thoroughly. Do not wash food down with liquid.

▶ Drink at least eight 8-ounce glasses of water each day to help your digestive system function properly.

▶ Avoid using food as a way of dealing with your emotions. Instead, take a walk or write in a journal when you feel stressed.

Practicing these healthy behaviors shows that you understand the potential impact of common risk behaviors on the quality of life.

Problems of the Digestive System

Problems of the digestive system include the minor discomfort caused by indigestion or an upset stomach, more serious bacterial infections or foodborne illness, and conditions that need immediate medical attention, such as appendicitis. Health-literate teens possess the ability to assess their own health. These teens are able to explain the relationship between eating habits and total health.

Functional Problems of the Digestive System

Problems such as indigestion, heartburn, gas, constipation, nausea, or diarrhea may result from illness, stress, and eating certain foods.

▶ **Indigestion** is *a feeling of discomfort in the upper abdomen.* This feeling of fullness can sometimes be accompanied by gas and nausea. Indigestion can be caused from eating too much food, eating too quickly, and eating foods that are spicy or high in fat. Stomach disorders and stress can contribute to indigestion.

▶ **Heartburn** is *a burning sensation in the center of the chest that may rise from the bottom, or tip, of the breastbone up to the throat.* It results from acid reflux, or the backflow of stomach acid into the esophagus. As the acid enters the esophagus, it irritates the tissues, causing a burning feeling. Heartburn can also be a symptom of a **hiatal hernia** (hy-AY-tuhl HER-nee-uh), *a condition in which part of the stomach pushes through an opening in the diaphragm.* Because frequent or prolonged heartburn can be an indication of more serious digestive disorders, it is important to discuss the symptoms with a medical professional.

▶ **Gas.** Although a certain amount of gas in the stomach and intestines produced from the breakdown of food is normal, excessive gas can result in cramps or an uncomfortable feeling of fullness in the abdomen. Most foods that contain carbohydrates or complex sugars, such as beans, cabbage, broccoli, onions, and starches, can cause gas.

How does viral hepatitis affect the liver?

Hepatitis, an inflammation of the liver, is caused by viral infections. Several different viruses exist, including hepatitis A, B, and C. Hepatitis A is spread by contaminated food or water and by the feces of infected people. Hepatitis B and C can be spread by sexual contact, by contact with infected blood, and by sharing needles with infected drug users. Hepatitis B and C viruses can cause chronic hepatitis, a disease that can last a lifetime.

▶ **Constipation** is a condition in which feces become dry and hard and bowel movements are difficult. Constipation can be caused by not drinking enough water or consuming enough **fiber** to move wastes through the digestive system. Some medications can also cause constipation. Following a diet that includes fruits and vegetables, drinking at least eight 8-ounce glasses of water each day, and getting regular physical activity are the best ways to avoid constipation.

When recommended by a health care professional, laxative drugs may be used to treat constipation. Laxatives can cause diarrhea, abdominal cramps, and gas. Some types of laxatives coat the intestine.

Reading Check

Explain What are some of the functional problems of the digestive system?

Hands-On Health ACTIVITY

Avoiding Stress for Healthy Digestion

What does stress have to do with digestion? More than you might think! Stress can affect how your digestive system functions. Plus, stress can lead to poor eating habits. Chronic stress can cause poor absorption of vitamins and minerals, which can lead to nutritional deficiencies. In this activity, you will design a poster displaying stress-management strategies to aid healthy digestion.

What You'll Need

- pencil and paper
- markers
- poster board

What You'll Do

1. Divide a piece of paper into four sections.
2. Write one of the following concepts in each section:
   - Eat regular meals, with a variety of foods, instead of over- or undereating.
   - Limit comfort foods, which are frequently full of fat and sugar.
   - Limit caffeine, which is a stimulant.
   - Don't rush through meals; sit down and relax.
3. Under each concept, list 5–10 positive stress-management strategies. For example, under "Limit comfort foods" you may write, "When I'm stressed, I will take a long walk instead of eating cookies." Under "Don't rush through meals," you may write, "I will get up ten minutes earlier every morning so I have time to eat a leisurely breakfast."
4. Working with a small group, create a poster about one of these four concepts, showing how teens can avoid stress and maintain digestive system health. Make your poster colorful and attractive. Be sure to include tips for stress-management techniques.

Apply and Conclude

Present your stress-management poster to the class. Consider displaying the posters in the cafeteria or other areas of the school.

Reading Check

Examine What is the cause of peptic ulcers?

The coating may prevent vitamin absorption. The body may also become dependent on laxatives and fail to function on its own.

► **Nausea** is the feeling of discomfort that sometimes precedes vomiting. Motion sickness, pathogens, some medications, and dehydration can cause nausea. Vomiting is a reflex in which the contents of the stomach are brought back up the esophagus and out of the mouth. Powerful contractions of the abdominal muscles compress the stomach, while the esophageal sphincter relaxes to allow the contents to exit the stomach.

► **Diarrhea** is the frequent passage of watery feces. When digested food passes too quickly through the large intestine, water cannot be absorbed and diarrhea results. Diarrhea may result from changes in eating style, overeating, emotional turmoil, or nutritional deficiencies. Bacterial or viral infections and certain medications can cause diarrhea. One of the greatest concerns about diarrhea, especially when it occurs in infants and young children, is dehydration. To avoid dehydration during an episode of diarrhea, drink plenty of water and other fluids. Fluids that contain electrolytes help maintain the body's fluid and chemical balance. Medical attention should be sought if diarrhea persists for more than 48 hours.

Structural Problems of the Digestive System

Although some digestive system problems are temporary or easily treated, others are very serious, requiring immediate medical attention.

GALLSTONES

Gallstones are formed when cholesterol in bile crystallizes and blocks the bile duct between the small intestine and the gallbladder. Symptoms include pain in the upper right portion of the abdomen, nausea, vomiting, and fever. Treatment includes taking medication that dissolves the stones or having the stones broken down by high-intensity ultrasound waves. Surgical removal of the stones and possibly the gallbladder itself is an option when symptoms are severe.

APPENDICITIS

Appendicitis is *the inflammation of the appendix,* a tube from 3 to 4 inches long that extends from the beginning portion of the large intestine. The appendix becomes swollen and inflamed if it is blocked or clogged by bacteria or other foreign matter that prevent the release of its secretions. Symptoms of appendicitis include pain in the lower right portion of the abdomen, fever, loss of appetite, nausea and vomiting, and tenderness in the area of the appendix. The appendix may burst, spreading infection throughout the abdomen, making the condition extremely serious. Medical care is essential. Treatment involves surgical removal of the appendix.

GASTRITIS

Gastritis, one of the most common disorders of the digestive system, is an inflammation of the mucous membrane that lines the stomach. An increase in the production of stomach acid, the use of tobacco or alcohol, infections caused by bacteria and viruses, and medications such as aspirin can irritate the stomach lining. Symptoms of gastritis include pain, indigestion, decreased appetite, and nausea and vomiting. Treatment includes avoiding irritants and taking medications or antibiotics to eliminate infection.

LACTOSE INTOLERANCE

Lactose, a type of sugar found in milk and other dairy products, is normally broken down by the enzyme lactase. People who are lactose intolerant do not produce enough lactase, so undigested lactose remains in the small intestine. Bacteria in the digestive tract ferment ingested lactose, producing such symptoms as abdominal cramps, bloating, gas, and diarrhea. Chewing lactase enzyme tablets can reduce symptoms. People who are lactose intolerant should choose alternate sources of calcium including dark green vegetables such as broccoli and kale, fortified soymilk, and yogurt with active cultures.

PEPTIC ULCER

A **peptic ulcer** is *a sore in the lining of the digestive tract.* Peptic ulcers can be caused by regular use of anti-inflammatory drugs such as aspirin and by a bacterial infection caused by *Helicobacter pylori (H. pylori).* Symptoms include nausea, vomiting, and abdominal pain that worsens when the stomach is empty. Ulcers can cause bleeding in the stomach, and without treatment, they may perforate, or break through, the stomach wall. Treatment includes medications that neutralize acid or eliminate infection and avoiding irritants such as aspirin, cigarette smoke, and alcohol.

CIRRHOSIS

Destruction of liver tissue, usually caused by prolonged and heavy alcohol use, results in cirrhosis, or scarring of the liver tissue. Alcohol interferes with the liver's ability to break down fats. Excess fat in the liver blocks the flow of blood in the liver cells. Liver tissue is destroyed and replaced with useless scar tissue, preventing normal liver function. Cirrhosis can lead to liver failure and may cause death unless a liver transplant is performed.

CROHN'S DISEASE

Crohn's disease causes inflammation of the lining of the digestive tract. Symptoms include diarrhea, weight loss, fever, and abdominal pain. Although no cause has yet been discovered, the disease seems to be associated with problems in the immune system.

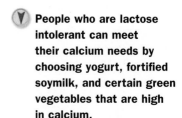

People who are lactose intolerant can meet their calcium needs by choosing yogurt, fortified soymilk, and certain green vegetables that are high in calcium.

HEALTH *Online*

TOPIC **The Digestive System**

Go to **health.glencoe.com** for links to more information about the digestive system.

ACTIVITY Using the information provided at these links, create a checklist of daily behaviors you can adopt to keep your digestive system healthy.

COLON CANCER

Cancer of the colon and rectum is the second leading cause of cancer deaths in the United States. This cancer usually develops in the lowest part of the colon, near the rectum. As the cancer grows larger, it either blocks the colon or causes bleeding, often during elimination. Cancers of this type are usually slow to spread. Seeking early medical help greatly increases a person's chance of survival.

COLITIS

Colitis is an inflammation of the large intestine or colon. It may be caused by bacterial or viral infections. Symptoms may include fever, abdominal pain, and diarrhea, which can contain blood.

HEMORRHOIDS

Hemorrhoids are veins in the rectum and anus that are swollen as a result of increased pressure. Hemorrhoids may occur with constipation, during pregnancy, and after childbirth. Signs of hemorrhoids include itching, pain, and bleeding. Regular physical activity and a diet high in fiber can help prevent hemorrhoids.

TOOTH DECAY

Teeth are very important to the digestive process. Brushing and flossing teeth daily is the best way to prevent tooth decay and to keep your teeth healthy.

The teeth are an important part of your digestive system. *What health behaviors do you practice every day to promote the health of your teeth?*

LESSON 2 REVIEW

Reviewing Facts and Vocabulary

1. Examine the effects of health behaviors on the digestive system, and list three behaviors that help prevent digestive system problems.
2. Define *indigestion* and describe its symptoms.
3. Name and describe two structural problems of the digestive system.

Thinking Critically

4. **Synthesizing.** How does fiber contribute to the health of the digestive system?
5. **Analyzing.** Why are early detection and treatment of digestive system disorders important?

Applying Health Skills

Goal Setting. Analyze the relationship between health promotion and disease prevention. Make a list of health behaviors you could practice to improve the health of your digestive system. Choose one behavior from your list and use the goal-setting steps to develop a plan to incorporate this behavior into your daily life.

After You Read

Problems and Solutions. Make a T chart. On one side, list the problems of the digestive system. On the other side, list some of the ways to care for the digestive system to avoid illness and disease.

Visit **health.glencoe.com** for the Interactive Study Guide for Lesson 2.

The Urinary System

Guide to Reading

Building Vocabulary

As you read this lesson, write each new highlighted term and its definition in your notebook.

- urine (p. 453)
- nephrons (p. 454)
- ureters (p. 454)
- bladder (p. 455)
- urethra (p. 455)
- cystitis (p. 456)
- urethritis (p. 456)
- hemodialysis (p. 457)

Focusing on the Main Ideas

In this lesson, you will learn how to:

- Describe the structures and functions of the urinary system.
- Examine the effects of health behaviors on the urinary system.
- Identify the problems and warning signs of the urinary system.

Reading Strategy

Predict

- Scan the headings, subheadings, and photo captions. Write a summary describing what you think will be included in this lesson.

Quick Write

Write a short paragraph describing how food and drink affect your urinary system.

While the digestive system removes solid wastes from the body, the urinary system functions to filter and remove liquid waste. A healthy urinary system helps maintain balance within the internal environment of the body. Because of this important role, problems in the urinary system, if left untreated, can affect the entire body and may result in death.

Function of the Urinary System

The main function of the urinary system is to filter waste and extra fluid from the blood. **Urine** is *liquid waste material* excreted from the body through the process of urination. Urine consists of water and body wastes that contain nitrogen. These wastes become toxic to cells if they remain in the body for too long.

The Kidneys

The kidneys, shown in **Figure 17.3** on the next page, are bean-shaped organs about the size of a fist. They are near the middle of the back, just below the rib cage.

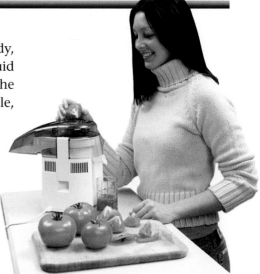

Avoid caffeine drinks, drink at least eight glasses of water daily, and include other healthful sources of fluids to help maintain the function of your urinary system.

Reading Check

Explain What vital function do the kidneys provide for the body?

The kidneys remove waste products from the blood through tiny filtering units called **nephrons** (NEH-frahnz), *the functional units of the kidneys.* Each kidney contains over 1 million nephrons. Each nephron consists of a ball formed of small capillaries, called a glomerulus (gluhm-ER-ruh-luhs), and a small tube called a renal tubule that functions as a filtering funnel.

FIGURE **17.3**

THE KIDNEY

The kidney, part of the urinary system, performs the vital function of removing wastes from the blood.

Kidney   Nephron

- glomerulus
- tubule
- capillary
- vein
- artery
- collecting tube
- urine to ureter

Did You Know ?

The urinary system filters about 50 gallons of blood and produces 1 to 2 quarts of urine each day.

As part of the filtering process, the kidneys adjust the amount of salts, water, and other materials excreted in the urine according to the body's needs. They monitor and maintain the body's acid-base and water balances. When the blood and body fluids become too acidic or too alkaline, the kidneys alter the acidity of the urine to restore the balance. When the body becomes dehydrated, the pituitary gland releases antidiuretic hormone (ADH), stimulating thirst and allowing the kidney to balance the fluid levels in the body.

The Ureters

From the kidneys, urine travels to the bladder through the ureters. The **ureters** are *tubes that connect the kidneys to the bladder.* Each ureter is 8 to 10 inches long. Muscles in the ureter walls tighten and relax to force urine down and away from the kidneys. The ureters are constantly working. Some amount of urine is passed from the ureters to the bladder about every 15 seconds.

The Bladder and the Urethra

The **bladder** is *a hollow muscular organ that acts as a reservoir for urine*. Located in the pelvic cavity, the bladder is held in place by ligaments attached to other organs and to the pelvic bones. Until the bladder is ready to be emptied, sphincter muscles close tightly, like a rubber band, around the opening into the **urethra**, *the tube that leads from the bladder to the outside of the body.*

Reading Check

Infer Which urinary conditions include infection and blockage of urine?

Health Behaviors and the Urinary System

Proper urinary function is important because wastes that are not removed from the body quickly become toxic. There are several health behaviors that can affect your urinary system.

Resilient TEENS

Jennie Bregande has an uncanny knack for finding silver linings in life's darkest clouds. Jennie's Asian features set her apart and she was teased about being adopted. "Kids can be so cruel," says Jennie. "They called me names, and I'd come home crying.

But Jennie's toughest challenge was coming to terms with having Attention Deficit Disorder (ADD). "I used to be so ashamed that I couldn't concentrate like other kids," says Jennie. "Then a therapist helped me see it as a gift. There are things I see, connections I make, that other kids don't."

These days Jennie offers advice to kids who call the weekly radio show "Teen Talk" that she hosts. "I've learned to surround myself with positive people," she says. "And that makes all the difference."

"I've learned to surround myself with positive people, and that makes all the difference."

Reading Check **Explain** Why was having ADD the toughest challenge Jennie faced?

A healthy individual who wishes to become an organ donor carries a card stating that preference. An organ donation card such as the one shown here is often carried with the person's driver's license.

▶ Drink at least eight 8-ounce glasses of water each day, and limit your intake of caffeine and soft drinks. Caffeine drinks can interfere with kidney function and increase the amount of water lost through urination.

▶ Eat a well-balanced diet.

▶ Practice good hygiene and personal health care to help prevent harmful bacteria from causing infection.

▶ Have regular medical checkups. Reporting to your doctor any changes in the frequency of urination and in the color or odor of urine is important to the early detection and treatment of urinary system disorders.

Health-literate teens are able to determine how heredity, environmental, and lifestyle factors place them at risk for disease.

Problems of the Urinary System

Urinary system problems can result from several different conditions, including infection and blockage of urine. **Cystitis** is *an inflammation of the bladder,* most often caused by a bacterial infection, which can spread to the kidneys. **Urethritis**, *the inflammation of the urethra,* can be caused by a bacterial infection. Symptoms of both conditions include burning pain during urination, increased frequency of urination, fever, and the presence of blood in the urine. Seeking medical help for these symptoms shows you know strategies for health enhancement and risk reduction. Health-literate teens can identify prevention, causes, warning signs, and treatments for non-communicable diseases.

Kidney Problems

Kidney disorders, some of which can be life threatening, should be treated and monitored by a medical professional. Kidney problems include the following conditions.

▶ **Nephritis** is the inflammation of the nephrons. Symptoms include fever, tissue swelling, and changes in urine production.

▶ **Kidney stones** form when salts in the urine crystallize into a solid stone, usually containing calcium. Small stones can pass through the urinary system naturally, with treatment to relieve symptoms. Treatment for larger stones includes a procedure in which high-intensity sound waves are used to break stones apart so they can pass through the urethra.

▶ **Uremia** is a serious condition associated with a decrease in blood filtration by the kidneys. As a result of decreased filtration, abnormally high levels of nitrogen waste products remain in the blood and can cause tissue damage.

KIDNEY FAILURE

Kidney failure can be acute, meaning sudden onset, or chronic, in which case the kidneys progressively lose their ability to function. Treatment includes reducing symptoms and slowing the progression of the disease. If kidney damage is extensive, dialysis or a kidney transplant may be required.

▶ **Hemodialysis** (HEE-moh-dy-AL-uh-suhs) is *a technique in which an artificial kidney machine removes waste products from the blood.* A needle connected to plastic tubing passes blood from the patient to a machine that filters the blood and returns it in much the same manner that a healthy kidney would.

▶ **Peritoneal dialysis** uses the peritoneum, a thin membrane that surrounds the digestive organs, to filter the blood. A catheter, a tube that provides a passageway for fluids, is inserted into the abdominal cavity to remove toxins.

▶ **Kidney transplant** is a third treatment option for chronic kidney failure. This involves the replacement of a nonfunctional kidney with a healthy kidney from a donor.

Kidney failure is treated by using medical technology to filter the blood artificially. *What options might a person with kidney failure have besides dialysis?*

LESSON 3 REVIEW

Reviewing Facts and Vocabulary

1. Describe the main function of the urinary system.

2. What is a *ureter* and what is a *urethra*?

3. Examine the effects of three health behaviors on the urinary system, and explain how these behaviors help reduce the risk of developing a urinary system disorder.

Thinking Critically

4. **Analyzing.** Explain why coffee, tea, and cola drinks should not be counted as part of your daily recommended eight glasses of water.

5. **Applying.** Relate the importance of early detection and warning signs that prompt individuals of all ages to seek health care for urinary system problems. What might a change in the appearance of one's urine indicate?

Applying Health Skills

Accessing Information. Research and discuss the health-related social issues of organ donation and kidney transplants. How are donors matched with potential recipients? What type of follow-up care is needed? Share with your classmates what you learned about organ donation and transplants.

After You Read

Explain. Write a brief paragraph describing the role of the kidneys. What vital function do they perform to maintain your health?

Visit **health.glencoe.com** for the Interactive Study Guide for Lesson 3.

Lesson 3 The Urinary System **457**

Think Drink

You know drinking lots of water is good for you—but what other fluids will help you stay healthy? Consider these options.

Sports Drinks

PROS: Most contain ideal levels of electrolytes, which reduce the chances you will cramp during workouts that last for more than an hour. Their simple sugars are easily converted to glycogen, giving your muscles much-needed fuel. Plus, the drink's added sodium stimulates the urge to drink, so you guzzle more often.

CONS: You may not love the taste—nor the calories (about 50 to 70 calories in 8 ounces), sugar, artificial flavorings, and cost (water and fruit tend to be much cheaper).

Water

PROS: Water is suitable for any type of activity, whether you're walking the dog or racing a friend. It's also cheap compared to sports drinks.

CONS: Water doesn't replenish all the electrolytes that you lose through sweat or help refuel muscle tissue during endurance activities. It also goes through your system faster, so you may find yourself taking more breaks than you'd like.

Fruits and Vegetables with High Water Content

PROS: Oranges, watermelon, grapes, cucumbers, celery, and many other fruits and vegetables are bursting with fluids. (Oranges, for example, are 87 percent water.) Plus, most produce is packed with such vital nutrients as fiber, folate, magnesium, potassium, and vitamin C.

CONS: Eating may be impractical or inconvenient during heavy exercise. Normal portions of fruits and veggies don't always provide enough fluid. On average, whole foods like these work best as a supplement to water or a sports drink.

TIME to THINK... About Drinks with Caffeine

Imagine that you're the coach of your school soccer team. The team members ask if they can each have a caffeinated cola drink at half time. What three reasons can you give them for saying they should drink water instead? (*Hint:* Research the effects of caffeine on the body and dehydration.)

Health Skills Application

1. **Goal Setting.** Examine the effects and benefits of physical activity for coping with stress and helping reduce the risk of developing certain digestive disorders. Use the steps of goal setting to develop a plan to incorporate 30 minutes of physical activity into each day. Make a table to help you organize your time to fit the activity into your day. *(LESSON 1)*

2. **Communicating.** You are worried about a close family member who appears to be using food as a coping mechanism for dealing with his or her emotions. Write a dialogue that includes how you could encourage this person to use more positive health behaviors to manage his or her emotions. Use "I" messages and active listening techniques in your dialogue. *(LESSON 2)*

3. **Accessing Information.** Research more about the elimination of waste products from the body. Identify the different types of wastes and which organs and body functions are responsible for eliminating each type. Make a poster that shows the results of your research. *(LESSON 3)*

 CAREER Corner

Urologist

A urologist is a doctor who specializes in treating diseases of the urinary tract. About 99,000 Americans die every year from causes related to kidney failure. This number is expected to grow in the near future as the American population ages. In order to meet this demand for medical services, more young people will be needed to pursue careers in this special field.

To become a urologist, you'll need a four-year college degree followed by five years of medical school. You can find out more about this and other health careers by clicking on Career Corner at **health.glencoe.com**.

 BEYOND the Classroom

Parent Involvement

Advocacy. With a parent, learn more about the services available in your community for patients suffering from digestive or urinary problems. Are there groups for people with colitis or irritable bowel syndrome, for example? Where do patients receive dialysis? Investigate programs that raise awareness of these services, and ask how you and your parents can participate.

School and Community

Tooth Care. Contact a dentist, and ask him or her to talk to your class about oral health. Ask the dentist to describe the specific role of teeth in digestion and how different teeth are shaped to carry out different functions.

After You Read

Use your Foldable to review chapter material by recalling what you have learned and then checking your knowledge by reviewing your notes under the tabs.

FOLDABLES™
Study Organizer

► **EXPLORING HEALTH TERMS** *Answer the following questions on a sheet of paper.*

Lesson 1 *Replace the underlined words with the correct term.*

absorption	bile
chyme	digestion
elimination	gastric juices
peristalsis	mastication

1. The mechanical and chemical breakdown of foods for use by the body's cells is <u>peristalsis</u>.

2. The process of <u>elimination</u> is the passage of food from the digestive tract into the cardiovascular and lymphatic systems.

3. <u>Chyme</u> is a yellow-green, bitter fluid important in the breakdown and absorption of fats.

4. <u>Digestion</u> is the expulsion of undigested food or body wastes.

Lesson 2 *Match each definition with the correct term.*

appendicitis	indigestion
heartburn	peptic ulcer
hiatal hernia	

5. A burning sensation in the center of the chest that may rise from the bottom, or tip, of the breastbone up to the throat.

6. A condition in which part of the stomach pushes through an opening in the diaphragm.

7. An inflammation of the appendix.

8. A sore in the lining of the digestive tract.

Lesson 3 *Fill in the blanks with the correct term.*

cystitis	urethra
hemodialysis	urethritis
nephrons	bladder
urine	ureters

(_9_) are the functional units of the kidneys. The (_10_) produced in the kidneys is carried to the (_11_), where it is stored until it exits the body through the (_12_).

► **RECALLING THE FACTS** *Use complete sentences to answer the following questions.*

1. Where does the process of digestion begin, and which digestive juice is involved?

2. Define the term *chyme*. In which part of the digestive process is it formed?

3. What is the purpose of villi?

4. What is the main function of the large intestine?

5. What is constipation? What causes it?

6. What are some problems that can be caused by overusing laxatives?

7. How do gastritis and a peptic ulcer differ?

8. Explain the causes and risks of cirrhosis of the liver.

9. Define the term *urine*. What are the main components of urine?

10. What is the function of the bladder?

11. Compare and contrast cystitis and urethritis.

12. Describe the two types of dialysis available for patients with chronic kidney failure.

For more review questions for Chapter 17, go to **health.glencoe.com**.

➤ WRITING CRITICALLY

1. Expository. Write a public service announcement describing how stress can affect digestion. Provide advice about what to do to avoid stress-related digestive problems and what to do if they should occur.

2. Descriptive. Write a one-page summary of why it is important to drink about 6 to 8 cups of water per day. Include information on how water helps the urinary system, including the kidneys, and other benefits of drinking water.

Standardized Test Practice

 Read the paragraph below and then answer the questions.

Liquids Fight Flu Symptoms

(1) Have you ever heard of the influenza epidemic of 1918–1919? (2) Many people died worldwide. (3) In the United States, nearly 800,000 people died. (4) That's more than the number of Americans who died in World War I, World War II, Korea, and Vietnam combined. (5) Influenza viruses still exist. (6) Why doesn't the flu kill as many people today?

(7) People in the health-care industry today know that they need to tell flu patients some things about how to feel better. (8) One of the most important treatments is simple — liquids. (9) People with the flu should drink lots of water, juice, and clear soups.

1. Which sentence below should be added after sentence (5) to support the ideas in the first paragraph?

A Sick people should not drink liquids.
B Washing your hands often is important.
C Even young kids can learn to wash their hands.
D You've probably had the flu yourself.

2. Which revision of sentence 7 is the most coherent and focused?

F Doctors and nurses need to know how to talk to sick people.
G Follow these logical and new rules of flu treatment to be safe.
H Health-care professionals understand better how to treat the flu.
I To keep you safe from catching the flu, follow simple, new steps.

3. Create a multimedia poster that uses familiar children's book characters, words, and pictures to teach young flu patients to drink lots of liquids.

CHAPTER 18

Endocrine and Reproductive Systems

Eye ON THE Media

Gender Representation in the Media

Is there gender bias in news coverage? Are women reporters seen as frequently on the news as men? Gender biases in the media may be reflected in

▶ television news reporting.

▶ magazine writing.

▶ newspaper writing.

Visit the Eye on the Media section at **health.glencoe.com** to learn more about gender bias in your city's media.

FOLDABLES™
Study Organizer

Before You Read

Make this Foldable to help you organize your notes on the structure and function of the endocrine system. Begin with a sheet of **11″ x 17″** paper.

▶ **Step 1**

Fold a sheet of paper into thirds.

▶ **Step 2**

Fold the bottom edge up **2** inches and crease.

Endocrine System

Structure	Function	Problems

▶ **Step 3**

Glue the outer edges of the fold to create three pockets. Label as shown. Place **3″ x 5″** notecards or pieces of paper in the pockets.

As You Read

As you read and discuss the material in the chapter, use notecards to record and define terms, draw diagrams, list main ideas and supporting facts, and give examples of how you might use what you've learned in your daily life. Place the notecards in the appropriate pocket in your Foldable.

SPOTLIGHT ON HEALTH

Using Visuals. Many hormonal changes take place during the teen years. How are the endocrine and the reproductive systems related?

The Endocrine System

Guide to Reading

Building Vocabulary

As you read this lesson, write each new highlighted term and its definition in your notebook.

▶ endocrine glands (p. 464)

▶ hormones (p. 464)

▶ thyroid gland (p. 465)

▶ parathyroid glands (p. 465)

▶ pancreas (p. 465)

▶ pituitary gland (p. 465)

▶ gonads (p. 466)

▶ adrenal glands (p. 466)

Focusing on the Main Ideas

In this lesson, you will learn how to:

▶ Describe the glands of the endocrine system and the function of each.

▶ Examine the effects of health behaviors on the endocrine system.

Quick Write

The endocrine system causes bodies to change during adolescence. Write a short paragraph describing why it is especially important to eat nutritious foods during the teen years.

Reading Strategy

Organize Information

▶ Make a two-column chart. On the left side of the chart, list facts about the structure of the endocrine system, including the function of the glands. On the right side of the chart, list facts about the problems of the endocrine system.

▼ When the brain recognizes a stressful situation, the endocrine system reacts by releasing the hormone adrenaline. *How do these changes help prepare the body to react under stress?*

All the cells in your body respond to messages sent by three of your major body systems—the nervous system, the immune system, and the endocrine system. These three systems work closely together to coordinate the functions of the body. The endocrine system is especially important during the teen years because one of its main functions is to regulate growth and development. Health-literate individuals can analyze and describe the relationship between the glands and hormones that control the secondary sex characteristics.

Structure of the Endocrine System

Endocrine glands are *ductless—or tubeless—organs or groups of cells that secrete hormones directly into the bloodstream.* **Hormones** are *chemical substances that are produced in glands and help regulate many of your body's functions.* Hormones are secreted by the endocrine glands and then carried to their destinations in the body by the blood. These chemical messengers influence physical and mental responses. Hormones produced during puberty trigger physical changes in the body. **Figure 18.1** describes the major glands of the endocrine system and the body functions they regulate.

FIGURE 18.1

THE ENDOCRINE SYSTEM

The glands of the endocrine system are located throughout the body. Each gland has at least one particular function.

Thyroid The **thyroid gland** *produces hormones that regulate metabolism, body heat, and bone growth.* The thyroid produces thyroxine, which regulates the way cells release energy from nutrients.

Parathyroid Glands The **parathyroid glands** *produce a hormone that regulates the body's calcium and phosphorus balance.*

Testes The testes are the male reproductive glands.

Ovaries The ovaries are the female reproductive glands.

Besides playing a role in reproduction (as described in Lessons 2 and 3), the testes and ovaries control the development of secondary sex characteristics during puberty.

Hypothalamus The hypothalamus links the endocrine system with the nervous system and stimulates the pituitary gland to secrete hormones.

Pineal Gland This gland secretes melatonin, which regulates sleep cycles and is thought to affect the onset of puberty.

Pituitary Gland The pituitary regulates and controls activities of other endocrine glands.

Thymus Gland The thymus regulates development of the immune system.

Adrenal Glands These glands produce hormones that regulate the body's salt and water balance. Secretions from the adrenal cortex and the adrenal medulla control the body's emergency response.

Pancreas The **pancreas** is *a gland that serves both the digestive and the endocrine systems.* As an endocrine gland, the pancreas secretes two hormones that regulate the level of glucose in the blood—glucagon and insulin.

Pituitary Gland

The **pituitary gland** *regulates and controls the activities of all of the other endocrine glands.* The pituitary is known as the master gland. It has three sections, or lobes—anterior, intermediate, and posterior.

▶ **Anterior lobe.** The anterior, or front, lobe of the pituitary gland produces six hormones. Somatotropic, or growth, hormone stimulates normal body growth and development by altering chemical activity in body cells. Thyroid-stimulating hormone (TSH) stimulates the thyroid gland to produce hormones. Adrenocorticotropic (uh-DREE-noh-kawr-ti-koh-TROH-pik) hormone (ACTH) stimulates production of hormones in the adrenal glands.

Reading Check

Analyze What are the functions of the thyroid gland and the parathyroid gland (Figure 18.1)?

Two hormones that stimulate production of all other sex hormones are secreted by the pituitary's anterior lobe during adolescence. Follicle-stimulating hormone (FSH) and luteinizing hormone (LH) control the growth, development, and functions of the **gonads**, another name for *the ovaries and testes.*

- In females FSH stimulates cells in the ovaries to produce estrogen, a female sex hormone that triggers the development of ova. LH is responsible for ovulation and stimulates ovarian cells to produce progesterone. The hormone prolactin stimulates milk production in females who have given birth.

- In males LH stimulates cells in the testes to produce the male hormone testosterone. FSH controls the production of sperm.

▶ **Intermediate lobe.** The intermediate, or middle, lobe of the pituitary secretes melanocyte-stimulating hormone (MSH), which controls the darkening of the skin by stimulating skin pigments.

▶ **Posterior lobe.** The posterior, or rear, lobe of the pituitary gland secretes antidiuretic hormone (ADH), which regulates the balance of water in the body. ADH also produces oxytocin, which stimulates uterine contractions during the birth of a baby.

Adrenal Glands

The **adrenal glands** are *glands that help the body recover from stress and respond to emergencies.* They each have two parts.

▶ The **adrenal cortex** secretes a hormone that inhibits the amount of sodium excreted in urine and serves to maintain blood volume and pressure. It also secretes hormones that aid the metabolism of fats, proteins, and carbohydrates. These hormones play a role in immunity and the body's response to stress.

▶ The **adrenal medulla** is controlled by the hypothalamus and the autonomic nervous system. It secretes the hormones epinephrine (also called adrenaline) and norepinephrine. Epinephrine increases heartbeat and respiration, raises blood pressure, and suppresses the digestive process during periods of high emotion.

Problems of the Endocrine System

Factors such as stress, infection, and changes in the balance of fluid and minerals in the blood can cause hormone levels to vary. Often these situations will correct themselves. More serious problems, including those described here, may require medication.

▶ **Diabetes mellitus** is a disorder in which the pancreas produces too little or no insulin, resulting in high blood glucose levels. Symptoms include fatigue, weight loss, thirst, and frequent urination.

Hormones produced by the pituitary gland play a role in determining height.
Appraise the significance of other body changes occurring during adolescence.

Reading Check

Apply How can you keep your endocrine system functioning at peak performance?

▶ **Graves' disease,** also called *hyperthyroidism,* is a disorder in which an overactive and enlarged thyroid gland produces excessive amounts of thyroxine. Symptoms include nervousness, weight loss, increased thirst, rapid heartbeat, and intolerance for heat. Low thyroxine production, called *hypothyroidism,* causes fatigue, dry skin, weight gain, constipation, and sensitivity to cold.

▶ **Cushing's disease** results from the overproduction of adrenal hormones. Symptoms include round face, humped upper back, thin and easily bruised skin, and fragile bones.

▶ **Goiter,** an enlargement of the thyroid gland, is caused mainly by a lack of iodine in the diet. Since the introduction of iodized salt, goiters have become rare in the United States.

▶ **Growth disorders** are caused by abnormal amounts of growth hormone. With early diagnosis and proper treatment, a child with a growth disorder can reach a normal height.

Care of the Endocrine System

To keep your endocrine system functioning at peak performance, take care of all of your body systems. Eat nutritious meals, get enough sleep, and avoid stress. A health care professional can perform medical tests to determine whether your endocrine function is normal.

Staying physically active is one way to reduce stress and to keep your endocrine system healthy. *What other healthful behaviors help ensure the health of this system?*

LESSON | **1** **REVIEW**

Reviewing Facts and Vocabulary

1. What is an *endocrine gland*?
2. What are the two parts of the adrenal glands, and what do they do?
3. What are the functions of FSH and LH?

Thinking Critically

4. **Evaluating.** Do you agree with the statement that the pituitary gland is the "master gland"? Explain your reasoning.
5. **Analyzing.** Which endocrine glands become more active during puberty? Name the hormones these glands produce, and appraise the significance of changes occurring during adolescence that they cause.

Applying Health Skills

Self Management. On a sheet of paper, write the names of two endocrine glands. List one important function of each gland. Then write a statement examining the effects of health behaviors on the endocrine system.

▬▬▬ **After You Read** ▬▬▬

Cause and Effect. Create a two-column chart. In one column, list the problems that may affect the endocrine system. In the second column, list some of the symptoms of that disorder.

 Visit **health.glencoe.com** for the Interactive Study Guide for Lesson 1.

The Male Reproductive System

Guide to Reading

Building Vocabulary

As you read this lesson, write each new highlighted term and its definition in your notebook.

▶ reproductive system (p. 468)

▶ sperm (p. 468)

▶ testosterone (p. 469)

▶ testes (p. 469)

▶ scrotum (p. 469)

▶ penis (p. 469)

▶ semen (p. 469)

▶ sterility (p. 472)

Focusing on the Main Ideas

In this lesson, you will learn how to:

▶ **Describe** the parts and functions of the male reproductive system.

▶ **Examine** care of the male reproductive system and identify situations requiring professional health services.

▶ **Describe** abstinence as it relates to the prevention of STDs.

Reading Strategy

Organize Information

▶ Create a chart with four boxes. In the top left box, list the functions of the male reproduction system. In the top right box, list the structure of the system. In the lower boxes, list ways to care for the system on the left and problems of the system on the right.

Quick Write

Write a short paragraph explaining what changes occur when the male reproductive system matures.

▶ There are 300 million to 400 million sperm in each ejaculation, but only one can fertilize an ovum.
What is the relationship of testosterone to sperm?

An essential function of all living things is reproduction, the process by which life continues from one generation to the next. In humans, as in many other animal species, reproduction results from the union of two specialized sex cells—one from the male and one from the female. These cells are made by the **reproductive system**, *the system of organs involved in producing offspring.*

Structure and Function of the Male Reproductive System

The male reproductive system includes both external and internal organs. The two main functions of the male reproductive system are the production and storage of **sperm**, *the male reproductive cells*, and the transfer of sperm to the female's body during sexual intercourse. During the early teen years, usually between the ages of 12 and 15, the male reproductive system reaches maturity. At that time hormones produced in the pituitary gland stimulate the production of **testosterone**, *the male sex hormone*. Testosterone initiates physical changes that signal maturity, including broadening of the shoulders, development of muscles and facial and other body hair, and deepening of the voice. Testosterone also controls the production of sperm. A physically mature male is capable of producing sperm for the rest of his life. Health-literate teens can describe gender differences, expectations, and biases. At this time in a teen's life, it is important to learn to identify ways of resisting persuasive tactics regarding sexual involvement.

External Male Reproductive Organs

The testes, the penis, and the scrotum are external structures involved in the process of reproduction. The **testes** (singular, *testis*), also called testicles, are *two small glands that produce sperm*. These glands secrete testosterone. The testes are located in the **scrotum**, *an external skin sac*. The **penis** is *a tube-shaped organ that extends from the trunk of the body just above the testes*. It is composed of spongy tissue that contains many blood vessels. When blood flow to the penis increases, it becomes enlarged and erect. This normal body function is called an *erection*. Males experience erections easily and frequently during puberty. Erections can occur for no reason. Sometimes an erection results when clothing the male is wearing causes friction.

The penis releases semen. **Semen** is *a thick fluid containing sperm and other secretions from the male reproductive system*. At the height of sexual arousal, a series of muscular contractions known as *ejaculation* may occur. **Fertilization**—the joining of a male sperm cell and a female egg cell—can result if ejaculation occurs during sexual intercourse.

Sperm cannot live in temperatures higher than the normal body temperature of 98.6°F. The scrotum protects sperm by keeping the testes slightly below the normal body temperature. When body temperature rises, muscles attached to the scrotum relax, causing the testes to lower away from the body. If body temperature lowers, the muscles tighten and the testes move closer to the body for warmth. Tight clothing that holds the testes too close to the body may interfere with sperm production.

When a male begins to produce sperm, he may experience nocturnal emissions, or ejaculations that occur when sperm is released during sleep. This is a normal function that relieves the buildup of pressure as sperm begin to be produced during puberty.

During puberty, teens should assess their lifelong health and other goals, and set personal goals for maintaining a healthy body.

▼ Development of facial hair is one of the changes that occur during a male's early teens. Another change is the ability to produce sperm. *Which hormone stimulates physical changes in a maturing male?*

Reading Check

Cause and Effect What physical changes are the result of the male sex hormone testosterone?

CHARACTER CHECK

Responsibility. Here are some ways a teen can show that he or she is mature and responsible.
- Demonstrate respect for yourself and others.
- Control sexual urges, and never impose them on others.
- Practice abstinence from sexual activity before marriage.

Internal Male Reproductive Organs

Although sperm are produced in the testes, which are suspended outside the body, they must travel through several structures inside the body before they are released. These structures include the vas deferens, the urethra, the seminal vesicles, the prostate gland, and Cowper's glands. **Figure 18.2** shows the path taken by sperm cells from the testes until they are released from the body.

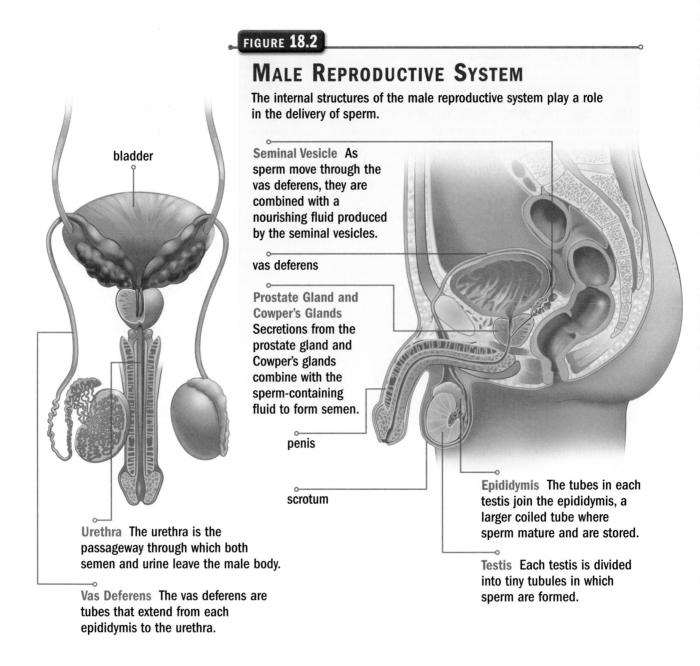

FIGURE **18.2**

MALE REPRODUCTIVE SYSTEM

The internal structures of the male reproductive system play a role in the delivery of sperm.

bladder

Seminal Vesicle As sperm move through the vas deferens, they are combined with a nourishing fluid produced by the seminal vesicles.

vas deferens

Prostate Gland and Cowper's Glands Secretions from the prostate gland and Cowper's glands combine with the sperm-containing fluid to form semen.

penis

scrotum

Epididymis The tubes in each testis join the epididymis, a larger coiled tube where sperm mature and are stored.

Testis Each testis is divided into tiny tubules in which sperm are formed.

Urethra The urethra is the passageway through which both semen and urine leave the male body.

Vas Deferens The vas deferens are tubes that extend from each epididymis to the urethra.

Hands-On Health ACTIVITY

Monthly TSE Reminder Card

It's important for males to do a testicular self-exam (TSE) every month. However, not all males are accustomed to performing it. In this activity you will create a reminder card for yourself or the males in your family.

What You'll Need

- paper
- colored pens
- lamination supplies (optional)

What You'll Do

1. Cut the paper into a wallet-sized card.
2. On one side of the card, write out the steps in performing a TSE (see page 472).
3. On the other side of the card, create a message that will remind and persuade you or males in your family to do a monthly exam. The exam could be scheduled for the same time each month, such as the first day of every month.
4. Laminate the card so that it will last.

Apply and Conclude

Keep the reminder card in a location where you (or males in your family) will see it often. Because the best time to examine yourself is after a warm bath or shower, consider placing the card in the bathroom. Explain the importance of taking responsibility for regularly performing a TSE.

Care of the Male Reproductive System

Caring for the male reproductive system involves medical checkups, hygiene, protection, and self-examination. A health-literate individual knows strategies for health enhancement and risk reduction.

▶ **Get regular checkups.** Have regular checkups by a physician every 12 to 18 months.

▶ **Bathe regularly.** Bathe daily, thoroughly cleansing the penis and scrotum.

▶ **Wear protective equipment.** Use a protective cup or supporter during physical activities to shield external organs.

▶ **Perform regular self-examinations.** Check the scrotum and testicles for signs of cancer. Report any change to a physician.

▶ **Practice abstinence.** Abstain from sexual activity before marriage to avoid contracting **STDs.**

Reading Check

Classify What are some of the STDs that affect the male reproductive system?

Sexually Transmitted Diseases (STDs)

The primary means of transmission of all STDs is sexual activity. An individual who practices abstinence before marriage understands the role of individual responsibility regarding personal risk behaviors and how abstinence from sexual activity prevents STDs. One of the important benefits of abstinence is the prevention of these STDs:

▶ **Chlamydia** and **gonorrhea** are bacterial infections that cause discharge from the penis and burning upon urination; both conditions can damage reproductive health. Treatment includes a course of antibiotics.

▶ **Syphilis** is another bacterial infection. Initially, a painless, reddish sore appears at the site of infection. If left untreated, syphilis can spread and damage internal organs. It is treated with antibiotics.

▶ **Genital herpes** is a virus that causes blisterlike sores in the genital area. Medication relieves symptoms, but the virus remains in the body for life.

Problems of the Male Reproductive System

The organs of the male reproductive system can be affected by functional and structural problems, as well as STDs. These situations require professional health services.

Inguinal Hernia

An inguinal (IN-gwuh-nuhl) hernia is a separation of tissue that allows part of the intestine to push into the abdominal wall near the top of the scrotum. Straining the abdominal muscles or lifting heavy objects can cause a tear in this tissue. Symptoms of inguinal hernia may include a lump in the groin near the thigh, pain in the groin, or in severe cases, partial or complete blockage of the intestine. Surgery is usually necessary to repair the opening in the muscle wall.

Sterility

Sterility is *the inability to reproduce.* In males it can result from too few sperm or sperm of poor quality. Sterility can result from environmental hazards, including exposure to X rays and other radiation, toxic chemicals, and lead. Hormonal imbalance, certain medications, and use of drugs, including anabolic **steroids,** can damage sperm. Some diseases, including STDs, and mumps contracted as an adult also can result in sterility.

Testicular Cancer and Problems of the Prostate

Testicular cancer can affect males of any age but occurs most often in males between the ages of 14 and 40. These factors increase the risk of developing the disease: undescended testicle, abnormal testicular development, and family history of testicular cancer. A monthly testicular self-exam is recommended by the American Cancer Society. Males should be prompted to seek health care if they notice any warning signs, such as a painless lump or swelling in either testicle or pain or discomfort in a testicle or in the scrotum. With early detection most testicular cancer is treatable through surgery, radiation therapy, or chemotherapy.

The prostate gland can become enlarged as a result of an infection, a tumor, and age-related problems. An enlarged gland presses against the urethra, resulting in frequent or difficult urination. Symptoms may also indicate more serious conditions, including prostate cancer. Prostate cancer screening is usually done during routine physical exams for males over age 50. Early detection increases the chance of survival. Treatment includes surgery, radiation, and hormone therapy.

National and world champion cyclist Lance Armstrong is a survivor of testicular cancer.

Why are testicular self-exams important for male reproductive health?

LESSON 2 REVIEW

Reviewing Facts and Vocabulary

1. What is the function of the testes?

2. Describe the path that sperm follow from the time they form until they leave the body.

3. What are the symptoms of testicular cancer? Identify situations requiring professional health services for preventive care.

Thinking Critically

4. **Analyzing.** Why would knowing the correct way to lift a heavy object be an important behavior to protect the health of the male reproductive system?

5. **Synthesizing.** Analyze the importance and benefits of abstinence as it relates to the prevention of STDs. How can problems related to STDs affect the male reproductive system?

Applying Health Skills

Practicing Healthful Behaviors. Analyze the relationship between unsafe behaviors related to drug use and the harmful effects of these substances on the male reproductive system. Write a paragraph stating how avoiding drugs, including steroids, can ensure the health of your reproductive system.

After You Read

Identify Problems and Solutions. List at least three problems that may affect the male reproductive system. After each problem, list some of the symptoms.

 Visit **health.glencoe.com** for the Interactive Study Guide for Lesson 2.

The Female Reproductive System

Guide to Reading

Building Vocabulary

As you read this lesson, write each new highlighted term and its definition in your notebook.

▶ ova (p. 474)

▶ uterus (p. 474)

▶ ovaries (p. 474)

▶ ovulation (p. 474)

▶ fallopian tube (p. 475)

▶ vagina (p. 475)

▶ cervix (p. 476)

▶ menstruation (p. 476)

Focusing on the Main Ideas

In this lesson, you will learn how to:

▶ Describe the parts and functions of the female reproductive system.

▶ Examine the care of the female reproduction system and identify situations requiring professional health services.

▶ Explain the importance of abstinence as it relates to the prevention of STDs.

Reading Strategy

Organize Information

▶ Make a three-column chart. In the first column, list facts about the structure and function of the female reproductive system. In the second column, list facts about the care of the system. In the third column, list facts about the problems of the system.

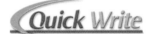 Quick Write

Write a short paragraph explaining how the endocrine and reproductive systems relate to one another.

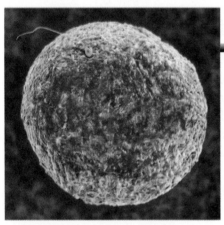

The female reproductive system stores ova that unite with sperm in the process of reproduction. *Name another function of the female reproductive system.*

The female reproductive system has several functions. It produces female sex hormones and stores *female reproductive cells,* called **ova** (singular, *ovum*). The **uterus**, *a hollow, muscular, pear-shaped organ inside a female's body,* nourishes and protects the fertilized ovum from conception until birth.

Structure and Function of the Female Reproductive System

The female reproductive system includes several organs and glands. **Ovaries** are *the female sex glands that store the ova and produce female sex hormones*. At birth a female's ovaries contain more than 400,000 immature ova, or eggs. One ovum matures each month, beginning at puberty when the pituitary gland produces hormones. **Ovulation** is *the process of releasing a mature ovum into the fallopian tube each month*. The right ovary will release a mature ovum one month, and the left ovary will release one the next month.

Female Reproductive Organs

Figure 18.3 shows the structures of the female reproductive system. Notice the tube that lies next to each ovary. When a mature ovum is released from the ovary, it moves to one of the **fallopian tubes**, *a pair of tubes with fingerlike projections that draw in the ovum.*

Tiny hairlike structures called cilia work, along with muscular contractions in the fallopian tubes, to move the ovum along. Sperm from the male enter the female reproductive system through the **vagina**, *a muscular, elastic passageway that extends from the uterus to the outside of the body.*

If sperm are present in the fallopian tubes, a sperm cell may unite with an ovum, resulting in fertilization. The fertilization of an egg by a sperm produces a cell called a *zygote*. When the zygote leaves the fallopian tube, it enters the uterus. There, the zygote attaches itself to the uterine wall and begins to grow. In preparation for receiving the zygote, the uterine wall has thickened and is rich in blood, which enables the uterus to nourish the zygote. The developing fetus will remain attached to the uterine wall until **birth.**

FIGURE 18.3

FEMALE REPRODUCTIVE SYSTEM

The female reproductive system produces sex cells called ova and provides a place for a fertilized ovum to grow.

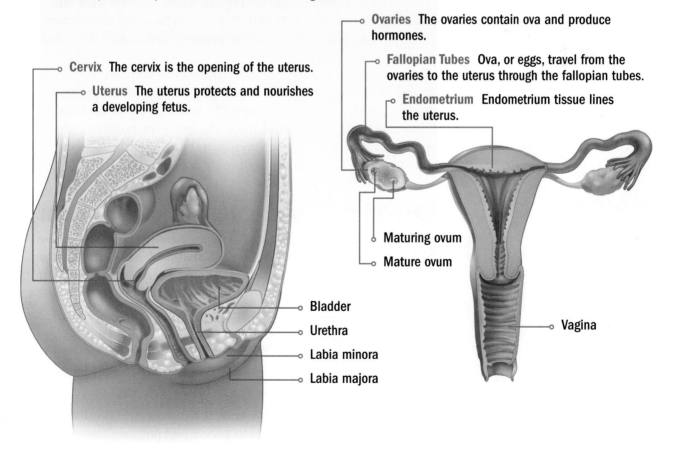

Ovaries The ovaries contain ova and produce hormones.

Fallopian Tubes Ova, or eggs, travel from the ovaries to the uterus through the fallopian tubes.

Endometrium Endometrium tissue lines the uterus.

Cervix The cervix is the opening of the uterus.

Uterus The uterus protects and nourishes a developing fetus.

Maturing ovum

Mature ovum

Bladder

Urethra

Labia minora

Labia majora

Vagina

FIGURE 18.4

THE MENSTRUAL CYCLE

Days 1–8	Days 9–23	Day 24	Days 25–28
After seven days, if the egg is not fertilized, menstruation begins.	A new egg is maturing inside the ovary.	The mature egg is released into one of the fallopian tubes.	The egg travels through the fallopian tube to the uterus.

Menstruation

In a mature female, each month the uterus prepares for possible pregnancy. If pregnancy doesn't occur, the thickened lining of the uterus, called the *endometrium,* isn't needed, and it breaks down into blood, tissue, and fluids. These materials pass through the **cervix**, *the opening to the uterus,* and into the vagina. This *shedding of the uterine lining* is called **menstruation** and is part of the menstrual cycle, which is summarized in **Figure 18.4.** Females wear either sanitary pads or tampons to absorb the blood flow. The start of menstruation, which typically lasts five to seven days, marks the beginning of the menstrual cycle.

Most females begin their first menstrual cycle between the ages of 10 and 15. The cycle may be irregular at first. As a female grows and matures, her menstrual cycle usually becomes more predictable. Endocrine hormones control the cycle, but poor nutrition, stress, and illness can influence it. Excessive exercise, which is associated with anorexia, may also disrupt the menstrual cycle.

Ⓨ **Eating nutritious foods and avoiding caffeine can often reduce discomfort related to menstruation.**
What other health behaviors will keep your reproductive system healthy?

Care of the Female Reproductive System

Good hygiene is important for maintaining the health of the female reproductive system. In a mature female, cells in the lining of the vagina are constantly being shed, causing a slight vaginal discharge. Cleanliness will help eliminate odors.

▶ **Bathe regularly.** It is especially important to shower or bathe daily during the menstrual period. During menstruation, change tampons or sanitary pads every few hours. Feminine deodorant sprays and douches are not necessary and may cause irritation or infection in the sensitive tissues around the vagina.

▶ **Practice abstinence from sexual activity.** This is is the only 100 percent effective method in preventing pregnancy and STDs.

BREAST SELF-EXAM

Breast cancer is the most common cancer and the second leading cause of death, after lung cancer, for women in the United States. The American Cancer Society recommends that females examine their breasts once a month, right after the menstrual period, when breasts are not tender or swollen. Early detection is an important factor in the successful treatment of breast cancer.

▶ Lie down and place a pillow under the right shoulder. Place the right arm behind the head. Use the fingers of the left hand to feel for lumps or thickening in the right breast. Move around the breast first in a circle, then up and down, and be sure to go over the entire breast area. Repeat the procedure the same way each month. Examine the left breast with the right hand.

▶ Repeat the examination of both breasts while standing, with one arm behind the head. In the upright position, check the upper and outer parts of the breasts, toward the armpit. Standing in front of a mirror, inspect the breasts for any dimpling of the skin, changes in the nipple, redness, or swelling.

Problems of the Female Reproductive System

Several disorders can affect the female reproductive system. Problems related to menstruation can range from minor discomfort to life-threatening illness.

▶ **Menstrual cramps** sometimes occur at the beginning of a menstrual period. Light exercise or applying a heating pad to the abdominal area may help relieve symptoms. A health care professional may recommend medication for pain relief. Severe or persistent cramping, called dysmenorrhea, may be an indication that professional health services are required.

▶ **Premenstrual syndrome (PMS)** is a disorder caused by hormonal changes. Its symptoms, which may be experienced one to two weeks before menstruation, include nervous tension, anxiety, irritability, bloating, weight gain, depression, mood swings, and fatigue. Regular physical activity and good nutrition may reduce the severity of symptoms.

▶ **Toxic shock syndrome (TSS)** is a rare but serious bacterial infection that affects the immune system and the liver, and can be fatal. To reduce the risk of TSS, use tampons with the lowest possible absorbency and change tampons often. Warning signs of TSS include fever, vomiting, diarrhea, a sunburnlike rash, red eyes, dizziness, and muscle aches. Any female with these symptoms should seek health care immediately.

Reading Check

Identify What are the stages of the menstrual cycle (Figure 18.4)?

Did You Know ?

The American Cancer Society recommends that females have pelvic exams by age 18 or when recommended by their physician. A pelvic exam is not painful.

• During a pelvic exam, a health care professional checks the shape, size, and position of pelvic organs and checks for any tumors or cysts.

• An examination of cells collected from the cervix, called a *Pap test*, can detect early changes in cells that may indicate a risk of cervical cancer.

• The health care professional also may test for certain sexually transmitted diseases.

Health Skills Activity

Communication: Asking Difficult Questions

"Hello, Brooke," says Dr. Morgan. "How are you? I see we're doing a basic summer camp physical."

Brooke smiles and nods. She has been coming to Dr. Morgan for years and feels comfortable with her.

"Before we begin," Dr. Morgan continues, "do you have any questions for me? Everything okay?"

"Well," Brooke begins, "about a week before my period, I get depressed. It seems much worse than the everyday blues. Once my period starts, I'm okay."

"It's important to ask about your concerns," Dr. Morgan replies. "Many girls and women feel a little blue before their periods, but if your depression is severe, there are treatments we can try. Let's talk more about your symptoms."

What Would You Do?
How would you bring up a reproductive health topic with your parents or guardian or a health care professional? Use the following guidelines for effective communication to help you develop a dialogue.

1. Use "I" messages.
2. Speak in a respectful tone.
3. Make eye contact.
4. Show appropriate body language.
5. Express clear, organized ideas.

Problems Related to Infertility

Infertility, the inability to conceive a child, can have several causes.

► **Endometriosis.** This painful, chronic disease occurs when tissue that lines the uterus migrates and grows in the ovaries, fallopian tubes, the uterus, or the lining of the pelvic cavity.

► **Pelvic inflammatory disease (PID).** PID is an infection of the fallopian tubes, ovaries, and the surrounding areas of the pelvis. It can damage a female's reproductive organs. PID usually is caused by **sexually transmitted diseases (STDs).**

► **Sexually transmitted diseases** are the most common causes of infertility and other disorders of the reproductive system. Often symptoms of STDs are not evident in females unless a medical examination is performed. Avoiding sexual contact until marriage shows you understand the role of individual responsibility regarding personal risk behaviors.

Reading Check

Describe What are the most common causes of infertility and other disorders of the reproductive system?

Other Female Reproductive Disorders

Other reproductive disorders include the following:

▶ **Vaginitis,** caused by bacterial vaginosis, is the most common vaginal infection in women of childbearing age, and it is often accompanied by discharge, odor, pain, itching, or burning. If not treated with antibiotics, vaginitis can sometimes lead to PID.

▶ **Blocked fallopian tubes,** the leading cause of infertility, may result from PID, abdominal surgery, STDs, or endometriosis.

▶ **Ovarian cysts** are fluid-filled sacs on the ovary. Small, noncancerous cysts usually disappear on their own. Larger cysts may require surgery.

▶ **Cervical, uterine, and ovarian cancer** occur in the female reproductive system. Early sexual activity and STDs such as human papillomavirus (HPV) are related to an increased incidence of cervical cancer. Regular checkups and pelvic exams are important for early detection and treatment.

LESSON 3 REVIEW

Reviewing Facts and Vocabulary

1. How do the structures in the fallopian tubes help move the ovum from the ovaries to the uterus?
2. Explain *ovulation*, *fertilization*, and *menstruation*.
3. List three causes of infertility in females.

Thinking Critically

4. **Synthesizing.** Analyze the importance of abstinence as it relates to the prevention of STDs. What behaviors can female teens practice to protect the health of their reproductive systems?

5. **Analyzing.** Relate the importance of early detection and warning signs for problems of the female reproductive system. Why is it important for every female to have regular pelvic exams starting at age 18 or when recommended by her physician?

Applying Health Skills

Advocacy. Make a card reminding yourself or the females in your family to perform a monthly breast self-exam. Provide step-by-step instructions. Add a catchy phrase that will remind users of the importance of early detection, and include warning signs that should prompt females to seek professional health services.

After You Read

Identify Problems and Solutions. List at least three problems that may affect the female reproductive system. After each problem, list some of the symptoms.

Visit **health.glencoe.com** for the Interactive Study Guide for Lesson 3.

Bodies on the Move

The teenage body is constantly changing. Just remember: It's all perfectly natural!

Hair Loss

If you notice that you're losing more hair than usual, don't panic. "People are constantly shedding hair, and you can lose a lot in a single day," says Dr. Patricia Simmons, M.D., a specialist in pediatric and adolescent medicine. She adds that it's normal to lose as many as 100 hairs a day. Boys generally have shorter hair, so the lost strands are less noticeable to them than to girls.

Stretch Marks

Have you spotted any little pinkish lines on your body? "These marks are usually a very normal part of your body's growth and change," says Dr. Simmons. For girls, stretch marks—which start out as raised red areas, become purple, and finally flatten and fade to shiny or barely visible thin streaks—usually appear on areas like the hips, thighs, or breasts. They are not as common for boys, but they occasionally turn up on the upper arms and the shoulders. There is no way to prevent or treat the marks (and you can forget about stretch-mark creams, which just just don't work). "Although they never completely go away, they do become far, far less obvious," assures Dr. Simmons.

Body Odor

"Another change that becomes apparent during the teen years is your body odor," says Dr. Simmons. "Hormones work on some of the cells that cause you to sweat, and they also stimulate some of the oil-producing cells. That combination leads to more intense body odor." Shower daily using any kind of soap to banish smelly sweat and bacteria. Just be sure to wash everywhere. Then apply an antiperspirant/deodorant to keep your underarms dry. ▄

TIME to THINK... About Changes During Adolescence

The article lists three changes a person might experience during puberty. Investigate what hormones are responsible for these changes. With a group, create a flow chart that details when and how one of these hormones is triggered, where it is produced, and how it causes the changes during adolescence.

1. **Practicing Healthful Behaviors.** Excessive weight has been shown to be a contributing factor for developing diabetes mellitus. Identify three things you can do each day to help maintain a healthy weight for life. *(LESSON 1)*

2. **Accessing Information.** Some athletes use anabolic-androgenic steroids—chemicals similar to testosterone—to increase muscle size and improve overall performance. Research and list the harmful effects of steroids on the body. Then create a visual presentation that informs others of the dangers of steroid use. *(LESSON 2)*

3. **Advocacy.** Annual Pap tests are important for all women over the age of 18. Relate the importance of early detection and warning signs that prompt females to seek health care. Prepare an informative, accurate, and persuasive pamphlet to encourage women to have an annual Pap test. *(LESSON 3)*

CAREER Corner

School Nurse

Are you caring and sympathetic, and are you concerned with the physical and mental/emotional needs of others? If so, a career as a school nurse may be right for you. School nurses perform screenings, provide emergency first aid, monitor state immunization laws, develop health-related curricula to meet the needs of students and teachers, and counsel students on personal health issues.

Nursing students need a strong background in science and mathematics. To become a registered nurse, a student must graduate from an accredited nursing school and pass a national licensing exam. For more information, click on **health.glencoe.com.**

BEYOND the Classroom

Parent Involvement

Advocacy. Share the information about breast and testicular self-exams with a parent. Work together to find a place to display the reminder cards you made. Then discuss with all family members the importance of these exams for early detection of cancers. In addition, discuss the warning signs that should prompt persons of any age to seek medical attention.

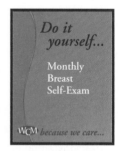

Do it yourself...

Monthly Breast Self-Exam

WCM *because we care...*

School and Community

School Health Services. Ask the school nurse to talk to your class about the importance of proper hygiene and care of the reproductive systems. Also, have the nurse describe the health services available through his or her office. How can students access these services? Which services require the approval of a parent?

After You Read

Use your Foldable notecards to review what you have learned about the endocrine system.

➤ **EXPLORING HEALTH TERMS** *Answer the following questions on a sheet of paper.*

Lesson 1 *Match each definition with the correct term.*

adrenal glands	pituitary gland
endocrine glands	parathyroid glands
hormones	thyroid gland
pancreas	gonads

1. The gland that regulates activities of all the other endocrine glands.

2. The gland that produces hormones that regulate metabolism and bone growth.

3. Glands that produce a hormone that regulates the body's calcium and phosphorus balance.

4. Glands that help the body recover from stress and respond to emergencies.

Lesson 2 *Identify each statement as True or False. If false, replace the underlined term with the correct term.*

penis	sperm
reproductive system	semen
scrotum	testes
sterility	testosterone

5. <u>Semen</u> is the male reproductive cell.

6. The testes are contained in the <u>penis</u>.

7. <u>Testosterone</u> is the male sex hormone.

Lesson 3 *Fill in the blanks with the correct term.*

cervix	ovulation
fallopian tubes	ovum
menstruation	uterus
ovaries	vagina

8. Ova mature in the _____ .

9. The _____ is a muscular, elastic passage-way that extends from the uterus to the outside of the body.

10. The hollow, pear-shaped organ inside a female's body where a fetus is nourished is the _____ .

➤ **RECALLING THE FACTS** *Use complete sentences to answer the following questions.*

1. What is the function of hormones?

2. Why are the ovaries and testes considered endocrine glands?

3. What is epinephrine, and what function does it have?

4. Why is a goiter an uncommon problem in the United States?

5. What are three physical changes initiated by testosterone in the male?

6. What are three ways to care for the male reproductive system?

7. What is an inguinal hernia?

8. Relate the importance of early detection and warning signs of prostate cancer that prompt males of all ages to seek health care.

For more review questions for Chapter 18, go to **health.glencoe.com**.

9. Name and describe the two processes that are part of the menstrual cycle.

10. How can menstrual cramps be relieved?

11. Relate the importance of early warning signs for seeking health care. Why should a female with symptoms of TSS contact a health care professional immediately?

12. Identify situations requiring professional health services for preventive care. What is PID, and what usually causes it?

► WRITING CRITICALLY

1. Personal. Write a one-page letter to yourself describing how puberty has affected you. Include information on how your body and emotions have changed and how you feel about yourself now that you're becoming an adult. Save the letter to read to yourself again when you're older.

2. Personal. Write a letter to your doctor or school nurse asking questions you might have about the structure and function of your reproductive system and how to care for your reproductive health.

Standardized Test Practice

MATH Read the paragraph below, examine the table, and then answer the questions.

The time between fertilization of an egg by a sperm and birth is a known as a *gestation period*. This amount of time varies from organism to organism. The table gives the average gestation periods (in days) for several different types of animals.

Animal	Gestation Period
Hamster	16.5 days
Ferret	42 days
Coyote	63 days
Lion	108 days
Human	267 days
Horse	337 days
Camel	406 days

1. What is the median of the gestation periods in the table?

Ⓐ 108 days

Ⓑ 177 days

Ⓒ 389.5 days

Ⓓ There is no median because all the numbers are different.

2. The actual gestation period can be stated as a range of days. For a human that range is from 250 to 285 days. If the value in the table is the average gestation period, the value is the

Ⓕ median.

Ⓖ mode.

Ⓗ mean.

Ⓘ first quartile.

3. Compare the size of each animal listed to its gestation period. Predict the relative gestation period of a rhinoceros. Explain your prediction.

Prenatal Development and Birth

Eye ON THE Media

Reading Programs for Children

Reading has many benefits for children. Being read to and learning to read helps children by

▶ **fostering the desire to read.**

▶ **teaching cooperation.**

▶ **developing listening skills.**

Visit the Eye on the Media section at **health.glencoe.com** to learn more about the importance of reading programs for children.

FOLDABLES™
Study Organizer

Before You Read

Make this Foldable to help you organize information on the beginning of life. Begin with a sheet of plain 8½" x 11" paper.

 Step 1

Fold a sheet of paper along the long axis, leaving a ½" tab along the bottom.

 Step 2

Fold in half, then fold again into fourths.

 Step 3

Unfold and cut along the three fold lines on the front flap. Label as shown.

Conception & Implantation | Embryonic Growth | Fetal Development | Labor

The Beginning of the Life Cycle

As You Read

As you read and discuss the material in the chapter, use your Foldable to take notes, define terms, sketch diagrams, and explain the early stages of the life cycle.

SPOTLIGHT ON HEALTH

Using Visuals. What steps can parents-to-be take to increase the chances of having a healthy baby?

485

The Beginning of the Life Cycle

Guide to Reading

Building Vocabulary

As you read this lesson, write each new highlighted term and its definition in your notebook.

► fertilization (p. 486)
► implantation (p. 486)
► embryo (p. 486)
► fetus (p. 486)
► amniotic sac (p. 487)
► umbilical cord (p. 487)
► placenta (p. 487)
► labor (p. 490)

Focusing on the Main Ideas

In this lesson, you will learn how to:

► Identify the stages of fetal development from conception through pregnancy and birth.
► Explain how a pregnant female transfers nutrients and other substances to her fetus.

Reading Strategy

Predict

► Scan the headings, subheadings, and photo captions. Write one paragraph describing what information you believe will be presented in this lesson.

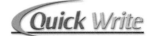
Quick Write

Write a short paragraph describing how important it is for mothers-to-be to eat a healthful diet.

This human egg cell is surrounded by sperm. Chemical changes take place in the egg's surface so that only one sperm can fertilize it.

Did you know that your body is made of trillions of cells? These cells form the tissues and organs in your body. Yet your heart, lungs, skin, bones, and other body organs all began as a single cell that is smaller than the period at the end of this sentence.

Conception and Implantation

The entire complex human body begins as one microscopic cell that is formed by the union of an egg cell, or ovum, from a female and a sperm cell from a male. The *union of a male sperm cell and a female egg cell* is called **fertilization**, which is also known as *conception*. The resulting cell is called a *zygote* (ZY-goht).

Look at **Figure 19.1** on page 487. Notice that within a day after the zygote forms, it begins dividing as it travels down the fallopian tube. By the time it reaches the uterus, the zygote has divided many times to form a cluster of cells with a hollow space in the center. Within a few days, *the zygote attaches to the uterine wall* in the process called **implantation**. *The cluster of cells that develop between the third and eighth weeks of pregnancy* is called an **embryo** (EM-bree-oh). *After about the eighth week, this developing group of cells* is called a **fetus** (FEE-tuhs).

Take the Health Inventory for Chapter 19 at **health.glencoe.com**.

Embryonic Growth

As the embryo grows, its cells continue to divide, forming three tissue layers that later become various body systems. One layer becomes the respiratory and digestive systems. A second layer develops into muscles, bones, blood vessels, and skin. A third layer forms the nervous system, sense organs, and mouth.

During this time two important structures form outside the embryo:

▶ The **amniotic** (am-nee-AH-tik) **sac** is *a thin, fluid-filled membrane that surrounds and protects the developing embryo.* It also insulates the embryo from temperature changes.

▶ The **umbilical** (uhm-BIL-uh-kuhl) **cord** is *a ropelike structure that connects the embryo and the mother's placenta.* The **placenta** (pluh-SEN-tuh) is *a thick, blood-rich tissue that lines the walls of the uterus during pregnancy and nourishes the embryo.*

Although the blood supply of the mother and the developing embryo are kept separate, materials diffuse from one blood supply to the other through the umbilical cord. Nutrients and oxygen pass from the mother's blood to the embryo, and wastes from the embryo diffuse into the mother's blood. The wastes are excreted from the mother's body along with her body wastes.

Substances that are harmful to the developing embryo can pass through the umbilical cord, too. If a pregnant female uses harmful substances, such as tobacco, alcohol, or other drugs, they can cross the placenta and harm the developing embryo.

How do twins form?
Identical twins result when a single egg that has been fertilized by a single sperm divides and forms two embryos. Because they develop from the same zygote, identical twins have the same genetic information, are the same gender, and look almost exactly the same.

Fraternal twins form when a female's ovaries release two eggs. Separate sperm fertilize each egg, and two embryos develop. Each twin has a different genetic makeup, and they may or may not be the same gender. Fraternal twins do not resemble each other any more than other brothers and sisters do. Fraternal twins are much more common than identical twins.

FIGURE 19.1

IMPLANTATION

Fertilization and implantation occur after an egg is released from the ovary.

Cell Division
As the zygote travels down the fallopian tube toward the uterus, it divides many times.

Fertilization
Only one sperm can fertilize an egg.

Implantation
About six days after fertilization, the zygote burrows into the lining of the uterus.

Fetal Development

The time from conception to birth is usually about nine full months. These nine months are divided into three 3-month periods called *trimesters*. Read about the changes that take place during each trimester in **Figure 19.2.** Compare the images to see the growth of the fetus in each trimester.

FIGURE 19.2

STAGES OF EMBRYONIC AND FETAL DEVELOPMENT

First Trimester (0 to 14 weeks)	Major Changes
0–2 weeks	A zygote may float freely in the uterus for 48 hours before implanting. The spinal cord grows faster than the rest of the body. The brain, ears, and arms begin to form. The heart forms and begins to beat.
3–8 weeks	The embryo is about 1 inch long at 8 weeks. The mouth, nostrils, eyelids, hands, fingers, feet, and toes begin to form. The nervous system can respond to stimuli. The cardiovascular system is fully functional.
9–14 weeks	The fetus develops a human profile. Sex organs, eyelids, fingernails, and toenails develop. By week 12 the fetus makes crying motions but no sound and may suck its thumb.

During the period of growth in the uterus, the fetus develops in preparation for living outside the mother's body. Organs develop and become ready to function on their own. The fetus grows and gains weight. After about the seventh month, fat deposits are added under the skin to help the baby maintain body heat after birth. The fetus stores nutrients and builds immunity and protection from diseases and infections.

Reading Check

Classify What are the stages of fetal development called? How long does each stage last?

Second Trimester (15 to 28 weeks)	Major Changes
15–20 weeks	The fetus can blink its eyes. The body begins to grow, growth of the head slows, and the limbs reach full proportion. Eyebrows and eyelashes develop. The fetus can grasp and kick and becomes more active.
21–28 weeks	The fetus can hear conversations and has a regular cycle of waking and sleeping. Weight increases rapidly. The fetus is about 12 inches long and weighs a little more than 1 pound. The fetus may survive if born after 24 weeks but will require special medical care.
Third Trimester (29 weeks to birth)	**Major Changes**
29–40 weeks	The fetus uses all five senses and begins to pass water from the bladder. Brain scans have shown that some fetuses dream during their periods of sleep in the eighth and ninth months of development. Approximately 266 days after conception, the baby weighs 6 to 9 pounds and is ready to be born.

Stages of Birth

In the final weeks of pregnancy, the fetus becomes more and more crowded in the uterus and puts increased demands on its mother's body. Most often the baby's head moves to the lower part of the uterus. Many females experience weak, irregular muscular contractions of the uterus for weeks or even months before the baby is born. As the time approaches for the baby to be born, however, these contractions become regular, stronger, and closer together. The stronger contractions induce **labor**, *the final stage of pregnancy in which the uterus contracts and pushes the baby out of the mother's body.* The stages of labor are summarized in **Figure 19.3.**

Real-Life Application

Fetal Ultrasound Technology

Ultrasound is a nonintrusive technology that uses the reflection of sound waves to monitor a fetus in the uterus. A moving image of the developing fetus can be viewed on a monitor. Doctors can measure how the fetus is growing and whether organs such as the heart are developing properly. Ultrasound is used to determine the position of the fetus before birth.

Fetal ultrasound is harmless for the mother and child.

Only a trained specialist should interpret an ultrasound image.

In many cases gender can be determined with ultrasound.

Ultrasound can be done quickly in a doctor's office.

Ultrasound is helpful for identifying twins and other multiple births.

ACTIVITY

Access print or online sources to investigate at least two other technologies used in fetal monitoring. Tell when and why each is used, cite your sources of information, and provide the criteria you used to evaluate your sources of valid health information. Write a paragraph explaining how fetal ultrasound technology helps protect the health of the mother and the unborn child.

FIGURE 19.3

LEAVING THE WOMB

A female goes through three stages of labor to deliver a baby. Labor can last from a few hours to several days.

Stage 1: Dilation	Stage 2: Passage Through Birth Canal	Stage 3: Afterbirth
The contractions of the uterus cause the cervix, the opening to the uterus, to begin to dilate, or widen. In about 95 percent of pregnancies, the baby's head is resting on the cervix. Toward the end of this stage, contractions break the amniotic sac that surrounds the baby.	When the cervix is fully dilated, the baby passes through the birth canal and emerges from the mother's body. Right after birth the baby takes its first breath and cries to clear the lungs of amniotic fluid.	The placenta is still attached to the baby by the umbilical cord. Contractions continue until the placenta, now called the *afterbirth,* is pushed from the mother's body. The umbilical cord is cut to separate the placenta from the baby.

REVIEW

LESSON 1

Reviewing Facts and Vocabulary

1. Define *fertilization* and *implantation.*
2. Explain fetal development from conception through pregnancy and birth.
3. How is a developing fetus nourished?

Thinking Critically

4. **Synthesizing.** Considering what you learned about the female reproductive system in Chapter 18, explain what would happen if the zygote did not implant in the uterus after leaving the fallopian tube.
5. **Applying.** Explain how harmful substances taken in by a pregnant female can be transferred to a developing fetus. How might fetal development be affected?

Applying Health Skills

Accessing Information. Research the changes that occur in a female's body during the nine months of pregnancy. Make an informative pamphlet that summarizes this information by trimester. Illustrate the pamphlet with pictures that show fetal development during each trimester.

After You Read

Explain. Write a few sentences explaining how twins form. Include information describing the difference between identical and fraternal twins.

Prenatal Care

Building Vocabulary

As you read this lesson, write each new highlighted term and its definition in your notebook.

▶ prenatal care (p. 492)

▶ birthing center (p. 492)

▶ fetal alcohol syndrome (FAS) (p. 494)

▶ miscarriage (p. 496)

▶ stillbirth (p. 496)

▲ Regular physical activity under the guidance of a health care professional, along with good nutrition, contribute to a healthy pregnancy.

Focusing on the Main Ideas

In this lesson, you will learn how to:

▶ Examine prenatal care and proper nutrition for the baby and the mother.

▶ Discuss the harmful effects of certain substances on the fetus, such as tobacco, alcohol, other drugs, and environmental hazards.

▶ List complications during pregnancy such as miscarriage and stillbirth.

Reading Strategy

Cause and Effect

▶ Draw a word web with "healthy baby" in the center, and Prenatal Care, Nutrition, Fetal Health, and Complications around the center. As you read, list facts under each heading.

Write a short paragraph describing some positive health behaviors you think would benefit a developing fetus.

A female should begin prenatal care as soon as her pregnancy is confirmed to promote optimal health for both the baby and the mother. **Prenatal** (pree-NAY-tuhl) **care** refers to *steps that a pregnant female can take to provide for her own health and the health of her baby.* Obtaining prenatal care shows that you understand the impact of personal health behaviors on body systems.

Importance of Prenatal Care

One of the first decisions a pregnant female must make is who will provide her prenatal care. An *obstetrician* (ahb-stuh-TRI-shuhn) is a doctor who specializes in the care of a female and her developing child. A *certified nurse-midwife* is an advanced practical nurse who specializes in prenatal care and delivering babies. In the United States, most births take place at a hospital, but some women choose to have the delivery at home or in a **birthing center**, *a facility in which women with low-risk pregnancies can deliver their babies in a homelike setting.*

During prenatal visits the female will have a complete physical that includes blood tests and a pelvic exam. The purpose of the exam is to identify problems so that they can be corrected or treated as early as possible. The obstetrician or nurse-midwife will monitor the mother's weight and blood pressure. Often the developing baby will be viewed with an ultrasound machine. These visits also give the parents-to-be the opportunity to ask questions and to learn about important behaviors that can help ensure the health of the baby.

Proper Nutrition During Pregnancy

An unborn baby depends on its mother for nourishment. For this reason, a pregnant female needs more nutrients than at any other time in her life. To ensure the optimal health of the developing fetus, increased amounts of many nutrients, including those below, are needed.

▶ **Calcium** helps build strong bones and teeth and healthy nerves and muscles. It is also important in developing heart rhythm.

▶ **Protein** helps form muscle and most other tissue.

▶ **Iron** makes red blood cells and supplies oxygen to cells.

▶ **Vitamin A** aids in cell and bone growth and eye development.

▶ **Vitamin B complex** aids in forming the nervous system.

▶ **Folic acid** is a critical part of spinal fluid and helps close the tube that contains the central nervous system. This neural tube forms 17 to 30 days after conception, so neural tube defects can occur before a female knows that she is pregnant. Health care providers suggest that all females of childbearing age consume 400 to 600 micrograms of folic acid daily to prevent these defects.

Although a pregnant female's nutritional requirements may increase, she must be careful not to gain too much weight. Most pregnant females need only 300 additional calories each day—about the number of calories found in two and a half cups of low-fat milk. Most health care professionals suggest that females who are at a healthy pre-pregnancy weight gain between 25 and 35 pounds during pregnancy. Excess weight can be a health risk for both mother and baby.

Reading ✓ Check

Explain Why is proper nutrition so important during pregnancy?

▼ Choosing nutritious foods, such as fruits and vegetables, and drinking milk during pregnancy can ensure that a mother-to-be receives the optimal amount of nutrients. *What nutrients are especially important for proper development of the fetus?*

Smokers inhale nicotine and carbon monoxide, both of which reach the fetus through the umbilical cord, preventing the fetus from getting enough nutrients and oxygen. *How might this affect fetal development?*

Weight-reduction diets during pregnancy can harm the developing fetus.

Caffeine, present in coffee, tea, chocolate, and many cola drinks, can affect the developing fetus. A high intake of caffeine during pregnancy has been linked to an increased risk of birth defects and low birth weight.

Physical activity can be beneficial to the pregnant female and developing child. Before starting any exercise program, the expectant mother should discuss the matter with her health care provider.

The Health of the Fetus

A pregnant female shows that she understands the potential impact of common risk behaviors on the quality of her life and that of her unborn fetus by being very careful about the substances she takes into her body. Tobacco, alcohol, and other drugs used by the mother can enter the body of the developing fetus and have harmful effects.

Tobacco and Pregnancy

Smoking during pregnancy is harmful to the fetus. It is estimated that smoking accounts for up to 30 percent of low birth weight babies, 14 percent of premature births, and 10 percent of all infant deaths. Studies suggest that a pregnant female's smoking may also affect the growth, mental development, and behavior of her child until he or she is 11 years old.

The responsibility to provide a smoke-free environment extends beyond the expectant mother. According to the American Lung Association, pregnant females exposed repeatedly to secondhand smoke also have an increased risk of having a low birth weight baby. Low birth weight is a leading cause of death for children under 12 months old.

Alcohol and Pregnancy

Any alcohol consumed during pregnancy quickly passes through the umbilical cord to the fetus. The fetus breaks down alcohol much more slowly than an adult does, so the alcohol level in the fetus's blood can be higher than that of the mother and remain higher for a longer period of time. An elevated alcohol level can result in permanent damage to the fetus and a condition known as **fetal alcohol syndrome (FAS)**, *a group of alcohol-related birth defects that includes both physical and mental problems.* The serious, lifelong consequences of FAS are listed at the left.

The tragedy of **FAS** is that it is entirely preventable. The safe decision for pregnant females and females considering pregnancy is not to drink any alcoholic beverages.

> ### Did You Know ?
>
> Children with FAS suffer lifelong consequences, including
> - mental retardation.
> - learning disabilities.
> - serious behavior problems.
> - slowed growth.
> - physical deformities, including a small skull, abnormal facial features, and heart defects.

Medicines, Other Drugs, and Pregnancy

Using **drugs** when pregnant can have serious consequences. During pregnancy even prescription and over-the-counter **medicines** should be taken only with the approval of a doctor or other qualified health care provider.

Using illegal drugs when pregnant poses a serious health threat to both the mother and the fetus. Drug abuse can harm the mother's health and make her less able to support the pregnancy. Drugs also can directly harm fetal development. The use of certain illegal drugs during pregnancy can cause serious birth defects, premature labor, or miscarriage. In addition, a baby can be born addicted to the drugs the mother uses during pregnancy. The infant will suffer withdrawal when it no longer receives the drugs after birth. The baby may be hypersensitive and irritable and may cry for hours. It may tremble and jerk. A baby born addicted to drugs may fail to bond with its parents as normal babies do.

Reading Check

Determine What are some of the lifelong consequences for children with fetal alcohol syndrome (FAS)?

Hands-On Health ACTIVITY

Tips for a Healthy Pregnancy

In this activity you will write and design a brochure explaining how to access health services to ensure a healthy pregnancy for pregnant females. Keep in mind that prenatal care isn't just the responsibility of the mother-to-be. Expectant fathers, for example, can buy and prepare healthful food and accompany their wives to medical visits and childbirth classes.

What You'll Need

- construction paper
- colored markers or pens
- magazines or newspapers

What You'll Do

1. Fold the construction paper to make a three-panel pamphlet.

2. Using the information in this chapter, write at least five tips for a healthy pregnancy. Under each tip, include actions both parents should take to ensure that their baby is healthy.

3. Illustrate your pamphlet with photos from magazines or newspapers, or draw your own illustrations. Make your pamphlet persuasive, and target it to expectant parents.

4. Share your pamphlet with the class.

Apply and Conclude

As a class, combine the best features of all the pamphlets to create one pamphlet. Make copies, and give them to family members who are expecting a child or planning a family.

Although most pregnancies progress without complications, certain environmental factors can affect the healthy development of a fetus. *What steps can a mother-to-be take to protect the health of her unborn child?*

Environmental Hazards

Harm to the fetus can result when a pregnant female is exposed to some common substances in the environment. Being familiar with these substances can help a female avoid exposing her unborn child to their harmful effects. A prepared family member understands how the environmental conditions of the community influence the health of individuals.

▶ **Lead.** Lead exposure has been linked to miscarriages, low birth weight, mental disabilities, and behavior problems in children. Lead can be found in the paint of houses built before 1978.

▶ **Smog.** Recent studies have linked air pollution with birth defects, low birth weight, premature birth, stillbirth, and infant death. The greatest risk occurs during the second month of pregnancy when most organs and facial features develop.

▶ **Radiation.** Ionizing radiation—the type found in X rays— can affect fetal growth and cause mental retardation.

▶ **Cat Litter.** Cat feces may contain a parasite that can cause a disease called toxoplasmosis (tahk-suh-plaz-MOH-suhs). This disease can result in miscarriage, premature labor, and health problems in a newborn. Pregnant females should wash their hands after petting a cat, have others clean the cat litter box, and wear gloves when gardening where cats may be present.

In addition, when using household chemicals, pregnant females should read the cautions on cleaning products, wear gloves, and work in well-ventilated areas.

Complications During Pregnancy

Most pregnancies proceed with few problems. However, complications can arise, some of them serious. Health-literate individuals can assess behaviors and decisions as to the likelihood of resulting in infant death and disability. One complication is **miscarriage**, *the spontaneous expulsion of a fetus that occurs before the twentieth week of a pregnancy. A dead fetus expelled from the body after the twentieth week* is called a **stillbirth**. Women who use tobacco or drugs during pregnancy are more likely to experience a miscarriage or stillbirth than those who abstain from these substances. A miscarriage or stillbirth doesn't necessarily mean that the mother did something wrong. Receiving the proper prenatal care during pregnancy can reduce the risk or severity of any problems that do arise.

Ectopic Pregnancy

Ectopic (ek-TAH-pik) pregnancies result when the zygote implants in the fallopian tube, the abdomen, the ovary, or the cervix. Ectopic pregnancy can occur when the fertilized egg can't pass to the uterus, sometimes because of inflammation or scar tissue that has developed as a result of **sexually transmitted diseases.** The fetus can't get the nourishment it needs to grow normally. The situation is a threat to the pregnant female's life. Ectopic pregnancy is the number one cause of death of females in the first trimester of pregnancy. The treatment of ectopic pregnancy is removal of the fetus from the female's body.

Preeclampsia

Preeclampsia (pree-ee-CLAMP-see-ah), also called toxemia, can prevent the placenta from getting enough blood. The condition may result in low fetal birth weight and problems for the mother. Symptoms of preeclampsia in a pregnant female include high blood pressure, swelling, and large amounts of protein in the urine. Treatment includes reducing blood pressure through bed rest or medicines. In some cases, hospitalization is necessary.

Did You Know ?

In the United States 2 to 5 percent of pregnant females are diagnosed with gestational diabetes mellitus, or GDM. It usually disappears after the baby's birth.

LESSON 2 REVIEW

Reviewing Facts and Vocabulary

1. Explain the importance of prenatal care in promoting optimal health for both the baby and the mother.

2. Define the term *stillbirth.*

3. Analyze the harmful effects of certain substances on the fetus. Why should pregnant females avoid drugs, alcohol, and tobacco?

Thinking Critically

4. **Evaluation.** Suppose someone told you that pregnancy is a natural process so prenatal care is not important. What information would you give such a person?

5. **Synthesizing.** Analyze the harmful effects on the fetus of environmental hazards. Name the factors that affect a developing fetus over which a pregnant female has control.

Applying Health Skills

Stress Management. Pregnancy causes extra stress on the body of the mother. Along with these physical stresses come concerns about the health of the baby and about parenthood. Make a list of healthful "stress-busters" pregnant females could use. Share your list with families who are expecting a child.

After You Read

Cause and Effect. Write a paragraph explaining the cause and effect of using tobacco, alcohol, and other drugs on the fetus.

Visit **health.glencoe.com** for the Interactive Study Guide for Lesson 2.

Lesson 2 Prenatal Care **497**

Heredity and Genetics

Guide to Reading

Building Vocabulary

As you read this lesson, write each new highlighted term and its definition in your notebook.

- heredity (p. 498)
- chromosomes (p. 499)
- genes (p. 499)
- DNA (p. 499)
- genetic disorder (p. 500)
- amniocentesis (p. 501)
- chorionic villi sampling (CVS) (p. 501)
- gene therapy (p. 503)

Focusing on the Main Ideas

In this lesson, you will learn how to:

- Examine genetics and its role in fetal development.
- Identify common genetic disorders.
- Analyze genetic research and technology and their impact on the health of people with genetic disorders.

Reading Strategy

Organize Information

- Make a word web with "heredity" at the center. Surround with bubbles labeled Chromosomes, Genes, DNA, Fetal Development, Genetic Disorders, and Gene Research. As you read, fill in the appropriate facts.

Quick Write

Make a list of some of the ways a family you know looks alike. Describe why you think this likeness might be genetic.

Ⓨ **Family members often share a strong physical resemblance.** *What inherited characteristics are visible in this family?*

No two individuals are exactly alike. Even identical twins have some differences. What accounts for this variety of traits? A number of factors influence the way an individual develops. One significant factor is heredity.

Heredity

The *passing of traits from parents to their children* is called **heredity**. Examples of traits that you inherited from your parents are your eye and hair color and the shape of your earlobes. Environment can also influence inherited traits. For example, height is an inherited trait, but poor nutrition may stunt a child's growth.

Chromosomes and Genes

Most cells in your body contain a nucleus—the cell's control center. Inside each nucleus is a set of **chromosomes** (KROH-muh-sohmz), *threadlike structures found within the nucleus of a cell that carry the codes for inherited traits.* Most cells in the body contain 46 chromosomes arranged as 23 pairs.

Sections of chromosomes, called genes, carry codes for specific traits. **Genes** are *the basic units of heredity.* Like chromosomes, genes occur in pairs. One gene from each pair is inherited from each parent. You have thousands of genes in every cell of your body.

DNA

The chemical unit that makes up chromosomes is called **DNA**, or deoxyribonucleic (dee-AHK-si-REYE-boh-nyoo-KLEE-ik) acid. All living things are made of DNA. Chemical compounds, called bases, make up the structure of DNA. The arrangement of the bases along each DNA molecule differs. Because several thousand pairs of bases are in each gene, countless numbers of arrangements are possible. The order of the bases is called the *genetic code.* Cells use the genetic code to make proteins. Proteins help to build and maintain body tissues. Different kinds of proteins result in various individual traits. All the characteristics that you have—the color of your eyes, the amount of curl in your hair, and your height—are determined by your genetic code. Unless you have an identical twin, your DNA is different from that of any other person.

Genetics and Fetal Development

Every living organism has a certain number of chromosomes. Although most human cells contain 46 chromosomes—23 pairs—sperm and egg cells have only half that amount, or 23 chromosomes. When a sperm and an egg unite, the resulting zygote will have 46 chromosomes—23 from each parent. These chromosomes carry the hereditary traits of the parents. Health-literate individuals understand the ways that heredity and environment affect human growth and development.

As you learned in Lesson 1, a zygote divides many times, producing the trillions of cells that make up the human body. Between each cell division, each chromosome in the cell nucleus duplicates itself, producing two sets of 46 chromosomes. As the cell divides, the two sets of chromosomes separate. Each new cell will contain one set of 46 chromosomes that are identical to those in the first cell of the zygote.

A DNA resembles a long twisted helix, with ladder-like chains. Nitrogen bases make up the rungs of the ladder. *Give an example of a trait that is determined by genes.*

▼ Human X and Y chromosomes determine gender. Each of the body cells in a male has an X and a Y chromosome. Each body cell in a female has two X chromosomes.

Explain why the sperm, not the ovum, determines the gender of a fetus.

Dominant and Recessive Genes

At least one pair of genes is responsible for each human trait. Some genes are *dominant,* and others are *recessive.* The traits of dominant genes generally appear in offspring whenever they are present. The traits of recessive genes usually appear only when dominant genes are not present. For example, suppose an individual receives two genes for eye color—one for brown eyes and one for blue eyes. The resulting individual will have brown eyes because the gene for brown eyes is dominant and the gene for blue eyes is recessive. An individual with blue eyes must have two recessive genes for blue eye color.

The situation is more complex than in the example above because traits that express a quantity or an extent—such as height, weight, or color—usually depend on many gene pairs, not just one.

Genes and Gender

In humans one pair of chromosomes determines the gender of an individual. If you are female, these two chromosomes look exactly alike and are called X chromosomes. If you are male, the two chromosomes differ—one is shorter than the other. The shorter chromosome is the Y chromosome. The longer one is the X chromosome.

Remember that sperm and egg cells contain only half the chromosomes of other cells, or one sex chromosome, not two. Sperm contain an X or a Y chromosome. Eggs have only an X chromosome. The gender of a child is determined by which type of sperm—X or Y—unites with an egg.

Genetic Disorders

Sometimes the genes that an individual inherits contain a *mutation,* or abnormality, in the base sequence of the genetic code. Often the mutation has little or no effect on the individual, but sometimes the mutation can result in defects or other health problems. **Genetic disorders** are *disorders caused partly or completely by a defect in genes.* Some genetic disorders, such as those that cause birth defects, are apparent right away. One example of such a defect is cleft palate. However, other genetic disorders do not show up until later in life. **Figure 19.4** gives information about some common genetic disorders.

FIGURE **19.4**

COMMON HUMAN GENETIC DISORDERS

Disorder	Characteristics
Sickle-cell anemia	Red blood cells have a sickle shape and clump together; may result in severe joint and abdominal pain, weakness, kidney disease, restricted blood flow
Tay-Sachs disease	Destruction of nervous system; blindness; paralysis; death during early childhood
Cystic fibrosis	Mucus clogs many organs, including lungs, liver, and pancreas; nutritional problems; serious respiratory infections and congestion
Down syndrome	Varying degrees of mental retardation, short stature, round face with upper eyelids that cover inner corners of the eyes
Hemophilia	Failure of blood to clot

Although most genetic disorders cannot be cured, in some cases they can be treated, especially if they are diagnosed early—often before birth. Two common technologies used to test for genetic disorders are amniocentesis (am-nee-oh-sen-TEE-sis) and chorionic villi (kor-ee-ON-ik VIL-eye) sampling.

▶ **Amniocentesis** is *a procedure in which a syringe is inserted through a pregnant female's abdominal wall into the amniotic fluid surrounding the developing fetus.* Doctors can examine the chromosomes in fetal cells taken from amniotic fluid for genetic abnormalities or to determine the gender and age of the fetus. Amniocentesis is usually performed 16 to 20 weeks after fertilization.

▶ **Chronic villi sampling**, or **CVS**, is *a procedure in which a small piece of membrane is removed from the chorion, a layer of tissue that develops into the placenta.* The tissue can be examined for genetic disorders or to determine fetal age and gender. The procedure is done around the eighth week of fetal development.

Tests for genetic disorders may also be done after a child is born. For example, many states require the testing of all newborns for phenylketonuria (PKU). If PKU is diagnosed soon after birth, a baby's diet can be altered to stop possible mental retardation caused by this genetic disorder.

Reading ✓ Check

Compare and Contrast What is the difference between dominant and recessive genes?

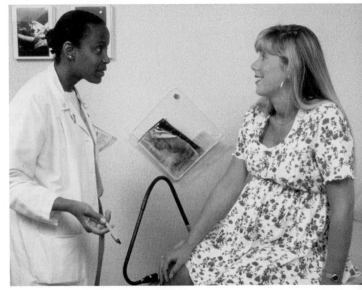

Health care professionals can check the health of a fetus using a variety of testing procedures. *How can the age of a fetus be determined?*

Resilient TEENS

Lara Brown was born in Korea and came into the world with a cleft lip and palette, and severe dyslexia. "I was always aware of my physical appearance," says Lara, "and embarrassed by the way I would mess up language."

Lara became depressed and withdrawn and for a year was bulimic. "I wouldn't face my own feelings," she says.

Gradually, however, Lara's natural love of self-expression began to assert itself. She began writing about her experiences that were eventually published as the book *121 Ways to Say "I Love You" to Your Teenage Daughter*.

"Over time I let go of all the feelings that were like pieces of broken glass inside me," says Lara. "I've learned that I don't have to go through issues alone."

"Over time I let go of all the feelings that were like pieces of broken glass inside me."

Reading Check

Explain How do you think writing helped Lara get in touch with her feelings?

Genetic Counseling

Research for diagnosing, preventing, and treating genetically related diseases has resulted in a wide variety of programs. Genetic counseling is one way that the prevention and control of health problems are influenced by research and medical advances. Genetic counselors can guide families of children with genetic disorders regarding possible treatment options.

Genetic Research to Cure Disease

Scientists have taken an important step in understanding and treating genetic disorders. The Human Genome Project has successfully identified the approximately 30,000 genes on the 46 human chromosomes. Gene maps can be used to diagnose genetic disorders.

Reading Check

Explain What can happen when a person's genes contain a mutation or abnormality?

Gene Therapy

Many disorders result when an individual lacks a functioning gene. Without the functioning gene, certain substances that the body needs are not produced. **Gene therapy** is *the process of inserting normal genes into human cells to correct genetic disorders.* When the defective gene is replaced with a normal one, the cells with the new gene begin to make the missing substance. The practice of placing fragments of DNA from one organism into another is called *genetic engineering,* and it is considered highly experimental. Genetic diseases for which scientists are researching gene therapies include cystic fibrosis and various types of cancer. It is important to know how the prevention and control of health problems are influenced by research and medical advances.

Genetically Engineered Drugs

Genes used to treat disease aren't usually inserted directly into human beings. Instead they are placed into other organisms, causing them to produce substances that can be used to treat human diseases and disorders. Genetic engineering is also used to produce some vaccines that prevent diseases. It's important to understand the impact of technology on personal, family, and community health.

Did You Know ?

Two purposes of the Human Genome Project are to identify all of the genes in human DNA and to determine the sequences of the 3 billion base pairs that make up human DNA. A working draft of the entire human genome sequence was announced in June 2000. Scientists hope to use the information from the project to improve diagnosis and treatment for approximately 4,000 human genetic disorders.

LESSON 3 REVIEW

Reviewing Facts and Vocabulary

1. What is *heredity?*
2. Name three human genetic disorders.
3. Explain the difference between *amniocentesis* and *chorionic villi sampling (CVS).*

Thinking Critically

4. **Analyzing.** Explain the significance of genetics and its role in fetal development.
5. **Synthesizing.** Explain how genetic research technology has impacted the health status of families. How might a genetic counselor help a family that has just learned that their child may have inherited a genetic disorder?

Applying Health Skills

Accessing Information. Research a particular genetic disorder. Prepare a presentation that summarizes the cause, symptoms, and treatment of the disorder and the latest research being conducted. Explain how technology has impacted the health status of individuals, families, communities, and the world.

After You Read

Explain. Write a brief paragraph explaining what causes genetic disorders and how can they be diagnosed.

Visit **health.glencoe.com** for the Interactive Study Guide for Lesson 3.

Lesson 3 Heredity and Genetics **503**

Infancy and Childhood

Guide to Reading

Building Vocabulary

As you read this lesson, write each new highlighted term and its definition in your notebook.

► developmental tasks (p. 504)
► autonomy (p. 505)
► scoliosis (p. 507)

Focusing on the Main Ideas

In this lesson, you will learn how to:

► Identify the developmental tasks of childhood.
► Discuss state laws and community services that provide vision and hearing screenings and immunization programs for children.

Reading Strategy

Describe

► Write a brief paragrah describing the four stages of childhood development.

Write a short paragraph describing why it is important to choose age-appropriate toys for children.

⚠ **Children often imitate the behavior of adults.** *What are some examples of positive behaviors adults can display when they are around children?*

Dramatic physical and mental changes take place as an infant grows through childhood. Many scientists have studied these changes, and they have developed different theories about them. One of the most widely accepted theories of development is that of psychologist Erik Erikson.

Childhood Development

According to Erikson, each individual passes through eight developmental stages during his or her life. Each stage is characterized by **developmental tasks**, *events that need to happen in order for a person to continue growing toward becoming a healthy, mature adult.* Success in each stage is dependent on an individual's experiences during that stage. Partial development at one stage can be overcome by developmental successes in following stages. The four stages that apply to infancy and childhood are summarized in **Figure 19.5.**

Infancy

Infancy is the period of fastest growth in a person's life. During this time a child's weight may triple, and his or her height may

FIGURE 19.5

STAGES OF INFANCY AND CHILDHOOD

Each stage of development is associated with a developmental task that involves a person's relationship with other people.

Stage 1	Stage 2	Stage 3	Stage 4
Infancy: Birth to 1 year **Task:** To develop trust **Description:** Infant is completely dependent on others to meet his or her needs. Must be able to trust others to provide for needs.	**Early Childhood:** 1 to 3 years **Task:** To develop ability to do tasks for oneself **Description:** Child learns to walk, talk, and dress and feed himself or herself. Self-control and confidence begin to develop, and child begins desiring independence.	**Middle Childhood:** 4 to 6 years **Task:** To develop responsibility, take initiative, to create one's own play **Description:** Child becomes more engaged in interactions with others. Models adult behavior by helping with household chores. Learns to control impulses.	**Late Childhood:** 7 to 12 years **Task:** To develop an interest in performing activities **Description:** Child completes transition from home to school; learns to make things, use tools, and acquire skills.

increase by 50 percent. Infancy is a time of learning—how to eat solid food and how to sit, crawl, and walk. An important task for an infant is developing trust. Infants of parents who are attentive—who play with and talk to the infant and give comfort—learn to view the world as a safe place. These children see people as being dependable. If parents ignore a child's needs, the child may learn to be distrustful.

Early Childhood

Children in early childhood begin to feel proud of their accomplishments, and they become eager to learn more. During this time children develop many new skills. They learn to talk, climb, push, and pull. They increase their vocabulary and begin talking in sentences. If parents accept the child's need to do whatever he or she is capable of, the child will develop a sense of **autonomy**, *the confidence that a person can control his or her own body, impulses, and environment.* If parents are overprotective or critical of the child's behaviors, the child may develop doubts about his or her abilities.

Reading Check

Describe What is a developmental task?

Middle Childhood

During middle childhood children learn to initiate play activities rather than merely following the lead of others. Children of this age display their intelligence by asking many questions. They must learn to recognize emotions and practice expressing them in appropriate ways. If parents show approval of these new abilities and encourage questions, children learn creativity, initiative, and the ability to start something on their own. Children of parents who are impatient with the child may develop a sense of guilt about self-initiated activities, resulting in low self-esteem.

Late Childhood

During late childhood school becomes an important part of a child's life. Children develop skills in reading, writing, and math. Children learn to get along with peers, learn appropriate roles in society, and develop a conscience. If their efforts are rewarded and

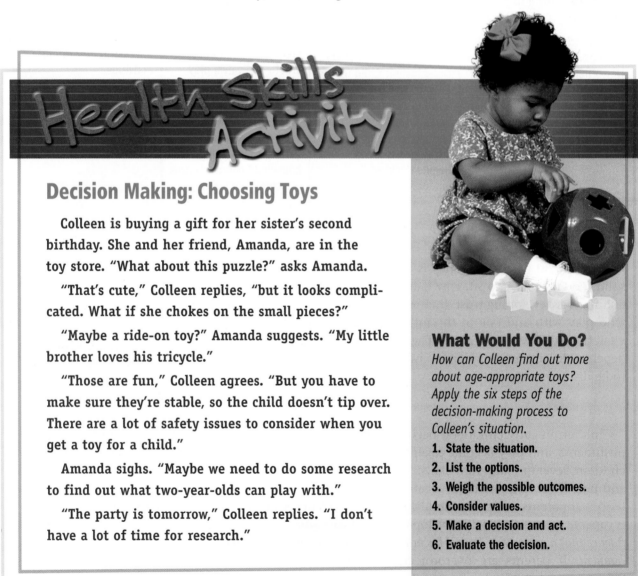

Health Skills Activity

Decision Making: Choosing Toys

Colleen is buying a gift for her sister's second birthday. She and her friend, Amanda, are in the toy store. "What about this puzzle?" asks Amanda.

"That's cute," Colleen replies, "but it looks complicated. What if she chokes on the small pieces?"

"Maybe a ride-on toy?" Amanda suggests. "My little brother loves his tricycle."

"Those are fun," Colleen agrees. "But you have to make sure they're stable, so the child doesn't tip over. There are a lot of safety issues to consider when you get a toy for a child."

Amanda sighs. "Maybe we need to do some research to find out what two-year-olds can play with."

"The party is tomorrow," Colleen replies. "I don't have a lot of time for research."

What Would You Do?

How can Colleen find out more about age-appropriate toys? Apply the six steps of the decision-making process to Colleen's situation.

1. **State the situation.**
2. **List the options.**
3. **Weigh the possible outcomes.**
4. **Consider values.**
5. **Make a decision and act.**
6. **Evaluate the decision.**

appreciated, their pride in their work increases. Children who are scolded for making a mess, getting in the way, or not following directions may develop feelings of self-doubt.

Health Screenings in Childhood

Vision and hearing impairments can affect a child's development as much as social factors do. Immunizations and health screenings can prevent many problems.

Vision and Hearing

According to the CDC, nearly one in every 1,000 children in the United States has low vision or is legally blind. The American Academy of Ophthalmology recommends that vision screenings be given to newborns and regularly throughout childhood. Schools often provide regular vision screenings for students.

In the United States, two to three of every 1,000 infants are born with a hearing impairment severe enough to affect language development. Some state laws require that newborns be screened at birth for hearing loss. Schools often provide periodic screenings.

Scoliosis

Scoliosis, *an abnormal lateral, or side-to-side, curvature of the spine,* may begin in childhood and go unnoticed until the teen years. Its exact cause is unknown, though it is more common in girls. Many public schools make it a policy check for scoliosis in middle school.

LESSON 4 REVIEW

Reviewing Facts and Vocabulary

1. Define *developmental tasks.* List three developmental tasks of infancy and childhood.

2. What developmental task must be accomplished in early childhood?

3. Which health screenings are usually provided by schools?

Thinking Critically

4. **Synthesizing.** How do the actions of parents contribute to the developmental tasks of their children?

5. **Evaluating.** Do you think that all states should have laws requiring regular health screenings for children? Explain your answer.

Applying Health Skills

Accessing Information. Research various school and community health services for people of all ages such as vision and hearing screenings and immunization programs. If appropriate, post your findings on a class Web site.

After You Read

Analyze a Graph. Using Figure 19.5, write a summary describing at least two activities that infants and children are likely to accomplish during that stage of their development.

Visit **health.glencoe.com** for the Interactive Study Guide for Lesson 4.

Lesson 4 Infancy and Childhood **507**

How DNA Works

DNA is a self-reproducing molecule that carries instructions from one generation to the next—and it's beautiful!

Cell Width 10 to 30 micrometers (a micrometer is one-thousandth of a millimeter)

Chromosome   Nucleus

DNA strand Length of one turn: 34 angstroms (an angstrom is one ten-millionth of a millimeter)

DNA is twisted into packets, called chromosomes, that are tucked into the nucleus of each cell. The blueprints for making proteins are stretches of DNA called genes. Genes spell out instructions in four–letter codes: *A, T, G,* and *C.*

Diameter: 20 angstroms

DNA backbone

DNA bases

To make a copy of itself, DNA unzips into two half-ladders that are reverse images of each other. Each half rebuilds itself from components stored in the cell. *A*s always bond with *T*s and *G*s bond with *C*s, so the copies are identical.

The base pairs attach to each other with hydrogen bonds.

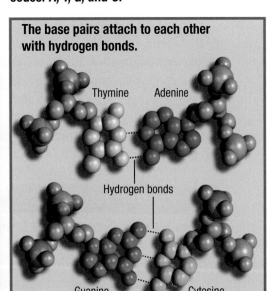

Thymine   Adenine

Hydrogen bonds

Guanine   Cytosine

TIME to THINK...   About DNA

The structure of DNA may seem simple, but discovering that structure was anything but simple. Using the Internet and your school's media center, explore the work of James Watson and Francis Crick. Report to class the role of these two scientists in uncovering the mysteries of DNA.

1. Accessing Information. Choose a human body system. Research its development before birth. Prepare a visual report of your findings. *(LESSON 1)*

2. Communicating. Research and analyze the effects of secondhand smoke on a developing fetus. Write a dialogue in which a pregnant woman uses this factual information and "I" messages to communicate her desire for a person not to smoke in her presence. *(LESSON 2)*

3. Advocacy. Research a genetic disorder that interests you. Find out what organizations are currently doing research on the disease and how this research is funded. Write a letter to the funding organization urging them to continue their support. *(LESSON 3)*

4. Practicing Healthful Behaviors. Identify screening and immunization programs in your community. What screenings and immunizations are required by your state? By your school district? How would you access these health services? Explain how to access these health services for people of all ages. *(LESSON 4)*

CAREER
Corner

Pediatrician

Being a physician who specializes in treating children from birth through the teen years takes patience, understanding, and a lot of education. Pediatricians get a four-year college degree and then complete four years of medical school. This is followed by three or more years of residency training in pediatrics. Some pediatricians have additional training in specialties such as neonatal care or heart diseases in children. Find out more about this and other health careers by clicking on Career Corner at **health.glencoe.com.**

BEYOND
the Classroom

Parent Involvement

Analyzing Influences. Talk with a parent or other adult family member about the responsibilities of parenthood. Share Erikson's stages of infancy and early, middle, and late childhood, and discuss how your family helped you move successfully from one stage to another.

School and Community

Child Care. Invite a child psychologist to your school to discuss the developmental tasks of children. Have the person explain the positive behaviors that caregivers can use to help ensure that the children they care for become healthy, mature adults. Then use the information to prepare a pamphlet for all babysitters to read.

After You Read

Use the notes you have taken in your Foldable to write an expository paragraph explaining the stages of fetal development from conception to birth.

FOLDABLES™
Study Organizer

➤ **EXPLORING HEALTH TERMS** *Answer the following questions on a sheet of paper.*

Lesson 1 *Replace the underlined words with the correct term.*

amniotic sac	implantation
embryo	labor
fertilization	placenta
fetus	umbilical cord

1. The final stage of pregnancy, in which the uterus contracts and pushes the baby out of the mother's body, is <u>fertilization</u>.

2. The ropelike structure that connects the embryo and the placenta is the <u>fetus</u>.

3. The <u>amniotic sac</u> is the thick, blood-rich tissue that lines the walls of the uterus and nourishes the embryo during pregnancy.

Lesson 2 *Match each definition with the correct term.*

birthing center	prenatal care
stillbirth	fetal alcohol syndrome (FAS)
miscarriage	

4. A facility in which females with low-risk pregnancies can deliver their babies in a homelike setting.

5. A group of alcohol-related birth defects.

6. The spontaneous expulsion of a fetus that occurs before the twentieth week of a pregnancy.

Lesson 3 *Fill in the blanks with the correct term.*

CVS	genetic disorder
DNA	chromosomes
genes	heredity
gene therapy	amniocentesis

7. The threadlike structures found within the nucleus of a cell that carry the codes for inherited traits are called _____.

8. The basic units of heredity are _____.

9. The chemical units that make up chromosomes are called _____.

10. A defect in genes can result in a(n) _____.

Lesson 4 *Fill in the blanks with the correct term.*

autonomy	scoliosis
developmental tasks	

11. _____ is/are a series of events that must happen in order for an individual to continue growing toward becoming a healthy, mature adult.

12. _____ is/are the confidence that a person can control his or her own body, impulses, and environment.

13. An abnormal sideways curvature of the spine is _____.

➤ **RECALLING THE FACTS** *Use complete sentences to answer the following questions.*

1. From where does a zygote's DNA originate?

2. What is the function of the amniotic sac?

3. Summarize the three stages of labor.

4. What happens during a prenatal visit to a doctor or certified nurse-midwife?

For more review questions for Chapter 19, go to **health.glencoe.com**.

5. Why is nutritional counseling during pregnancy important?

6. List four environmental hazards that can harm a fetus.

7. Explain the role of genetics in fetal development. If a baby boy receives a dominant gene for brown eyes and a recessive gene for blue eyes, what color will his eyes be?

8. How does the genetic makeup of a male differ from that of a female?

9. How might impatience toward someone in middle childhood affect the development of that child?

10. How soon after birth should an infant have a hearing screening?

11. When is a child commonly checked for scoliosis?

▶ WRITING CRITICALLY

1. **Descriptive.** Write an article providing information for future mothers on how to care for their unborn babies during pregnancy. Include quotes from an expert and from a mother describing the types of things she did to care for her baby and herself.

2. **Narrative.** Write a one-page story describing a child in one of the childhood developmental stages. In the story, use specific examples showing how the child demonstrates characteristics of that particular stage. Make sure that your story includes interesting characters, setting, and plot that tells a clear story arranged in a logical order.

Standardized Test Practice

 The purpose of persuasive writing is to convince the reader to accept your opinion or to take a specific action. The *Writing Situation* focuses on the effects of positive reinforcement and encouragement on young children. The *Directions for Writing* suggests that you think about these effects as you demonstrate how parents and caregivers can give children positive reinforcement and encouragement in different situations.

PROMPT

Writing Situation: In this chapter you learned about the infancy and childhood stage of development. You have been asked to create a brochure that teaches new parents the importance of positive reinforcement and encouragement on young children ages 2–4.

Directions for Writing: Think about the effects of positive reinforcement and encouragement of young children. Keep in mind the effects of the lack of such reinforcement on a child's growth and development.

Now write to convince parents and caregivers to provide positive reinforcement and encouragement daily. Remind your audience that positive reinforcement and encouragement can be shown in a variety of situations, such as at home, in preschool, in parks, restaurants, and other public places. Use specific situations and suggestions to get your point across.

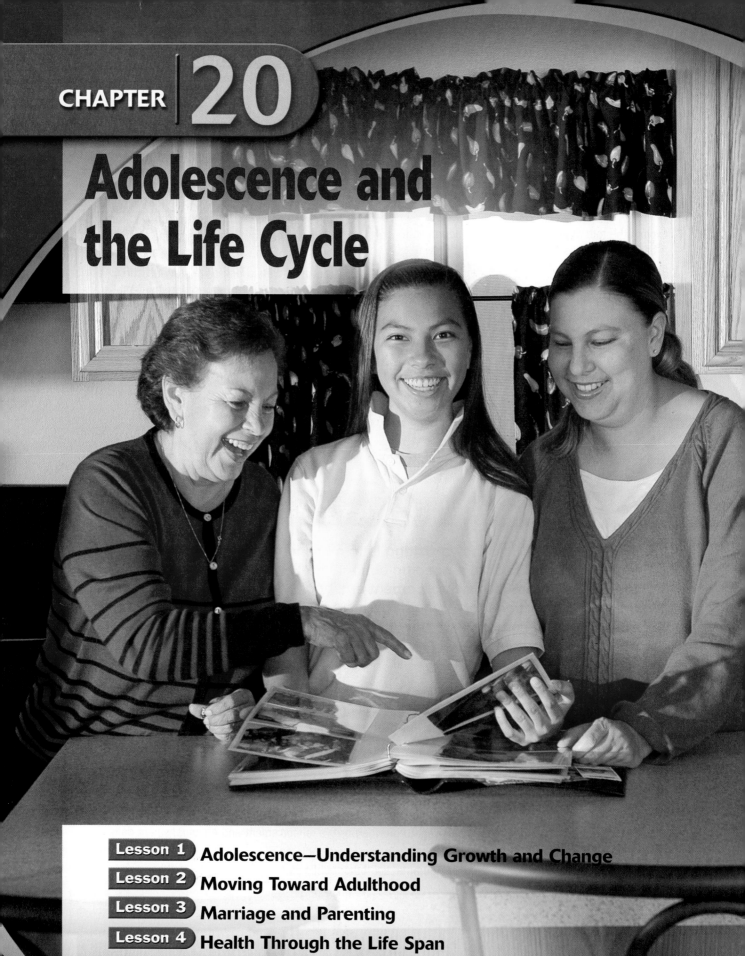

Adolescence and the Life Cycle

Eye ON THE Media

Representation of Older Adults in the Media

How common is it to see older adults in movies and television programs? In many cases, older adults are seen only in small or supporting roles. What message does this send to you?

Visit the Eye on the Media section at health.glencoe.com to learn more about how to examine your attitudes about the number of older adults seen in the media.

FOLDABLES™
Study Organizer

Before You Read

Make this Foldable to help you organize what you learn about growth and changes taking place during adolescence. Begin with a sheet of plain 8½" x 11" paper.

▶ **Step 1**

Fold a sheet of paper in half along the long axis.

▶ **Step 2**

Fold into thirds.

▶ **Step 3**

Cut the top flap along the fold lines. Draw two overlapping ovals, and label as shown.

Male | Both | Female

As You Read

As you read and discuss the material in the chapter, use your Foldable to record what you learn about the changes taking place in males and females during adolescence under the appropriate tabs.

SPOTLIGHT ON HEALTH

Using Visuals. How can the healthy behaviors you practice now positively affect your health at each stage of adulthood?

Adolescence–Understanding Growth and Change

Guide to Reading

Building Vocabulary

As you read this lesson, write each new highlighted term and its definition in your notebook.

- adolescence (p. 514)
- puberty (p. 514)
- hormones (p. 514)
- sex characteristics (p. 515)
- gametes (p. 515)
- cognition (p. 516)

Focusing on the Main Ideas

In this lesson, you will learn how to:

- Examine the physical, mental, emotional, and social changes that occur during adolescence.
- Demonstrate the use of decision-making and problem-solving skills during adolescence.

Reading Strategy

Predict

- Write each of the Building Vocabulary terms on a sheet of paper. Before reading the lesson, write a definition based on your current knowledge. At the end of the lesson, review your definitions and make changes as needed.

Quick Write

Write a brief paragraph describing the ways that adolescents differ from children.

Learning to cope with the changes of adolescence can help to make your teen years happy and fulfilling.

The *period from childhood to adulthood*, called **adolescence**, is a time of many exciting challenges and changes. One of the most noticeable of these changes is physical growth. Many of your friends have gotten taller. Voices are changing and bodies are filling out. After infancy, adolescence is the fastest period of growth. Changes are also taking place in your mental/emotional and social life.

Puberty

Sometime between the ages of 12 and 18, individuals go through Erikson's fifth stage of development—**puberty**, *the time when a person begins to develop certain traits of adults of his or her own gender.* Puberty marks the beginning of adolescence. **Hormones** are *chemical substances that are produced in glands and that help regulate many of your body's functions.* The male hormone, testosterone, and the female hormones, estrogen and progesterone, are responsible for the changes that affect teens during puberty.

Take the Health Inventory for Chapter 20 at **health.glencoe.com**.

Physical Changes During Adolescence

Growth isn't the only body change that occurs during adolescence. Perhaps the most significant body change that takes place is the development of **sex characteristics**, *the traits related to a person's gender.* Some sex characteristics, called primary sex characteristics, are related directly to the production of *reproductive cells,* called **gametes**. The male gametes are **sperm.** In males the production of sperm by the testes begins in puberty. The female's gametes are the **eggs,** or *ova.* All eggs are present at birth, but they don't mature until puberty, when ovulation begins. In females the uterus and ovaries enlarge at this time. Other changes during puberty are those associated with secondary sex characteristics, which are described in **Figure 20.1.**

Look at any group of teens, and you'll notice great variation in the size and shape of adolescents of the same age. This variation can be a source of concern among teens who sometimes compare themselves with others. For example, since boys tend to start their growth spurts later, girls who grow taller than their classmates may feel self-conscious about their height. A boy may be embarrassed when his voice "cracks" because of the growth of the larynx.

Each individual goes through the changes of puberty at his or her own rate. You may experience the changes sooner or later than others, and you may feel uncomfortable about the differences. Just remember that every teen experiences these changes, which are completely normal and will resolve themselves as time passes.

Reading Check

Cause and Effect What is the relationship between hormones and sex characteristics?

Health Minute

Strategies for Avoiding Acne

Acne is caused by a bacterial infection in the oil glands, which can cause pimples.

Tips for dealing with acne:

► Avoid oil-based makeup and greasy lotions.
► Keep your face and hair clean.
► Change washcloths and towels often.
► Don't squeeze or scratch pimples.
► In cases of severe acne, consult your family health care professional or a dermatologist, a doctor who specializes in problems of the skin.

FIGURE 20.1

SECONDARY SEX CHARACTERISTICS

The exact age at which puberty begins is determined primarily by heredity. These changes do not occur overnight but gradually unfold over several months or years.

In females:
• Breasts develop
• Waistline narrows
• Hips widen
• Body fat increases
• Menstruation starts

In males:
• Facial hair appears
• Voice deepens
• Shoulders broaden
• Muscles develop
• Hairline begins to recede

In both:
• Body hair appears
• All permanent teeth grow in
• Perspiration increases

Mental Changes During Adolescence

Not only does your body grow during adolescence, but so does your **brain.** By the time a person reaches the age of six, his or her brain is 95 percent of its adult size. However, the cerebrum—the thinking part of the brain—continues to develop in adolescence, increasing memory and **cognition**, *the ability to reason and think out abstract solutions.* As a child you could see only limited solutions to a problem; but as an adolescent, you become increasingly capable of solving problems in more complex ways. This new ability enables you to anticipate the consequences of a particular action, think logically, and understand different points of view.

As you are making the transition from child to adult, you will begin to understand the role of individual responsibility regarding personal risk behaviors.

What specific changes take place in your brain that enable you to develop these new skills? Examine **Figure 20.2,** and read what scientific research is uncovering about the brain during adolescence.

HEALTH Online

TOPIC The Human Brain

Go to health.glencoe.com for links to more information about the human brain.

ACTIVITY Using the links, research discoveries about the human brain and its development. Write a short paragraph about your findings.

Reading ✓ Check

Analyze How does brain development that occurs during the teen years enable you to develop new skills?

FIGURE 20.2

BRAIN DEVELOPMENT IN TEENS

Over the past 25 years, neuroscientists have discovered a great deal about the human brain. Recent imaging techniques have enabled scientists to examine the brains of people throughout their life spans—including the teen years.

Cerebellum
The cerebellum coordinates muscles and physical movement. Recently scientists have found evidence that it is also involved in the coordination of thinking processes. The cerebellum undergoes dramatic growth and change during adolescence.

Amygdala
The amygdala is associated with emotion. New studies suggest that teens use this part of the brain rather than the more analytical frontal cortex that adults use in emotional responses. Scientists think this might explain why teens sometimes react so emotionally.

Frontal Cortex
The frontal cortex is responsible for planning, strategizing, and judgment. The area undergoes a growth spurt when a child is 11 to 12 years of age. This is followed by a growth period when new nerve connections form.

Corpus Callosum
The corpus callosum connects the two sides of the brain. It is thought to be involved in creativity and problem solving. Research suggests that it grows and changes significantly during adolescence.

Source: National Institute of Mental Health

Emotional Changes in Adolescence

Teens often experience bursts of energy and waves of strong emotions in addition to the physical and mental changes taking place. Teens may feel that puberty is like being on a roller coaster, with constantly changing feelings that go up and down quickly. You may feel on top of the world one day and down in the dumps the next. The intensity of these feelings can be overwhelming, but it is important to know that every teen experiences these changing feelings. Support and love from family and friends are especially important and can give you a sense of security when you need it. This support can help you become more confident both emotionally and socially.

Social Changes During Adolescence

During adolescence teens also experience social changes. The need to make friends and be accepted into a peer group becomes important. Close friends are a major part of your social experience. At this time, you will develop techniques for communicating care, consideration, and respect for self and others. By taking a variety of classes, and through extracurricular activities, you will meet people from many cultural and social backgrounds. The teen years are a time when you will begin to appreciate how ethnic and cultural diversity both enrich and challenge healthy living. Peers may challenge what you stand for, what you believe, and what you think is right or wrong. Good friends, however, will not ask you to do something that goes against your personal values. Strong friendships generally begin when people realize that they have the same goals, experiences, and values.

Discovering who you are is a lifelong process. *How can having close friendships be a positive experience in your development?*

Developmental Tasks of Adolescence

You have read about some of the physical, mental/emotional, and social changes teens experience. Adolescents don't move through these changes separately. At any given time a teen may be dealing with several of them at once. Robert Havighurst, a well-known sociologist, identified more specific tasks connected to the transition from adolescence to adulthood. Some of these developmental tasks include achieving emotional independence from parents, developing your identity, and adopting a personal value system. You will begin to establish goals for a career, and you will find that practicing appropriate behaviors will help you achieve these goals.

As you recognize the adjustments you are going through, evaluate your progress by asking yourself the questions that follow each task on the next two pages to help you assess your personal growth.

► **Establish emotional and psychological independence.** You may move back and forth between the desire for independence and the security of knowing your family supports you. Teens who have an ongoing, open communication with their parents learn the advantages of seeking advice and feedback regarding the use of decison-making and problem-solving skills. When parents or guardians discuss and explain situations, rules, or reasons in the decision-making process, teens can learn from their modeling of problem-solving skills. You will discover ways that your family's support and guidance can help you become more emotionally and socially independent.

Resilient TEENS

Taushia Brooks has faced many difficulties. When she was eight her parents divorced and she and her brother went to live with their father. "My father was fun because he took us fishing and to monster truck rallies," says Taushia. "But he forgot to take care of us." Before long, Taushia and her brother moved back with their mother.

Taushia has responded to the upheavals in her life by turning to friends and keeping herself busy with hobbies and volunteer activities. "I have two friends whose parents treat me like family," she says, "and everyone I work with has been super supportive. They've inspired me to stay on the right track."

Taushia is currently involved in seven volunteer groups. Her dream is to attend college and study psychology. "It might sound strange, but I'm thankful for all I've been through," says Taushia. "I'm stronger now, and I know I can always take care of myself."

"I'm stronger now, and I know I can always take care of myself."

 Reading Check **Explain** How did Taushia's experiences make her stronger?

▶ **Develop a personal sense of identity.** Your identity began to develop when you were a child and your parents were your role models. During adolescence you develop confidence and become more independent. *In what ways are you a different person than you were two years ago?*

▶ **Adopt a personal value system.** When you were a young child, your parents provided you with a set of rules for appropriate and inappropriate behavior. As an adolescent you can begin to assess your own values when they differ from the values expressed by your peers and others. *Have you begun to establish personal beliefs and values that enhance your health and well-being? Are you acting in ways that support those standards?*

▶ **Establish adult vocational goals.** The teen years are the time during which you begin to identify your vocational goals. *Have you set long-term goals and identified steps to reach your goals?*

▶ **Develop control over your behavior.** Adolescents make decisions daily about whether to participate in risk behaviors that may harm their health. Considering your values and your short-term and long-term goals will give you a firm idea on the importance of making healthy decisions and avoiding risky situations. *Consider two recent events that challenged you to show emotional maturity and avoid a risk behavior.*

Explore opportunities and find ideas to help you establish educational and vocational goals. *Where can you get information that will help you make important decisions about your future?*

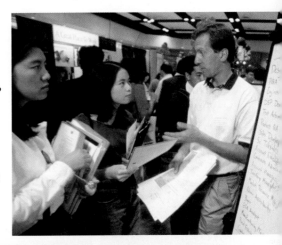

LESSON 1 REVIEW

Reviewing Facts and Vocabulary

1. What is *adolescence*?
2. Describe and appraise the significance of two body changes that occur in males and two that occur in females during adolescence.
3. What is *cognition*?

Thinking Critically

4. **Synthesizing.** Choose one developmental task of adolescence. Explain what steps you might take to accomplish this task.
5. **Analyzing.** Summarize the advantages of seeking advice and feedback regarding the use of decision-making and problem-solving skills during adolescence.

Applying Health Skills

Analyzing Influences. Make a two-column chart. In the first column, list changes other than physical changes that you have observed in yourself since you became an adolescent. In the second column, identify any person, event, or idea that influenced the change.

After You Read

Compare and Contrast. Draw two overlapping circles. In one circle, record the changes that take place in females during puberty. In the other circle, record changes that take place in males. In the overlapping section, record changes that occur in both sexes.

Moving Toward Adulthood

Guide to Reading

Building Vocabulary

As you read this lesson, write each new highlighted term and its definition in your notebook.

▶ physical maturity (p. 520)

▶ emotional maturity (p. 520)

▶ emotional intimacy (p. 523)

Focusing on the Main Ideas

In this lesson, you will learn how to:

▶ **Examine** the positive effects of relationships with peers, family, and friends on physical and emotional health.

▶ **Identify** the developmental tasks of adulthood.

Reading Strategy

Predict

▶ Scan the headings, subheadings, and photo captions. Write three questions you believe will be answered in this lesson.

Quick Write

Write a brief paragraph describing your vision of yourself as an adult.

▲ Physical maturity is just one component of adulthood. *What other changes took place as this individual became a healthy, emotionally mature adult?*

Many of the changes that occur in adolescence prepare you for the role of an adult. Clearly adulthood isn't something that suddenly appears on the morning of your twenty-first birthday. There is much more than chronological age to be considered. One term often used when defining adulthood is *maturity*. Maturity has several components, including both physical and emotional aspects.

Physical and Emotional Maturity

In late adolescence or the early twenties, most people reach **physical maturity**, *the state at which the physical body and all its organs are fully developed.* However, an adult physique doesn't mean that you are an adult. To be an adult, you'll need to develop emotionally.

Emotional maturity is *the state at which the mental and emotional capabilities of an individual are fully developed.* An emotionally healthy person not only has a strong personal identity but also has developed close relationships. The individual possesses positive values and goals. He or she has the ability to give and receive love, the ability to face reality and deal with it, and the capacity to relate positively to life experiences and learn from them. Relationships with peers, family, and friends can have a positive effect on your physical and emotional health.

Considering the Entire Life Cycle

Psychologist Erik Erikson's theory of social development covers the entire life span. Each stage of adulthood is characterized by its own accomplishments, as shown in **Figure 20.3.**

Young Adulthood

Erikson's stages of life illustrate that as a person progresses through life, his or her goals continue to evolve. Health-literate individuals know strategies when making decisions related to health needs and risks of young adults. Although physical growth occurs automatically, emotional maturity develops as each individual focuses on four major aspects of life: personal independence, occupational choices, intimate relationships, and contributions to society.

Reading Check

Compare and Contrast
What is the difference between physical maturity and emotional maturity?

FIGURE 20.3

ERIKSON'S STAGES OF ADULTHOOD

The adult years are made up of three major stages. Each stage is associated with a goal that involves a person's relationships with other people.

Stage 6 – Young Adulthood 19 to 40 years	Stage 7 – Middle Adulthood 40 to 65 years	Stage 8 – Late Adulthood 65 years to death
Goal: To develop intimacy **Description:** Person tries to develop close personal relationships. **Positive Outcomes:** Individual can form close relationships and share with others; families are started. **Negative Outcomes:** Individual may fear commitment, feel isolated, and be unable to depend on others.	**Goal:** To develop a sense of having contributed to society **Description:** Individual looks outside self and cares for others, often through grandparenting or volunteering. **Positive Outcomes:** Individual helps others and the next generation. **Negative Outcomes:** Person may remain self-centered and have little involvement with others.	**Goal:** To feel satisfied with one's life **Description:** Person tries to understand meaning of own life. **Positive Outcomes:** Adult will have a sense of fulfillment and satisfaction with life choices. **Negative Outcomes:** Person may feel disappointment with life's achievements.

Health Skills Activity

Decision Making: Exploring Careers

"I just had a talk with the school counselor," Jason says to his friends over lunch. "He gave me tips on how to decide on a career. I'm glad summer is almost here so I can get started!"

"You mean you're going to spend your summer exploring careers?" Kim asks. "Just what did the counselor say?"

Jason replies, "Well, because I'm interested in health care, the counselor advised that I volunteer at the hospital. In fact, the hospital has a Medical Explorers Club that I can get involved in."

"What's the rush?" Lonnie asks, "You've got plenty of time to do these things, right, Kim?" "Lonnie's right," Kim agrees. "Just take it easy this summer and hang out with us. What's your hurry, anyway?"

Jason wonders what he should do.

What Would You Do?
Apply the six steps of the decision-making process to Jason's dilemma. Identify a health-promoting decision that will positively affect Jason's future.

1. State the situation.
2. List the options.
3. Weigh the possible outcomes.
4. Consider values.
5. Make a decision and act.
6. Evaluate the decision.

Developing Personal Independence

The desire for independence during adolescence is a part of the quest for *self-actualization*, which includes developing one's capabilities to the fullest. When leaving home or beginning to work full-time, young adults may substitute the emotional support of friends for the support they once received from parents. As they mature, however, they become more self-sufficient.

Making Occupational Choices

As a teen you probably are giving some thought to what you want your life to be like when you are an adult. Part of that thought process may include your ideas about a career or occupation. Your ideas may be influenced by a part-time job, a role model, or the amount of education beyond high school required for a specific career.

Establishing Intimate Relationships

As individuals grow into adulthood, they begin to develop emotional intimacy with other individuals. **Emotional intimacy** is *the ability to experience a caring, loving relationship with another person with whom you can share your innermost feelings.* During this time, some people may have several successive romantic relationships. This may result in marriage when individuals are ready for a permanent commitment. Individuals who are occupied with establishing a career or determining their own identity may decide to seek romantic relationships later or not at all. Some people choose to remain single. Practicing abstinence until marriage gives a person freedom from sexually transmitted diseases and maintains options for a healthy future.

Contributing to Society

Another task of young adulthood includes determining where and how a person fits into society. You have probably already developed some of your own political ideas and religious views. Voting in elections and taking part in community projects is a way of increasing self-esteem and confidence and of contributing to society in a positive and effective manner.

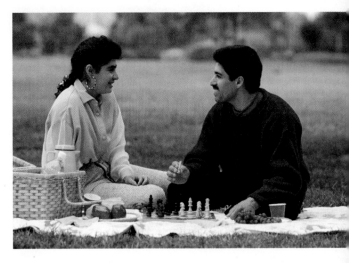

Forming intimate relationships allows two people to spend time together enjoying shared interests. *How might a close, committed relationship help a person throughout later adulthood?*

LESSON 2 REVIEW

Reviewing Facts and Vocabulary

1. When do most people reach physical maturity?
2. What is the difference between *emotional maturity* and *emotional intimacy?*
3. What are the four developmental tasks of adulthood?

Thinking Critically

4. **Analyzing.** What does Erikson say is the goal of young adulthood? Why might this goal be the most challenging? Explain your reasoning.
5. **Synthesizing.** Evaluate positive and negative effects of relationships with peers, family, and friends on a person's physical and emotional health.

Applying Health Skills

Goal Setting. Identify two occupations of interest to you. Using the goal-setting process discussed in Chapter 2, list steps you can take as an adolescent to prepare for each occupation. Share these steps with a parent or your school counselor, and incorporate into your plan any additional steps they suggest.

After You Read

Explain. Write a brief paragraph explaining what physical maturity and emotional maturity mean. How will physical maturity affect your body? How will an adult's thinking change with emotionally maturity?

Marriage and Parenting

Guide to Reading

Building Vocabulary

As you read this lesson, write each new highlighted term and its definition in your notebook.

► commitment (p. 524)
► marital adjustment (p. 525)
► adoption (p. 527)
► self-directed (p. 528)
► unconditional love (p. 528)

Focusing on the Main Ideas

In this lesson, you will learn how to:

► Compare the differences between a dating relationship and marriage.
► List ways married couples use effective communication in maintaining healthy relationships.
► Discuss the roles of parents and other family members in promoting a healthy family.

Reading Strategy

Describe

► Write a one-page essay describing some of the responsibilities of marriage.

 Quick Write

Make a list of some of the responsibilities of parenthood.

▼ When a man and a woman decide to marry, they sometimes attend premarital counseling sessions to build skills for a healthy, lasting relationship. *Why is making a commitment for life important to a successful marriage?*

Although many first marriages end in divorce, most individuals who marry begin with the intent of making a lifetime commitment. A **commitment** is *a promise or a pledge* that partners make to each other.

Marriage

Most people marry because they fall in love and are ready to enter into a lasting, intimate relationship. Couples in a marriage are able to share togetherness and give each other support in hard times as well as good times.

Choosing Marriage

There are several differences between a dating relationship and a marriage. When a couple understands that marriage is their goal, their relationship becomes more thoughtful, they make deeper commitments to each other, and they consider long-term consequences when making decisions. In this way, this couple shows they understand the relationships among physical, mental/emotional, and social health. If an individual has any doubts or questions about a partner's reasons for marrying, these questions should be fully explored before the marriage takes place.

Conflict-Resolution Skills for a Healthy Marriage

Good communication is critical for a successful marriage. Spouses who share feelings and express concerns in a respectful way are more likely to settle conflicts effectively. In this activity you will role-play a solution to a challenging marital situation using good communication and conflict-resolution skills.

What You'll Need

- scenarios provided by your teacher
- paper and pencils or pens

What You'll Do

1. Each group will be given a scenario that poses a potential challenge to a marriage. Topics may include moving because of a spouse's job, struggling to pay the mortgage, and caring for a sick relative.

2. Using content from this chapter, brainstorm several ways that the conflict can be resolved successfully. For example, for moving because of a spouse's job the partners may work together to find a new home both spouses love; budget for long-distance phone calls; agree to visit old friends and family often.

3. Plan a dialogue or skit showing ways the situation can be resolved. Use conflict-resolution skills that include "I" messages, listening skills, and agreeing on a solution that benefits both sides. Present your skit to the class.

Apply and Conclude

Write a paragraph explaining what you have learned about the importance of good communication and problem-solving skills in a marital relationship.

Successful Marriages

Making a life commitment is only the first step in a successful marriage. **Marital adjustment**—*how well a person adjusts to marriage and to his or her spouse*—depends on these factors:

▶ **Good communication.** Couples need to be able to share their feelings and express their needs and concerns. Demonstrating communication skills helps couples build and maintain a healthy marriage relationship.

▶ **Emotional maturity.** People who are emotionally healthy try to understand their partners' needs and are willing to compromise. They don't always think of themselves first; they consider what is best for the relationship.

▶ **Similar values and interests.** When couples share attitudes about the importance of good health, spirituality, ethical standards, morality, family, and friendships, they spend more time together, which strengthens a marriage.

Reading Check

Compare and Contrast What are some of the differences between a dating relationship and a marriage?

Resolving Conflicts in Marriage

Even in the best marriages, conflict occasionally results because no two people will always agree on everything. Some common issues that cause problems in marriages include the following:

▶ Differences in spending and saving habits

▶ Conflicting loyalties involving family and friends

▶ Lack of communication

▶ Lack of intimacy

▶ Jealousy, infidelity, or lack of attention

▶ Decisions about having children and arranging child care

▶ Abusive tendencies or attitudes

In a successful marriage both partners respect, trust, and care for each other. Conflicts are resolved fairly without damaging the self-esteem of either partner. Couples can reduce the impact of conflict by developing good communication and **conflict-resolution** skills. Sometimes resolving marital conflict requires that a couple seek counseling.

Teen Marriages

One of the most important factors for a successful marriage is maturity. Emotional maturity enables partners to deal with the problems and decisions of marriage. Most teens are still struggling to figure out their own identity and to set goals for their own future. It is unlikely that they have had a chance to determine what is important to them or what they want in a marriage partner. That's one reason that about 60 percent of marriages involving teens end in divorce. Statistics from the CDC indicate a high probability that a teen marriage will end in its first few years.

Once in a marriage relationship, teens begin to realize that they have increased responsibilities that may interfere with personal freedoms and educational or career goals. They also recognize that they do not have enough life experience to make this important and lasting life choice. Overwhelming financial pressures add stress to the relationship. Marriage difficulties arise as the newness wears off and teens recognize the responsibilities required to make the marriage succeed.

Reading Check

Explain What are some of the issues that create difficulty in teen marriages?

(V) Teens have the responsibility to finish school and set personal goals before considering marriage. *What added responsibilities come with a marriage commitment?*

Responsibilities of Parenthood

After marriage many couples decide to start a family. Some couples choose to adopt a child. **Adoption** is *the legal process of taking a child of other parents as one's own.* Mature couples also may make a choice to bring foster children into their lives. Becoming a parent can be an exciting experience. Most parents find raising a child to be both challenging and rewarding, and they take great joy in loving and caring for their children. It is important that prospective parents analyze the changes in lifestyle and responsibility before and after the birth of their baby. Parenting is a serious, ongoing responsibility. Parents must provide protection, food, clothing, shelter, education, and medical care. Parenting also involves providing guidance, instilling values, setting limits, and giving unconditional love.

Providing Guidance

Parenting involves providing guidance and teaching children that each individual is responsible for his or her own successes and failures. One way to do this is by encouraging children and helping them develop a sense of pride in their accomplishments. Another aspect of parenthood is guiding and protecting children while teaching them to make their own decisions. Watching children learn to get along with others and solve their own problems is a satisfying experience for a parent. When parents are joined by the extended family—grandparents and other family members—in their role of promoting a healthy family, the joy of raising children becomes a shared experience. When children see family members interacting in a mature, loving, and caring manner, they are more likely to grow up to be healthy and productive.

Instilling Values

Parents with a strong commitment to their value system and spirituality wish to pass on these important aspects of life to their children. As children grow, they develop a set of *values,* the system of beliefs and standards of conduct that they find important and that will guide the way they live. Values help children develop strong character and resiliency to resist the negative influences they may encounter. Parents who teach positive values help their children become happy, mature adults. It is also important that parents know how ethnic and cultural diversity both enrich and challenge healthy living. This is a value they can pass on to their children.

A child can bring pride and joy, but he or she also brings new responsibilities. *What role does this father have in promoting a healthy family?*

Setting Limits

When children learn limits, they become **self-directed**, or *able to make correct decisions about behavior when adults are not present to enforce rules*. When children must be disciplined, parents should follow these guidelines:

▶ Act quickly so that children understand the link between misbehavior and consequences.

▶ Distinguish between the behavior and the child so that children think of themselves as people who sometimes misbehave rather than as bad children.

▶ Be consistent with rules and consequences so that children can easily establish a connection between certain behaviors and resulting consequences. Praise positive behavior.

Giving Unconditional Love

Another responsibility of parenthood is providing children with **unconditional love**, *love without limitation or qualification*. Parents need to show their children love at all times—whether the child is well-behaved, happy, sad, sick, or afraid. Receiving unconditional love helps a child thrive. Before having children, it is important that couples examine the lifelong responsibilities and requirements of being a parent.

▼ **Unconditional love is an important responsibility of parenthood.** *How can unconditional love contribute to a healthy childhood experience?*

LESSON 3 REVIEW

Reviewing Facts and Vocabulary

1. What commitment do two people make to each other when they marry?
2. What are two communication skills that help determine a successful marital adjustment?
3. Describe how parents, grandparents, and others contribute to a healthy family.

Thinking Critically

4. **Analyzing.** Explain why choosing to become a parent is one of the most serious decisions a person can make.
5. **Synthesizing.** Distinguish between a marriage and a dating relationship. Discuss ways that responsibilities of marriage are different from dating.

Health Skills Activity

Advocacy. List important techniques and responsibilities involved in raising a healthy, happy child. Create a pamphlet of parenting tips for married couples thinking of starting a family.

After You Read

Identify Problems and Solutions. List four areas that may cause conflict in marriage. Write a few sentences describing how you might attempt to work out this problem if you were married.

Visit **health.glencoe.com** for the Interactive Study Guide for Lesson 3.

Health Through the Life Span

Guide to Reading

Building Vocabulary

As you read this lesson, write each new highlighted term and its definition in your notebook.

▶ transitions (p. 529)

▶ empty-nest syndrome (p. 531)

▶ integrity (p. 532)

Focusing on the Main Ideas

In this lesson, you will learn how to:

▶ Describe the physical, mental/emotional, and social transitions that occur during middle and later adulthood.

▶ Identify lifestyle behaviors and health programs that promote health and prevent disease.

Reading Strategy

Predict

▶ After scanning the lesson headings, subheadings, and pictures, write a few sentences describing what you think you'll learn in this lesson.

Think about some healthy, happy older adults you know. Write a short paragraph describing what characteristics they share.

I n the United States in 1900, life expectancy was only about 47 years. Today it is almost 77 years and continues to rise. What has contributed to this increase? One factor is the advances in health care that occurred throughout the twentieth century. Another factor is the public's increased awareness about the importance of practicing healthful behaviors at all ages. Yet another is the influence of laws, policies, and practices on health-related issues, particularly those related to disease prevention.

Middle Adulthood

E rikson's seventh developmental stage is middle adulthood, encompassing the ages from 40 to 65. These years are often full of **transitions**, *critical changes that occur at all stages of life*. It can be a time of family and individual accomplishments, such as children graduating from college, the arrival of the first grandchild, achievement of a satisfying career goal, or recognition of the individual's contributions to community and friends. When a person understands the relationships among physical, mental, emotional, and social health throughout adulthood, these accomplishments can be more fulfilling.

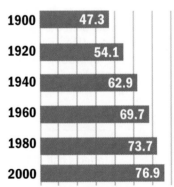

1900	47.3
1920	54.1
1940	62.9
1960	69.7
1980	73.7
2000	76.9

10 20 30 40 50 60 70 80
Average Age

 The average life expectancy in the United States has increased dramatically in the last 100 years. *Why has life expectancy risen?*

Reading ✓ Check

Analyze What are some of the effects age has on specific parts of the body (Figure 20.4)?

Physical Transitions

Change doesn't stop when adolescence ends; it continues throughout the life span. People in middle adulthood experience physical changes as their bodies begin to age. Skin loses its elasticity, the functioning of the body's organs slows, and the body's immune system becomes less effective. Females experience menopause around ages 45 to 55. This is the stopping of ovulation and menstruation, after which a female cannot get pregnant. Hormonal changes during menopause often cause physical effects that may include hot flashes.

FIGURE 20.4

KEEPING YOUR BODY HEALTHY THROUGHOUT THE LIFE SPAN

Many of the health habits you develop as an adolescent will affect the way you feel as you grow older. Practicing healthful behaviors and avoiding tobacco, alcohol, and other drugs during your teen years will reduce your risk of developing serious problems such as diabetes and heart disease in the future.

Eyes Eyesight changes with age. The eyes have more difficulty bringing images into focus. Eating plenty of leafy green vegetables, controlling blood pressure, and avoiding tobacco use promotes eye health. Sunglasses protect your eyes from damaging UV rays.

Brain Scientists say that like your muscles, your brain needs exercise to stay healthy. Read and keep learning to exercise your brain.

Mouth Teeth and gums can become decayed and diseased without proper care. Brush and floss regularly. See a dentist every six months.

Ears Loud sounds take a toll on your hearing. Limit your exposure to noise. Keep the stereo at a low volume. Use earplugs when operating noisy equipment.

Heart Lack of physical activity and a diet high in saturated fats are known risk factors for heart disease. Engaging in regular aerobic activity and choosing foods low in saturated fats greatly reduce the risk of heart disease.

Muscles and Joints Arthritis affects half of those over age 65. Maintaining a healthy weight and being physically active can help keep joints healthy and pain free.

Skin Aging skin may become wrinkled, spotted, and dry. Reduce exposure to harmful UV rays by covering up and wearing a sunscreen. Avoid using tanning beds.

Research indicates that most people who have practiced healthy behaviors such as weight management, nutritious eating, and regular physical activity as teens and young adults find these changes to be less severe. Adults who have developed lifelong healthy habits and continue to be active stay healthy by eating low-fat, high-fiber diets and avoiding tobacco, alcohol, and other drugs. Strength training has been proven to provide significant benefits to most adults. Those benefits include increasing muscle mass, preserving bone density, and protecting the major joints from injury. **Figure 20.4** on page 530 describes some healthy behaviors you can begin now to reduce your risk of developing the illnesses and disabilities that historically have been common among older adults.

Mental Transitions

Just as exercise strengthens the muscles of people at any age, mental activities strengthen the brain. Solving puzzles, reading, and playing board games provide mental stimulation. An adult who "exercises" his or her brain remains mentally active. Learning is a lifelong pursuit. At midlife many adults start new careers, return to school, and learn new hobbies. The use of computers gives older adults opportunities to broaden their access to information. People reach middle adulthood with a great deal of knowledge and experience, which they can use to pursue new interests.

Emotional Transitions

The emotional transitions for some people in middle adulthood are much like the "growing pains" of adolescence. Most people have by this time experienced many of life's greatest joys, including children, pride in their personal accomplishments, and some disappointments. The midlife crisis for some individuals results from questions and concerns about whether they have met their goals, feel loved and valued, and have made a positive difference in the lives of others. Keeping the health triangle in balance and continuing to set goals along the way will help people avoid these concerns.

Social Transitions

Most social transitions during middle adulthood focus on the family. Many adults of this age are faced with the death of a parent or the need to adjust to their children's growing up and leaving home. *The feelings of sadness or loneliness that accompany children's leaving home and entering adulthood* are called **empty-nest syndrome**.

People who maintain healthy relationships with family and friends have less difficulty adjusting to these changes. For many this is a time to apply their talents and life experience to community and social programs. They use their time to pursue new interests and make new friends. Developing good social skills as an adolescent helps ease these transitions.

▼ **Meeting new challenges is just one way to maintain physical health.** *How can your actions as a teen help prepare you for the physical, mental, emotional, and social transitions of adulthood?*

Reading Check

Cause and Effect What is the relationship between integrity and a sense of fulfillment in late adulthood?

Late Adulthood

Erikson's final stage of development, late adulthood, occurs after age 65. One of the goals of people at this stage is to look at life with satisfaction and a sense of fulfillment. Older adults evaluate the events of their lives and their achievements. If they have lived their lives with **integrity**, making their decisions with *a firm adherence to a moral code,* they are likely to be satisfied. For example, a person who considered family a high priority may have also succeeded in a career while providing for family. Older adults who have maintained intimate relationships and remained committed to a system of values will have a sense of satisfaction. They can look back without regret and feel content with their accomplishments.

Real-Life Application

Government Spending for Health Research

The National Institutes of Health (NIH) gathers information from many sources to establish research priorities for the prevention and treatment of diseases, including those that affect older people. Study the illustration and captions. Then complete the activity to advocate for one of the following aging-related health issues.

Setting Research Priorities: Every Voice Counts

Patients and Their Advocacy Groups
Scientific Review Committees
Voluntary Organizations
President and Administration
Industry Scientists
Public Members of Advisory Councils
Physicians and Other Health Professionals
General Public
Congress
Professional Societies
Industry Managers

Source: National Institutes of Health, 2002

Advocacy groups
The Alzheimer's Association advocates increased funding for **Alzheimer's disease** research.

Volunteer groups
Stroke survivors have testified to Congress about increased funding for **stroke** and heart research.

Professional groups
The American Academy of Orthopaedic Surgeons advocates increases in NIH funding for **osteoarthritis** and other musculoskeletal disorders.

ACTIVITY

Choose one disease related to aging that you believe should receive additional research funding from the NIH. Then compose a letter to a voluntary health organization, a member of Congress, or a patient advocacy group. Write with conviction, and target your letter to the people who will be reading it. Support your letter with data from your research.

Expanding Opportunities in Late Adulthood

Because of the increase in life expectancy in the United States, most adults can enjoy many years of late adulthood. Many look forward to retirement so that they can pursue new interests. Others choose to continue to work or even change careers. For many, volunteering is another way of staying active.

Public Health Policies and Programs for Older Adults

The Social Security system, first created in 1935, provides benefits to older adults, as well as people with disabilities. To assist retirees with their health care needs, the government offers Medicare to people 65 years of age and older and Medicaid to people with low incomes and limited resources. An informed health consumer understands how public health policies and government regulations influence health conditions.

Because of better health care, people can now expect to live longer after retirement. For this reason, financial planning is essential. Although some companies provide retirement benefits, many workers must plan for their own retirement with personal or company-run long-term savings plans. Through use of these funds in conjunction with Social Security benefits, the poverty rate for older adults has been reduced. Many older adults are finding that, because of a lifetime of healthy behaviors, the years after retirement are their best.

What are Social Security credits?

As you work and pay taxes, you earn "credits" that count toward eligibility for future Social Security benefits. You can earn a maximum of 4 credits each year. Most people need 40 credits (ten years of work) to qualify for benefits.

LESSON 4 | REVIEW

Reviewing Facts and Vocabulary

1. What transitions do people in middle adulthood face?
2. What causes empty-nest syndrome?
3. What is *integrity*?

Thinking Critically

4. **Analyzing.** Name specific examples of the relationship between health decisions you make as a teen and disease prevention later in life.

5. **Evaluating.** How have programs such as Social Security and personal retirement plans changed the lifestyles of older adults? Analyze how laws providing Social Security and Medicare benefits can enhance health and prevent disease in older adults.

Applying Health Skills

Goal Setting. Write a list of goals indicating where you would like to be when you reach middle and late adulthood. The list should include physical, mental, emotional, and social goals. Next to each goal, write a healthful behavior that you can start now to ensure that you will reach your goal.

After You Read

Compare and Contrast. Make a T chart. On one side, list factors about middle adulthood. On the other side, list factors about late adulthood. Look for similarities and differences.

Visit **health.glencoe.com** for the Interactive Study Guide for Lesson 4.

Lesson 4 Health Through the Life Span **533**

Why more and more teens are making smart choices.

By most measures, Beth is a typical teenager. She lives in suburban New Jersey, likes to read, and loves to go out dancing with her friends. When it comes to her ideas about sex, Beth gets a lot of support from her peers. This 17-year-old believes that having sex before marriage is the wrong thing to do. "I'm not ready emotionally," she says. "I think I should wait for my true love."

Beth and her friends abstain from sex to avoid unplanned pregnancy and STDs, and because of their beliefs. The National Campaign to Prevent Teen Pregnancy has sponsored a poll of high school seniors. Many who responded said that morals, values, and/or religious beliefs play the biggest role in their decisions to remain abstinent. Whether it's a personal code, their family's values, or religious teachings, these principles can be a powerful deterrent.

Take Bill, 17, of Uniontown, Pennsylvania. He feels that having sex before marriage would be letting himself and his principles down. He had a relationship that "constantly tested" him, he says, but "no matter how tempting things got, we stuck to our guns and never gave in."

Jane, 17, of Harbor Springs, Michigan, is another example. She made a commitment to herself two years ago not to have sex until she was married—because of her faith and her feeling that sex required a long-term commitment. Eventually, her boyfriend of a year and a half

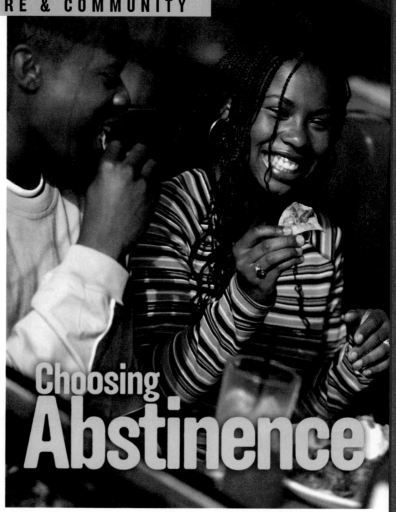

Choosing **Abstinence**

threatened to break up with her unless she had intercourse with him. "I realized that he didn't really care about what I really want out of life," says Jane, who stood her ground against the boyfriend's demands. "I broke up with him. Now I'm dating a guy who understands what's important to me." ◼

TIME to THINK... | About Abstinence

With a small group, write a short dialog in which you advise a friend who is being pressured into sexual behavior to avoid sex. Use the list of reasons you brainstormed in your dialog.

ANALYZING INFLUENCES

1. **Analyzing Influences.** Adolescence is a stage marked by change. List three changes teens experience. Appraise and explain how each influences and contributes to personal growth for a healthy life. *(LESSON 1)*

 REFUSAL SKILLS

2. **Refusal Skills.** You have your sights set on a career goal, but your friends want you to go against a school rule that might cause you to jeopardize that goal. Write three refusal statements that are based on your goals. *(LESSON 2)*

 ACCESSING INFORMATION

3. **Accessing Information.** Poll friends and acquaintances who want to get married about why they would like to do so. Identify similar reasons, and use the information to create a graph showing the number of individuals choosing each reason. *(LESSON 3)*

 PRACTICING HEALTHFUL BEHAVIORS

4. **Practicing Healthful Behaviors.** Analyze the dynamics of family roles and responsibilities relating to health behaviors. Work with an older adult in your family to identify one health behavior that you can do together. *(LESSON 4)*

CAREER Corner

Gerontologist

If you get along well with older adults, you might want to consider a career as a gerontologist. A gerontologist often works with other professionals, such as occupational and physical therapists, dietitians, and lawyers, to improve the quality of life for older persons. Some gerontologists work in nursing homes, senior centers, and other community facilities. Still others teach or work in research facilities. Because the population of the United States is aging, the job outlook for individuals working in gerontology is excellent. Find out more about this and other careers in Career Corner at **health.glencoe.com.**

BEYOND *the* Classroom

Parent Involvement

Advocacy. Find out about community resources available to help parents with their parenting roles and child-care options. Are there programs associated with local schools or colleges? Find out how you and your parents can become involved in such programs.

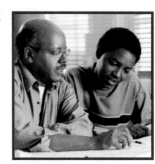

School and Community

Active Older Adults. Visit a senior center in your community. Meet some of the older adults who use the center. Find out why they visit the center and what other resources they use. If possible, volunteer at the center.

After You Read

Use the notes you have taken in your Foldable to review what you have learned about growth and changes that take place during adolescence.

FOLDABLES™
Study Organizer

➤ EXPLORING HEALTH TERMS *Answer the following questions on a sheet of paper.*

Lesson 1 *Replace the underlined words with the correct term.*

adolescence	hormones
cognition	puberty
gametes	sex characteristics

1. A person begins to develop sex characteristics during <u>cognition</u>.

2. <u>Gametes</u> are produced in glands and help regulate many of the body's functions.

3. During adolescence, <u>puberty</u>, the traits related to a person's gender, develop.

Lesson 2 *Match each definition with the correct term.*

emotional intimacy   **physical maturity**
emotional maturity

4. The state in which the physical body and all its organs are fully developed.

5. The state in which the mental and emotional capabilities of an individual are fully developed.

Lesson 3 *Fill in the blanks with the correct term.*

commitment	self-directed
marital adjustment	unconditional love
adoption	

6. When someone adjusts to marriage or to his or her spouse, that person makes a _____ .

7. Making decisions about behavior when adults are not present to enforce the rules is an indication that a child is _____ .

8. When parents show their child love at all times without limitation or qualification, the parents are giving _____ .

Lesson 4 *Identify each statement as True or False. If false, replace the underlined term with the correct term.*

empty-nest syndrome   **transitions**
integrity

9. The critical changes that take place during adulthood are called <u>integrity</u>.

10. <u>Empty-nest syndrome</u> may result when children move from home.

➤ RECALLING THE FACTS *Use complete sentences to answer the following questions.*

1. What are two physical changes that take place in the teen brain? How are these changes significant?

2. Why is it important for adolescents to expand their verbal skills?

3. How does the value system of an adolescent differ from that of a child?

4. What are two characteristics of an emotionally mature person?

5. Why does emotional maturity take longer to achieve than physical maturity?

6. What are some ways that young adults can contribute to society?

7. Why do most people marry?

8. How can couples reduce the impact of conflict on their marriage?

9. Why are teen marriages often unsuccessful?

10. How can a parent help a child become self-directed?

11. How do mental activities such as reading and solving puzzles help older adults?

12. What are some ways in which older adults can use the freedom that comes from having children move away from home?

13. How has increased life expectancy affected the way people view retirement?

---

536 **Chapter 20** Review

For more review questions for Chapter 20, go to **health.glencoe.com**.

► WRITING CRITICALLY

1. Personal. Write a journal entry describing some of the physical, mental/emotional, or social changes that occur during adolescence. Describe how these changes can affect your total health and your overall sense of identity.

2. Descriptive. Write a one-page script showing how a married couple would work together to solve one of the following problems: developing and following a budget, deciding to have children, or addressing a communication problems.

Standardized Test Practice

 Read the passage below and then answer the questions.

A Workforce of Teenagers

(1) Teenagers are working in greater numbers than ever before. (2) Some teenage workers choose jobs in fields that they feel strongly about, like cleaning local streams or working at an organic-gardening nursery. (3) Or they might join the parks department to plant trees in a city park. (4) Teenagers interested in working with younger children can apply in community centers or tutor them after school. (5) Many teens work in their own neighborhoods, mowing lawns and doing other yard work.

(6) Studies show that teens are successful workers. (7) They relate well to other teens as well as to older adults. (8) Most teenage workers find a pleasant surprise—they like their jobs more than they expected to. (9) Many teens make lasting friendships on the job. (10) They also learn new skills and gain insight about their future career and educational choices.

1. Which detail below supports the idea that teenagers are successful in the workforce?

A Large numbers of teenagers have entered the workforce.
B Many work for their town's parks department.
C Some teens have taken jobs at organic-gardening nurseries.
D They relate well to other teens and to older adults.

2. The writer wants to add the following detail to this passage:

Some teenagers—girls and boys—babysit neighborhood children.

Based on the organization of this piece, after which number on the list should this detail be added?

F after sentence 1
G after sentence 4
H after sentence 6
I after sentence 7

3. Write a paragraph discussing why you think the world needs to invite the energy and enthusiasm of teenagers into many areas of life. Give specific reasons and examples to back up your ideas.

NO SMOKING: LUNGS AT WORK

GLA

Which Antismoking Ads Are Most Effective with Teens?

Antismoking campaigns use satire or recite facts to influence teens not to smoke. These ads may be sponsored by

► **nonprofit organizations.**

► **government agencies.**

► **tobacco companies.**

Visit the Eye on the Media section at **health.glencoe.com** to learn more about this topic.

FOLDABLES™ Study Organizer

Before You Read

Make this Foldable to help you organize what you learn about the effects of tobacco use. Begin a sheet of plain 8½" x 11" paper or a sheet of notebook paper.

► **Step 1**

Fold a sheet of paper in half along the long axis.

► **Step 2**

Fold into fourths, then again into eighths.

► **Step 3**

Unfold and cut up the fold lines on the front flap to create eight tabs. Label as shown.

| Addictive Drug |
| Nicotine |
| Stimulant |
| Carcinogen |
| Tar |
| Carbon Monoxide |
| Smokeless Tobacco |
| Leukoplakia |

As You Read

As you read and discuss the material in the chapter, use your Foldable to define terms and list examples under the appropriate tabs.

SPOTLIGHT ON HEALTH

Using Visuals. Using tobacco can seriously damage a person's health. What strategies can you use to prevent the use of tobacco?

MOKING IS NOT OROUS

The Effects of Tobacco Use

Guide to Reading

Building Vocabulary

As you read this lesson, write each new highlighted term and its definition in your notebook.

- addictive drug (p. 540)
- nicotine (p. 541)
- stimulant (p. 541)
- carcinogen (p. 541)
- tar (p. 541)
- carbon monoxide (p. 541)
- smokeless tobacco (p. 542)
- leukoplakia (p. 542)

Focusing on the Main Ideas

In this lesson, you will learn how to:

- List harmful substances in tobacco and tobacco smoke.
- Examine the harmful effects of tobacco use on body systems.
- Compare the physical, mental, social, and legal consequences of tobacco use.

Reading Strategy

Organize Information

- As you read, create a list of some of the short-term and long-term effects of using tobacco.

Write a short paragraph describing why you think some people continue to use tobacco despite the health effects.

Tobacco products, which are made from the leaves of tobacco plants, contain nicotine. Experts say that nicotine is more addictive than heroin or cocaine. *Analyze the harmful physical and mental consequences of tobacco.*

Trends in tobacco use are changing, and that's good news for public health, according to the American Lung Association. The public is becoming more aware of the health costs of tobacco use, and more individuals are making the choice to be tobacco free.

Tobacco Use—A Serious Health Risk

According to the Surgeon General, tobacco use, particularly smoking, is the number one cause of preventable disease and death in the United States. Because tobacco use has been linked to many health risks, the government requires that all tobacco products carry warning labels. Avoiding *all* forms of tobacco can prevent many serious health problems. Still, every day some teens begin to smoke, chew, or dip tobacco. Many people begin to use tobacco products thinking that they can quit whenever they want to. Tobacco use can be habit-forming, but like other chemical dependencies, it is treatable.

Nicotine

One of the reasons that tobacco users find it difficult to quit is that tobacco contains an **addictive drug**, *a substance that causes*

Take the Health Inventory for Chapter 21 at **health.glencoe.com**.

physiological or psychological dependence. All tobacco products contain **nicotine**, *the addictive drug found in tobacco leaves.* Nicotine is classified as a **stimulant**—*a drug that increases the action of the central nervous system, the heart, and other organs.* Nicotine raises blood pressure, increases heart rate, and contributes to heart disease and stroke. Once addicted, people need more and more tobacco to satisfy the craving for nicotine.

Cigarette Smoke—A Toxic Mixture

Not only is tobacco addictive, but the smoke from burning tobacco is toxic. In 1992 the Environmental Protection Agency classified environmental tobacco smoke, or secondhand smoke, as a Group A carcinogen. This is the most dangerous class of carcinogen. A **carcinogen** is *a cancer-causing substance.* Other compounds in tobacco smoke are described below.

Tar and Carbon Monoxide

Cigarette smoke contains **tar**, *a thick, sticky, dark fluid produced when tobacco burns.* As tar penetrates the smoker's respiratory system, it destroys cilia, tiny hairlike structures that line the upper airways and protect against infection. Tar damages the alveoli, or air sacs, which absorb oxygen and rid the body of carbon dioxide. It also destroys lung tissue, making the lungs less able to function. Lungs damaged by smoking are more susceptible to diseases such as bronchitis, pneumonia, emphysema, and cancer.

Carbon monoxide, another compound found in cigarette smoke, is *a colorless, odorless, and poisonous gas* that is taken up more readily by the blood than oxygen. Carbon monoxide replaces oxygen in the blood, thereby depriving the tissues and cells of oxygen. It also increases the risk of high blood pressure, heart disease, and hardening of the arteries.

Harmful Effects of Pipes and Cigars

Like smoking cigarettes, smoking pipes or cigars presents major health risks. Cigars contain significantly more nicotine and produce more tar and carbon monoxide than cigarettes do. One cigar can contain as much nicotine as a pack of cigarettes. Pipe and cigar smokers have an increased risk of developing cancers of the lip, mouth, and throat.

Did You Know ?

→ **S**pecialty cigarettes carry many health risks.

- Testing has shown that imported cigarettes contain two to three times the amount of tar and nicotine found in American cigarettes.
- Smokers of low-nicotine, low-tar cigarettes smoke more and inhale more deeply to maintain their body's accustomed nicotine level.
- Bidis and clove cigarettes can contain up to seven times as much nicotine and twice as much tar as regular cigarettes.

Cigarettes contain 43 known carcinogens, including cyanide, formaldehyde, and arsenic. They also contain poisonous chemicals used in insecticides, paint, toilet cleaners, antifreeze, and explosives. *How can you use this knowledge to help others stay tobacco free?*

Your decision not to smoke can help keep your lungs healthy. *Compare the healthy lung (top) with the one damaged from smoking (bottom). Discuss how tar and other components in tobacco smoke affect the respiratory system and its function.*

Reading Check

Identify Name some of the drugs and compounds in tobacco and tobacco smoke.

Harmful Effects of Smokeless Tobacco

Smokeless tobacco is *tobacco that is sniffed through the nose, held in the mouth, or chewed*. These products are *not* a safe alternative to smoking. Like tobacco that is smoked, smokeless tobacco contains nicotine in addition to 28 carcinogens, all of which are absorbed into the blood through the mucous membranes and the digestive tract.

Because smokeless tobacco is often held in the mouth for a length of time, it delivers both nicotine and carcinogens to the body at levels that can be two to three times the amount delivered by a single cigarette. As a result, people who chew eight to ten plugs of tobacco each day take in the same amount of nicotine as a two-pack-a-day smoker. Smokeless tobacco is as addictive as smoked tobacco. In addition, it irritates the mouth's sensitive tissues, causing **leukoplakia**, or *thickened, white, leathery-looking spots on the inside of the mouth that can develop into oral cancer*. Cancers of the throat, larynx, esophagus, stomach, and pancreas are also more common among users of smokeless tobacco.

How Tobacco Affects the Body

For several decades health officials have warned the public about the health risks of tobacco. The chemicals in tobacco products can cause damage to many body systems. **Figure 21.1** on page 543 illustrates some of the effects of tobacco on the body.

Short-Term Effects of Tobacco Use

Some effects of tobacco use can occur immediately after using the product. Here are some of these short-term effects:

▶ **Changes in brain chemistry.** The addictive properties of nicotine cause the body to crave more of the drug. The user may experience withdrawal symptoms such as headaches, nervousness, and trembling as soon as 30 minutes after his or her last tobacco use.

▶ **Increased respiration and heart rate.** Breathing during physical activity becomes more difficult; and in some cases, nicotine may cause an irregular heart rate.

▶ **Dulled taste buds and reduced appetite.** Tobacco users often lose much of their ability to enjoy food.

▶ **Bad breath and smelly hair, clothes, and skin.** These unattractive effects may cause people to avoid the tobacco user.

Long-Term Effects of Tobacco Use

Over time, tobacco use takes a serious toll on many body systems, including the respiratory, cardiovascular, and digestive

FIGURE 21.1

HEALTH RISKS OF TOBACCO

Tobacco use damages several important body systems, causing severe health problems that may result in death.

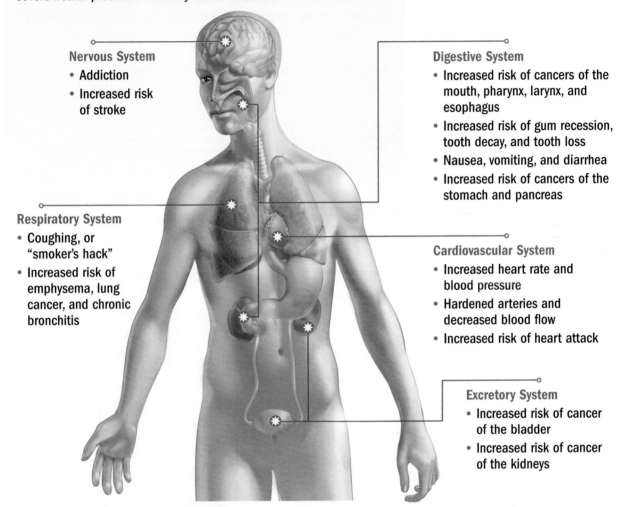

Nervous System
- Addiction
- Increased risk of stroke

Respiratory System
- Coughing, or "smoker's hack"
- Increased risk of emphysema, lung cancer, and chronic bronchitis

Digestive System
- Increased risk of cancers of the mouth, pharynx, larynx, and esophagus
- Increased risk of gum recession, tooth decay, and tooth loss
- Nausea, vomiting, and diarrhea
- Increased risk of cancers of the stomach and pancreas

Cardiovascular System
- Increased heart rate and blood pressure
- Hardened arteries and decreased blood flow
- Increased risk of heart attack

Excretory System
- Increased risk of cancer of the bladder
- Increased risk of cancer of the kidneys

systems. The immune system is weakened, making the body more vulnerable to disease. Long-term tobacco use can lead to health problems such as:

▶ **Chronic bronchitis.** Repeated tobacco use can damage the cilia in the **bronchi** until the cilia no longer function. This leads to a buildup of tar in the lungs, causing chronic coughing and excessive mucus secretion.

▶ **Emphysema.** This is a disease that destroys the tiny air sacs in the lungs. The air sacs become less elastic, making it more difficult for the lungs to absorb oxygen. A person with advanced emphysema uses up to 80 percent of his or her energy just to breathe.

Reading Check

Cause and Effect What happens to a person's health when tobacco has damaged several body systems?

▶ **Lung cancer.** When the cilia in the bronchi are destroyed, extra mucus cannot be expelled. Cancerous cells can grow in these conditions, block the bronchi, and move to the lungs. Unless detected early, lung cancer causes death.

▶ **Coronary heart disease and stroke.** Nicotine constricts **blood vessels,** which cuts down on circulation, or blood flow. Nicotine also contributes to plaque buildup in the blood vessels, which can lead to hardened arteries, a condition called arteriosclerosis. Arteries may become clogged, increasing the risk of heart attack and stroke. The risk of sudden death from

Resilient TEENS

In sixth grade, Roni Dixon was hanging out with what she calls an "older crowd." She started smoking cigarettes in an effort to fit in.

Then something happened that changed Roni's perspective. She nearly passed out after a cross-country race at school. "Mom always said I'd have to choose between sports and smoking," says Roni. She was so frightened by her inability to breathe that she vowed never to smoke again.

Roni not only kept her promise never to smoke but began focusing on school and volunteer work in the community. Today, she belongs to 10 different organizations. "I want people to know that low-income people in the not-so-good communities can get good grades, be active in programs, and go to college."

> "Mom always said I'd have to choose between sports and smoking."

Roni dreams of returning to her hometown and helping kids turn their lives around. "If I could do it, they can too," she says. "It's all about thinking positively and believing in yourself."

Reading Check

Describe What did you learn about the effects of smoking on athletes from Roni's story?

heart disease is three times greater for smokers than for nonsmokers. A nonsmoker knows how to delay the onset of and reduce the risk for potential health problems during adulthood.

▼ Most teens choose healthy alternatives and avoid the harmful effects of tobacco use.

Other Consequences

Tobacco use brings many other serious consequences, especially for teens.

▶ **Legal consequences.** Selling tobacco products to persons under the age of 18 is illegal in all states. Schools prohibit the use of tobacco products on school property, and a student may be suspended or expelled for breaking these rules.

▶ **Social consequences.** Many people find secondhand smoke and the smell of tobacco offensive, so tobacco users may be excluded from social gatherings.

▶ **Financial consequences.** Use of tobacco products can be very expensive. Someone who smokes a pack of cigarettes a day can spend more than $2,000 each year just on cigarettes. According to a recent report, the total economic cost of tobacco use to taxpayers in the United States, including medical costs, is about $97 billion a year.

LESSON 1 | REVIEW

Reviewing Facts and Vocabulary

1. What is *nicotine?* Why is it harmful?
2. Explain why cigarette smoke is toxic.
3. List the short-term and long-term effects of tobacco use.

Thinking Critically

4. **Applying.** Examine the effects of tobacco use on the respiratory and cardiovascular systems.
5. **Synthesizing.** Analyze the harmful effects of tobacco, such as physical, mental, social, and legal consequences.

Applying Health Skills

Advocacy. Help others recognize how tobacco use can harm body systems. Write a letter to your parents or other adult members of your family explaining what damage can occur as a result of using tobacco products.

After You Read

Cause and Effect. Create a T chart. On one side, list factors about tobacco use and cigarette smoke. On the other side, list the ways that tobacco affects the body and other consequences of tobacco use.

Choosing to Live Tobacco Free

Guide to Reading

Building Vocabulary

As you read this lesson, write each new highlighted term and its definition in your notebook.

▶ nicotine withdrawal (p. 548)

▶ nicotine substitute (p. 549)

Focusing on the Main Ideas

In this lesson, you will learn how to:

▶ **Discuss** the benefits of a tobacco-free lifestyle.

▶ **Develop** strategies for preventing tobacco use.

▶ **List** community services that relate to the prevention of tobacco-related diseases.

Reading Strategy

Explain

▶ Write a brief paragraph summarizing whether you believe tobacco to be addictive. Defend your belief.

Make a list of all the negative effects of tobacco use that you can think of.

Knowing the health risks of tobacco use has helped people make the healthful decision to stay tobacco free.

Reduced Tobacco Use Among Teens

According to the Centers for Disease Control and Prevention (CDC), smoking rates among teens have fallen sharply in recent years. Reports show that nationally 22 percent of high school students smoke. This is down from 36 percent in 1997. Some factors contributing to this ongoing trend include:

▶ **Antismoking campaigns.** In 1998 tobacco companies and 46 states reached a legal settlement that restricted tobacco advertising and promotion. Tobacco companies are now required to fund ads that discourage young people from smoking.

▶ **Financial cost.** Tobacco use is expensive. Many teens find that they would rather spend their money on healthier alternatives.

▶ **Societal pressures.** Legislative acts have limited smoking in public places. More young people are growing up in an environment that is less tolerant of secondhand smoke.

▶ **Family influence.** Many teens avoid tobacco use because their parents strongly disapprove of the use of tobacco products.

 After peaking in 1997, teen smoking has fallen sharply. *What has contributed to the drop in teen smoking in recent years?*

High school students who reported smoking a cigarette in the last 30 days

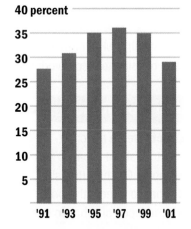

Source: Centers for Disease Control and Prevention, 2001

Benefits of Living Tobacco Free

People who have never used tobacco and people who have quit enjoy the many benefits of a tobacco-free lifestyle. Avoiding tobacco lowers the risk of lung cancer, heart disease, and stroke. It improves cardiovascular endurance and lung function, which increases physical fitness and enhances athletic performance.

Living tobacco free has mental, emotional, and social benefits, too. Tobacco-free people have a sense of freedom because they know that they are not dependent on an addictive substance. They experience less stress because they don't have to worry about health-related problems caused by tobacco use. A tobacco-free lifestyle also helps a person look and feel better. Having higher energy levels, healthier skin, fresher breath, and better-smelling clothes and hair increases confidence in social situations. Health-literate teens recognize that tobacco use can impact personal goals, educational opportunities, and occupational choices.

Strategies for Preventing Use of Tobacco

The best way to avoid the negative consequences of tobacco use is never to start using tobacco products. Nearly 90 percent of all adult smokers started when they were teens, so if you avoid tobacco use during middle school and high school, you are likely to stay tobacco free throughout your life. A tobacco-free individual knows strategies for health enhancement and risk reduction. Below are some strategies to help you stick to your decision to become and stay tobacco free. Health-literate teens know how the social environment influences the health of the community.

▶ **Choose friends who don't use tobacco.** Being around people who share your values and beliefs will strengthen your commitment to lead a tobacco-free life.

▶ **Avoid situations where tobacco products may be used.** By staying away from such situations, you reduce the chance of being pressured to use tobacco.

▶ **Practice and use refusal skills.** Prepare in advance what you will say if someone offers you tobacco. Your refusal may be a simple "No thanks," or you may give a reason, such as, "No, I need to stay fit for the track competition." Be assertive, and leave the situation if the pressure continues.

Reading Check

Examine What are some of the benefits of a tobacco-free lifestyle?

▼ A tobacco-free lifestyle improves heart and lung function, which helps your athletic performance. *List some other benefits of living tobacco free.*

What Happens When a Smoker Quits?

Benefits of Quitting:

► **Within 20 minutes** blood pressure and pulse rates drop. Body temperature in limbs returns to normal.

► **Within eight hours** oxygen levels return to normal.

► **In 24 hours** the chance of heart attack begins to decrease.

► **In 48 hours** nerve endings begin to regrow. Senses of taste and smell improve.

► **In three days** breathing becomes easier as lung capacity increases.

► **Within two weeks to three months** lungs function up to 30 percent better.

► **Within one to nine months** lung cilia regrow, and coughing, sinus congestion, and shortness of breath decrease.

► **In one year** the risk of coronary heart disease is cut in half.

► **In five years** the risk of lung cancer and cancers of the mouth, throat, and esophagus is reduced by 50 percent. Stroke risk is also decreased.

► **In ten years** the risk of cancer of the bladder, kidney, cervix, and pancreas decreases.

Why Some Teens Use Tobacco

In spite of the many benefits of a tobacco-free lifestyle, some teens choose not to resist the pressure to start smoking. Some teens think that smoking will help them control their weight or cope in times of stress and crisis. Other teens believe that smoking will make them seem mature and independent. These beliefs are far from the truth about tobacco use. Because smoking reduces the body's capacity for physical activity, it may actually lead to weight gain. In addition, health problems and nicotine dependency will increase the tobacco user's stress level.

Other reasons for teen tobacco use are peer pressure and media influences. Some teens try their first cigarette with a friend who already smokes. Other teens may try tobacco to imitate, or model, celebrities or other adults who smoke. Some teens are influenced by ads that depict tobacco use as glamorous and sophisticated.

Being aware of these influences and being informed about the harmful effects of tobacco can help teens resist the pressure to use tobacco products. Teens who analyze these influences realize that most people who use tobacco products suffer from health problems and wish they could quit the habit.

Reasons to Give Up Tobacco Use

Many teens who start using tobacco do decide to quit. Here are just a few of the reasons they cite:

► They begin to have health problems, such as asthma or respiratory infections.

► They have the desire, will, and commitment to stop.

► They realize how expensive the habit is.

► They realize that using tobacco can lead to other risky behaviors, such as the use of alcohol and other drugs.

► They find it difficult to purchase tobacco products because selling tobacco products to persons under the age of 18 is illegal in all 50 states.

► They realize the damaging effects of secondhand smoke and don't want to harm their families and friends.

Stopping the Addiction Cycle

Millions of people have succeeded in their effort to quit tobacco use. Overcoming nicotine addiction can be difficult, but it's not impossible. Most people who stop using tobacco will experience symptoms of **nicotine withdrawal**, *the process that occurs in the body when nicotine, an addictive drug, is no longer used.* The cravings and discomfort caused by these symptoms are temporary, and smokers trying to quit should remember that success will lead to better health.

Withdrawal

Symptoms of nicotine withdrawal include irritability, difficulty concentrating, anxiety, sleep disturbance, and cravings for tobacco. To relieve the symptoms, some people use a **nicotine substitute**, *a product that delivers small amounts of nicotine into the user's system while he or she is trying to give up the tobacco habit.* Many nicotine substitutes are available, including gum, patches, nasal sprays, and inhalers. Nicotine gum products are OTC products; the other nicotine substitutes require a doctor's prescription.

Reading Check

Speculate The nicotine in tobacco is an addictive drug. How difficult do you think it is for people to stop using tobacco?

Real-Life Application

Help a Friend STOP Using Tobacco

Studies have shown that most people who try to quit have a greater success rate if they have support from others. A smoke-free advocate knows positive ways to influence others to make positive choices. Use the **STOP** approach to help someone stop using tobacco.

Show concern. Approach the person in a caring, nonjudgmental manner. Use "I" messages to let the person know that you care about his or her health.

Take time to plan. Putting a plan on paper makes it easier to set objectives. You may need to help the person create a physical activity program. Set a date to quit, locate formal tobacco cessation programs, and devise strategies to cope with tobacco cravings.

Offer support. Put the plan into action. For example, you might bring the person sugarless gum. Ride a bike, shoot hoops, or take a walk together to help him or her get physical activity. Arrange to attend a class together to learn relaxation techniques.

Promote success. Let the person know that you are proud of him or her for quitting. Celebrate each week of abstinence. If the person relapses, continue to encourage him or her. Keep in touch with the person after he or she has quit.

ACTIVITY

Write a plan that addresses each of the STOP guidelines. If you have a family member or a friend who uses tobacco, create the plan for that person, or work with a classmate who knows someone who uses tobacco. Make sure that your plan contains messages that promote the health benefits of stopping tobacco use. Consider the person, and tailor the plan to that person's needs and interests.

Getting Help—Tips for Quitting

People who are trying to give up tobacco can try the following strategies:

▶ **Prepare for the day.** Set a target date for quitting.

▶ **Get support and encouragement.** Support from family, friends, and peers will increase a person's chance of success.

▶ **Identify available health-related services in the community.** It may be necessary to seek advice from a doctor, enroll in a tobacco cessation program, or join a support group. Other helpful resources include the American Lung Association and local hospitals.

▶ **Replace tobacco use with healthier alternatives.** Sugarless gum, carrots, and cinnamon sticks are substitutes that people can use when they feel an urge to have a cigarette.

▶ **Change daily behavior.** Avoiding other tobacco users, preparing one's environment for a tobacco-free life, and changing daily routines can also help smokers avoid their tobacco triggers.

▶ **Engage in healthful behaviors.** Physical activity, good nutrition, stress-management techniques, and abstinence from alcohol and other drugs will help people through the withdrawal process.

HEALTH Online

TOPIC Helping People Quit

Go to health.glencoe.com and click on Web Links for information about the American Lung Associations programs to help people quit smoking.

ACTIVITY Using these links, identify a program you think would be particularly effective in helping people quit smoking. Write a short paragraph explaining your choice.

LESSON 2 REVIEW

Reviewing Facts and Vocabulary

1. List three benefits of staying tobacco free.
2. List four strategies for preventing tobacco use.
3. What is *nicotine withdrawal*, and what are *nicotine substitutes?*

Thinking Critically

4. **Evaluating.** Why might tobacco advertisements target teens?
5. **Synthesizing.** Identify available health-related services in the community that relate to the prevention of tobacco-related disease, and explain how helping people quit tobacco use promotes health.

Applying Health Skills

Refusal Skills. Make a two-column chart. In the first column, write five situations in which a teen might be pressured to use tobacco. In the second column, develop effective refusal statements and strategies for preventing the use of tobacco.

After You Read

Problems and Solutions. Many teens are faced with peer pressure to use tobacco. Make a T chart. On one side, list some of the reasons why teens might use tobacco. On the other side, list strategies for preventing and quitting tobacco use.

Promoting a Smoke-Free Environment

Guide to Reading

Building Vocabulary

As you read this lesson, write each new highlighted term and its definition in your notebook.

▶ environmental tobacco smoke (ETS) (p. 551)

▶ mainstream smoke (p. 551)

▶ sidestream smoke (p. 551)

 Quick Write

Write a brief paragraph describing the benefits of a smoke-free environment.

Focusing on the Main Ideas

In this lesson, you will learn how to:

▶ Discuss the harmful effects of tobacco on fetuses, infants, and young children.

▶ Examine laws, policies, and practices that help prevent tobacco-related disease.

▶ Demonstrate ways of reducing tobacco-related illnesses and working to meet the nation's health goals.

Reading Strategy

Organize Information

▶ Create a two-column table. Label one column Unborn Children and Infants. Label the other column Young Children. As you read, list some of the effects of environmental tobacco smoke on these groups.

The dangers of ETS have prompted some states to pass laws that prohibit all tobacco use in public buildings. *What other measures can be taken to protect the health and well-being of nonsmokers?*

As more and more people become aware of the harmful effects of tobacco, efforts to curb tobacco use in public places are gaining ground. By participating in advocacy efforts to curb tobacco use in public places, teens show that they understand how the environmental conditions of the community influence the health of individuals.

Risks for Smokers and Nonsmokers

Both smokers and nonsmokers who breathe air containing tobacco smoke are at risk for health problems. **Environmental tobacco smoke (ETS)**, or secondhand smoke, is *air that has been contaminated by tobacco smoke.* Environmental tobacco smoke is composed of **mainstream smoke**, *the smoke exhaled from the lungs of a smoker,* and **sidestream smoke**, *the smoke from the burning end of a cigarette, pipe, or cigar.* Sidestream smoke is more dangerous than mainstream smoke because it has higher concentrations of carcinogens, nicotine, and tar.

Effects of Smoke on Nonsmokers

Environmental tobacco smoke from cigarettes and cigars contains more than 4,000 different chemical compounds, 43 of which are identified as carcinogens. Inhaling this smoke either by smoking or by breathing in ETS brings these carcinogens into the body. ETS affects people of all ages, causing eye irritation, headaches, ear infections, and coughing. It worsens asthma conditions and other respiratory problems. Every year 3,000 people are diagnosed with lung cancer caused by secondhand smoke.

Effects of Smoke on Unborn Children and Infants

Choosing to live tobacco free is one of the best things a pregnant woman can do to make sure that her baby will be born healthy. Smoking during pregnancy can seriously harm the developing fetus. Nicotine passes through the placenta, constricting the blood vessels of the fetus. Carbon monoxide reduces the oxygen levels in the mother's and the fetus's blood. These negative effects increase the risk of impaired fetal growth, miscarriage, prenatal death, premature delivery, low birth weight, deformities, and stillbirths. The infant may also suffer from growth and developmental problems throughout early childhood.

Babies of smokers are two and a half times more likely to die of sudden infant death syndrome (SIDS). One study found that nearly 60 percent of all SIDS cases could be prevented if babies and pregnant females were protected from tobacco smoke. Infants exposed to ETS have an increased risk of asthma, tonsillitis, and respiratory tract infections.

Effects of Smoke on Young Children

Young children are also particularly sensitive to environmental tobacco smoke. Children of smokers are nearly twice as likely to be in poor health as those of nonsmokers. Consider these facts:

▶ Children of smokers tend to have a higher incidence of sore throats, ear infections, and upper respiratory problems than children of nonsmokers.

▶ Children who live with smokers have double the risk of developing lung cancer than children of nonsmokers.

Because children learn by example, it's not surprising that children of smokers are nearly three times as likely to smoke as children of nonsmokers. Being a positive role model is another good reason to make the choice to be tobacco free.

Parents protect the health of their children by staying tobacco free. *Analyze the harmful effects of tobacco on the fetus.*

Reading Check

Compare and Contrast What are the differences between mainstream and sidestream smoke?

Reducing Your Risks

What can you do to protect yourself from ETS? If you and your family want your home to be smoke free, politely ask visitors to refrain from smoking inside. If someone in your household smokes, open windows to allow fresh air to circulate, and request that certain rooms remain smoke free. Consider using air cleaners to help remove contaminants from the air. If you are visiting a home in which someone smokes, go outside or to another room. Ask to open the window slightly to provide fresh air. Suggest meeting elsewhere, such as in your home or at a library. In restaurants and other public places, request seating in a nonsmoking area. If no smoke-free area is available, go to another restaurant.

Reading Check

Infer Why is environmental smoke especially harmful to fetuses, infants, and young children?

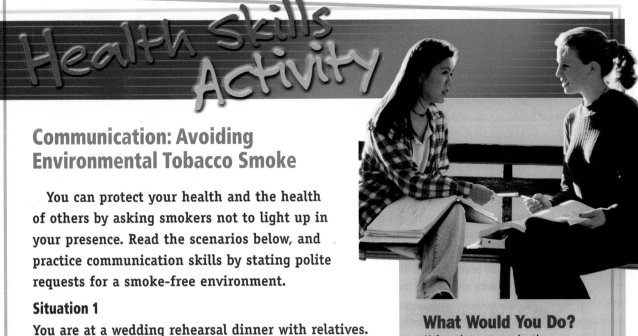

Health Skills Activity

Communication: Avoiding Environmental Tobacco Smoke

You can protect your health and the health of others by asking smokers not to light up in your presence. Read the scenarios below, and practice communication skills by stating polite requests for a smoke-free environment.

Situation 1

You are at a wedding rehearsal dinner with relatives. Your favorite cousin, whom you haven't seen for a long time, is seated next to you. As you begin catching up on family news, your cousin lights a cigarette.

Situation 2

You and your friends have been waiting for 30 minutes to be seated in a restaurant. A table becomes available in the smoking section, where several people are smoking heavily. Your friends want to take it.

What Would You Do?

Using the communication skills you have learned, write a response to each scenario. Be prepared to role-play your response for the class.

1. Use "I" statements.
2. Keep your tone respectful.
3. Maintain appropriate body language.
4. Give reasons for your request.

Toward a Smoke-Free Society

As people realize that smoking causes diseases and harms not only their own health but also the health of others, the drive to become a smoke-free society increases. Today's consumer understands how public health policies and government regulations influence health conditions. Many states have taken steps to prohibit smoking in all public buildings and private workplaces. Many people are promoting laws that would ban smoking and eliminate ETS in public places such as restaurants, civic buildings, business offices, and lobbies. Laws prohibiting the sale of tobacco products to minors are being strictly enforced. Tobacco licenses are being revoked when stores sell tobacco products to people under the age of 18.

Hands-On Health ACTIVITY

Smoking Out Underage Tobacco Sales

Federal law prohibits the sale of tobacco products to all persons under 18. In some states buyers must be 21. The easier it is to buy tobacco products, the more likely it is that teens will experiment with tobacco and become addicted. Promote health in your community by reminding peers that it's illegal for stores to sell tobacco products to minors.

What You'll Need

- information provided by your teacher
- poster board
- masking tape
- markers

What You'll Do

1. In a small group, use the information your teacher has provided on tobacco control in your state to answer these questions:
   - What is the legal age to purchase tobacco products?
   - What is the penalty for minors who use or possess tobacco products?
   - What are the penalties for merchants who sell tobacco to minors?
   - What is your state doing to curb underage tobacco sales?
2. With your group, discuss your findings. Recall signs you have seen that explain store policies regarding the sale of tobacco products. How do you think these signs affect teens who wish to purchase tobacco products?

Apply and Conclude

With your group, create a poster that is targeted at teens who wish to purchase tobacco products even though it is against the law. Include the responses to at least two of the questions you answered in the activity. Your poster should be attention-getting, persuasive, and accurate. Ask a local merchant to display your poster.

Increasingly, the law is taking into consideration the rights of the nonsmoker. Certain states have successfully sued tobacco companies to recover the cost of treating tobacco-related diseases. The money awarded in these cases is often used to fund statewide antismoking campaigns or to offset the medical costs related to tobacco use.

Working Toward National Health Goals

The Department of Health and Human Services has launched a program called *Healthy People 2010* to promote health and prevent disease nationwide. One of the nation's health goals, according to *Healthy People 2010,* is to reduce the number of people who use tobacco and of deaths associated with tobacco use. Decreasing tobacco use and reducing exposure to secondhand smoke are important steps in increasing the years of healthy life among people in the United States.

Your health as an individual, as well as the health of your family and community, are related to this national health objective. Become involved in activities that promote a healthy lifestyle, and encourage others to practice healthful behaviors, too. You can start a tobacco prevention program at school or join a youth group campaigning for stricter government control of tobacco and its availability.

 These teens are asking the storeowner to remove a tobacco ad because their state prohibits such ads from appearing within 1,000 feet of a school. *What other actions can teens take to promote health in their communities?*

LESSON 3 REVIEW

Reviewing Facts and Vocabulary

1. Define *mainstream smoke* and *sidestream smoke.* Explain what they have in common.

2. Explain how tobacco settlement money helps disease prevention and health promotion.

3. What strategies can you use to limit the amount of ETS you breathe?

Thinking Critically

4. **Evaluating.** Analyze the influence of laws on the health-related issue of teen tobacco use, and explain how this issue is related to disease prevention.

5. **Analyzing.** Analyze the harmful effects of certain substances and environmental hazards, such as environmental tobacco smoke, on fetuses, infants, and young children.

Applying Health Skills

Advocacy. You can help others make the decision to stay tobacco free. Using the goals of *Healthy People 2010,* create a pamphlet that will educate people about the harmful effects of tobacco use and secondhand smoke. Relate the nation's health goals and objectives for reducing tobacco-related illnesses to individuals, family, and community health in your pamphlet.

After You Read

Problems and Solutions. Create a two-column chart. On one side, list risks for smokers and nonsmokers. On the other side, list ways to work toward a smoke-free society.

Clearing the Air

A growing number of teen activists has declared a media war on big tobacco companies.

"**D**o you want to be deceived?" yells the speaker at the podium, 17-year-old Andy Berndt. "No!" roar the more than 700 teenage antismoking activists who have packed New Jersey's Liberty Science Center. The shout seems loud enough to be heard all the way across the Hudson River—at Philip Morris's Manhattan headquarters. That's where this protest is aimed: at the giant cigarette companies that, the activists believe, target teen smokers.

A Stand Against Smoking

Each of the teens in the auditorium wears a white T-shirt declaring "Not for Sale." This means that they can't be bought by the millions of dollars tobacco companies spend every day advertising cigarettes. They've come here to declare something else—the creation of a statewide teen antitobacco group called REBEL (Reaching Everyone by Exposing Lies). It's the newest in a pack of teen-led antismoking organizations starting up nationwide. Their mission: to teach teens not just about the health risks of smoking, but about the tactics tobacco companies use to hook young people on their products.

Recently "Not for Sale" commercials began airing on MTV and Nickelodeon.

Over the last decade, the audience meant to benefit from that message has been growing. Every day, 6,000 teen-agers try smoking for the first time and 1,200 Americans die from tobacco-related disease. Studies show that nearly 80 percent of regular smokers light up their first cigarette by their 18th birthday.

Andy Berndt doesn't think that lectures about health risks that can occur years down the road will convince teens to stop smoking. "No adult can make kids understand the issues like another kid," he says. "If we educate other kids about all the ways the tobacco industry is trying to deceive them, we'll win the war." ◼

TIME to THINK... | About Smoking

By yourself or in a small group, create your own antismoking advertisement for a magazine or a newspaper. Pay careful attention to the message you want to send by your choice of words and images. Share your ad with the class.

1. **Decision Making.** What would you do if a close friend wanted to use tobacco to relieve stress? Use the six steps of decision making to form a plan of action. *(LESSON 1)*

2. **Accessing Information.** Conduct research to identify, describe, and assess available health services in the community that provide tobacco cessation programs to prevent disease and promote health. Make a list of resources that will provide help for tobacco users who want to quit. *(LESSON 2)*

3. **Communication Skills.** What would you say to a pregnant female to encourage her to live tobacco free? *(LESSON 3)*

4. **Advocacy.** Write a letter to a state or local official expressing your opinions on what the government should do to promote the health of its citizens. Include in your letter information on the benefits of a smoke-free environment for all people. *(LESSON 4)*

CAREER Corner

Respiratory Therapist

Do you enjoy interacting with people of all ages? Are you interested in working in the medical field? A respiratory therapist works with patients who need respiratory care. Therapists provide temporary relief to patients suffering from asthma or emphysema and emergency care to patients who are suffering from a heart attack, stroke, drowning, or shock.

Formal training is required to enter this profession. Training programs vary in length and in the credentials and degrees awarded. Find out more about this and other health careers by clicking on Career Corner at **health.glencoe.com.**

BEYOND the Classroom

Parent Involvement

Advocacy. With your parents, brainstorm ways your family can help promote a smoke-free environment in your community. What actions can you take to contribute to a healthy environment for all people in your community?

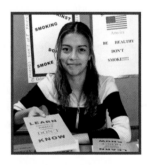

School and Community

Antitobacco Programs. Work with classmates, teachers, and administrators to start a Teens Against Tobacco Use (TATU) program at your school. As a group, design a plan for promoting health in your school and community by reducing tobacco use. Ask members of the community to support your goals.

After You Read

Use the notes you have taken in your Foldable to review what you have learned. Use the vocabulary terms to write an expository paragraph on the effect of tobacco use.

▶ EXPLORING HEALTH TERMS *Answer the following questions on a sheet of paper.*

Lesson 1 *Match each definition with the correct term.*

stimulant	carcinogen
addictive drug	smokeless tobacco
carbon monoxide	nicotine
tar	leukoplakia

1. The addictive drug in tobacco.

2. A drug that increases the action of the central nervous system, the heart, and other organs.

3. A cancer-causing substance.

4. A thick, sticky, dark fluid produced when tobacco burns.

Lesson 2 *Fill in the blanks with the correct term.*

nicotine withdrawal
nicotine substitute

(**_5_**) is the process that occurs in the body when nicotine is no longer used. A (**_6_**) can be used to ease the side effects associated with this process.

Lesson 3 *Replace the underlined words with the correct term.*

mainstream smoke
sidestream smoke
environmental tobacco smoke (ETS)

7. Sidestream smoke is another name for secondhand smoke.

8. Environmental tobacco smoke is the smoke exhaled from the lungs of a smoker.

9. Mainstream smoke is tobacco smoke from the burning end of a cigarette, pipe, or cigar.

▶ RECALLING THE FACTS *Use complete sentences to answer the following questions.*

1. What effect does tar in cigarette smoke have on the respiratory system?

2. What effect does carbon monoxide have on the body?

3. Examine the harmful effects of tobacco use on the digestive and excretory systems.

4. How does smoking lead to lung cancer?

5. How do tobacco companies encourage teen tobacco use?

6. List two refusal skills you can use to say no to tobacco.

7. What are some reasons why teens stop using tobacco?

8. Identify three sources of help for people who want to quit tobacco use.

9. List three health problems associated with environmental tobacco smoke.

10. How does ETS harm infants and young children?

11. How do state laws discourage teen smoking?

12. Describe the goals of *Healthy People 2010* that relate to tobacco use.

For more review questions for Chapter 21, go to **health.glencoe.com**.

➤ WRITING CRITICALLY

1. **Expository.** Write an antismoking advertisement targeted at teens that persuades them to abstain from smoking and tobacco use. In your ad, explain the harmful effects and health risks of tobacco use.

2. **Persuasive.** Write a letter to the editor stating your opinion on teen smoking and urging teens not to use tobacco products. Conduct research on tobacco marketing. Is it legal to market tobacco products to teens? Do tobacco companies market directly to teens? Are tobacco products marketed indirectly to teens? Include facts in your letter. Support your statements with evidence that provides logical reasons, examples, and quotes from experts.

Standardized Test Practice

 The purpose of persuasive writing is to convince the reader, or in this case, the listener, to accept your opinion and take a specific action. The *Writing Situation* focuses on the effects of smoking on public playgrounds. The *Directions for Writing* suggests that you think about these effects and then write a speech that will convince people to accept your views and change their behavior if necessary.

PROMPT

Writing Situation: You have been asked to give a speech urging people to stop smoking on public playgrounds.

Directions for Writing: Think about effects of smoking on public playgrounds—both on the space and on the children who use the playground.

Now, write to convince people to accept your point of view and change their behavior. Be prepared to present your ideas orally to the class or to a group of adults in the community.

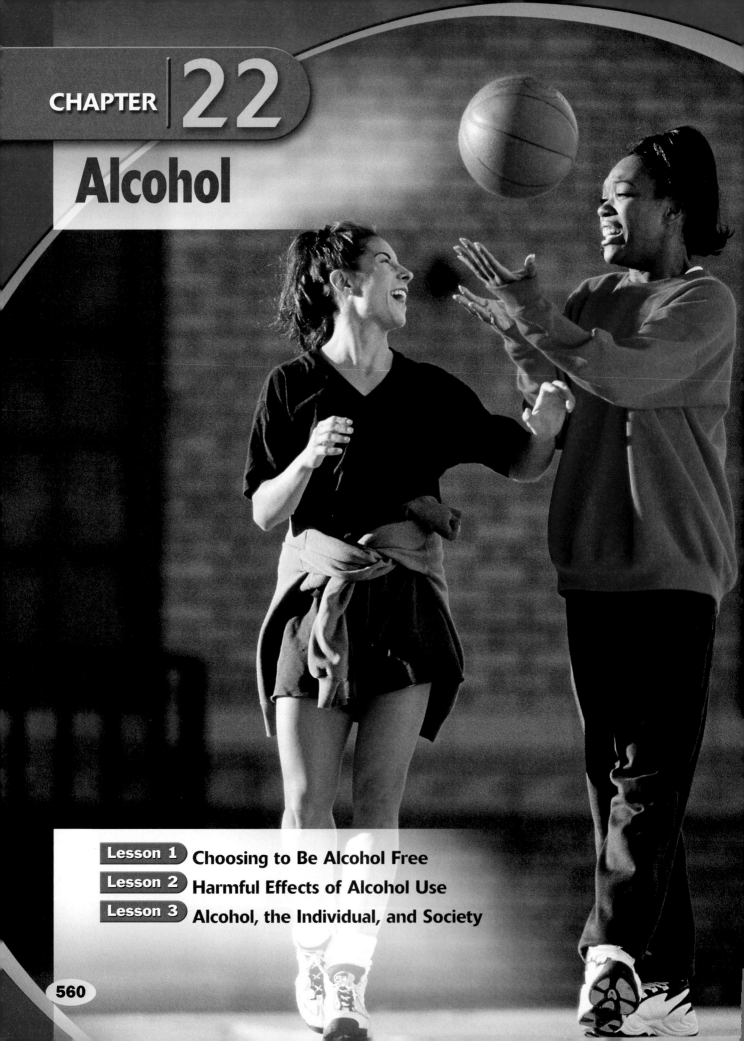

CHAPTER 22

Alcohol

Lesson 1 Choosing to Be Alcohol Free

Lesson 2 Harmful Effects of Alcohol Use

Lesson 3 Alcohol, the Individual, and Society

Eye ON THE Media

Researching Alcohol Issues on the Internet

The Internet can be a useful tool for finding information about health issues such as alcohol use and abuse. However, it is important to analyze the source of information found on the Web. Some credible Web resources may include

▶ **nonprofit organizations.**

▶ **government departments.**

▶ **parent groups.**

Visit the Eye on the Media section at **health.glencoe.com** to learn more about how to evaluate Web sources.

FOLDABLES™
Study Organizer

Before You Read

Make this Foldable to help you organize what you learn about alcohol and about choosing to be alcohol free. Begin with four sheets of 8½" x 11" paper or four sheets of notebook paper.

▶ **Step 1**

Fold four sheets of paper in half along the short axis.

▶ **Step 2**

On each sheet, make a cut 1" from the edge of the paper. Cut through the top flap only.

▶ **Step 3**

Staple the four sheets together at the 1" tabs and label them: The Facts About Alcohol, Factors That Influence Alcohol Use, Avoid Alcohol: Avoid Unsafe Situations, and Being Alcohol Free.

The Facts About Alcohol

As You Read

As you read and discuss the material in the chapter, use your Foldable to define terms and record what you learn under the appropriate tabs.

SPOTLIGHT ON HEALTH

Using Visuals. How can you and your peers let others know that you've decided to live alcohol free?

Choosing to Be Alcohol Free

Guide to Reading

Building Vocabulary

As you read this lesson, write each new highlighted term and its definition in your notebook.

▶ ethanol (p. 562)

▶ fermentation (p. 562)

▶ depressant (p. 563)

▶ intoxication (p. 563)

▶ alcohol abuse (p. 565)

Focusing on the Main Ideas

In this lesson, you will learn how to:

▶ **Identify** factors that influence decisions about alcohol use and your health.

▶ **Examine** the physical, mental/emotional, social, and legal consequences of alcohol use.

▶ **Discuss** the role alcohol plays in unsafe situations.

▶ **Develop** strategies for preventing the use of alcohol.

Reading Strategy

Predict

▶ Scan all the headings, subheadings, and pictures in this lesson. Write a few sentences describing what information you believe this lesson contains.

Write a short paragraph describing what you think might help a teen choose to be alcohol free.

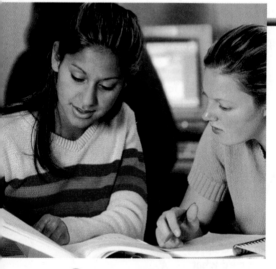

Recognizing the health risks of alcohol will help you make the decision to stay alcohol free. *How can avoiding alcohol use help you succeed in school?*

For many people the image is a familiar one: energetic young adults playing sports, cooking out, living life to the fullest. The purpose of this attractive advertisement scene is to promote and sell a drug—alcohol—that is addictive, physically damaging, and often an entry into the use of other drugs. In reality, alcohol is a lethal drug with harmful effects that include physical, mental/emotional, social, and legal consequences, including serious health problems to the drinker and those around him or her and even death caused by disease, violence, and motor vehicle accidents.

The Facts About Alcohol

Alcohol, or more accurately, **ethanol**—*the type of alcohol in alcoholic beverages*—is a powerful and addictive drug. Ethanol can be produced synthetically and naturally through the fermentation of fruits, vegetables, and grains. **Fermentation** is *the chemical* *action of yeast on sugars.* Water, flavoring, and minerals are mixed with ethanol to produce a variety of beverages, such as beer and wine. Alcohol also can be processed to create spirits, or liquors, such as whiskey, rye, and vodka.

Immediate Effects of Alcohol Consumption

At first drinking alcohol may provide a kind of energy "rush." This initial reaction masks alcohol's true effects as a **depressant**, *a drug that slows the central nervous system.* Alcohol quickly affects a person's motor skills by slowing reaction time and impairing vision. Clear thinking and good judgment also diminish. A variety of factors, including a person's body size and stomach contents, determines alcohol's effect. For this reason, the amount of alcohol that leads to intoxication varies from person to person. **Intoxication** is *the state in which the body is poisoned by alcohol or another substance and the person's physical and mental control is significantly reduced.*

Factors That Influence Alcohol Use

Despite the many problems associated with alcohol use, many teenagers still choose to drink. Why? Several reasons influence teens in their choice to use—or not use—alcohol:

▶ **Peer pressure.** It's normal for teens to want to feel accepted within a group. The desire to fit in is strong. Teens who choose friends who avoid alcohol use are more likely to be alcohol free than teens whose friends accept alcohol use.

▶ **Family.** Family members can help teens be alcohol free. Parents who discourage and avoid the use of alcohol are more likely to have teens who do the same. In fact, teens cite parental disapproval as the number one reason for not using alcohol.

▶ **Media messages.** Many media messages on TV and radio and in movies make alcohol use appear exciting, attractive, and fun. Many of these messages feature elements targeted to a teen audience, such as young, attractive people engaging in problem-free drinking in a partylike atmosphere. The message of many ads is "To fit in, drink alcohol." However, teens who recognize these messages and their meanings are more likely to resist negative influences.

Ⓐ Your family, friends, and peers influence your decisions about avoiding the use of alcohol. *Analyze the importance of alternatives to alcohol and substance use.*

Did You Know ?

Through the media teens are exposed to alcohol use in many forms.

- By the time teens reach ninth grade, most will have seen more ads for beer or wine than for any other product.
- A recent study found that 93 percent of the 200 most popular movie rentals depicted alcohol use.
- A review of top-selling rap recordings found alcohol mentioned in 47 percent of the songs.

Reading Check

Describe What are some factors that determine alcohol's effect on different people?

Advertising Techniques

Companies that produce alcoholic beverages spend billions of dollars each year and use various strategies to advertise and sell their products. Advertisements appear on billboards, can be seen or heard on television and radio, and fill magazines and newspapers. Alcohol companies sponsor sporting events, music concerts, art festivals, exhibits, and other community events. They do this to

Real-Life Application

Seeing Through Alcohol Advertising

What media images come to mind when you think of advertisements for alcohol? Many advertisers appeal to emotions and desires to influence people to buy their products. By understanding the ways in which advertisers market alcohol, teens can make the informed choice to avoid using it.

JOIN THE FUN!

What is really being advertised?
The ad is "selling" physical attractiveness. It appeals to an internal influence that most people share: the desire to be among friends who enjoy being together.

What is the hidden message?
"You need our beer to have fun with your friends."

What is the truth?
Drinking beer is not the reason people are enjoying the party. This picture is staged. In fact, drinking alcohol impairs coordination; the ability to play volleyball would be affected. None of the risks of alcohol use are shown.

ACTIVITY

Use a critical eye when looking at advertisements in magazines and newspapers and on billboards, television, and the Internet. Select three examples of alcohol advertising. For each example, ask yourself these questions:

1. **What is really being advertised?** Write a paragraph that analyzes how the ad appeals to an emotion or a desire in a particular audience.

2. **What is the hidden message?** Create a caption that describes what the advertisers want the intended audience to believe about drinking alcohol.

3. **What is the truth?** Explain why the ad is misleading, using at least three facts about alcohol use that the ad does not mention.

Demonstrate what you have learned from your analysis by writing a statement on the truthfulness of alcohol advertising.

associate their products with attractive and healthy people having fun. It is important to thoroughly analyze and interpret media messages that encourage the consumption of alcohol.

Alcohol's Role in Unsafe Situations

Alcohol use can be dangerous and even deadly. Alcohol-related motor vehicle accidents are the number one cause of death and disability among teens. Alcohol use also is linked with deaths by drowning, fire, suicide, and homicide. Even if you are not drinking but are around people who are, you have an increased risk of being seriously injured, involved in a vehicle crash, and affected by violence. Alcohol-related incidents can be damaging to the health and safety of the user and those associated with the user.

Alcohol and the Law

If you are under 21, it is illegal to buy, possess, or consume alcohol. For teens who break the law, the legal consequences can be very negative. Teens can be arrested, fined, and sentenced to a youth detention center. By breaking the law, the offender risks both damaging his or her reputation and losing the trust and respect of friends and family members.

Alcohol, Violence, and Sexual Activity

Teens can protect their health by avoiding situations where alcohol is present. Teens who drink alcohol are more likely to be victims or perpetrators of violent crimes such as rape, aggravated assault, and robbery. They are also more likely to become involved in fights, resulting in school or police action.

Alcohol use and sexual activity are a dangerous mixture. Alcohol impairs a person's judgment, lowers inhibitions, and compromises moral standards. Teens who use alcohol are more likely to become sexually active at earlier ages, to engage in sexual activity more often, and to engage in unprotected sexual activity more often than teens who do not use alcohol. The effects of such careless sexual activity can be unplanned pregnancy, HIV, STDs, and negative mental and social consequences.

Alcohol Abuse

Most young people do not live in families in which alcohol abuse is a problem. However, it is estimated that 25 percent of all youth *are* exposed to family **alcohol abuse**—*the excessive use of alcohol*—at some time before they reach the age of 18. Young people who live in a household in which a family member abuses alcohol are at a high risk for neglect, abuse, economic hardship, and social isolation. Sometimes these problems can lead a young person to try alcohol

CHARACTER CHECK

Responsibility. Demonstrate your commitment to a lifestyle that does not include alcohol use by taking responsibility for your decisions. **Write and sign a pledge to stay alcohol free. Share your pledge with your parents and friends. Encourage your friends to sign pledges, too.**

Did You Know

Alcohol use is a serious matter. It is a key factor in
- 33 percent of suicides.
- 50 percent of homicides.
- 62 percent of assaults.
- 68 percent of manslaughter cases.
- 50 percent of head injuries.
- 41 percent of traffic fatalities.
- domestic abuse and injury, child abuse and neglect, and workplace injuries.
- more than half of all drowning incidents.

Health Skills Activity

Refusal Skills: Avoiding Alcohol

Chantelle has been invited to a party at her friend Natasha's house. When Chantelle arrives, she is surprised to see people drinking alcoholic beverages. Natasha's parents are not at home.

Chantelle walks over to Natasha. "What kind of party is this?" she asks.

"It's a *high-school* party," Natasha says. "Here, have a beer."

"No, thanks," Chantelle responds. "Won't your parents be upset if they see this?"

"Don't worry," Natasha says. "They won't be home for hours. Here, have a drink. It'll loosen you up."

Chantelle knows she needs to communicate her refusal and leave the party. What should she do?

What Would You Do?
Apply the following refusal skills to write a response for Chantelle.

1. Say no in a firm voice.
2. Explain why you are refusing.
3. Suggest alternatives to the proposed activity.
4. Back up your words with body language.
5. Leave if necessary.

---

as an escape. However, drinking only makes the situation worse. Studies indicate that a person who begins drinking as a teen is four times more likely to develop alcohol dependence than an adult is.

Alcohol and Extracurricular Activities

The negative consequences of alcohol use for teens can extend to their eligibility for participation in extracurricular activities, including athletics. Most schools have adopted a zero-tolerance policy for students found using alcohol. If caught, students may become ineligible to participate or may be suspended from their activities or from school. A student's future social, college, and job prospects could be damaged.

Being Alcohol Free

Deciding to be alcohol free is an important step in achieving a healthy lifestyle. Many people, especially teens, make the commitment to stay alcohol free. This commitment helps you:

A Choosing to be alcohol free allows you to reach your potential and achieve your goals.

▶ **Maintain a healthy body.** Avoiding alcohol use protects body organs from damage and decreases the chance of injury.

▶ **Make responsible decisions.** Having a clear head helps you make decisions to protect your health and the health of others.

▶ **Avoid risky behavior.** Teens who avoid alcohol reduce their risk of drinking and driving, participating in sexual activity, and being a victim or perpetrator of a violent crime.

▶ **Avoid illegal activities.** Purchasing and possessing alcohol are against the law for anyone under the age of 21. You can avoid arrest and legal problems by being alcohol free.

Strategies for Preventing Use of Alcohol

Even if the pressure to use alcohol becomes intense, saying no is much easier when you're prepared. If you find yourself in a situation in which alcohol is present, be assertive: refuse to drink, leave the situation quickly, and call for a ride home. Your best defense is to avoid situations in which alcohol is present. Practice refusal skills to build confidence. A prepared individual knows methods for effectively expressing feelings and opinions on health issues.

Call home for a ride if you find yourself in a situation where alcohol is present. *What other refusal strategies can you demonstrate to avoid unsafe situations?*

LESSON 1 REVIEW

Reviewing Facts and Vocabulary

1. Define the terms *alcohol*, *depressant*, and *intoxication*.

2. Identify and explain ways families can have a positive influence on teens' decisions about alcohol use.

3. Describe and demonstrate two effective refusal strategies for avoiding the use of alcohol.

Thinking Critically

4. **Analyzing.** Explain the depressant effects of alcohol. How might alcohol affect your ability to make healthful decisions?

5. **Synthesizing.** Explain the role alcohol plays in unsafe situations such as HIV, STDs, unplanned pregnancies, and motor vehicle accidents.

Applying Health Skills

Advocacy. Prepare a pamphlet or an article for your school newspaper that advocates an alcohol-free lifestyle. Describe the risks and consequences of alcohol use. Be sure to explain the benefits of being alcohol free and to include strategies you have developed for preventing use of alcohol.

After You Read

Problems and Solutions. Make a T chart. On the left side, list facts about alcohol and its role in unsafe situations. On the right side, list ways to be alcohol free.

Harmful Effects of Alcohol Use

Guide to Reading

Building Vocabulary

As you read this lesson, write each new highlighted term and its definition in your notebook.

▶ metabolism (p. 569)

▶ blood alcohol concentration (p. 570)

▶ binge drinking (p. 571)

▶ alcohol poisoning (p. 571)

Focusing on the Main Ideas

In this lesson, you will learn how to:

▶ Describe the short-term effects of alcohol use.

▶ Discuss the consequences of drinking and driving.

▶ Explain the dangers of drug/alcohol use.

▶ Develop refusal strategies concerning alcohol use.

Reading Strategy

Predict

▶ Scan the headings, subheadings, and photo captions. Write a short paragraph predicting what you think will be taught in this lesson.

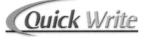

Make a list of all the negative effects of alcohol use that you can think of.

Ⓐ **Many over-the-counter and prescription drugs carry warning labels about alcohol interactions.** *Analyze how these warnings help protect users from health risks.*

Statistics confirm that drinking alcohol is a high-risk behavior. Nevertheless, some teens feel pressured to drink alcohol. Finding out about the physical effects alcohol has on the body can help you strengthen your commitment to staying alcohol free.

Short-Term Effects of Drinking

The short-term effects of alcohol are different for each individual. Many of these effects are described in **Figure 22.1.** Some factors that influence the onset of these effects include:

▶ **Body size and gender.** A small person feels the effect of the same amount of alcohol faster than a large person does. In general, alcohol moves into the bloodstream faster in females.

▶ **Food.** Food in the stomach slows down the passage of alcohol into the bloodstream.

▶ **Amount and rate of intake.** As the amount of alcohol consumed increases, the level of alcohol in the bloodstream also rises. When a person drinks alcohol faster than the liver can break it down, intoxication results. When blood alcohol levels become too high, alcohol poisoning can occur.

Alcohol and Drug Interactions

Interactions between medications and alcohol can lead to illness, injury, and even death. In fact, alcohol-drug interactions are a factor in about one-fourth of all emergency room admissions. To understand why these interactions occur, you must understand how the body works. When a drug enters the body, it travels through the bloodstream to its target organ or tissue. Over time, the body metabolizes the drug. **Metabolism** is *the process by which the body breaks down substances.* Alcohol travels through the bloodstream to the brain. At the same time, the liver metabolizes the alcohol in the bloodstream and makes it less active. Then the kidneys filter the neutralized particles and other waste products from the blood and produce urine, which is excreted.

The presence of both alcohol and medication or another drug within a person's body can be very dangerous. Most over-the-counter medicines and prescription drugs warn users against drinking alcohol while on that drug. It is important that you recognize that use of alcohol and other drugs contributes to accidents, crime, and suicide. This is because alcohol combined with medicines or other drugs can result in a *multiplier effect,* in which the medication has a greater or different effect than if it were taken alone. Both prescription drugs and over-the-counter medicines, such as aspirin, can alter the ways in which alcohol affects the body. Labels on medicines that might cause reactions warn against combining them with alcoholic beverages.

FIGURE 22.1

SHORT-TERM EFFECTS OF ALCOHOL

Physical and mental impairment begin with the first drink of alcohol and increase as more alcohol is consumed.

Nervous System	Cardiovascular System	Digestive System	Respiratory System
• **Brain.** The brain becomes less able to control the body. Movement, speech, and vision may be affected. • **Memory.** Thought processes are disorganized, and memory and concentration are dulled. • **Judgment.** Judgment is altered and coordination is impaired.	• **Heart.** With a low intake, alcohol causes an increase in heart rate and blood pressure. At higher intake levels, heart rate and blood pressure decrease and heart rhythm becomes irregular. Risk of cardiac arrest increases. • **Blood Vessels.** Alcohol causes the blood vessels to expand. The increased surface area of the blood vessels allows body heat to escape and the body's temperature to drop.	• **Stomach.** Some alcohol passes quickly from the stomach into the bloodstream. Stomach acid production increases and often results in nausea and vomiting. • **Liver.** Toxic chemicals are released as the liver metabolizes alcohol. These chemicals cause inflammation and scarring. • **Kidneys.** Alcohol causes the kidneys to increase urine output, which can lead to dehydration.	• **Lungs.** Carbon dioxide formed by the liver is released from the body through the lungs. • **Breathing.** Alcohol depresses nerves that control involuntary functions such as breathing. If an excessive amount of alcohol is consumed, breathing may slow, become irregular, or stop.

These are some typical alcohol-drug interactions:

▶ Alcohol may slow down a drug's absorption by the body. This increases the length of time that the alcohol or drug is in the body and increases the risk of harmful side effects from the drug.

▶ Frequent drinking may increase the number of metabolizing enzymes in the body. This can cause medications to be broken down faster than normal, decreasing their effectiveness.

▶ Metabolizing enzymes can change some medications into chemicals that can damage the liver or other organs. For example, when taken with alcohol, acetaminophen, a common painkiller and fever reducer, can cause serious liver damage even when it is used in small amounts.

▶ Alcohol can increase the effects of some drugs. For example, antihistamines, which are taken for colds or allergies, react with alcohol and cause excessive dizziness and sleepiness. This effect is especially dangerous if you are operating machinery or driving.

Driving Under the Influence

Drinking alcohol impairs vision, reaction time, and coordination. When drinking is mixed with driving, the results can be disastrous and even deadly. In fact, *driving while intoxicated* (DWI), also known as *driving under the influence* (DUI), is the leading cause of death among teens. A person is said to be intoxicated when his or her blood alcohol concentration exceeds the state's legal limit. **Blood alcohol concentration (BAC)** is *the amount of alcohol in a person's blood, expressed as a percentage.* In most states driving while intoxicated is defined as having a 0.1 percent BAC, although in some states the figure is 0.08. However, signs of intoxication can begin to appear at BACs as low as 0.02. **Figure 22.2** on the next page illustrates the alcohol content of some common alcoholic beverages. Remember that for anyone under 21, there is no acceptable BAC percentage. Medical researchers have found that drinking of any sort

▶ slows reflexes.

▶ reduces a person's ability to judge distances and speeds.

▶ increases risk-taking behaviors.

▶ reduces a person's concentration while increasing forgetfulness.

Alcohol-related vehicle fatalities are a leading cause of death for teens. *What other consequences are associated with risk-taking such as drinking and driving?*

Consequences of DWI

When a person is stopped for drinking and driving, a police officer will administer a field sobriety test before the person is given a breathalyzer test to measure BAC. The consequences for a teen caught driving while intoxicated or driving under the influence may include

▶ harm to the driver and others.

▶ severely restricted driving privileges and/or immediate confiscation of a driver's license.

▶ alcohol-related injuries, property damage, and death.

▶ living with regret and remorse from these consequences.

▶ loss of parental trust and respect.

▶ arrest, jail time, court appearance, and a heavy fine or bail.

▶ a police record and possible lawsuits.

▶ higher insurance rates.

Like drinking and driving, riding in a vehicle with a driver who has been drinking is also a serious matter. Every day at least a dozen teens are killed in alcohol-related crashes. Never ride in a vehicle with a driver who has been drinking. If you are faced with this situation, demonstrate refusal strategies: find a ride with someone who has not been drinking, or call home to have someone come to get you. Using refusal skills shows that you understand the role of individual responsibility regarding personal risk behavior.

Binge Drinking

Recent studies show that **binge drinking**, *drinking five or more alcoholic drinks at one sitting,* is a serious problem among young people. Rapid binge drinking is especially dangerous because it is possible to consume a fatal dose of alcohol.

Alcohol Poisoning

It is very dangerous, and can be deadly, to drink a large amount of alcohol. **Alcohol poisoning** is *a severe and potentially fatal physical reaction to an alcohol overdose.* Alcohol acts as a depressant and shuts down involuntary actions such as breathing and the gag reflex that prevents choking. It's common for a person who has consumed too much alcohol to vomit because alcohol is a stomach irritant. If the involuntary actions are shut down, a person can choke and be asphyxiated by his or her own vomit.

FIGURE 22.2

COMPARING BEER, WINE, AND SPIRITS

Each of these beverages contains the same amount of pure alcohol—about 0.5 ounces.

Drink	Alcohol by Volume	Alcohol Content
Beer 12 oz.	4%	0.5 oz.
Wine 5 oz.	10%	0.5 oz.
Vodka or Whiskey 1.25 oz.	40%	0.5 oz.

Hands-On Health   ACTIVITY

Saying No to a Driver Who Has Been Drinking

You've heard the statement "Don't drink and drive." It's also dangerous to ride in a car if you suspect the driver has been drinking. Here are some strategies you can demonstrate to refuse that ride.

- Make a firm commitment to yourself not to ride with someone who has been drinking. If you know that alcohol will be available at a party, don't go.
- When you suspect a driver has been drinking, be prepared to make the right choice for your health and safety. Be strong. Find another way home.

Direct Statements: "I am not riding with you. You have been drinking."

Excuses: "I forgot to tell you—my dad is picking me up."

Insults: "You are really crazy to drive after drinking."

Humor: "I'm not getting in that car with you; I value my life."

Alternate suggestion: "Give me the keys; I'll drive."

What You'll Need

- 1 index card per student
- colored pencils or markers
- hole punch
- scissors

What You'll Do

1. Working with a small group, brainstorm a list of refusal strategies a teen can use to avoid riding in a car with a driver who has been drinking.

2. Write and present a skit that has dialogue showing one or more successful refusal skills. Be sure that every group member has a part.

3. Act out your skit for the class. Analyze each skit for the dialogue you think is most effective. Remember

and practice these statements so that you'll be prepared if a drinking driver offers you a ride.

Apply and Conclude

On your own, cut a 3″ × 5″ index card in half so that you have a 3″ × 2½″ card. Write "Don't Ride with a Drunk Driver" on the card. Then write at least two statements you can use to refuse such a ride. Use markers to make the card eye-catching. After your teacher laminates the card, punch a hole in it and place it on your key ring.

Effects of Alcohol Poisoning

Passing out is a common effect of drinking too much alcohol. Alcohol doesn't stop entering a person's bloodstream after he or she passes out, however. Instead, alcohol in the stomach and intestines continues to enter the bloodstream, and blood alcohol concentration continues to rise. For this reason, it's dangerous to assume that a person who has consumed a lot of alcohol will be fine if left to "sleep it off."

Symptoms that indicate alcohol poisoning include

▶ mental confusion, stupor, coma, inability to be roused, vomiting, and seizures.

▶ slow respiration—10 seconds between breaths or fewer than 8 breaths a minute.

▶ irregular heartbeat.

▶ hypothermia, or low body temperature—pale or bluish skin color.

▶ severe dehydration from vomiting.

A person who exhibits any of these signs or has passed out may die if left untreated. If you suspect that a person has alcohol poisoning, call 911 immediately.

The consequences of binge drinking can have serious effects on a person's health. *What should you do if you suspect someone has alcohol poisoning?*

LESSON 2 REVIEW

Reviewing Facts and Vocabulary

1. Define *blood alcohol concentration* and *metabolism.*

2. Examine the short-term effects of alcohol use. List three ways alcohol impairs the functioning of the nervous system.

3. What are the signs of alcohol poisoning?

Thinking Critically

4. **Analyzing.** Explain why it's dangerous to mix alcohol and medications or other drugs.

5. **Synthesizing.** Associate risk-taking with consequences such as drinking and driving. Describe the legal and financial consequences of operating a motor vehicle while under the influence of alcohol.

Applying Health Skills

Advocacy. Prepare a public service announcement to get the word out about the health risks of binge drinking. Include facts about alcohol's effects on the body, as well as the risks involved with rapid binge drinking and how it can cause alcohol poisoning. Demonstrate effective refusal strategies to avoid these risks.

After You Read

Analyze a Graph. After reviewing Figure 22.2, on page 571, determine how many of each drink would need to be consumed to meet your state's BAC.

Visit **health.glencoe.com** for the Interactive Study Guide for Lesson 2.

Lesson 2 Harmful Effects of Alcohol Use **573**

Alcohol, the Individual, and Society

Guide to Reading

Building Vocabulary

As you read this lesson, write each new highlighted term and its definition in your notebook.

▶ fetal alcohol syndrome (FAS) (p. 576)

▶ alcoholism (p. 576)

▶ alcoholic (p. 576)

▶ recovery (p. 578)

▶ detoxification (p. 578)

▶ sobriety (p. 578)

Focusing on the Main Ideas

In this lesson, you will learn how to:

▶ Identify the goals of *Healthy People 2010* to reduce risk behaviors associated with alcohol use.

▶ Compare the effects of alcohol use on body systems and the risk of disease caused by alcohol use.

▶ Describe the harmful effects of alcohol on a fetus.

▶ List community health-related services for prevention and treatment of alcoholism and alcohol use.

Reading Strategy

Organize Information

▶ Fold your paper into three sections. Label the sections Physical, Mental/Emotional, and Social. As you read, list ways that the use of alcohol affects each part of the health triangle in the appropriate sections.

One devastating effect of alcohol use is alcoholism. Write a short paragraph describing the effects of alcoholism on society.

(A) **Compare the healthy liver (top) with the liver that has been damaged by alcohol use.** *Explain the relationship between a healthy liver and an alcohol-free lifestyle.*

The costs of alcohol use are far-reaching and relate to individual, family, and community health. One goal of *Healthy People 2010* is to reduce a number of risk behaviors associated with alcohol. This includes reducing average annual alcohol consumption, binge drinking, and the total number of alcohol-related deaths and deaths due to alcohol-related vehicle crashes. Health-literate teens are able to determine how the use of alcohol and other drugs contributes to accidents, crime, and suicide.

Long-Term Effects of Alcohol on the Body

Alcohol use has long-term effects on the user and on others as well. Excessive alcohol use over a prolonged period of time can damage most body systems. These effects are more severe in the body of a young person. In teens alcohol use can interfere with growth and development. **Figure 22.3** shows some of the long-term effects of alcohol abuse.

FIGURE 22.3

LONG-TERM EFFECTS OF ALCOHOL ABUSE

Alcohol affects many of the major organs in the body, and long-term drinking can cause death. The worst damage occurs after years of abuse, but some damage occurs with only moderate drinking.

Changes to the Brain

• **Addiction**—inability to stop drinking.

• **Loss of brain functions**—loss of verbal skills, visual and spatial skills, and memory.

• **Brain damage**—long-term excessive use of alcohol can lead to major brain damage and even to a reduction of brain size. Moderate drinking can destroy brain cells; however, the brain can regain some of its lost abilities over time if a person stops drinking.

Cardiovascular Changes

• **Heart**—damage to heart muscle.

• **Enlarged heart**—from increased workload caused by alcohol.

• **High blood pressure**—damages the heart and can cause heart attack and stroke.

Liver Problems

• **Fatty liver**—fats build up in the liver and cannot be broken down; excess fat blocks the flow of blood to liver cells, leading to cell death.

• **Alcoholic hepatitis**—inflammation or infection of the liver.

• **Cirrhosis**—liver tissue is replaced with useless scar tissue; the disease can lead to liver failure and death unless a liver transplant is performed.

Digestive System Problems

• **Irritation**—digestive lining is damaged; can lead to stomach ulcers and cancer of the stomach and esophagus.

Pancreas Problems

• **Lining of the pancreas**—swells to block the passage from the pancreas to the small intestine. Chemicals the small intestine needs for digestion can't pass through the blocked area. The chemicals begin to destroy the pancreas itself, causing pain and vomiting. A severe case can lead to death.

Alcohol During Pregnancy

When a pregnant female drinks, so, in effect, does her fetus. Alcohol passes from the mother's body into the bloodstream of the fetus. Unlike the adult liver, the fetus's liver is not developed enough to process the alcohol. As a result, a female who drinks during pregnancy risks permanent damage to the fetus. Drinking

Reading Check

Describe How does alcohol abuse affect many of the body's major organs (Figure 22.3)?

during the first few weeks of pregnancy—when many women do not yet realize they are pregnant—can be especially harmful to a baby's central nervous system. Infants born to mothers who drink during pregnancy may be at risk of **fetal alcohol syndrome (FAS)**, *a group of alcohol-related birth defects that include physical and mental problems.*

Effects of Fetal Alcohol Syndrome (FAS)

The effects of fetal alcohol syndrome are both severe and lasting. An FAS baby may be born with a small head and deformities of the face, hands, or feet. Heart, liver, and kidney defects, as well as vision and hearing problems, are common. FAS babies experience slow growth and coordination and have difficulties with learning, attention, memory, and problem solving.

FAS is the leading known cause of mental retardation in the United States. The good news is that it's totally preventable—provided that expectant mothers understand two things: there is no safe amount of alcohol to drink and no safe time in which to drink it. Even small amounts of alcohol can harm a fetus.

Alcoholism

One of the most devastating effects of alcohol use is **alcoholism**, *a disease in which a person has a physical or psychological dependence on drinks that contain alcohol.* Alcoholism is characterized by an impaired ability to study, work, and socialize normally.

Alcoholics

An **alcoholic** is *an addict who is dependent on alcohol.* Some alcoholics may display harmful behaviors such as drunken driving and violent or aggressive actions. Others may become quiet and withdrawn. Alcoholism is not limited to any age, race, ethnic, or socioeconomic group. Alcoholics may be middle-aged business people or high-school athletes. Regardless of background, alcoholics can develop serious health problems, such as cirrhosis of the liver and brain damage. An alcoholic might display these symptoms:

▶ **Craving.** An alcoholic has a compulsion, or strong need, to drink; he or she cannot manage tension and stress without drinking.

▶ **Loss of control.** An alcoholic cannot limit his or her drinking and is preoccupied with alcohol.

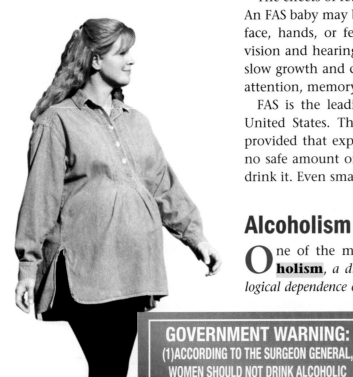

GOVERNMENT WARNING: (1)ACCORDING TO THE SURGEON GENERAL, WOMEN SHOULD NOT DRINK ALCOHOLIC BEVERAGES DURING PREGNANCY BECAUSE OF THE RISK OF BIRTH DEFECTS. (2)CONSUMPTION OF ALCOHOLIC BEVERAGES IMPAIRS YOUR ABILITY TO DRIVE A CAR OR OPERATE MACHINERY AND MAY CAUSE HEALTH PROBLEMS.

Avoiding tobacco, alcohol, and other drugs is an important decision a female can take toward a healthy pregnancy. *Analyze the harmful effects on the fetus of alcohol.*

▶ **Physical dependence.** When not drinking, an alcoholic may experience withdrawal symptoms, such as nausea, sweating, shakiness, and anxiety.

▶ **Tolerance.** An alcoholic experiences a need to drink increasingly greater amounts of alcohol in order to feel its effects.

▶ **Health, family, and legal problems.** An alcoholic often suffers repeated injuries, receives multiple drunk driving citations, and has frequent arguments and generally poor relationships with family members.

Factors Affecting Alcoholics

Growing scientific evidence suggests a genetic link to alcoholism. In fact, the American Academy of Child and Adolescent Psychiatry reports that children of alcoholics are four times more likely than other children to become alcoholics. However, this does not necessarily mean that a person with such a genetic pre-disposition will become an alcoholic. Other environmental factors, such as family, friends, culture, peer pressure, availability of alcohol, and stress, also put a person at risk for alcoholism. There is, however, one guarantee: You can protect yourself against this disease by making the healthy choice to stay alcohol free.

Stages of Alcoholism

According to the American Medical Association, alcoholism develops in three stages. All alcoholics do not experience each stage equally.

▶ **Stage 1—Abuse.** Typically, alcoholism begins with social drinking in an attempt to relax. Over time, a physical and psychological dependence on alcohol to manage stress develops. At this point a person begins to drink and become intoxicated regularly, which can result in blackouts and memory loss. Often, a person begins to lie or make excuses about his or her drinking. The person needs to consume more alcohol to feel the desired effect. He or she may be a problem drinker.

▶ **Stage 2—Dependence.** The person reaches a point where he or she cannot stop drinking and is physically dependent on the drug. Alcohol becomes the person's central focus. The drinker tries to hide the problem, but performance on the job, at school, and at home soon suffers. The drinker makes excuses and blames others for problems.

Family members of alcoholics also experience the negative effects of alcoholism. *List ways a person can avoid the risks of alcoholism.*

▶ **Stage 3—Addiction.** In the final stage of alcoholism, drinking is the *most* important thing in a person's life. The person is addicted to the drug and his or her life is out of control, although frequently he or she does not realize or acknowledge this fact. Because liver damage is common at this stage, less alcohol may be required to produce intoxication. If the alcoholic stopped drinking, he or she would experience severe withdrawal symptoms.

Effects on Family and Society

There are an estimated 14 million alcoholics in the United States. Health-literate teens understand how the social environment influences the health of the community. Alcohol use is a major factor in the four leading causes of accidental death—car accidents, falls, drownings, and house fires. Alcohol also plays a major role in violent crimes, such as homicide, forcible rape, and robbery. For example:

▶ About 40 percent of violent crimes, totaling about 3 million annually, are alcohol-related.

▶ Two-thirds of victims who encounter **domestic violence** report that alcohol was a factor in the crime.

▶ Nearly half of all homicide victims have alcohol in their bloodstreams.

Often, alcoholism has indirect, as well as direct, effects on people associated with alcoholics. These people may be involved in a process known as *codependency*. Codependents learn to ignore their own needs and focus their energy and emotions on the needs of the alcoholic. In the process codependents lose their trust in others, their self-esteem, and, at times, their own health.

Treatment for Alcohol Abuse

Although alcoholism cannot be cured, it *can* be treated. A health-literate individual knows how to access school and community health services for self and others. *The process of learning to live an alcohol-free life* is called **recovery**. As many as two-thirds of all alcoholics who try to recover do so with proper treatment. The goal of treatment programs is to stop or control the intake of alcohol. Counseling and medication can help an alcohol user set goals to deal with problems of alcohol abuse. **Sobriety**, *living without alcohol,* is a lifelong commitment. Many resources are available to help people who have a drinking problem. Help is also available for the families and friends of problem drinkers. Some of these programs are described in **Figure 22.4.**

Reading Check

Infer How does alcoholism affect the family and friends of an alcoholic?

STEPS TO RECOVERY

Step 1: Admission
The person admits to having a drinking problem and asks for help.

Step 2: Detoxification
The person goes through **detoxification,** *a process in which the body adjusts to functioning without alcohol.*

Step 3: Counseling
The person receives counseling to help him or her learn to live without alcohol.

Step 4: Recovery
The person takes responsibility for his or her own life.

FIGURE 22.4

WHERE TO GET HELP FOR ALCOHOL ABUSE

There are many places to get information about treatment for alcohol dependency. The goal of these programs is to provide support for alcoholics, family members, and friends affected by alcoholism.

Al-Anon/ Alateen	Alcoholics Anonymous	National Association for Children of Alcoholics	National Clearinghouse for Alcohol and Drug Information	National Drug and Treatment Referral Routing Service
helps families and friends of alcoholics deal with and recover from the effects of living with an alcoholic	provides help for alcohol users of all ages	provides help for children of alcoholics	provides information about alcohol and other drugs	provides treatment referral and information about treatment facilities

It's Not Your Fault!

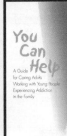

LESSON 3 REVIEW

Reviewing Facts and Vocabulary

1. Identify three serious effects of alcohol abuse.

2. Define *sobriety.* Explain why sobriety is a lifelong commitment.

3. What steps must an alcoholic take during the recovery process?

Thinking Critically

4. **Analyzing.** Explain how damage can occur in the body of the developing fetus when a pregnant woman drinks alcohol.

5. **Synthesizing.** Alcoholism can have devastating effects on people associated with an alcoholic. Explain ways that these individuals can be affected, and tell how and where those living with an alcoholic can get help.

Applying Health Skills

Accessing Information. Consult your school counselor or use the phone book to identify available health-related services in the community for families with alcohol-related problems. Research the availability of family counseling. Explain why these sources are valid. Share your information in a flyer or pamphlet.

After You Read

Explain. Write a summary describing the three stages of alcoholism. After completing the summary, write a brief paragraph describing what sources of help are available in your community.

Reducing Underage Drinking Through Coalitions

Keeping the Lid on the Bottle

Teens can make a difference when it comes to preventing underage drinking.

Kasey Folse, 16, is a member of the Louisiana Alliance to Prevent Underage Drinking. He works to enact laws that make it harder for those who are underage to buy alcohol, such as registration tags for beer kegs. These tags would allow police to trace kegs back to whomever purchased it and punish that person if the beer was being served to underage drinkers. Kasey is also working to offer teens a place to talk about alcohol issues. "Kids don't really have anywhere to turn at my school," says Kasey. "It would definitely help if we had someone to talk one on one with students to deal with alcohol and drug questions."

Things weren't all that different at Andrew Araiza's Mary Carroll High School in Corpus Christi, Texas. Andrew says that many teens "don't consider all the problems associated with alcohol, like poisoning, accidents, and suicide."

Andrew is executive vice president of Texans Standing Tall, a coalition of youths and adults against underage drinking. He has successfully lobbied to remove liquor ads from the state's hunting license handbook and helped lower the legal blood alcohol limit from .1 to .08. Andrew says, "Having peer-group talks, where a teen with a problem describes what happened to him or her—that would get the message across."

Thanks to Ann Miller, 18, that message is coming through loud and clear at Oregon's Canby High. She educates teens about drinking, counsels those with problems, and encourages them to attend a local youth-oriented Alcoholics Anonymous meeting. The result is a greater awareness in the school of the drawbacks of alcohol use and a population of teens who aren't afraid to ask for help. "People with a drinking problem have got to have good treatment available and good support from the adults around them," says Miller.

TIME to THINK...

About Blood Alcohol Level

On the Internet or your school's media center, look up government statistics about alcohol-related traffic accidents. Use those statistics to come up with three powerful reasons why people should not drink and drive.

Health Skills Application

1. **Practicing Healthful Behaviors.** What physical, mental, social, and legal consequences are faced by students who are caught using or possessing alcohol? *(LESSON 1)*

2. **Communication Skills.** Suppose a friend who has been drinking is going to drive himself or herself and others home. How would you respond to this situation? *(LESSON 2)*

3. **Advocacy.** Find out about groups at your school that advocate for an alcohol-free lifestyle. Get involved with a group, using what you have learned about the consequences of drinking to get local stores to advocate for less advertising of alcohol products. *(LESSON 3)*

CAREER Corner

BEYOND the Classroom

Substance Abuse Counselor

Do you like helping friends with their problems? Would you enjoy counseling people who need to find help for alcohol abuse problems in their families? As a substance abuse counselor, you would assess and treat people with substance problems and help those who live with alcoholics or substance abusers.

More than half of all counselors in the United States have a master's degree. Most states require some form of credentials, certification, license, or registry before someone can become a counselor. Find out more about this and other health careers by clicking on Career Corner at **health.glencoe.com.**

Parent Involvement

Advocacy. With your parents or guardians, learn about SADD—Students Against Destructive Decisions. Learn when, where, and why it was founded, what its mission is, and how you and your family can get involved. Draw up a contract for all family members to sign that includes a commitment never to drink and drive and never to ride with any driver who has been drinking—even a family member.

School and Community

Support Programs. Locate an alcohol treatment program in your community. Contact the agency and find out how the program works, what is required of participants, and how people are supported during the recovery process. Report to your class what you have learned.

After You Read

Use the notes you have taken in your Foldable to review what you have learned. Look at the labels, recall what you know about that main idea, then check your responses by looking under the tabs.

▶ EXPLORING HEALTH TERMS *Answer the following questions on a sheet of paper.*

Lesson 1 *Fill in the blanks with the correct term.*

alcohol abuse	fermentation
depressant	intoxication
ethanol	

Drinks that contain (_1_) act as a (_2_) on the central nervous system. Drinking alcohol can lead to physical and mental impairment that is called (_3_). (_4_) puts family members at risk for neglect, physical abuse, and economic hardship.

Lesson 2 *Match each definition with the correct term.*

blood alcohol concentration	metabolism
binge drinking	alcohol poisoning

5. The process by which the body breaks down substances.
6. Drinking five or more alcoholic drinks at one sitting.
7. The amount of alcohol in a person's blood expressed as a percentage.
8. A severe and potentially fatal physical reaction to an alcohol overdose.

Lesson 3 *Fill in the blanks with the correct term.*

alcoholism	alcoholic
detoxification	fetal alcohol syndrome
sobriety	recovery

9. _____ is a condition in which a fetus has been adversely affected mentally and physically by the mother's alcohol use during pregnancy.
10. A(n) _____ has an addiction to alcohol.
11. _____ is a process in which the body adjusts to functioning without alcohol.

▶ RECALLING THE FACTS *Use complete sentences to answer the following questions.*

1. List three factors that influence alcohol use.
2. What are some of the risks of alcohol use?
3. Describe the effects that alcohol has on the body.
4. What impact can alcohol use have on a teen's education and career goals?
5. Describe one typical alcohol-drug interaction.
6. What are some factors that affect an individual's short-term reaction to alcohol?
7. What are some physical, mental, social, and legal consequences of driving while intoxicated or driving under the influence?
8. Explain how alcohol poisoning can cause a person's blood alcohol concentration to continue to rise even after the person stops consuming alcohol.
9. What are some specific goals of *Healthy People 2010* for reducing ways in which alcohol affects the family and society?
10. What is a safe amount of alcohol that a mother can drink during pregnancy?
11. Describe the symptoms an alcoholic might display.
12. Describe two programs that offer help to alcoholics and their families. Explain the services they provide.

For more review questions for Chapter 22, go to **health.glencoe.com**.

➤ WRITING CRITICALLY

1. Narrative. Write a one-page story describing how a teen uses refusal skills when asked to go to a party where no adults will be present and alcohol will be served. Show how an alcohol-free activity is both healthy and fun.

2. Descriptive. Write a scenario describing two teens. One teen has developed a drinking problem. The other teen is a friend who wants to help. Should the friend talk to the problem drinker or consult with a trusted adult? What steps would you take to help the friend?

Standardized Test Practice

 Read the paragraph below and then answer the questions.

Law enforcement officers use special machines that people breathe into to determine the blood alcohol level of the person being tested. How can a person's breath show how much alcohol is in the person's blood? Alcohol travels through the bloodstream to many parts of the body. As the blood passes through the lungs, a certain amount of alcohol moves from the blood to the lungs and is exhaled. The amount of alcohol exhaled depends on the concentration of alcohol in the blood. When body temperature and blood cell composition are normal, the relationship between breath alcohol and blood alcohol is shown on the machine's graph.

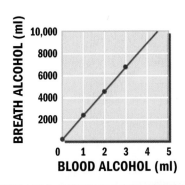

1. Kim breathes into the machine and exhales 3150 mL of air. According to the graph, how many milliliters of blood alcohol are equivalent to this volume of air?

- **A** 1 mL
- **B** 1.5 mL
- **C** 3 mL
- **D** 2100 mL

2. What type of function is shown on the graph?

- **F** exponential
- **G** higher degree
- **H** linear
- **I** quadratic

3. An increase in body temperature of 1.8°F results in an increase of 7 percent in the machine's test results. If a graph similar to the one shown were drawn for a person with a temperature of 97°F, would the slope be greater or less than the slope of this graph? Explain.

Medicines and Drugs

Eye ON THE Media

Interview About Steroid Use

News stories describing steroid use among amateur and professional athletes have grabbed the headlines in recent years. Steroid use can result in negative consequences, including an increased risk of

▶ cancer, heart disease, stroke, or kidney failure.

▶ emotional problems, such as "roid rages."

▶ alteration of sexual characteristics.

Visit the Eye on the Media section at health.glencoe.com to learn more about this topic.

FOLDABLES™
Study Organizer

Before You Read

Make this Foldable to help you organize what you learn about the role of medicines. Begin with a plain sheet of 11" x 17" paper.

▶ **Step 1**

Fold the short sides of a sheet of paper into the middle to form a shutterfold.

▶ **Step 2**

Fold the shutterfold in half.

▶ **Step 3**

Unfold. Cut along the inside fold lines on both sides to form four tabs. Label as shown.

| Medicines That Prevent Disease | Medicines That Fight Pathogens |
| Medicines That Relieve Pain | Medicines That Promote Health |

As You Read

As you read and discuss the material in the chapter, use your Foldable to take notes and to list examples under the appropriate tabs.

SPOTLIGHT ON HEALTH

Using Visuals. Illegal drugs can seriously damage a person's physical, mental/emotional, and social health. In what specific ways can drugs affect an athlete's life?

The Role of Medicines

Guide to Reading

Building Vocabulary

As you read this lesson, write each new highlighted term and its definition in your notebook.

► medicines (p. 586)
► drugs (p. 586)
► vaccine (p. 587)
► analgesics (p. 588)
► side effects (p. 589)
► additive interaction (p. 589)
► synergistic effect (p. 589)
► antagonistic interaction (p. 589)

Focusing on the Main Ideas

In this lesson, you will learn how to:

► **Compare** the relationships between medicines, health promotion, and disease prevention.
► **Discuss** the differences between prescription and over-the-counter medicines.
► **List** laws, policies, and practices that relate to the safe use of medicine.

Reading Strategy

Classify

► Fold your paper into four parts. Label the parts for medicines that Prevent Disease, Fight Pathogens, Relieve Pain, and Promote Health. As you read, list facts in the appropriate sections.

Write a short paragraph describing some of the ways medicine can promote good health.

▲ Medicines are taken to fight illness, promote health, prevent disease, and reduce pain. *When was the last time you needed to use some type of medication?*

Medicines are taken for many different reasons. A person may sustain a painful injury while playing a sport or perhaps develop a chest cold accompanied by a hacking cough. To help promote health and to help prevent or treat disease, people often take medicines.

Classification of Medicines

There are countless medicines that treat a wide range of health problems. **Medicines** are *drugs that are used to treat or prevent disease or other conditions.* **Drugs** are *substances other than food that change the structure or function of the body or mind.* All medicines are drugs, but not all drugs are medicines. Medicines can be sorted into four broad categories: medicines that

► help prevent disease.
► fight pathogens, or infectious agents that cause disease.
► relieve pain.
► help maintain or restore health and regulate the body's systems.

586 **Chapter 23** Medicines and Drugs

Take the Health Inventory for Chapter 23 at **health.glencoe.com**.

Medicines That Prevent Disease

One main purpose of medicines is to promote health by preventing diseases before they occur. There are two main types of preventive medicines:

▶ **Vaccines.** A **vaccine** is *a preparation introduced into the body to stimulate an immune response.* These medicines contain weakened or dead pathogens that stimulate your body to produce specific **antibodies** against those pathogens. Once the antibodies are produced, they give your body long-lasting protection against those specific pathogens in the future.

▶ **Antitoxins.** These extracts of blood fluids contain antibodies and act more quickly than vaccines. They are produced by inoculating animals, such as sheep, horses, or rabbits, with specific toxins that stimulate the animal's immune system to produce antibodies. In humans the injection of antitoxins neutralizes the effect of toxins such as those that cause tetanus and diphtheria.

Reading Check

Compare and Contrast
What are the differences between medicines and drugs?

Medicines That Fight Pathogens

Antibiotics are a class of chemical agents that destroy disease-causing microorganisms while leaving the patient unharmed. Antibiotics work either by killing harmful bacteria in the body or by preventing bacteria from reproducing. The chemical composition of each antibiotic is effective against a particular range of bacteria.

Athlete's foot can be controlled with antifungal medicines. *Why is it important to use the correct medicine for a particular treatment?*

In recent years strains of bacteria have emerged that are resistant to penicillin and other antibiotics. This drug resistance occurs when a bacterial strain undergoes a change in genetic structure as a result of overexposure to an antibiotic, making the bacterium "immune" to the medicine. For example, a bacteria called *pneumococcus* that causes ear and sinus infections and pneumonia is now resistant to penicillin. The overuse of antibiotics and failure to finish a prescription medication are two reasons why bacteria develop resistance. A new generation of broad-spectrum antibiotics has been developed that kill a wide variety of bacteria, including some penicillin-resistant strains.

ANTIVIRALS AND ANTIFUNGALS

Antibiotics have no effect on viruses. However, a new group of drugs called antivirals has been developed to treat some viral illnesses. Antiviral medicines often only suppress the virus; they don't kill it. Antifungals can cure or suppress infections such as athlete's foot and ringworm.

Medicines help many people with conditions such as asthma and diabetes live active, normal lives. *How are these diseases kept under control?*

Medicines That Relieve Pain

Probably the most common medicines are **analgesics**, or *pain relievers*. Analgesics range from comparatively mild medicines such as aspirin to strong narcotics such as the opium-based morphine and codeine. Aspirin contains acetylsalicylic (uh-SEE-tuhl-sal-uh-SIL-ik) acid. Aspirin is used to relieve pain, to reduce fever, and to treat arthritis.

Because of its widespread use, many people don't realize that aspirin can be dangerous. Even small amounts can irritate the stomach, especially when it's empty. Aspirin can cause dizziness and ringing in the ears. Children who take aspirin are at risk of developing Reye's syndrome, a potentially life-threatening illness of the brain and liver. Aspirin, therefore, should not be given to anyone under the age of 20 unless a health care professional directs otherwise. Some people who are sensitive to aspirin take acetaminophen (uh-see-tuh-MIH-nuh-fuhn) or ibuprofen (eye-byoo-PRO-fuhn) instead. Acetaminophen is the recommended analgesic for children.

Medicines That Promote Health

Medicines that maintain or restore health enable many people with chronic disease to function at an increased level of wellness. Such medicines include:

▶ **Allergy medicines.** Many people rely on antihistamines and other medications to reduce the sneezing, itchy or watery eyes, and runny nose that often accompany allergies.

▶ **Body-regulating medicines.** Some medicines maintain health by regulating body chemistry. Insulin is used to treat diabetes. Asthma sufferers use inhalers to relieve the swelling of bronchial tubes. Cardiovascular medicines are taken to regulate blood pressure, normalize irregular heartbeats, or regulate other functions of the cardiovascular system.

▶ **Antidepressant and antipsychotic medicines.** These medicines help regulate brain chemistry. For example, mood stabilizers are often used in the treatment of mood disorders, depression, and schizophrenia. Proper medication can help people with these disorders live healthy, productive lives.

▶ **Cancer treatment medicines.** These medicines reduce rapid cell growth and help stop the spread of cancer cells. For instance, chemotherapy is used to kill fast-growing cancer cells. This medication, either applied to the skin or injected, results in serious side effects that usually disappear after treatment stops.

Medicines and the Body

Medicines can have a variety of effects on individuals, or can cause different reactions. A person's reaction to a given medicine depends on how that medicine mixes with the chemicals in his or her body. Most medicines cause **side effects**, *reactions to medicine other than the one intended*. It's important to be aware of your reactions to medicines and report them to your health care provider. Patients should always tell their doctors about any medicines they are already taking when a new medicine is prescribed.

When medicines are taken together or when a medication is taken in combination with certain foods, the combination may produce different effects. In some cases, physicians make use of interactions to increase the effectiveness of a treatment. Other interactions may be harmful.

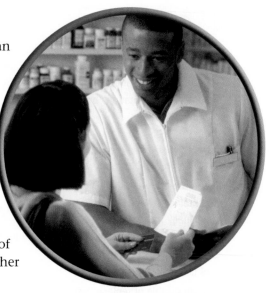

► **Additive interaction** occurs when *medicines work together in a positive way*. For example, both an anti-inflammatory and a muscle relaxant may be prescribed to treat joint pain.

► **Synergistic effect** is an *interaction of two or more medicines that results in a greater effect than when the medicines are taken alone*—one medicine increases the strength of the other. One medicine may boost the rate of digestion, for example, enabling a second medicine to be absorbed faster.

► **Antagonistic interaction** occurs when *the effect of one medicine is canceled or reduced when taken with another medicine*. For example, someone who receives an organ transplant must take antirejection medicines. If the person is diabetic and takes insulin, the antirejection medicine may decrease the effectiveness of the insulin.

(A) In addition to your health care provider, your local pharmacist is a person who can answer questions about medications. *What questions should you ask your pharmacist before taking a new medication?*

Other Problems

A person may experience other problems when taking medicines:

► **Tolerance** is a condition in which the body becomes used to the effect of a medicine. The body then requires increasingly larger doses of the medicine to produce the same effect. Sometimes a person will experience "reverse tolerance." In this condition, the body requires less of the substance to produce the desired effect.

► **Withdrawal** occurs when a person stops using a medicine on which he or she has a chemical dependence. For example, medicines containing codeine can lead to dependence. Symptoms of withdrawal, which include nervousness, insomnia, severe headaches, vomiting, chills, and cramps, gradually ease over time. Withdrawal sometimes requires medical intervention.

Reading Check

Describe What are the side effects or other problems a person may experience when taking medicine?

Medicine Safety

To minimize risks to the public, the federal government has established laws and policies for testing and approving new medicines. In the United States all medicines must meet standards set by the Food and Drug Administration (FDA) before being approved and made available for sale. The FDA requires manufacturers to supply information about a medicine's chemical composition, intended use, effects, and possible side effects. An informed consumer understands how public health policies and government regulations influence health conditions. One practice of the FDA is to determine how medicine should be released to the public.

▶ **Prescription medicines.** Some medicines, called prescription medicines, are available only by means of a doctor's written instructions and can be dispensed only by a licensed pharmacist. **Figure 23.1** shows the information that must appear on every prescription medicine label.

▶ **Over-the-counter (OTC) medicines.** This group includes a wide variety of medicines that you can buy without a prescription. Although the FDA considers it safe to use these

FIGURE 23.1

PRESCRIPTION MEDICINE LABEL

Prescription labels must carry certain information about the medicine. In order to use a medicine safely, always read the label carefully, and talk to your doctor or pharmacist if you have any questions.

Name of prescribing doctor

Pharmacy name, address, and phone number

Name of patient

Prescription number

Directions from the doctor

Number of refills allowed

Name of medicine

Strength

Date prescription was filled

Expiration date

Number of tablets in container

ABC Pharmacy
500 Carter Road
Anytown, NY 78060
Tel: (214) 555-8888

Rx 7531000
Dr. Fisher, MD
Refills: 0

Marcus Smith
Take one tablet 4 times daily.
Finish all medication. Take with food.

Erythromycin Tab   500mg   ACS QTY: 24

Date filled: 01/20/04   Discard after 01/20/05

medications without medical supervision, any drugs can be harmful if not used properly.

When the FDA approves a medicine, it is saying that the medicine is safe when used as directed. FDA approval also means that a medicine is effective in treating the condition for which it is prescribed.

Medicine Misuse

Medicines can promote health and prevent disease, but it is the responsibility of individuals and families to use medicines and supplements as they are prescribed or intended by law, policy, or commonly accepted practice. All medicines are packaged with instructions for use. Failing to follow these instructions can have serious health consequences. Other types of medicine misuse include:

▶ giving a prescription medicine to a person for whom it was not prescribed or taking another person's medicine.

▶ taking too much or too little of a medicine or taking a medicine for a longer or shorter period than prescribed.

▶ discontinuing use of a medicine without informing the health care professional.

▶ mixing medicines.

LESSON 1 REVIEW

Reviewing Facts and Vocabulary

1. What are the four broad categories of medicines?
2. What government organization tests and approves all new medications?
3. List three specific examples of medicine misuse.

Thinking Critically

4. **Synthesizing.** Analyze the influence of laws, policies, and practices on the public release of medicine in the United States.
5. **Evaluating.** Analyze the relationship and use of medicines that promote health and those that prevent disease. Give two examples.

Applying Health Skills

Accessing Information. Using reliable resources, research the known benefits and risks of aspirin. Integrate the information you have found into a poster about safe aspirin use. Make sure your poster explains why dosages vary for infants, children, adults, and the elderly.

After You Read

Analyze a Graph. After reviewing Figure 23.1, on page 590, write a summary explaining why it is important to review a medicine label before taking a drug.

Visit **health.glencoe.com** for the Interactive Study Guide for Lesson 1.

Lesson 1 The Role of Medicines **591**

Drug Use—A High-Risk Behavior

Guide to Reading

Building Vocabulary

As you read this lesson, write each new highlighted term and its definition in your notebook.

▶ substance abuse (p. 592)
▶ illegal drugs (p. 592)
▶ illicit drug use (p. 592)
▶ overdose (p. 594)
▶ psychological dependence (p. 595)
▶ physiological dependence (p. 595)
▶ addiction (p. 595)

Focusing on the Main Ideas

In this lesson, you will learn how to:

▶ Describe substance abuse and examine the health risks involved.
▶ Identify the harmful effects of drugs on the fetus.
▶ Examine the physical, mental/emotional, social, and legal consequences of drug use.

Reading Strategy

Predict

▶ Scan the headings, subheadings, and photo captions. Write three questions that you believe will be answered in this lesson.

Make a list of the dangerous and harmful effects of drugs and their effect on the user, the user's family and friends, and the rest of society.

▼ Substance abuse harms concentration and coordination. You cannot do your best if your body and mind are not functioning properly. *How will you protect your health and avoid substance abuse?*

No one starts using drugs with the intention of causing a drug-related injury or getting addicted to the drug. Health-literate individuals understand the role of individual responsibility regarding personal risk behaviors. It is important that you recognize that drug misuse and substance abuse are life-threatening activities.

What Is Substance Abuse?

Some people misuse medicines intentionally to achieve a "high." This is **substance abuse**, *any unnecessary or improper use of chemical substances for nonmedical purposes.* Substance abuse includes overuse or multiple use of a drug, use of an illegal drug, and use of a drug in combination with alcohol or other drugs.

Not all abused substances are medicines. Many are **illegal drugs**, or street drugs, *chemical substances that people of any age may not lawfully manufacture, possess, buy, or sell.* People who use illegal drugs are guilty of a crime called **illicit drug use**, *the use or sale of any substance that is illegal or otherwise not permitted.* This includes the selling of prescription drugs on the street.

Factors That Influence Decisions About Drugs

All teens are faced with choices about drug abuse. Many factors influence a teen's response to the opportunities to experiment with drugs, including the following:

▶ **Peer pressure** is the influence that people your age may have on you. Teens whose friends and acquaintances avoid drug use can say no to drugs more easily than teens whose friends accept and even encourage drug use.

Reading Check

Define What is substance abuse?

Real-Life Application

Analyzing Trends: Drug-Prevention Programs

According to findings by a National Household Survey on Drug Abuse (NHSDA), more and more teens are getting involved in drug-prevention programs. What effect do you think this has on teens' making the decision to avoid drug use?

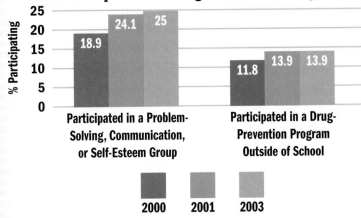

Youth Participation in Drug-Prevention Programs

Participated in a Problem-Solving, Communication, or Self-Esteem Group
- 18.9
- 24.1
- 25

Participated in a Drug-Prevention Program Outside of School
- 11.8
- 13.9
- 13.9

2000   2001   2003

Source: Substance Abuse and Mental Health Services Administration: NHSDA Survey, 2003

- In 2003, 25 percent of youths surveyed participated in a problem-solving, communication, or self-esteem group. The percentage of students who had participated in a drug-prevention program outside of school was 13.9 percent.

- According to the results of this survey, teens reporting an increase in the use of illicit drugs did not participate in such a program. What does this indicate about the influence drug-prevention programs can have on a teen's decision to avoid drugs?

- Survey results also showed 58.9 percent of youths age 12 to 17 indicated that they had talked with a parent in the past year about the dangers of alcohol and drug use. What effect do you think support from parents has on teens' participation in drug-prevention programs?

ACTIVITY

Write a newspaper article that describes factors that influence teens' choices about whether to use drugs. Include internal and external influences. How can teens benefit from participating in drug-prevention programs and influence others in a positive and healthful way?

▶ **Family members** can help teens resist drugs. Parents and other adults who avoid drug use and who discourage drug experimentation influence their teens to abstain from drugs.

▶ **Role models** are people you admire and want to imitate. Teens who look up to coaches, athletes, actors, and professionals who avoid and discourage drug use have an advantage in resisting drugs.

▶ **Media messages** can influence your impression of drug use. Messages from TV, digital media, film, and music, for example, may be misleading about the harmful effects of drugs.

▶ **Perceptions** of society's drug behavior are often inaccurate. According to the 2003 Youth Risk Behavior Survey, almost 80 percent of 13 year olds had never used drugs.

A strong, supportive system of family and friends can help a teen make the healthful decision to avoid drugs. *What other factors help you remain drug free?*

In order to make the right choice about drug use, it is important that a teen knows how information from peers, family, and the community influences personal health.

Health Consequences of Drug Use

Illegal drugs have harmful side effects that can range from minor to deadly. Unlike medicines, these substances are not monitored for quality, purity, or strength. The effects of such drugs are unpredictable. Drug abuse affects all sides of the health triangle.

▶ **Physical consequences.** Once a drug enters the bloodstream, it can harm a user's brain, heart, lungs, and other vital organs. A serious danger of drug abuse is the risk of overdosing. An **overdose** is *a strong, sometimes fatal reaction to taking a large amount of a drug.* Some drug use involves injecting substances through a needle, which can increase the risk of contracting diseases such as **hepatitis B** and **HIV.**

▶ **Mental/emotional consequences.** Drugs cloud reasoning and thinking, and users lose control of their behavior. As shown in **Figure 23.2** on page 595, the drug ecstasy alters the brain's structure and function. While under the influence of drugs, teens may no longer recall the positive beliefs, values, and ideals they have used to guide their own conduct.

▶ **Social consequences.** Substance abuse can have a negative effect on relationships with friends and family members. It can cause teens to be expelled from school or dropped from a school team, and it often has legal consequences. Substance abuse is a major factor in many crimes, suicides, and unintentional injuries.

FIGURE 23.2

DRUG USE AND THE BRAIN

Ecstasy, a stimulant drug that speeds up the nervous system, affects parts of the brain that control thinking, mood, memory, and perception.

- neocortex
- basal ganglia
- amygdala
- hypothalamus
- hippocampus

Understanding the Addiction Cycle

Teens who experiment with drugs will experience side effects, or unwanted reactions. The side effects can range from nausea and headaches to a loss of consciousness and even death, and can occur with a teen's first use of a drug. What may begin as a seemingly harmless pastime can result in serious consequences, including:

▶ **Tolerance.** The body of the substance abuser needs more and more of the drug to get the same effect.

▶ **Psychological dependence.** *A condition in which a person believes that a drug is needed in order to feel good or to function normally,* **psychological dependence** develops over time. The user has a continuing desire to take the drug for its effect.

▶ **Physiological dependence.** A person who experiences the severe effects of withdrawal when he or she stops taking a drug has a **physiological dependence**, *a condition in which the user has a chemical need for the drug.* Symptoms of withdrawal can include nervousness, insomnia, severe nausea, headaches, vomiting, chills, and cramps. In some cases, death can result.

▶ **Addiction.** Anyone who takes drugs risks one of the most frightening side effects: **addiction**, *a physiological or psychological dependence on a drug.* Addiction causes persistent, compulsive use of a substance known by the user to be harmful. People who are addicted to a substance have great difficulty in stopping without professional intervention.

Reading Check

Compare and Contrast
What is the difference between psychological dependence and physiological dependence?

Other Consequences of Drug Use

The consequences of drug use extend beyond the physical risks to a person's health. Drug use also damages a teen's performance in school and in sports. It can also harm relationships with friends and family. Finally, the teen years are filled with pressure and stress. Using drugs adds to that pressure and stress.

Consequences for the Individual

Drug use affects all aspects of a person's health. Mental/emotional and physical health suffer as tolerance, dependence, and addiction develop. People who experiment with drugs tend to lose control more readily than those who do not. This tendency can lead to violence. Substance abuse is also a major factor in violent crimes, suicides, and both unintentional and intentional deaths. Drug use can lead to a relaxing of inhibitions. As a result, drug users are at risk for engaging in sexual activity, which can lead to unintended pregnancy and exposure to **STDs.**

LEGAL CONSEQUENCES

Teens possessing, using, manufacturing, or selling drugs are committing the crime of illicit drug use. Being arrested leads to court fines and legal fees. Some states automatically suspend the driving privileges of minors convicted of a drug offense. Suspension from school, jail time, and probation also are consequences of arrest and conviction.

Consequences for Family and Friends

Some people believe that their decision about drug use is their business and doesn't involve anyone else. That is not true. When an individual chooses to abuse drugs, the decision affects everyone in the user's life. Teens who become involved with drugs lose their interest in healthy activities and have little time for friends who value a drug-free lifestyle. Family members have a responsibility to be aware of the warning signs of drug use and to encourage the individual to seek professional help.

Experimenting even once with a drug can quickly lead to a harmful and damaging addiction. *What consequences of drug use affect family and friends?*

Consequences for Babies and Children

A pregnant female who uses drugs passes the drug through the placenta to her unborn child. The baby may be spontaneously aborted or born with birth defects, behavioral problems, or an addiction. If either parent is using injected drugs, the baby may be born with HIV caused by the sharing of infected needles by one or both parents. A nursing mother who uses drugs passes these substances through breast milk to her child. Babies born to mothers who used depressants or other drugs during pregnancy may be physically dependent on drugs and show severe withdrawal symptoms at birth.

Children of drug users are often neglected and abused because their addicted parents cannot properly care for them. These children may suffer a lifetime of physical and emotional problems and may need to seek help from health professionals later in life.

Costs to Society

Drug abuse has consequences beyond the individual and family. One of the biggest burdens placed on society is a rise in drug-related crime and violence because the use of drugs decreases inhibitions, increases aggressiveness, and clouds judgment. Driving under the influence of an illegal substance can result in vehicle collisions and cause countless injuries and deaths.

Drug abuse also affects the nation's economy. According to a recent study by the Office of National Drug Control Policy, illegal drugs costs the American economy $160 billion per year. The costs result from lost work hours and productivity caused by drug-related illnesses, jail time, accidents, and deaths; health costs and legal fees resulting from illegal drug use; and law enforcement costs and insurance costs from drug-related damages, injuries, and deaths.

The consequences of drug abuse—physical, mental/emotional, social, and legal—are 100 percent preventable. By choosing a drug-free lifestyle, you avoid these consequences.

These teens recognize that using illegal drugs results in suspension or expulsion from school as well as legal consequences. *How can these consequences interfere with a teen's goals?*

LESSON 2 REVIEW

Reviewing Facts and Vocabulary

1. What are *substance abuse* and *illegal drugs?*
2. What are the factors that influence a teen's decision about substance abuse?
3. Analyze and explain the harmful effects of drugs on the fetus.

Thinking Critically

4. **Synthesizing.** List three costs of drug use to society, and give examples of how each of these costs might affect you.
5. **Evaluating.** What are some of the reasons that a substance abuser may have difficulties in achieving long-term goals?

Applying Health Skills

Advocacy. With classmates, analyze the physical, mental/emotional, social, and legal consequences of drug use. Put your ideas in the form of a video or public service announcement to advocate a drug-free lifestyle.

After You Read

Cause and Effect. Make a T chart. On the left side, list facts about substance abuse. On the right side, list the consequences of drug use.

Marijuana, Inhalants, and Steroids

Guide to Reading

Building Vocabulary

As you read this lesson, write each new highlighted term and its definition in your notebook.

▶ marijuana (p. 598)

▶ paranoia (p. 600)

▶ inhalants (p. 600)

▶ anabolic-androgenic steroids (p. 601)

Focusing on the Main Ideas

In this lesson, you will learn how to:

▶ **Identify** the harmful effects of marijuana, inhalants, steroids, and other substances.

▶ **Develop** strategies for avoiding the use of marijuana, inhalants, and steroids.

Reading Strategy

Organize Information

▶ Make a three-column chart. Label the columns Marijuana, Inhalants, and Steroids. As you read, list facts in the appropriate columns.

Knowing the risk of substance abuse can help you stay drug free. Make a list of reasons for saying no to drugs.

Marijuana is an illegal drug. It affects your memory, concentration, coordination, and reaction time. *What strategies do you have for avoiding marijuana use?*

Suppose that someone dared you to go into your school's chemistry lab and swallow a mixture of unfamiliar chemicals. You'd think the idea was pretty crazy, wouldn't you? Yet this is exactly what people do when they experiment with illegal drugs and other substances. Saying no to illegal drug use is one way that you can show you know various strategies when applying the decision-making process regarding healthy habits.

Marijuana

Marijuana, the common name for the Indian hemp plant cannabis, is *a plant whose leaves, buds, and flowers are usually smoked for their intoxicating effects*. It is one of the most widely used illegal drugs and is also known as grass, weed, and pot. It is often the first drug teens experiment with after alcohol. Hashish, or hash, is a stronger form of marijuana. Studies have shown that an individual who uses marijuana is 17 times more likely to use cocaine than one who has never used marijuana. Contrary to popular opinion, this drug is not harmless. All forms of marijuana are mind altering and can damage the user's health. When combined with other drugs and other substances, such as alcohol, marijuana can be deadly.

Marijuana and Addiction

As with other mood-altering drugs, marijuana raises levels of a brain chemical called dopamine. This chemical produces a pleasurable feeling. In some users the drug triggers the release of so much dopamine that a feeling of intense well-being or elation is reached. When the drug wears off, however, the pleasure sensation stops, often dramatically. This abrupt letdown is called a crash. Marijuana contains *more* cancer-causing chemicals than tobacco smoke and carries the same health risks as smoking tobacco. Marijuana also interferes with the immune system, so the user becomes more susceptible to infections. Many of the physical effects of marijuana use are summarized in **Figure 23.3.**

FIGURE 23.3

THE HEALTH RISKS OF MARIJUANA

The effects of marijuana use vary from person to person and can be influenced by an individual's mood and surroundings. In all cases, however, marijuana poses serious health risks.

- Hallucinations and paranoia
- Impaired short-term memory, reaction time, concentration, and coordination
- Distorted sense of time, sight, touch, and sound
- Decreased initiative and ambition
- Bloodshot eyes
- Dry mouth

- Lung irritation, coughing
- Heart and lung damage
- Increased risk of lung cancer
- Weakened immunity; increased susceptibility to colds, flu, and viral infections

- Increased appetite, leading to weight gain
- In pregnant females, increased risk of stillbirths and birth defects
- Changed hormone levels, affecting normal body development in teens
- In females, increased testosterone levels and risk of infertility
- In males, lowered sperm count and testosterone levels

Mental/Emotional Health Consequences

Marijuana users experience slow mental reflexes and may suffer sudden feelings of anxiety and **paranoia**, *an irrational suspiciousness or distrust of others.* The user may feel dizzy, have trouble walking, and have difficulty remembering events that just happened. Because short-term memory is adversely affected, problems at school and at work may develop. Users often experience distorted perception, loss of coordination, and trouble with thinking and problem solving.

Physical Consequences

For teens, marijuana poses physical risks to the **reproductive organs.** In males, regular use interferes with sperm production and lowers levels of testosterone. Females experience the opposite effect—an increase in testosterone levels. This may result in unwanted facial hair and can lead to infertility. Avoiding marijuana and other illicit drug use shows that you understand the impact of personal health behaviors on body systems.

Risks and Consequences of Driving Under the Influence

Driving under the influence of marijuana can be as dangerous as driving under the influence of alcohol because marijuana interferes with depth perception, impairs judgment, and slows reflexes. The penalties and legal consequences of driving under the influence of any drug, including marijuana, are strict. They include suspension of a driver's license, a fine, and possibly a jail term. Insurance premiums are increased when the driver's license is restored. If injury or death results from a drug-related accident, the impaired driver may face serious legal prosecution.

Reading Check

Describe How do the health risks of marijuana vary from person to person (Figure 23.3)?

(A) Driving under the influence of marijuana can be dangerous. *What are some effects of marijuana use that could impair a person's ability to drive safely?*

Inhalants

Inhalants are *substances whose fumes are sniffed and inhaled to achieve a mind-altering effect.* Most inhalants go immediately to the brain, causing damage and actually killing brain cells that will never be replaced. Inhalants include solvents and aerosols such as glues, spray paints, gasoline, and varnishes. They also include nitrates and nitrous oxides, which have medical uses. All inhalants are extremely dangerous, and many are labeled as poisons. These substances were never designed to be taken into the body, and they cause permanent nervous system and brain damage.

Most inhalants depress the central nervous system and produce effects that include a glassy stare, slurred speech, and impaired judgment. Inhalant use or huffing, inhaling the fumes from aerosol cans, can cause sudden death by increasing heart rate, resulting in cardiac arrest, or it can cause death by suffocation.

Anabolic-Androgenic Steroids

Anabolic-androgenic steroids are *synthetic substances that are similar to the male sex hormone testosterone. Anabolic* refers to muscle building, and *androgenic* refers to increased male characteristics.

Reading Check

Describe What are some of the mental/emotional consequences of drug use?

Resilient TEENS

Angelina Gonzalez was devastated by something her father told her. "He said he didn't know why I was bothering with school," says Angelina. "It's as if he never expected me to amount to anything."

Shy and unsure of herself, she found it hard to make friends. Then, at the age of 12, Angelina was prescribed painkillers following some dental work. The medication eased her physical pain. Emotionally, she felt better too. "It put a wall around me," she says, "so I didn't care what people said."

Angelina continued to take the painkillers until a special teacher entered her life. "Mr. Santos told us we could accomplish anything," says Angelina. For the first time Angelina felt supported and began to make plans for her future. "I plan to become a mentor and share my story with other teenagers," says Angelina. "I want them to know that if I can make it they can too."

"I want them to know that if I can make it they can too."

Reading Check

Describe How did having a mentor help Angelina?

Improving athletic performance through hard work and practice shows that you are a healthy, responsible person.

How could use of steroids harm rather than help an athlete's career?

Steroid use can cause mood swings; impaired judgment resulting from feelings of invincibility; and paranoia.

Legal and Social Consequences of Steroid Use

All steroid use other than that prescribed by a licensed physician is illegal and dangerous. Although steroids can increase muscle strength, the associated tendons and ligaments don't get stronger. This discrepancy can result in injuries that take a long time to heal and can end an athlete's career. In addition to causing health problems, steroid users often turn to other illegal, addictive drugs to combat the side effects of steroids. Abusers may take anabolic steroids as pills or by injection. If needles are shared or contaminated, steroid users run the risk of exposure to disease-causing bacteria and viruses, including HIV.

Serious health risks are not the only consequences of steroid use. According to the Anabolic Steroids Control Act of 1990, the nonmedical use of steroids is illegal for people of all ages in the United States. As drug testing for athletes becomes more prevalent, athletes who fail a drug test for steroids can face exclusion from an event, expulsion from the team, monetary fines, and jail time.

LESSON 3 REVIEW

Reviewing Facts and Vocabulary

1. Explain the relationship between marijuana use, alcohol use, and the use of other drugs and substances.

2. How does marijuana interfere with driving ability?

3. Analyze and examine the harmful effects of inhalants and steroids on body systems.

Thinking Critically

4. **Analyzing.** Analyze the harmful effects of marijuana and other substances, such as the physical, mental, social, and legal consequences of using marijuana.

5. **Synthesizing.** Why are younger students especially at risk for inhalant use? What can you do to help prevent younger students from trying inhalants?

Applying Health Skills

Practicing Healthful Behaviors. Write a short story in which a teen is being pressured to use one of the drugs discussed in this lesson. Your story should show how the teen effectively analyzes and applies strategies to avoid the dangers associated with drug use.

After You Read

Explain. Write an essay explaining why athletes should avoid using steroids. In your essay, include at least two points you learned while reading the lesson.

Visit **health.glencoe.com** for the Interactive Study Guide for Lesson 3.

Psychoactive Drugs

Guide to Reading

Building Vocabulary

As you read this lesson, write each new highlighted term and its definition in your notebook.

- psychoactive drugs (p. 603)
- stimulants (p. 605)
- euphoria (p. 605)
- depressants (p. 606)
- narcotics (p. 608)
- hallucinogens (p. 609)
- designer drugs (p. 610)

Focusing on the Main Ideas

In this lesson, you will learn how to:

- Identify the harmful effects of psychoactive drugs on body systems.
- Examine the role psychoactive drugs and other substances play in unsafe situations.
- Discuss the importance of alternatives to drug and substance use.
- Develop strategies for avoiding drug use.

Reading Strategy

Classify

- Fold your paper into four parts. Label the parts Stimulants, Depressants, Narcotics, and Hallucinogens. As you read, list the types of drugs and facts in the appropriate categories.

Quick Write

Make a list of some of the strategies you can use to avoid drug use.

The central nervous system (CNS), which includes the brain and the spinal cord, is an amazingly complex part of the body. Every form of activity, from bending a finger to solving abstract problems, involves the central nervous system. **Psychoactive drugs**, *chemicals that affect the central nervous system and alter activity in the brain,* change the functioning of the CNS.

Classification of Psychoactive Drugs

There are four main groups of psychoactive drugs: stimulants, depressants, narcotics, and hallucinogens (huh-LOO-suhn-uh-juhnz). Some of these drugs have medicinal value when properly used. However, even under a doctor's supervision, they carry risks. When psychoactive drugs are misused or abused, a person's health and the proper function of all body systems are seriously affected. **Figure 23.4** on page 604 shows the health risks of these drugs on body systems. The effects on the developing brain and body of a teen can be especially damaging.

Your decision to stay healthy and drug free will help you succeed in school.

FIGURE 23.4

HEALTH RISKS OF PSYCHOACTIVE DRUGS

Types of Drugs	Consequences for Your Health
STIMULANTS	
Cocaine	• Nausea, abdominal pain, malnutrition • Chest pain, respiratory failure • Headache, stroke, seizure, heart attack, death • Exposure to HIV through contaminated needles, addiction
Crack	• Extreme addiction, with the same effects as pure cocaine • Rapid increase in heart rate and blood pressure can cause death
Amphetamines	• Decreased appetite, weight loss, malnutrition • High blood pressure, rapid heartbeat, heart failure, death • Loss of muscle coordination, delirium, panic • Aggressiveness, increased tolerance, addiction
Methamphetamine	• Memory loss, heart and nerve damage • Increased tolerance, addiction
DEPRESSANTS	
Barbiturates	• Reduced heart rate and blood pressure • Fatigue, confusion, impaired muscle coordination • Impaired memory, loss of judgment • Reduced respiratory function, respiratory arrest, death
Tranquilizers	• Depression, unusual excitement, fever, irritability • Loss of judgment, dizziness
Rohypnol	• Confusion, inability to remember what happened • Decreased blood pressure, drowsiness, gastrointestinal disturbances
GHB	• Drowsiness, nausea, vomiting, loss of consciousness • Impaired breathing, coma, death
NARCOTICS	
Opium	• Nausea, constipation
Morphine	• Rapid onset of tolerance, addiction
Heroin	• Confusion, sedation, unconsciousness, coma
Codeine	• Reduced respiratory function, respiratory arrest, death • Exposure to HIV through contaminated needles
HALLUCINOGENS	
PCP	• Loss of appetite, depression • Panic, aggression, violent actions • Increased heart and respiratory function
LSD	• Delusions, illusions, hallucinations, flashbacks, convulsions, coma, death
Ecstasy (MDMA)	• Confusion, depression, paranoia, muscle breakdown
Ketamine	• Kidney and cardiovascular system failure, death • Memory loss, numbness, impaired motor function • Nausea, high blood pressure, fatal respiratory reaction

Health Risks of Stimulants

Stimulants are *drugs that speed up the central nervous system.* Some foods, such as coffee, tea, and cola, contain small amounts of a stimulant called caffeine. The **nicotine** in tobacco products is also a stimulant. Sometimes stimulants are prescribed for specific medical conditions, for example, the medication used to treat hyperactivity. Although some stimulants have medical uses, many of these substances are used illegally. The most dangerous of the illegal stimulants are cocaine, amphetamines (am-FE-tuh-meenz), and methamphetamine (me-tham-FE-tuh-meen).

Cocaine

Cocaine is a rapid-acting, powerful, highly addictive stimulant that interrupts normal functioning of the central nervous system. The purchase and possession of cocaine is illegal everywhere in the United States. Cocaine is a white powder extracted from the leaves of the coca plant. Cocaine users can experience a surge of self-confidence and **euphoria**, *a feeling of intense well-being or elation.* Effects of cocaine use can last from 20 minutes to several hours.

The feeling of confidence induced by cocaine use is followed by an emotional letdown. Regular use can lead to depression, fatigue, paranoia, and physiological dependence. Cocaine use can cause malnutrition and, especially among teens, cardiac problems. When cocaine is snorted, it shrinks the tiny blood vessels in the nose. Repeated use can lead to collapse of the nasal septum, the wall dividing the two halves of the nose. When users inject cocaine, they risk contracting HIV or hepatitis B from infected needles. Overdosing can result in cardiac arrest, respiratory failure, seizures, and death.

Crack

An even more dangerous form of cocaine is crack. Also known as crack cocaine, rock, or freebase rock, crack is one of the most deadly drugs available. It is a very pure form of cocaine that reaches the brain seconds after being smoked or injected. Once in the blood, it causes heart rate and blood pressure to soar to dangerous levels. Death may result from cardiac or respiratory failure. Mixing cocaine and alcohol is extremely dangerous. These substances are combined in the liver, increasing the risk of death from liver failure.

Reading Check

Define What are the four main groups of psychoactive drugs?

▼ Crack cocaine is a concentrated form of cocaine that can cause death. *What are the dangers of mixing cocaine with other drugs such as alcohol?*

Source: National Institute on Drug Abuse

Amphetamines

Amphetamines are stimulants used in prescription medicines to reduce fatigue and drowsiness and to suppress the appetite. However, some people use amphetamines illegally to stay awake and alert, to improve athletic performance, and to lose weight. The easily developed tolerance to amphetamines causes a user to ingest more of the substance. Regular use of amphetamines can result in twitching, irregular heartbeat, paranoia, and heart and blood vessel damage.

Methamphetamine

Methamphetamine, or meth, is a stimulant used in treating certain diseases, including Parkinson's disease and obesity. It is a white, odorless powder that easily dissolves in alcohol or water. Because it is produced in makeshift labs, the drug is readily available, but its quality is uncertain. In recent years, this drug has been identified as one of the many dangerous and illegal substances called club drugs, drugs associated with concerts and all-night parties called raves. Meth may provide a short-term feeling of euphoria. Often the use of this drug results in depression, paranoia, damage to the central nervous system, increased heart rate and blood pressure, and damage to brain cells. It can also cause death.

Using or misusing illegal drugs and prescription medicines can have devastating effects on your life. You are more likely to become a victim of crime, or engage in criminal activity, are at risk for disease, and your personal relationships may suffer.

The red areas in the normal brain scan (top) show memory and motor skill control. The brain scan on the bottom, taken one month after the subject's use of methamphetamine, indicates loss of memory and of motor control.

Health Risks of Depressants

Depressants, or sedatives, are *drugs that tend to slow down the central nervous system.* Depressant drugs relax muscles, relieve feelings of tension and worry, and cause drowsiness. They can be dangerous because they slow the heart rate, lower blood pressure to dangerous levels, and interrupt the normal rate of breathing. One of the most commonly used depressants is alcohol. Two types of sedative medications are barbiturates (bar-BICH-uh-ruhts) and tranquilizers. Other widely used depressants include Rohypnol and GHB. Combining depressants, even in small amounts, produces a *synergistic* effect. For example, a user combining alcohol and tranquilizers can overdose, causing shallow breathing, weak and rapid pulse, coma, and even death.

Barbiturates

Barbiturates belong to a family of sedative-hypnotic drugs, or drugs that induce sleepiness. Barbiturate use can result in mood changes, sleeping more than normal, and coma. Barbiturates are rarely used for medical purposes. They are used illegally to produce a feeling of intoxication and to counteract the effects of stimulants. Combining barbiturates with alcohol can be fatal.

Tranquilizers

Tranquilizers are depressants that reduce muscular activity, coordination, and attention span. Tranquilizers are prescribed to relieve anxiety, muscle spasms, sleeplessness, and nervousness. However, when tranquilizers are overused, physiological and psychological dependence occurs. Withdrawal from tranquilizers causes severe shaking. In extreme cases, coma or death can result.

Hands-On Health ACTIVITY

Refusing Drugs

Learning to say no to drugs is an important component in maintaining a drug-free life. By practicing refusal skills, you will find it easier to uphold your commitment to a substance-free lifestyle. In this activity you will practice effective ways to say no to drugs.

What You'll Need

- pencil and paper
- one classmate

What You'll Do

1. Divide a sheet of paper into two columns. In the left column, list five pressure lines someone might use to persuade you to use drugs.

2. Trade your paper with a classmate. Read your partner's list. In the right column, write an effective refusal statement responding to each pressure line. Possibilities include: "No thanks, I don't do drugs"; "I'm on medication"; or "That stuff makes me sick."

3. Working with your partner, review your lists and role-play some of the most realistic scenarios. Take turns practicing refusal skills.

4. Which refusal statements did you find to be most effective? Remember and practice them to be prepared when someone tries to offer you drugs.

Apply and Conclude

With your partner, plan a public service announcement that emphasizes the importance of refusal skills. Your announcement should demonstrate how to say no to drugs effectively.

Rohypnol

Rohypnol is a widely available club drug. This depressant, which is ten times as strong as tranquilizers, is better known as the date rape drug, used in crimes of dating violence. Rohypnol comes in tablet form and looks like ordinary aspirin. The drug's harmless appearance has made it a dangerously effective drug in **date-rape crimes.** The victims may be given the tablets without their knowledge. Rohypnol dissolves in carbonated beverages and may easily be slipped into a soft drink. The victim wakes up much later with no recollection of what may have happened during the last several hours. Unplanned pregnancies and exposure to HIV and STDs can result from such unsafe situations.

GHB

Another club drug is gammahydroxy butyric acid (GHB). Like Rohypnol, it has been used in date-rape crimes. GHB is available as a clear liquid, a white powder, and in a variety of tablets and capsules. A person can easily overdose on GHB. The drug leaves the blood relatively quickly, making it hard for emergency room personnel to determine that an overdose has occurred.

Narcotics

Narcotics are *specific drugs that are obtainable only by prescription and are used to relieve pain.* Morphine, OxyContin, and codeine are examples of narcotics. Morphine is sometimes prescribed by medical professionals, and codeine is an ingredient in some cough medications. These drugs relieve pain by blocking pain messengers in the brain. Narcotic use can cause euphoria, drowsiness, constipation, pinpoint pupils, slow and shallow breathing, convulsions, coma, and death. Abuse of narcotics can cause addiction. Because narcotics are so addictive, pharmacists are required to keep records of all sales of these drugs.

Heroin

Heroin, a highly addictive narcotic, is a processed form of morphine that is injected, snorted, or smoked. Heroin depresses the central nervous system and slows breathing and pulse rate. Heroin abuse can cause infection of the heart lining and valves, as well as liver disease. Infectious diseases such as pneumonia, HIV, and hepatitis B can result from the use of infected needles. Large doses may result in coma or death. Users easily develop tolerance, prompting increased usage. Withdrawal can be very painful. Fetal death may occur if the user is pregnant.

What is OxyContin?

OxyContin is a prescription drug that contains oxycodone, a strong narcotic. When used properly under a doctor's supervision, it helps relieve moderate to severe chronic pain. When used illegally and in combination with alcohol or other depressants, however, OxyContin can be deadly. A side effect of this drug is suppression of the respiratory system, which can cause death from respiratory failure.

Hallucinogens

Hallucinogens are *drugs that alter moods, thoughts, and sense perceptions including vision, hearing, smell, and touch.* These drugs have no medical use. Phencyclidine (PCP), lysergic acid diethylamide (LSD), ketamine, and ecstasy are examples of powerful and dangerous hallucinogens. These drugs overload the sensory controls in the brain. The brain then confuses and intensifies sensations and hallucinates. Hallucinogens also impair judgment and reasoning and increase heart and respiratory rates. The altered mental states caused by hallucinogens can last for several hours or several days. The effects are extremely unpredictable, and users sometimes harm themselves physically or demonstrate other violent behaviors.

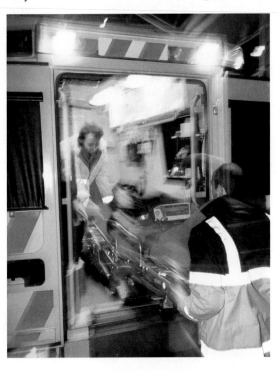

Illegal drugs can affect the human body in unpredictable ways. *What are some of the life-threatening effects of hallucinogens?*

PCP

PCP is considered one of the most dangerous of all drugs, and its effects vary greatly from user to user. Users report distorted sense of time and space, increased muscle strength, and inability to feel pain. Overdoses of PCP can cause death, but most PCP-related deaths are caused by the destructive behavior that the drug produces. PCP users have died in fires because they became disoriented and had no sensitivity to the pain of burning. Flashbacks can occur at any time, causing panic, confusion, and lack of control.

LSD

LSD is an extremely strong hallucinogen. Even a tiny amount can cause hallucinations and severe distorted perceptions of sound and color. Higher doses increase the risk of convulsions, coma, heart and lung failure, and death. Because LSD affects the brain's emotional center and distorts reality, users may experience emotions ranging from extreme euphoria to panic to deep depression. Flashbacks can involve a frightening range of emotions long after actual use of the drug.

Ketamine

Ketamine is an anesthetic used for medical purposes, mostly in treating animals. Misused as a club drug, ketamine is often sold as a white powder to be snorted, like cocaine, or injected. The drug is also smoked with marijuana or tobacco. Ketamine causes hallucinations and dreamlike states. Its use may result in death by respiratory failure. The misuse of ketamine and the use of all other hallucinogens is illegal.

Ecstasy and Other Dangerous Drugs

Designer drugs are *synthetic substances meant to imitate the effects of hallucinogens and other dangerous drugs.* Designer drugs vary greatly in potency and strength and can be several hundred times stronger than the drugs they are meant to imitate. One of the most recognized designer drugs is *ecstasy,* or MDMA. A combination stimulant and hallucinogen, ecstasy may give a short-term feeling of euphoria but often causes confusion, depression, paranoia, psychosis, and even long-term damage to brain cells. Overdoses are common. Use can also result in uncontrollable tremors, paralysis, and irreversible brain damage.

Consequences of Drug Use

Using illegal drugs and other substances can have negative consequences, including health problems, addiction, and difficulties in school. Furthermore, drug use often leads to poor judgment, which may put teens at risk for unintentional injuries, motor vehicle accidents, violence, STDs, unplanned pregnancies, and suicide. Avoiding places where drugs may be present may be the most effective strategy for dealing with individuals who are exhibiting dangerous behaviors. Choosing a drug-free life is one of the most important decisions you can make to protect your health.

Did You Know ?

The use of ecstasy among teens appears to be increasing, probably because teens are being led to think that no significant risks are involved in the use of this drug. However, ecstasy is extremely dangerous. Over 4,500 visits to emergency rooms for ecstasy-related incidents were reported in one year.

Ecstasy can cause dramatic increases in body temperature and may lead to muscle breakdown, kidney failure, and cardiovascular system damage.

LESSON 4 REVIEW

Reviewing Facts and Vocabulary

1. Examine and identify the body systems most affected by psychoactive and designer drugs.

2. Examine and explain the harmful effects of stimulants and hallucinogens on the central nervous system.

3. What are the health risks of narcotic abuse?

Thinking Critically

4. **Synthesizing.** Analyze the importance of alternatives to drug and substance use. Develop and explain your strategy for preventing the use of addictive substances and for avoiding psychoactive drugs.

5. **Analyzing.** Explain the role psychoactive drugs and other substances play in unsafe situations, such as HIV, STDs, unplanned pregnancies, and motor vehicle accidents.

Applying Health Skills

Accessing Information. Choose one of the drugs you learned about in this lesson. Research to evaluate its medical uses (if any), possible effects, and damage to body systems. Organize your findings in a chart similar to Figure 23.4. Share the chart with your class.

After You Read

Explain. Write a script showing how to use refusal skills to avoid drug use. Your script should include at least two characters.

Living Drug Free

Guide to Reading

Building Vocabulary

As you read this lesson, write each new highlighted term and its definition in your notebook.

▶ drug-free school zones (p. 612)

▶ drug watches (p. 612)

Focusing on the Main Ideas

In this lesson, you will learn how to:

▶ **Develop** strategies to prevent the use of drugs and other addictive substances.

▶ **Identify** school and community efforts to curb drug use.

▶ **List** community health-related services that relate to drug addiction and abuse.

▶ **Discover** alternatives to drug and substance abuse.

Reading Strategy

Explain

▶ Based on your current knowledge, write a newsletter article explaining why it's important to live drug free. Include strategies you currently use to avoid drug use.

Quick Write

It can be hard to say no to your peers. Make a list of refusal statements you could say to a peer who is pressuring you to use drugs.

Public opinion polls and national surveys clearly show that most Americans—children, teens, and adults—have taken a stand against illegal drugs. By working together, you and your family, peers, and community can stop the effects of drug abuse. Campaigning for a drug-free school and community shows that you know effective techniques for supporting community, state, and federal agencies that advocate for healthier communities.

Resisting Pressure to Use Drugs

Peer pressure can be intense during the teen years, particularly in settings where using alcohol and other drugs may seem the norm. You may be told that "everybody's doing it," but the fact is that illegal drugs never become a part of most teens' lives. In this country, almost 60 percent of high school students have never tried marijuana, and more than 90 percent have never tried cocaine. So the claim that "everybody's doing it" is simply not true. Resisting pressure to use drugs may be as easy as responding, "Not everybody's doing it. I'm not."

Let others know your reasons for living drug free. *What can you do to share your opinion with others?*

If you're offered a drug:

▶ Be firm in saying that you're
   not interested.

▶ Keep it simple. Say "No
   thanks," or "I don't need drugs."

▶ If the pressure continues,
   walk away.

Protect yourself against risks:

▶ Choose friends who share
   your commitment to staying
   drug free.

▶ Maintain your self-respect
   and be confident about
   your abilities.

▶ Take pride in your
   accomplishments.

▶ Use physical activity and
   relaxation techniques to
   handle stress.

▶ Stay involved in healthy
   activities and interests.

▶ Be aware of your surroundings,
   know what you are drinking,
   and cover drinks at parties.
   Never ride with people who
   are using drugs.

▶ Stay away from parties and
   places where drugs are
   present.

Commitment to Be Drug Free

The first step in staying drug free is to make a firm and deliberate decision. The only way to avoid the pitfalls and dangers of substance abuse is to be fully committed to refusing drugs before they are offered. In many cases it also means steering clear of people who use drugs and of places where drugs are likely to be used or offered.

Making the commitment to abstain from drugs is a life-enhancing decision. It does not mean that you will be deprived of friends or fun. Quite the opposite is true—being drug free means being able to enjoy life and deal with its challenges and problems in healthful ways. It also shows the strength of your values and demonstrates good character and respect for yourself and others.

REFUSAL SKILLS

To honor your commitment to living drug free, you can practice refusal skills. These are techniques that you can use to say no when others pressure you to use drugs. Consider all the harmful effects of drug use and all the benefits of a drug-free lifestyle. Doing so will help you stand up for what you believe without apologizing for or compromising your convictions.

Strategies for Preventing Use of Drugs

Individuals are only part of the key to curbing substance abuse. Schools and communities are working together on strategies for preventing use of drugs and other addictive substances.

School Efforts

All over the United States, **drug-free school zones** have been established. These are *areas within 1,000 feet of schools and designated by signs, within which people caught selling drugs receive especially severe penalties.* Efforts in and around schools to cut down on drug use include drug education classes, zero-tolerance policies, and expulsion of students found using drugs. In some areas police officers are assigned to patrol campuses. Security guards and locker searches also help protect teens from the dangers of drug abuse.

Community Efforts

Communities across the nation are taking positive action to stop drug abuse. **Drug watches** are *organized community efforts by neighborhood residents to patrol, monitor, report, and otherwise try to stop drug deals and drug abuse.* Becoming involved in antidrug programs in your community is a good way to protect your family and friends from the dangers and violence associated with drug abuse. A health advocate knows methods for working cooperatively with others to advocate for healthy communities.

The Importance of Alternatives to Drug and Substance Use

There are healthier ways to cope with day-to-day problems than turning to drugs. You can find many ways to feel good about yourself without depending on harmful substances. Getting involved in school or community activities can give teens the focus they need to follow through on a commitment toward a more healthful life.

Becoming Drug Free

For those teens already in trouble with drugs, it is never too late to get help. Admitting that there is a problem is the first step, and getting help is the essential next step in overcoming that problem. Teens may turn to individual counseling, support groups, or drug treatment centers for help. Support from parents, guardians, school counselors, or family doctors can guide teens to get help. **Figure 23.5** lists some warning signs of drug abuse. If you know someone who shows these signs, encourage him or her to seek help. The following steps can guide you in offering help to a friend or family member who is using alcohol or other drugs.

▶ Identify specific sources of help in your community—drug counselors, treatment centers, and support groups.

▶ Talk to the person when he or she is sober. Express your affection and concern for the person, and describe his or her behavior without being judgmental.

▶ Listen to the person's response. Be prepared for anger and denial.

▶ Offer to go with your friend or family member to a counselor or support group.

A drug-free advocate knows positive ways to influence others to make positive choices.

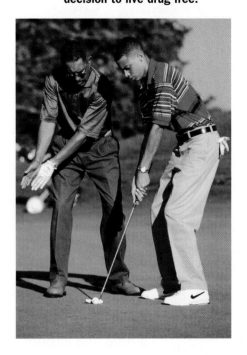

Spending time with a parent or trusted adult can reinforce a teen's decision to live drug free.

FIGURE 23.5

WARNING SIGNS OF DRUG USE

Be alert to these signs that a person may have a drug problem.

- Gets drunk or high regularly, is often hung over
- Lies about the drugs he or she is using, constantly talks about drugs
- Stops participating in activities that once were an important part of his or her life
- Changes eating or sleeping habits, shows rapid weight loss
- Takes unnecessary risks, participates in unsafe behaviors

- Gets in trouble with authorities, such as school administrators and police
- Seems withdrawn, depressed, tired, and cares less about personal grooming and appearance
- Has red-rimmed eyes and runny nose not related to cold or allergies
- Has "blackouts" and forgets what he or she did while under the influence
- Has difficulty concentrating

Getting Help

Drug abuse is a treatable condition. Support groups, counseling services, and treatment centers are available in most communities. For teens, the first step in getting help is talking to a parent, teacher, school counselor, health care provider, or another trusted adult. If an adult is unable to recommend a treatment option, teens can call a toll-free hot line or a drug treatment center.

Treatment Centers

For the most serious addictions, drug users attend treatment centers, facilities that provide medical supervision while a person goes through withdrawal and detoxification, or the removal of drugs from the user's body. Many of these centers provide medications to help with the physical and psychological effects of withdrawal.

Reading Check

Explain What is the first step in staying drug free?

Resilient TEENS

Loren Saenz didn't have to do drugs to learn that they can have a devastating effect on a person's life. "My brother's closest friend died of a drug and alcohol overdose, " she says. Just as disturbing, one of her friends was taking drugs and cutting herself. "I was scared she'd kill herself, so I convinced her talk to a counselor," says Loren.

To help others the way she'd helped her friend, Loren joined Students Against Destructive Decisions (SADD).

So what does the future hold for Loren? "I think I'd like to work with kids someday," she says softly. "I want them to realize what drugs and alcohol can do to their bodies before they try it."

"I want them to realize what drugs and alcohol can do to their bodies before they try it."

Reading Check   **Explain** How is Loren a role model for other teens?

Types of drug treatment centers include these:

▶ **Outpatient Drug-Free Treatment.** These programs usually do not include medications and often consist of individual or group counseling.

▶ **Short-Term Treatment.** These centers can include residential, medication, and outpatient therapies.

▶ **Maintenance Therapy.** Intended for heroin addicts, this treatment usually includes medication therapy.

▶ **Therapeutic Communities.** These are residences for people with a long history of drug abuse. The centers include highly structured programs that usually last from 6 to 12 months.

For people who have less serious addictions, or for those who are released from a treatment center, drug counseling is usually recommended. Drug counselors help people adjust to life without drugs. In conjunction with counseling, many recovering drug users attend support groups. These meetings are gatherings of people who share a common problem and who work together to help one another cope and recover. Support groups are a popular strategy for treating addiction because they provide the long-term moral support that the recovering user needs to remain drug free.

 Drug counseling and treatment can help a drug user break the cycle of addiction. *Identify health-related services in the community that relate to the prevention and treatment of addiction.*

LESSON 5 REVIEW

Reviewing Facts and Vocabulary

1. Identify some strategies that schools and communities have used to decrease the availability of drugs.

2. List five signs of substance abuse.

3. How do support groups help substance abusers?

Thinking Critically

4. **Analyzing.** Analyze the importance of healthy alternatives to drug and substance use.

5. **Synthesizing.** Develop a list of strategies for preventing use of addictive substances in your school. Write these in a formal list, and submit your ideas to the school principal or school board.

Applying Health Skills

Refusal Skills. Analyze and develop strategies for preventing the use of drugs. Prepare an insert on drug-refusal strategies for your school newspaper. Explain the dangers of drug abuse, and include examples of appropriate and effective refusal skills to avoid unsafe situations.

After You Read

Problems and Solutions. Make a T chart. On the problem side, list reasons some teens feel pressure to take drugs and the warning signs of drug use. On the solutions side, list strategies for preventing drug use and ways to become drug free.

Visit **health.glencoe.com** for the Interactive Study Guide for Lesson 5.

Lesson 5 Living Drug Free **615**

Vaccine:
The Battle Within

To create better vaccines, scientists must study the immune system's complex network of cellular guards.

Pathogen

1. B lymphocytes seek specific pathogens.

Identifies target **pathogen**.

Pathogen is exposed.

2. Antigen-presenting cell uncovers pathogens.

3. Helper T cell sounds alarm.

Searching for the Bad Bugs...

1. Spotting the Enemy
Formed in bone marrow, B lymphocytes are the only immune cells that can make antibodies—the first line of immune defense. Antibodies are proteins that detect and bind themselves to pathogens in the blood to neutralize them.

2. Exposing the Bad Guys
Often pathogens camouflage themselves against detection by antibodies with proteins called antigens. Antigen-presenting cells (APCs) chop up the proteins. This exposes the pathogens to destruction.

3. Sounding the Alarm
Helper T cells recognize and bind to bugs exposed by APCs. Once activated, helper Ts secrete hormones called cytokines. These signal the immune system to send more macrophages, B cells, and T cells to destroy the invaders, as well as more white blood cells containing enzymes that digest antigens.

...And Then Destroying Them

4. Building the Bombs
After they encounter antigens in the blood, some B cells retreat to the lymph nodes, where they become plasma cells and churn out antibodies that can bind to the antigens.

5. Going in for the Kill
Killer T cells must recognize antigens. Then they mature quickly to perform their second function—destroying pathogens. Killer T cells attach to a pathogen and douse it with a lethal toxin. Then they detach and go off to kill again, leaving the infected cell to die.

6. Bringing in the Big Guns
Natural killer cells are unspecialized fighters. They flood infected cells with toxins and destructive enzymes, but don't need to have the antigens exposed by APCs.

Pathogen is exposed.

4. B lymphocyte plasma cell releases antibody designed to kill specific pathogen.

5. Killer T cell binds and destroys its target pathogen.

6. Natural killer cell kills any invading bug in its path.

TIME to THINK...   About Vaccines

Every year nearly 2 million children worldwide die from diseases that vaccination could have prevented. Use the Internet or your school's media center to learn what diseases cause the most deaths among unvaccinated children. Why are these children not being vaccinated? Report your findings to the class.

Health Skills Application

1. **Accessing Information.** Research and analyze laws regulating the information that is required to be on all over-the-counter (OTC) medicine labels. Why does the FDA require this information to appear? *(LESSON 1)*

2. **Communication Skills.** Write a skit in which a teen expresses concern for a friend's drug problem. The teen should use effective communication skills to discuss the dangers of drug use and to encourage the friend to seek help. *(LESSON 2)*

3. **Refusal Skills.** Imagine that you are at a party and someone you know suddenly offers you marijuana. Analyze and explain the refusal strategies you could apply. *(LESSON 3)*

4. **Stress Management.** Derek, who has been under a lot of stress, confides in you that he wants to take depressants to relax. What would you say to persuade him not to do so? What healthy alternatives for managing stress would you recommend? *(LESSON 4)*

5. **Goal Setting.** Make a goal to live drug free. Use the goal-setting steps to develop an action plan for honoring your commitment. *(LESSON 5)*

Medical Records Technician

Do you enjoy managing information? Do you have strong organizational skills and an eye for detail? If you can keep track of a variety of important data, consider a career as a medical records technician. These professionals maintain medical records of patients in hospitals, clinics, and doctors' offices. They track prescription medicines and other health information to ensure that the right treatments and medications are given to patients.

Medical records technicians are required to have an Associate's degree in information management from a community college or vocational/technical school. Find out more about this and other health careers by clicking on Career Corner at **health.glencoe.com.**

After You Read

Use the notes you have taken in your Foldable to review what you have learned. On the back of your Foldable, write a descriptive paragraph about the effects medicines have on the human body.

FOLDABLES
Study Organizer

▶ EXPLORING HEALTH TERMS *Answer the following questions on a sheet of paper.*

Lesson 1 *Match each definition with the correct term.*

analgesics   antagonistic interaction
additive interaction   vaccines
side effects   synergistic effect
drugs   medicines

1. Drugs that are used to treat or prevent disease or other conditions.
2. Pain relievers.
3. Reactions to medicine other than the one intended.
4. An interaction of two or more medicines that results in a greater effect than when each medicine is taken separately.

Lesson 2 *Fill in the blanks with the correct term.*

substance abuse   illegal drugs
illicit drug use   overdose
psychological dependence   addiction
physiological dependence

When a person uses (_5_), he or she is committing the crime of (_6_). In addition to legal problems, using drugs carries the risk of (_7_), which can be fatal. (_8_), a condition in which the body develops a chemical need for a drug, is another health risk of drug use.

Lesson 3 *Match each definition with the correct term.*

anabolic-androgenic steroids   paranoia
marijuana   inhalants

9. An irrational suspicion or distrust of others.
10. Substances whose fumes are sniffed to give a mind-altering effect.
11. Synthetic substances that are similar to male sex hormones.

Lesson 4 *Match each definition with the correct term.*

euphoria   designer drugs
stimulants   narcotics
hallucinogens   psychoactive drugs
depressants

12. Pain-relieving drugs legally obtainable only by prescription.
13. Drugs that alter moods, thoughts, and sense perceptions, including vision, hearing, smell, and touch.
14. Synthetic substances made to imitate the effects of hallucinogens and other dangerous drugs.

Lesson 5 *Identify each statement as True or False. If false, replace the underlined term with the correct term.*

drug-free school zones   drug watches

15. Drug-free school zones are/is organized community efforts by neighborhood residents to patrol, monitor, report, and try to stop drug deals and drug abuse.
16. Drug watches are/is a designated area surrounding schools within which people caught selling drugs receive especially severe penalties.

▶ RECALLING THE FACTS *Use complete sentences to answer the following questions.*

1. Analyze and describe two types of medicines that fight diseases.
2. What is the difference between an additive interaction and an antagonistic interaction?
3. Compare and contrast OTC and prescription medicines.
4. Why are illegal drugs dangerous to the user?
5. List three legal consequences of drug use for teens.

For more review questions for Chapter 23, go to **health.glencoe.com**.

6. Analyze and explain the harmful effects of drugs on a fetus.

7. Marijuana raises the level of dopamine in the brain. What effect does this have on the body?

8. Examine and describe the physical consequences of inhalant use.

9. What can happen if an athlete uses steroids?

10. How does a stimulant affect the central nervous system?

11. What are the symptoms of a hallucinogen overdose?

12. List five harmful effects of club drugs.

13. List and analyze three strategies you can apply for avoiding drugs.

14. How are communities helping in the effort to promote health by stopping drug use?

15. List three types of centers in which drug users can be treated.

► WRITING CRITICALLY

1. **Expository.** Write a public service announcement educating teens about the health and social consequences of drug use. Encourage teens to use refusal skills to avoid drug use or to get help if they have a drug problem.

2. **Personal.** Write a letter to yourself outlining your commitment to stay drug free. In your letter, explain your reasons for abstaining from drug use, and write a drug prevention strategy for yourself. You can look back at your letter if you are ever in a situation in which you need to reinforce your commitment.

Standardized Test Practice

MATH Read the paragraph below, look at the table, and then answer the questions.

Grade	8th	10th	12th
Ever used	1.9%	2.4%	3.4%
Used in past year	1.1%	1.5%	2.5%
Used in past month	0.5%	0.8%	1.6%

Nonmedical use of substances known as *anabolic steroids* is considered substance abuse. The table shows the abuse of anabolic steroids in a 2004 study that involved students from both public and private schools.

1. If 12,000 of the students studied were tenth graders, how many of them have not used anabolic steroids in the past month?

Ⓐ 96   Ⓒ 11,820
Ⓑ 180   Ⓓ 11,904

2. If 20,000 of the students were eighth graders, how many of them have not ever used anabolic steroids?

Ⓕ 380   Ⓗ 16,200
Ⓖ 3800   Ⓘ 19,620

3. Examine the values in the table. Provide a logical explanation as to why the percentages are higher for older students.

Communicable Diseases

Media Messages on Emerging Infections

National health organizations such as the Centers for Disease Control and Prevention rely on the media to convey important health messages to the public about

▶ **diseases and epidemics.**

▶ **emerging infections.**

▶ **health data and statistics.**

Visit the Eye on the Media section at health.glencoe.com to learn more about the role of the media in conveying public health information.

Before You Read

Make this Foldable to help you organize what you learn about communicable diseases. Begin with two sheets of 8½" x 11" paper.

▶ Step 1

Stack two sheets of paper with the short edges 1½" apart.

▶ Step 2

Roll the bottom edges of the paper up so that the bottom edges are 1½" from the top edges.

▶ Step 3

Fold and staple to hold the tabs in place. Label as shown.

Communicable Diseases

Causes of Communicable Diseases
How Communicable Diseases Are Transmitted
Preventing the Spread of Disease

As You Read

As you read and discuss the material in the chapter, use your Foldable to record supporting facts under the appropriate tabs.

Using Visuals. What can you do to prevent the spread of communicable diseases?

What Are Communicable Diseases?

Guide to Reading

Building Vocabulary

As you read this lesson, write each new highlighted term and its definition in your notebook.

▶ communicable disease (p. 622)

▶ pathogen (p. 622)

▶ infection (p. 622)

▶ viruses (p. 623)

▶ bacteria (p. 623)

▶ toxin (p. 623)

▶ vector (p. 625)

Focusing on the Main Ideas

In this lesson, you will learn how to:

▶ Identify the types of pathogens that cause communicable diseases.

▶ Describe the ways in which communicable diseases are spread.

▶ Develop strategies to help prevent communicable diseases.

Reading Strategy

Organize Information

▶ Fold your paper into three parts labeled Causes, Ways to Transmit, and Strategies for Preventing. As you read, record facts about communicable diseases in each column.

Write a brief paragraph describing the symptoms you experienced the last time you had a cold, and explain how you think you caught the cold.

The HIV virus (top), pneumonia virus, and cold virus (bottom), are pathogens.

Most of us don't spend much time thinking about microorganisms, but they often impact our lives. Although most microorganisms—living things too small to be seen without a microscope—are harmless, a few, such as the viruses shown on this page, can cause communicable diseases. A **communicable disease** is *a disease that is spread from one living thing to another or through the environment.* Knowing how communicable diseases spread can help you choose behaviors to reduce your risk of getting them.

Causes of Communicable Diseases

An *organism that causes disease* is called a **pathogen**. Common pathogens include certain viruses, bacteria, fungi, protozoans, and rickettsias (rik-ET-see-uhz). **Figure 24.1** lists some of the diseases caused by pathogens. An **infection** is *a condition that occurs when pathogens enter the body, multiply, and damage body cells.* If the body is not able to fight off the infection, a disease develops.

Take the Health Inventory for Chapter 24 at **health.glencoe.com**.

Viruses

You're already familiar with two diseases caused by viruses—the common cold and influenza, or the flu. **Viruses** are *pieces of genetic material surrounded by a protein coat.* By themselves they are inactive. They need living cells to reproduce. Viruses invade all known forms of life—mammals, birds, reptiles, insects, plants, and even bacteria.

After a virus penetrates a cell, called the host cell, the virus takes control of the cell to manufacture more viruses. The new viruses burst from the cell, usually killing it, and take over other cells. Like other pathogens, viruses usually run their course and eventually are killed by the immune system. Antibiotics do not work against viruses.

Bacteria

Bacteria are *single-celled microorganisms* that live almost everywhere on earth. Most bacteria are harmless, and many types are essential for life. For example, bacteria in your digestive system help digest food and make some of the vitamins you need. When bacteria enter the body, they multiply through cell division. Some bacterial pathogens, such as the ones that cause tetanus, produce a **toxin**, a *substance that kills cells or interferes with their functions.* Like most other microorganisms that enter the body of a healthy individual, bacteria are usually destroyed by the immune system. Most bacterial diseases can be treated with **antibiotics.**

Reading Check

Explain What is a communicable disease?

FIGURE 24.1

DISEASES BY TYPE OF PATHOGEN

Viruses	Bacteria	Fungi	Protozoans	Rickettsias
• common cold • influenza (flu) • viral pneumonia • viral hepatitis • polio • mononucleosis • measles • AIDS • viral meningitis • chicken pox • herpes • rabies • smallpox • West Nile virus	• bacterial foodborne illness • strep throat • tuberculosis • diptheria • gonorrhea • Lyme disease • bacterial pinkeye • bacterial pneumonia • bacterial meningitis	• athlete's foot • ringworm • vaginal yeast infection	• malaria • amoebic dysentery • sleeping sickness	• typhus • Rocky Mountain spotted fever

Try to reduce your risk of infection when you participate in outdoor activities where vectors are common. *How is this teen protecting himself from deer ticks?*

Other Types of Pathogens

Other types of organisms also can cause communicable diseases.

▶ **Fungi** are plantlike organisms, such as molds and yeasts. Some types can cause diseases of the skin, such as athlete's foot; diseases of the mucous membranes; or of the lungs.

▶ **Protozoans** are single-celled organisms that are larger and more complex than bacteria. Most are harmless, but some can cause disease, especially in people with weakened immune systems.

▶ **Rickettsias** are pathogens that resemble bacteria. Like viruses, they multiply by invading the cells of another life form. Often these organisms enter humans through the bites of insects such as fleas or lice. Rocky Mountain spotted fever is the most frequently reported illness spread by rickettsias.

How Communicable Diseases Are Transmitted

There are several means of transmitting, or spreading, pathogens. Transmission can occur through direct and indirect contact and through breathing contaminated air. Some diseases can be transmitted in more than one way. If you know how they are spread, you can take precautions and avoid infection.

Direct Contact

Many pathogens are transmitted by direct contact with an infected person or animal or with something in the environment. Direct contact includes touching, biting, kissing, and sexual contact. Sneezing and coughing can spray infectious droplets of saliva or mucus into a nearby person's eyes, nose, or mouth. A pregnant woman may also transmit an infection to her unborn child through the placenta. A person can get tetanus from a puncture wound by a rusty nail.

Indirect Contact

Some communicable diseases can be transmitted indirectly, without being close to an infected person. The following are ways diseases can be transmitted through indirect contact:

▶ **Contaminated objects.** Inanimate objects can become contaminated with infectious discharges or secretions. Suppose that a person with a cold sneezes onto a table or into his or her hand and then touches the table. The cold viruses can be transmitted to you if you touch the table and then touch your nose or eyes. Use proper handwashing techniques to avoid transmitting infections.

▶ **Vectors.** An *organism, usually an arthropod, such as a tick, that carries and transmits pathogens to humans or other animals* is known as a **vector**. For example, a mosquito may take in pathogens when it feeds on an infected person. The mosquito then injects some of those pathogens into the next person it bites, thus spreading the disease. Common vectors include flies, mosquitoes, and ticks. Lyme disease and malaria are spread by vectors.

▶ **Water and food.** Careless handling and storage of food are major sources of contamination and illness. For example, salmonella (sal-muh-NE-luh) bacteria in undercooked poultry can cause food poisoning. Water supplies that become contaminated with human or animal feces can cause illnesses such as hepatitis A.

Airborne Transmission

Pathogens from a sneeze or a cough may float in the air for a long time and travel long distances. Airborne transmission is different from direct contact because the pathogens don't settle quickly on surfaces. Diseases that are transmitted this way include chicken pox, tuberculosis, and influenza. A person can get inhalation anthrax by inhaling soil containing the bacteria.

Strategies for Preventing Communicable Disease

Reducing your risk of communicable diseases isn't complicated. Practicing healthful behaviors is a strategy for preventing communicable diseases. An informed individual understands the impact of personal health behaviors on body systems.

Washing Hands

Handwashing is the single most effective strategy for preventing the spread of disease. Wash your hands before you prepare food, before you eat, and after you use the bathroom. Clean hands carefully before inserting contact lenses or putting on makeup. After handling animals, especially reptiles, or animal wastes, wash your hands. When someone in your home is ill, keep hands clean to prevent the spread of pathogens.

Handling Food Properly

Foodborne illness occurs in places where food is handled improperly. Always wash your hands before you handle food. Use paper towels, not dishcloths or sponges, to keep surfaces and equipment clean. Separate raw meat from other foods. Cook food to its proper temperature. Chill cold and leftover foods quickly to the proper temperature.

Health Minute

Strategies for Avoiding Diseases Transmitted by Vectors

Use these strategies where mosquitoes or ticks are common:

▶ Wear long-sleeved shirts, long pants, socks, and hats.

▶ Tuck shirts in at the waist, and tuck pants into socks.

▶ Wear boots, not sandals.

▶ Apply repellents to clothing, boots, socks, and all exposed skin.

▶ Check yourself and your clothing frequently. Wearing light-colored clothing can help you spot ticks and mosquitoes.

Reading Check

Compare and Contrast How is an airborne transmission different from direct contact?

Handwashing is important since your hands easily pick up and transfer bacteria. *List other strategies you can use to avoid the spread of disease.*

Other Prevention Strategies

Here are some other strategies that will help you reduce your risk of getting or spreading communicable diseases.

▶ Eat a balanced diet. Participate in regular physical activity. Avoid the use of tobacco, alcohol, and other drugs.

▶ Avoid sharing eating utensils, makeup, combs and brushes, and other personal items.

▶ Prepare and store food safely.

▶ Avoid unnecessary contact with people who are ill.

▶ Take care of yourself when you're ill. Cover your mouth when you cough or sneeze. Wash your hands after using a tissue.

▶ Use mosquito repellant when outside during warm months. Avoid direct contact with dead birds.

▶ Practice abstinence from sexual activity.

▶ Learn to manage stress. Stress makes you vulnerable to illness if you do not find ways to manage it effectively.

LESSON 1 — REVIEW

Reviewing Facts and Vocabulary

1. List five types of common pathogens, and identify one disease each type of pathogen causes.

2. Describe three ways in which pathogens spread and three healthful behaviors to limit their spread.

3. What are five ways you can reduce your risk of getting a communicable disease?

Thinking Critically

4. **Applying.** The fungus that causes athlete's foot lives in warm, moist places. What can you do to prevent getting this pathogen when you use gym or other common showers?

5. **Analyzing.** You wake up one morning with a headache, body aches, and a fever. You think you might be coming down with something. Analyze the relationship between healthful behaviors you can practice and the ways that communicable diseases are spread. What should you do?

Applying Health Skills

Practicing Healthful Behaviors. Work with a family member to identify ways in which you can reduce your risk of contracting a foodborne illness at home. Develop and analyze strategies related to the prevention of food poisoning.

After You Read

Problems and Solutions. Write a public service announcement describing how communicable diseases are spread. Include information describing how to avoid spreading these diseases.

Visit **health.glencoe.com** for the Interactive Study Guide for Lesson 1.

Preventing Communicable Diseases

Guide to Reading

Building Vocabulary

As you read this lesson, write each new highlighted term and its definition in your notebook.

▶ immune system (p. 627)

▶ inflammatory response (p. 628)

▶ phagocyte (p. 629)

▶ antigen (p. 630)

▶ immunity (p. 630)

▶ lymphocyte (p. 630)

▶ antibody (p. 631)

▶ vaccine (p. 631)

Quick Write

Think about the last time you had a small cut or injury that became red and painful. Write a short paragraph describing what the area of the injury looked like over several days.

Focusing on the Main Ideas

In this lesson, you will learn how to:

▶ Examine the ways the body protects itself against invading pathogens.

▶ Develop strategies for caring for your immune system and preventing disease.

▶ Analyze the ways in which technology has impacted the world in the prevention of communicable diseases.

▶ Identify health-related community services related to disease prevention.

Reading Strategy

Organize Information

▶ Make a word web with *Preventing Communicable Diseases* in the center. Surround the center with five circles titled Physical/ Chemical Barriers, Immune System, Specific Defenses, Memory Lymphocytes, and Vaccines. As you read, record facts in the appropriate spaces.

You can't see it, but the teen in the picture is waging a battle. The battle is not against other players who are trying to score a point. It's a battle to fight off the pathogens that constantly attack his body. Every day, 24 hours a day, your body is exposed to millions of pathogens. Most of the time, your body manages to stay free of infection because of your immune system. The **immune system** is *a network of cells, tissues, organs, and chemicals that fights off pathogens.*

Physical and Chemical Barriers

Physical and chemical barriers make up your body's first line of defense, as shown in **Figure 24.2** on page 628. They protect

▲ Compare the protective equipment worn by this goalie to your physical and chemical barriers. *How might behaviors such as wearing appropriate safety equipment help protect you from pathogens?*

against a wide variety of invaders. Physical barriers, such as skin and mucous membranes, block pathogens from invading your body. Chemical barriers, such as enzymes in tears, destroy pathogens.

The Immune System

The immune system has two major defense strategies. The inflammatory response is general, or nonspecific; it works against all types of pathogens. Specific defenses work against particular pathogens. Together, these defenses work to prevent disease.

The Inflammatory Response

The **inflammatory response** is *a reaction to tissue damage caused by injury or infection.* Its purpose is to prevent further tissue injury and to halt invading pathogens. Suppose that a splinter enters your finger. Your body immediately reacts to the damage caused by the splinter and to any pathogens on the splinter. If you've ever had the area around an injury become hot, swollen, red, and painful, you've experienced the inflammatory response.

Reading Check

Explain What occurs during the inflammatory response?

FIGURE 24.2

PHYSICAL AND CHEMICAL BARRIERS— THE BODY'S FIRST LINE OF DEFENSE

These elements work together as your body's first line of defense to prevent pathogens from entering and causing disease.

Skin is the first line of defense against many pathogens. Few pathogens can pass through the tough layer of dead skin cells that surrounds the body.

Tears and saliva contain enzymes that destroy or disable many pathogens.

Mucous membranes line many parts of the body, including your mouth, nose, and bronchial tubes. Cells in these membranes produce *mucus*, a sticky substance that traps pathogens. The mucus then carries the trapped pathogens to other areas of the body for disposal.

Cilia, the hairlike projections that line parts of the respiratory system, sweep mucus and pathogens to the throat, where they can be swallowed or coughed out.

Gastric juice in the stomach destroys many pathogens that enter the body through the nose and mouth.

In response to invasion by microorganisms and to tissue damage, blood vessels near the site of an injury expand to allow more blood flow to the area. As blood vessels expand, fluid and cells from the bloodstream leak into the area. The collection of fluid and white blood cells causes swelling and pain because of pressure on nerve endings. One type of cell that responds to injury is called a **phagocyte** (FA-guh-site), *a white blood cell that attacks invading pathogens.* Phagocytes engulf pathogens and then destroy them with chemicals. Pus, a collection of dead white blood cells and damaged tissue, may collect at the site of inflammation as a response to bacteria. After the pathogens are killed and tissue damage is under control, tissue repair can begin. However, regardless of whether pathogens survive the inflammatory response, specific defenses are activated. This activation is an effort to prevent this same infection from occurring again.

Injury and infection caused by this splinter may trigger an inflammatory response. *What immediately happens in the body as a response to injury?*

Health Skills Activity

Decision Making: Caring for Your Immune System

Aaron has been getting a lot of colds lately. Today he woke up with a bad sore throat. Aaron knows that he should stay home and rest, both for his own health and to avoid infecting others at school. However, Aaron plays the lead saxophone in the marching band, and today is the last band practice before the big game. This practice will even be a full-dress rehearsal to make sure everything goes right for the half-time show.

Saturday's game will be the playoff, and everyone is sure the school will win. If Aaron doesn't show up, he thinks he will be letting the band down. Besides, he doesn't want to admit that he is getting sick because then he won't be there on Saturday when the team wins.

Aaron wonders what he should do.

What Would You Do?
Apply the six steps of the decision-making model to Aaron's situation.

1. State the situation.
2. List the options.
3. Weigh the possible outcomes.
4. Consider values.
5. Make a decision and act.
6. Evaluate the decision.

Specific Defenses

Specific defenses react to invasion as a result of the body's ability to recognize certain pathogens and destroy them. The process by which this happens, the immune response, is described in **Figure 24.3.** During the immune response, certain types of white blood cells react to antigens. An **antigen** is *a substance that is capable of triggering an immune response.* Antigens are found on the surfaces of pathogens and in toxins. Macrophages are a type of phagocyte that destroys pathogens by making antigens recognizable to white blood cells. The result of the immune response is **immunity**, *the state of being protected against a particular disease.*

Lymphocytes

A **lymphocyte** (LIMP-fuh-site) is *a specialized white blood cell that coordinates and performs many of the functions of specific immunity.* There are two types of lymphocytes: T cells and B cells.

T CELLS AND B CELLS

There are different types of T cells with different functions. They all work together to protect against infection.

▶ *Helper T cells* trigger the production of B cells and killer T cells.

▶ *Killer T cells* attack and destroy infected body cells. Killer T cells don't attack the pathogens themselves, only the infected cells.

FIGURE 24.3

THE IMMUNE RESPONSE

The immune response is a complex interaction between your body and an invading pathogen. It can be broken down into eight distinct stages.

1. Pathogens invade the body.
2. Macrophages engulf the pathogen.
3. Macrophages digest the pathogen and T cells recognize antigens of the pathogen as an invader.
4. T cells bind to the antigens.
5. B cells bind to antigens and helper T cells.
6. B cells divide to produce plasma cells.
7. Plasma cells release antibodies into the bloodstream.
8. Antibodies bind to antigens to help other cells identify and destroy the pathogens.

▶ *Suppressor T cells* coordinate the activities of other T cells. They "turn off" or suppress helper T cells when the infection has been cleared.

In conjunction with the work of T cells, lymphocytes called B cells produce antibodies. An **antibody** is *a protein that acts against a specific antigen.* Each B cell is programmed to make one type of antibody, specific to a particular pathogen. Some antibodies attach to foreign antigens to mark them for destruction. Some destroy invading pathogens. Others block viruses from entering body cells.

The Role of Memory Lymphocytes

Your immune system actually has a "memory." Some T cells and B cells that have been activated by antigens become *memory cells*. These memory cells circulate in your bloodstream and through the lymphatic system, shown in **Figure 24.4** on page 632. When memory cells recognize a former invader, the immune system uses antibodies and killer T cells in a quick defense to stop it. For example, if you have had measles or an immunization against measles, your immune system remembers the antigens for the measles virus. If it enters your body again, antibodies will attack the virus immediately, protecting you from becoming ill.

Active Immunity

The immunity your body develops to protect you from measles and from other diseases is called *active immunity.* Naturally acquired active immunity develops when your body is exposed to antigens from invading pathogens. Artificially acquired active immunity develops in response to a **vaccine**, *a preparation of dead or weakened pathogens that are introduced into the body to stimulate an immune response.* In this way vaccines cause your body to produce antibodies without actually causing the disease. Today, more than 20 serious human diseases can be prevented by vaccination. Active immunity to many diseases can last a lifetime, but some immunizations need to be repeated to maintain immunity.

Passive Immunity

In active immunity your body produces its own antibodies. You also can be protected from pathogens by *passive immunity*—receiving antibodies from another person or an animal. This immunity is short-lived; it usually lasts only weeks to months. Natural passive immunity occurs when antibodies pass from mother to child during pregnancy or while nursing. Artificial passive immunity results from the injection of antibodies produced by an animal or a human who is immune to the disease.

Is there a vaccine to prevent colds?
Developing a vaccine to prevent colds is difficult. More than 200 different viruses can cause the common cold. This means that more than 200 different vaccines would have to be developed to prevent this illness.

FIGURE 24.4

IMMUNITY AND THE LYMPHATIC SYSTEM

The lymphatic system circulates antibodies to give you protection against many diseases. This protection can last throughout your life.

The **lymphatic system** is part of your immune system. It includes your tonsils, lymph nodes, and a network of vessels, similar to blood vessels, that transport lymph, or tissue fluid.

Lymph nodes can become enlarged when your body is fighting an infection because of the increased number of lymphocytes. If swelling lasts for three days, see your health care professional.

Lymphocytes are produced by lymph nodes. These nodes occur in groups and are concentrated in the head and neck, armpits, chest, abdomen, and groin.

Care of the Immune System

Your health behaviors can greatly reduce your chance of contracting a disease or getting an infection. When you keep your body strong and healthy, your immune system is better able to fight off pathogens. Taking positive steps in every area of your health will give you the boost needed to reduce your chance of illness.

▶ Follow a sensible eating plan to maintain your overall health and keep your immune system strong. Include whole grains and nutrient-rich foods such as fruits and vegetables, and reduce intake of fats, sugar, and salt. Drink six to eight 8-ounce glasses of water each day.

▶ Get plenty of rest. Fatigue reduces the effectiveness of the immune system. To function at their best, teens should average nine hours of restful sleep each night.

- Get about an hour of physical activity each day. This is especially important to relieve stress.

- Avoid sharing personal items such as towels, toothbrushes, hairbrushes, and makeup.

- Avoid tobacco, alcohol, and other drugs.

- Avoid sexual contact. Some **STDs,** such as HIV, actually destroy the immune system.

- Keep your immunizations up to date.

Vaccines to Aid the Body's Defenses

Reading Check

Explain What are some of the positive steps you can follow to reduce your chance of illness?

When a new disease emerges or a familiar one becomes a greater health threat than in the past, health care workers begin to look for ways to prevent the disease. Research and advances in medical technology have allowed scientists to develop vaccines. A health-literate individual knows how the prevention and control of health problems are influenced by research and medical advances. Today, vaccines prevent diseases that once claimed millions of lives around the world. Vaccines can be one of four types.

- **Live-virus vaccines** are made from pathogens grown under special laboratory conditions to make them lose most of their disease-causing properties. Although weakened, the organism can still stimulate the production of antibodies. The vaccines for measles, mumps, and rubella (MMR) and for chicken pox are produced in this way.

- **Killed-virus vaccines** use inactivated pathogens. Even though they are dead, the organism still stimulates an immune response and antibodies are produced. Flu shots, the Salk vaccine for polio, and the vaccines for hepatitis A, rabies, cholera, and plague are all killed-virus vaccines.

- **Toxoids** are inactivated toxins from pathogens. They are used to stimulate the production of antibodies. Toxoids can be used to protect the body against illnesses. Both tetanus and diphtheria immunizations use toxoids.

- **New and second-generation vaccines** are being developed by scientists using new technologies. An example is the vaccine for hepatitis B, which is made from genetically altered yeast cells.

These and many other common diseases can be prevented with vaccines:
- Chicken pox
- Hepatitis B
- Measles
- Mumps
- Whooping cough (pertussis)
- Tetanus
- Diphtheria
- Polio
- Rubella

Check with your parents or your health care professional to find out how many of these diseases you have been vaccinated against.

Immunization for All

Vaccines help prevent the spread of communicable disease by reducing the number of people who may become infected. When you are vaccinated against a disease, you show that you know strategies for health enhancement and risk reduction. It's also important to make sure your vaccinations are current. For some diseases, such as tetanus, it is necessary to be revaccinated every ten years. Keeping a record of your vaccinations will help you keep track of when you need booster shots.

You should have up-to-date immunizations, including those for tetanus, diphtheria, measles, mumps, rubella, and hepatitis B. Vaccination against chicken pox is recommended if you have not had this disease. Some vaccines require more than one dose over time, or "booster shots." Your family physician and your local health department can advise you on the immunizations you need and provide them for you. Most high schools and colleges require that students show proof of current immunizations before admission. Each state has its own laws governing immunizations and school attendance. By following these laws, you show that you understand how public health policies and government regulations influence health conditions in your community.

LESSON 2 REVIEW

Reviewing Facts and Vocabulary

1. List three physical and chemical barriers that pathogens encounter when they try to enter the human body.

2. What is the difference between active immunity and passive immunity?

3. Where can you go to find out which immunizations you need?

Thinking Critically

4. **Analyzing.** How do you think vaccines have impacted the health status of individuals, families, communities, and the world?

5. **Evaluating.** What would you say to someone who says that he or she is careful never to come into contact with pathogens and therefore will not become ill?

Applying Health Skills

Accessing Information. Research those vaccinations suggested for someone your age, and make a table of this information. Work with a parent or guardian to determine which of your immunizations are current, and fill in the information on the table. Plan to get any immunizations you lack. Use this table to track when you should update your immunizations.

After You Read

Analyze a Graph. After reviewing Figure 24.3 on page 630, write an essay describing how your immune system works. Include information describing how you can protect your immune system.

Visit **health.glencoe.com** for the Interactive Study Guide for Lesson 2.

Common Communicable Diseases

Guide to Reading

Building Vocabulary

As you read this lesson, write each new highlighted term and its definition in your notebook.

▶ pneumonia (p. 636)

▶ jaundice (p. 638)

▶ emerging infection (p. 640)

Quick Write

Make a list of all the communicable diseases you know of. What can you do to prevent them?

Focusing on the Main Ideas

In this lesson, you will learn how to:

▶ Explain the causes, transmission, symptoms, and treatment of several communicable diseases.

▶ Develop strategies to reduce the risk of contracting some communicable diseases.

▶ Examine the ways technology impacts world health status.

Reading Strategy

Predict

▶ Scan the headings, subheadings, and photo captions. Write a list of at least three questions you believe will be answered in this lesson.

Y ou probably have experienced a fever or the stuffy or runny nose of a cold. In this lesson you'll learn about some common communicable diseases, their symptoms, and how they are treated. Most important, you will learn how the environmental conditions of the community influence the health of individuals.

Respiratory Infections

T he most common communicable diseases are those of the respiratory tract. These infections can occur any-where from the nose to the alveoli of the lungs. Most are caused by viruses or bacteria. You can reduce your risk of most respiratory illnesses by avoiding close contact with people who are infected, washing your hands often, keeping your hands away from your eyes and nose, and keeping your immune system healthy. Smoking can contribute to illness by damaging cilia and irritating respiratory passages. In addition, symptoms of these diseases may be more severe in smokers. Smoking has also been shown to suppress the immune system.

⚑ When you have a cold, the best thing to do is rest, eat nutritious foods, and drink plenty of fluids such as water or fruit juice. *How might these strategies help your body fight cold viruses?*

Compare and Contrast
What are some of the similarities and differences between the common cold and the flu?

Is It a Cold
or the Flu?

Cold symptoms include:

▶ Runny or stuffy nose
▶ Sneezing
▶ Sore throat
▶ Headache

Flu symptoms include:

▶ High fever
▶ Chills
▶ Dry cough
▶ Muscle and joint pain
▶ Runny nose
▶ Sore throat
▶ Extreme fatigue

Common Cold

The common cold is a viral infection that causes inflammation of the mucous membranes that line the nose and throat. Symptoms include a runny nose, sneezing, and sore throat. Some common ways of getting a cold include rubbing your eyes or nose after picking up the virus directly through hand-to-hand contact or indirectly by handling a contaminated object. Colds can also be spread through the air when an infected person sneezes or coughs, releasing droplets containing the virus.

There is no cure for the common cold. Treatment is for relief of symptoms, and most colds clear up in a week or so. Often treatment includes the use of **analgesics.** It's important to note that anyone under 20 years of age should avoid use of medications containing salicylates, such as aspirin. Such use is linked to Reye's syndrome, a condition that can be fatal. Avoid these products no matter what disease you might have. Use acetaminophen or ibuprofen instead.

Influenza

Influenza, or the flu, is a viral infection of the respiratory tract. It is most often spread through airborne transmission but also may spread through direct or indirect contact. Symptoms of flu include high fever, fatigue, headache, muscle aches, and cough. The flu can lead to **pneumonia** (noo-MOH-nyah), *an infection of the lungs in which the air sacs fill with pus and other liquid.* This is a serious disease that is more likely to occur in the elderly and people with lung and heart problems.

Antiviral drugs for treatment of the flu are available but need to be given as soon as the first symptoms of the illness arise. Persons who have the flu should get proper nutrition and plenty of rest and fluids. Older adults and persons of any age with chronic health problems should get a flu shot every year. However, anyone who wants to avoid the flu can be given the vaccine.

Pneumonia

Along with influenza, pneumonia is one of the top ten causes of death in the United States. Viral pneumonia is relatively short-lived and produces symptoms similar to those of influenza. Antiviral drugs are used in some cases. Bacterial pneumonia can be treated with antibiotics if diagnosed early. The bacteria that cause pneumonia are often present in healthy throats. When body defenses are weakened in some way, the bacteria can get into the lungs and multiply. For example, if a person is elderly or has influenza, he or she may be more at risk for complications leading to pneumonia.

Strep Throat

Strep throat is a bacterial infection spread by direct contact, often through droplets that are coughed or sneezed into the air. Symptoms of strep throat include a sore throat, fever, and enlarged lymph nodes in the neck. Untreated, strep throat can lead to serious complications, including inflammation of the kidneys and rheumatic fever, which can cause permanent heart damage. Strep throat can be treated with antibiotics. A doctor cannot always diagnose strep by examination. If a sore throat lasts more than three days, a culture is taken to identify the bacteria.

Tuberculosis

Tuberculosis, or TB, is a bacterial disease that usually attacks the lungs. Since the 1940s, the incidence of TB has decreased in the United States. Today, the risk of TB infection is highest among people with compromised immune systems. That includes people with HIV, the very young whose immune systems are not fully developed, and those whose immune systems are compromised by disease or illness. TB is spread through the air when a person with the disease coughs or sneezes. Most people who are infected carry the bacteria in their lungs but never develop the disease because the body's defenses prevent the bacteria from multiplying and spreading to others. People with weakened immune systems are more likely to develop the active disease with symptoms that include fatigue, coughing (sometimes coughing up blood), fever, night sweats, and weight loss. People with the active disease can spread TB. Prolonged or repeated exposure is usually required for infection. Some strains have developed resistance to antibiotics. Physicians may have to prescribe several antibiotics at one time until tests are conducted to determine which are effective for a particular person.

Hepatitis

Hepatitis is inflammation of the liver and can be caused by chemicals, including drugs and alcohol, and by many different pathogens. The hepatitis A, B, and C viruses are some of the most common causes of this type of liver damage, and there is no cure for them. However, vaccines for hepatitis A and B are available.

Hepatitis A

Hepatitis A is another of the top ten communicable diseases reported in the United States. About 1.4 million people worldwide are newly infected each year. The hepatitis A virus is most commonly spread through contact with feces of an infected person. Infected persons who do not wash their hands properly may contaminate inanimate objects or food or spread the virus through direct contact.

Many employers in the health care industry require applicants to show proof of a negative TB test. *Why may patients in hospitals or in long-term care facilities be at increased risk for tuberculosis?*

Did You Know ?

Many people mistakenly believe that tuberculosis is no longer a problem, but experts estimate that about 10 million people in the United States are currently infected with TB bacteria and that about 10 percent of these people will develop the disease.

TB is increasingly a worldwide problem. In 2003, almost 2 million deaths were attributed to TB.

Symptoms of hepatitis A are generally mild and may include fever, nausea, vomiting, fatigue, abdominal pain, and **jaundice**, *a yellowing of the skin and eyes*. Most infected individuals recover completely. Chronic, or long-lasting, infection is rare. The best way to reduce your risk of hepatitis A is to practice careful handwashing and avoid close contact with people who are infected.

About 30 to 40 percent of people with hepatitis B don't know how they got the infection. *How can you protect yourself from exposure to hepatitis B?*

Hepatitis B

Hepatitis B is a more serious disease than hepatitis A. The hepatitis B virus (HBV) is found in most bodily fluids of an infected person, especially blood. It is most often transmitted through sexual contact. It also can be transmitted through needles shared by infected drug users. Though most people who are infected never experience symptoms, the hepatitis B virus frequently causes severe liver damage, including liver failure and cirrhosis, or scarring, of the liver. Hepatitis B may be responsible for up to 80 percent of all cases of liver cancer worldwide. More than 2 billion people worldwide have been infected with HBV. About 1.25 million people in the United States have chronic HBV infection.

You can reduce your risk of hepatitis B by practicing abstinence from sexual contact and from illegal drug use. Do not share personal items, such as toothbrushes and razors, which could have trace amounts of saliva or blood. Body piercing and tattooing using contaminated needles can spread the disease. The CDC recommends that all children and teens receive the hepatitis B vaccine.

Hepatitis C

Hepatitis C is the most common chronic bloodborne infection in the United States; about 4 million Americans are infected. It is most often transmitted by direct contact with infected blood through contaminated needles shared by drug users. Hepatitis C can lead to chronic liver disease, liver cancer, and liver failure. It is the leading reason for liver transplants in the United States. Up to 90 percent of those infected with the hepatitis C virus (HCV) don't realize they have the disease until years later when routine tests show liver damage. You can reduce your risk of hepatitis C by practicing abstinence from illegal drug use. In addition, don't share personal care items such as razors and toothbrushes. As with other viral infections, there is no cure for hepatitis. Treatment includes rest, proper nutrition, and drinking plenty of fluids.

Other Diseases

Several other communicable diseases are common among adolescents and young adults. **Figure 24.5** on page 640 provides a summary of these diseases.

Emerging Infections

Some diseases have been effectively controlled with the help of modern technology. Yet new diseases, such as West Nile Virus, AIDS, and Lyme disease, are constantly appearing. Others, such as malaria and tuberculosis, are occurring in forms that are resistant

Real-Life Application

Reducing Your Risk of Lyme Disease

In 1982 fewer than 1,000 cases of Lyme disease were reported in the United States. In 2002, more than 23,000 cases were reported. Lyme disease is transmitted to humans by the bite of an infected deer tick. Ticks favor a moist, shaded environment, such as forests. Coastal ticks thrive in areas of high rainfall. Ticks are most active in the spring and summer. Study the graph to help you analyze the environmental and geographical factors that influence the distribution and rate of disease in the United States. Use this information to develop a plan to reduce your risk.

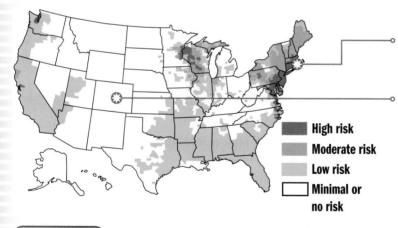

High risk
Moderate risk
Low risk
Minimal or no risk

What does the concentration of cases here tell you about the environment in which ticks live?

What is different about this part of the country that could account for the lower incidence of Lyme disease?

What human activities (leisure and industrial) could have influenced the increase in cases from 1982 to the present?

ACTIVITY

Work with a small group of students. Together, analyze the graph and discuss the questions. Use what you've learned to develop an action plan to decrease your risk of contracting Lyme disease. Include specific steps to protect yourself. Consider clothing, insect repellents, where you live or travel, and the time of year.

FIGURE 24.5

OTHER COMMON COMMUNICABLE DISEASES

Disease	Cause/Transmission	Symptoms	Treatment/Prevention
Mononucleosis	Virus attacks lymphocytes; spreads through direct contact, including sharing eating utensils and kissing	Chills, fever, sore throat, fatigue, and swollen lymph nodes	Rest if tired
Measles	Virus spreads when an infected person coughs, sneezes, or talks; highly contagious	High fever, red eyes, runny nose, cough, bumpy red rash usually starting on head or face	No definite treatment; vaccine for prevention
Encephalitis	A virus usually carried by mosquitoes; causes inflammation of the brain	Headache; fever; hallucinations; confusion; paralysis; and disturbances of speech, memory, behavior, and eye movement	If caused by herpes simplex virus, antiviral medicine; if caused by another virus, no known treatment
Meningitis	Virus or bacteria cause inflammation of the membranes that cover the brain	Fever, severe headache, nausea, vomiting, sensitivity to light, stiff neck	Viral meningitis: antiviral medicine if severe; bacterial meningitis: antibiotics; vaccine is available

Reading Check

Explain How do emerging infections spread from one area to another?

to drug treatments. These diseases are known as "emerging" diseases. An **emerging infection** is *a communicable disease whose incidence in humans has increased within the past two decades or threatens to increase in the near future.* Many factors are contributing to the development of emerging infections:

▶ **Transport across borders.** Infected people and animals carry pathogens from region to region, often to places where those pathogens previously were not a problem. Two examples of this are the appearance of dengue fever and West Nile encephalitis, which is caused by West Nile virus. Dengue fever is found mostly in South and Central America and parts of Asia and has appeared in the southwestern United States. West Nile encephalitis appears in Asia, Africa, and Europe and is now expanding across the Western Hemisphere, including most of the United States. Both diseases are carried by mosquitoes.

▶ **Population movement.** A factor in the increase in Lyme disease is the movement of people into heavily wooded areas where ticks are prevalent. Symptoms include a rash, fatigue, fever, headache, stiff neck, sore muscles, and joint pain. Lyme disease can be treated with antibiotics.

- **Resistance to antibiotics.** The widespread use of antibiotics has resulted in pathogens that have become resistant. The pathogens that cause tuberculosis, gonorrhea (a sexually transmitted disease), and a type of pneumonia all have developed resistance to one or more antibiotics.

- **Changes in food technology.** Mass production and distribution of food increases the chance that contaminated food will infect a great number of people. *E. coli* has been responsible for outbreaks affecting thousands.

- **Agents of bioterrorism.** Because of the ease and frequency of travel, a contagious bioterrorist agent such as smallpox can spread rapidly from country to country.

Public health officials in the United States are addressing infectious diseases elsewhere in the world because pathogens can emerge in one region and spread. Information on emerging diseases is widely available—on the Internet, in books and magazines, and through news reports. With health information readily available, individuals can become more proactive and responsible for reducing their risk of communicable diseases, including emerging infections.

Health Minute
What You Can Do

Precautions to avoid emerging or reemerging infections:

- Take all of the antibiotics prescribed by your doctor.
- Eat only fully cooked eggs.
- Avoid swallowing water at water parks.
- Take precautions to prevent bites by vectors such as ticks and mosquitoes.

LESSON 3 REVIEW

Reviewing Facts and Vocabulary

1. Compare and contrast the common cold and the flu.
2. What are three ways you can reduce your risk of getting influenza?
3. What are emerging infections?

Thinking Critically

4. **Synthesizing.** What healthful behaviors can students in your class practice to reduce everyone's risk of respiratory infection?
5. **Analyzing.** Why might emerging infections be an important area to receive funding for research? How can technology impact the reduction of diseases worldwide?

Applying Health Skills

Advocacy. Choose one emerging infection to research. Prepare a script for a public service announcement describing this disease. Be sure to include information on how the disease is transmitted and what the symptoms are. Urge individuals who suspect they may be infected to seek medical attention immediately. Share your script with the class.

After You Read

Problems and Solutions. Make a T chart. On the left side, list the Problems—the types of common communicable diseases. On the other side, list the Solutions—the strategies to reduce the risk of contracting some communicable diseases.

A Smallpox Shot

The smallpox vaccine works but carries real risks. Who should take it?

Outside of military personnel, who should get a shot to protect themselves against smallpox? It's a tricky question, because this particular vaccine is one of medicine's most dangerous. Most people just get a blister at the injection site and maybe some swelling of the arm. About a third will feel ill enough to miss work or school. Out of 1 million people, between 15 and 60 will develop serious complications, including encephalitis (swelling of the brain). If the entire population of the United States were to be vaccinated, 250 to 500 Americans would probably die.

Luckily, doctors can often tell in advance who is most at risk. Pregnant women and small children, for example, are particularly vulnerable. So is anyone whose immune system is compromised. All told, 60 million Americans would probably be well advised to take a pass.

Is It Worth the Risk?

According to a survey, two out of three Americans are willing to risk their health to protect themselves against a disease that doesn't really exist. There hasn't been an outbreak of smallpox for 25 years, thanks in large part to Dr. D. A. Henderson. He ran the World Health Organization's smallpox-eradication program and has been the chief smallpox adviser to the federal government. Henderson believes a smallpox outbreak in the United States would be "very controllable." The strategy he used in the 1960s and 1970s was to vaccinate only infected patients and people in contact with those patients, moving outward geographically in concentric circles until the virus stopped spreading. For those who don't get a precautionary vaccination, the smallpox vaccine still protects against the disease if given within two or three days after infection. ■

TIME to THINK...   About Preventing Infection

Discuss with the class:
1. What are the pros and cons of smallpox vaccinations?
2. What was Dr. Henderson's plan to prevent massive smallpox outbreaks in the 1960s and 1970s? Under that plan, would all citizens receive a vaccination if there was an outbreak in the U.S.? Why or why not?

Health Skills Application

1. **Goal Setting.** Identify three things you can do to lower your risk of contracting a communicable disease. Make a plan to incorporate these strategies into your daily life. Prepare a "Staying Healthy" checklist that gives strategies you can use to reduce the number of infections. *(LESSON 1)*

2. **Advocacy.** Check with state and local governments to find out what immunizations are required for admission to schools at various levels from preschool through college. Use this information to create a public service pamphlet that identifies and describes health-related services available in the community that relate to disease prevention and health promotion. *(LESSON 2)*

3. **Accessing Information.** Visit **health.glencoe.com** to link to a site on communicable diseases. Choose one of the diseases to research, and create a poster on your chosen disease. Include information about what symptoms accompany the disease, how it is transmitted, what lasting effects it can have on the body, what the trends are, who is most at risk, whether a cure or an effective treatment is available, and whether a vaccination is under development. *(LESSON 3)*

Epidemiologist

Did you ever wonder why and how diseases move the way they do? Why is the incidence of a particular disease suddenly on the increase? If these questions interest you, consider a career as an epidemiologist.

Epidemiology is a branch of medical science that deals with the incidence, distribution, and control of disease. Epidemiologists complete at least six years of college, studying science, human behavior, and biostatistics. People who want to become epidemiologists should be logical, patient, organized, and curious. Find out more about epidemiology and other health careers by clicking on Career Corner at **health.glencoe.com.**

Parent Involvement

Advocacy. Many diseases and emerging infections are spread by vectors. Contact a state or local health department to determine which vector-borne diseases occur most often in the state in which you live. Choose one of these diseases, and interview a local public health official about precautions that can be taken to avoid infection. Be sure to ask what treatments are available to an infected person. Prepare a fact sheet with this information, including a picture of the vector.

School and Community

Vaccine clinics. Gather information about clinics and other public sites where free or low-cost flu vaccines are offered. Prepare a flyer that explains the need for this immunization. Include the dates, times, and locations for these vaccination opportunities.

After You Read

Use the notes you have taken in your Foldable to review what you have learned. On the back of your Foldable, describe an experience you have had with a communicable disease and suggest ways that you might prevent future occurrences.

FOLDABLES
Study Organizer

▶ **EXPLORING HEALTH TERMS** *Answer the following questions on a sheet of paper.*

Lesson 1 *Match each definition with the correct term.*

communicable disease	pathogen
toxin	vector
viruses	bacteria

1. A microscopic organism that causes disease.
2. A substance that kills cells or interferes with their function.
3. An organism that carries and transmits pathogens to humans and other animals.

Lesson 2 *Fill in the blanks with the correct term.*

antibody	antigen
immune system	immunity
inflammatory response	lymphocyte
phagocyte	vaccine

4. The swelling and pain that accompany an injury such as a splinter are part of the body's _____ .
5. A white blood cell that attacks an invading pathogen is a(n) _____ .
6. The state of being protected against a particular disease is _____ .

Lesson 3 *Identify each sentence as True or False. If false, replace the underlined term with the correct term.*

emerging infection	jaundice
pneumonia	

7. Jaundice can be a complication of the flu.
8. A person with pneumonia will have skin and eyes that are slightly yellow.
9. An emerging infection is an infectious disease that has become more common within the past two decades or that threatens to increase in the near future.

▶ **RECALLING THE FACTS** *Use complete sentences to answer the following questions.*

1. What is one way that some bacteria are helpful to the human body? How do some bacteria harm the body?
2. How do pathogens spread when a person sneezes?
3. Analyze how handwashing can help prevent communicable diseases from spreading.
4. How do mucous membranes help fight pathogens?
5. How are antibodies and antigens related?
6. Describe how vaccines work, and evaluate their impact on disease prevention.
7. Explain how technology, such as the development of vaccines, has impacted the health status of individuals, families, communities, and the world in the prevention of communicable disease.
8. With what do the air sacs in the lungs fill in a person infected with pneumonia?
9. What healthful behaviors will reduce your risk of contracting hepatitis A, B, and C?
10. Identify three emerging infections.

For more review questions for Chapter 24, go to **health.glencoe.com**.

▶ WRITING CRITICALLY

1. **Expository.** Write a health bulletin to post in the office of your school nurse that informs others of strategies for preventing common communicable diseases. In your bulletin, make sure that you first define communicable diseases and list some common communicable diseases.

2. **Personal.** Write a journal entry describing how you felt the last time you were sick. Describe the favorite activities that you missed because of the illness, how long it took to catch up on schoolwork, and how long it took to feel better. In your journal, discuss any prevention strategies you might have taken to avoid the illness.

Standardized Test Practice

Read the paragraph below and then answer the questions.

If you have ever had a bacterial infection, you have seen how quickly bacteria can multiply in your body. Bacteria reproduce by dividing in two in a process known as binary fission. If conditions are ideal, binary fission takes about 15 minutes. However, this time can vary from about 10 minutes to about 24 hours.

Starting with a single bacterium, how can you find out how many bacteria exist after a certain length of time? After one reproductive cycle, you have two bacteria, or 2^1. After two cycles, you have four, or 2^2. You can summarize this pattern by the formula $B = 2^n$, where B is the number of bacteria, and n is the number of reproductive cycles.

1. One bacterium has a reproductive cycle of 30 minutes. How many bacteria will there be at the end of four hours?

A 16
B 120
C 256
D 512

2. How many bacteria exist after seven reproductive cycles?

F 14
G 64
H 128
I It depends on the length of the reproductive cycle.

3. What would be the shape of the graph where time is plotted on the x-axis and the number of bacteria is plotted on the y-axis? Where is the slope of the line the steepest?

Sexually Transmitted Infections and HIV/AIDS

Eye ON THE Media

Mock Radio Call-in Program

Radio call-in programs provide listeners with the opportunity to ask an expert questions. These programs also give listeners the chance to express their opinions. Radio call-in programs can

► **convey new information.**

► **analyze issues.**

Visit the Eye on the Media section at **health.glencoe.com** to learn more about how radio call-in programs can be useful in health advocacy.

FOLDABLES™ Study Organizer

Before You Read

Make this Foldable to help you organize what you learn about the risks of sexually transmitted infections. Begin with a sheet of 8½″ x 11″ paper.

► **Step 1**
Fold a sheet of paper along the long axis so the bottom edge lies 2″ from the top edge.

► **Step 2**
Fold into thirds.

► **Step 3**
Unfold and cut along the inside fold lines. Label as shown.

THE RISKS OF STDs

Behaviors   Consequences   Prevention

As You Read

As you read and discuss the material in the chapter, use your Foldable to define terms and record what you learn.

SPOTLIGHT ON HEALTH

Using Visuals. What can you do to raise funds for research for HIV/AIDS?

The Risks of STIs

Guide to Reading

Building Vocabulary

As you read this lesson, write each new highlighted term and its definition in your notebook.

▶ sexually transmitted diseases (STDs) (p. 648)

▶ sexually transmitted infections (STIs) (p. 648)

▶ epidemics (p. 648)

▶ abstinence (p. 651)

Focusing on the Main Ideas

In this lesson, you will learn how to:

▶ **Examine** the role alcohol and other drugs play in relation to HIV/AIDS and STDs.

▶ **Discuss** the benefits of abstinence as it relates to the prevention of STDs.

▶ **Develop** strategies to help prevent communicable diseases such as STDs.

Reading Strategy

Predict

▶ Before reading, write a brief essay describing ways that you can prevent the transmission of HIV/AIDS.

Quick *Write*

Your health is affected by the decisions you make. Write a short paragraph about the strategies you use to avoid risk behaviors.

▲ STDs are the most common communicable diseases in the United States. *Why do you think this has been called the hidden epidemic?*

Some communicable diseases, such as the cold or flu, can be transmitted through actions as simple as shaking hands. Other communicable diseases are not so easily spread. **Sexually transmitted diseases (STDs)**, also referred to as **sexually transmitted infections (STIs)**, are *infectious diseases spread from person to person through sexual contact*. For an infection to occur, a person must have sexual contact with someone who is infected with an STD. It's also possible that one person will show symptoms of the disease, while the other will not. A person can have an infection, and pass the infection to others, without necessarily having the disease.

STDs: The Hidden Epidemic

Throughout history people have been faced with **epidemics**, *occurrences of diseases in which many people in the same place at the same time are affected.* Today in the United States, we are now facing another epidemic—an epidemic of STDs. An estimated 65 million people in the United States are living with an incurable STD. Many of these cases go undiagnosed and untreated. Why?

► Many people with STDs are asymptomatic—without symptoms. They do not seek treatment because they don't know they are infected. Individuals who don't know that they are infected can continue to transmit STDs. Some people who suspect they have an STD may be too embarrassed to seek treatment.

► Even when STDs are diagnosed, they may not be reported to health departments so that contacts can be notified and treated. These contacts can continue to unknowingly transmit the disease to others.

High-Risk Behavior and STDs

In the United States teens make up one quarter of the estimated 15 million new cases of STDs each year. That's more than 10,000 young people infected every day. Why are teens at particularly high risk for infection from STDs? Teens who are sexually active are likely to participate in one or more of the following high-risk behaviors:

► **Being sexually active with more than one person.** This includes having a series of sexual relationships with one person at a time. However, being sexually active with even one partner puts a person at risk. Most teens are unaware of a partner's past behavior and whether he or she already has an STD.

► **Engaging in unprotected sex.** Even protected sex, or barrier protection, is not 100 percent effective in preventing the transmission of STDs, and it is not effective at all against HPV—the human papillomavirus. Abstinence from sexual activity is the only method that is 100 percent effective in preventing STDs.

► **Selecting high-risk partners.** Such partners include those with a history of being sexually active with more than one person and those who have injected illegal drugs.

► **Using alcohol and other drugs.** Alcohol use can lower inhibitions. In a recent survey, more than 25 percent of teens who engaged in sexual activity had been under the influence of alcohol or drug use.

To reduce the risk of STDs, teens must understand the causes, consequences, and prevention of major health risk behaviors, including the transmission of HIV/AIDS.

Reading ✓ Check

Explain Why are STDs a hidden epidemic?

Ⓨ Avoid high-risk behaviors by forming friendships with people who share your commitment to abstinence. *Develop and analyze other strategies related to the prevention of communicable diseases such as STDs.*

The Consequences of STDs

Most people, including teens, are not fully aware of the consequences of STDs. These are serious infections that can dramatically change the course of a person's life.

► **Some STDs are incurable.** The pathogens that cause these STDs cannot be eliminated from the body by medical treatment, such as antibiotics. The viruses that cause genital herpes and AIDS (the human immunodeficiency virus, or HIV), for example, remain in the body for life.

► **Some STDs cause cancer.** The hepatitis B virus can cause cancer of the liver. The human papillomavirus (HPV) can cause cancer of the cervix. These STDs also cannot be cured and may last a lifetime.

Reading Check

Infer What is the relationship between sexual intercourse and sexually transmitted infection?

Hands-On Health ACTIVITY

The Benefits of Abstinence

Practicing abstinence from sexual activity can benefit you in many ways. By encouraging your friends to abstain, you can be a positive influence on their health and well-being.

What You'll Need

- paper and pencil
- number cube (one for each group)
- paper cup (one for each group)
- construction paper
- markers

What You'll Do

1. Roll the cube from the cup onto your desk five times and record each number. Complete the following steps at your teacher's instruction.

2. Stand if you rolled one 5. Imagine that you have just found out that you have an STD. Tell how this will affect your life now and in the future.

3. Stand if you rolled a 5 more than once. Tell what you think and how you feel about having more than one STD.

4. As a class, brainstorm reasons for practicing abstinence.

5. Work in small groups to cut out a sheet of construction paper as your teacher instructs.

6. Write a different reason to practice abstinence on each of the six sides of the paper. Target the message to teens and be persuasive.

7. Fold and tape the paper to form a cube, then hang the cube from the ceiling.

Apply and Conclude

Imagine how you want your life to be in five years. Write it down. Be specific. Add how practicing abstinence now can help you achieve the life you want.

▶ **Some STDs can cause complications that affect the ability to reproduce.** Females can develop pelvic inflammatory disease (PID), which damages reproductive organs and can cause sterility.

▶ **Some STDs can be passed from an infected female to her child before, during, or after birth.** STDs can damage the bones, nervous system, and brain of a fetus. Premature births can result, and infants infected with STDs at delivery may become blind or develop pneumonia and some may die.

The Importance and Benefits of Abstinence

A clear cause-and-effect relationship exists between sexual intercourse in any form and sexually transmitted infection. If you have sexual contact with an infected person, you put yourself at risk of being infected with an STD. Sexual activity is the cause—an STD is the effect. An informed individual understands the role of individual responsibility regarding personal risk behaviors.

Prevent exposure to STDs by practicing **abstinence**, *the deliberate decision to avoid harmful behaviors, including sexual activity before marriage and the use of tobacco, alcohol, and other drugs.* Use refusal skills to avoid situations in which you may be at risk. Choose friends who are abstinent and who support your decision to abstain.

HEALTH Online

TOPIC **Hepatitis B**

Go to health.glencoe.com for Health Updates on hepatitis B.

ACTIVITY Using the information found in these articles, find the facts about the rise in hepatitis B infection. Share your findings with the class.

LESSON 1 | **REVIEW**

Reviewing Facts and Vocabulary

1. Identify three reasons why teens are at high risk for getting an STD.

2. Explain the relationship between alcohol and other drugs and substances used by adolescents and the role these substances play in unsafe situations such as HIV/STDs.

3. How are refusal skills related to STD prevention?

Thinking Critically

4. **Analyzing.** Analyze, discuss, and communicate the importance and benefits of abstinence as it relates to the prevention of STDs.

5. **Evaluating.** Explain and discuss why abstinence from sexual activity is the only method that is 100 percent effective in preventing STDs.

Applying Health Skills

Advocacy. Write an article for your school newspaper to inform students about the STD epidemic. Include the negative consequences that can affect a person's life, as well as strategies related to the prevention of STDs that you have developed and analyzed.

After You Read

Cause and Effect. Make a two-column chart. On the left side, list the high-risk behaviors that can lead to infection from STDs. On the right side, list some of the consequences of STDs.

Visit **health.glencoe.com** for the Interactive Study Guide for Lesson 1.

Common STIs

Guide to Reading

Building Vocabulary

As you read this lesson, write each new highlighted term and its definition in your notebook.

▶ human papillomavirus (HPV) (p. 652)

▶ chlamydia (p. 654)

▶ genital herpes (p. 654)

▶ gonorrhea (p. 655)

▶ trichomoniasis (p. 655)

▶ syphilis (p. 655)

Focusing on the Main Ideas

In this lesson, you will learn how to:

▶ Describe the symptoms and treatments for some common STDs.

▶ List community health services that help with the prevention and treatment of STDs.

▶ Examine public health policies and practices regarding STDs.

▶ Discuss the harmful effects of STDs on the fetus.

Reading Strategy

Predict

▶ Scan the headings, subheadings, and photo captions. Write a short paragraph summarizing what information you believe is in this lesson.

Quick Write

Write a short paragraph listing the STDs you have heard of and what to do to avoid the risk of contracting STDs.

 Learning about STDs can help you avoid the behaviors that lead to infection. *In addition to having accurate information, what else should you know or do to avoid infection from STDs?*

You have already learned why STDs are referred to as a hidden epidemic in the United States, which has the highest rates of STDs in the industrialized world. The Centers for Disease Control and Prevention (CDC) reports that STDs account for more than 85 percent of the most common communicable diseases in the United States. The estimated incidence and prevalence of STDs is shown in **Figure 25.1.** The most important fact to remember is this: The primary means of transmission of STDs is sexual activity. Teens who practice abstinence from sexual activity greatly reduce their risk of contracting STDs.

Human Papillomavirus

The **human papillomavirus**, or **HPV**, is *a virus that can cause genital warts or asymptomatic infection.* HPV is considered the most common STD in the United States. The CDC estimates that 50 to 75 percent of sexually active males and females acquire HPV infection at some time during their lives. About 30 different types of HPV can infect the genital area.

Most types of HPV infections are asymptomatic. A **Pap test** and other medical examinations may detect changes associated with HPV. There is no treatment. However, most asymptomatic HPV infections appear to be temporary and are probably cleared by the immune system. Almost all cases of cervical cancer are caused by certain types of HPV. HPV also can cause cancers of the penis and anus.

Genital Warts

Genital warts are pink or reddish warts with cauliflowerlike tops that appear on the genitals, the vagina, or the cervix one to three months after infection from HPV. Genital warts are highly contagious and are spread by any form of sexual contact with an infected person. It may take up to three months for warts to appear, but they often disappear, even without treatment. Diagnosis is determined by a health care worker by examination of the warts. If a person suspects he or she has been infected, examination and treatment are essential, because once infected, a person has the virus for the rest of his or her life. Treatments can rid the body of the warts but not the virus. Complications of HPV and genital warts can result in cervical cancer and cancer of the penis. Infants born to females infected with HPV may develop warts in their throats, obstructing the breathing passages, which can be life-threatening.

To reduce their risk, teens should understand that a mutually faithful, monogamous heterosexual relationship in the context of marriage is the best lifelong means of avoiding STDs.

Reading Check

Identify How many new cases of genital herpes occur each year (Figure 25.1)?

FIGURE 25.1		
ESTIMATED INCIDENCE AND PREVALENCE OF STDS IN THE UNITED STATES		
STD	**Incidence (Estimated number of new cases every year)**	**Prevalence (Estimated number of people currently infected)**
Human Papillomavirus (HPV)	6.2 million	20 million
Chlamydia	3 million	2 million
Genital Herpes	1 million	45 million
Gonorrhea	700,000	Not Available
Trichomoniasis	7.4 million	Not Available
Syphilis	70,000	Not Available
Hepatitis B	120,000	417,000

Source: CDC, Tracking the Hidden Epidemics. Trends in STDs in the United States, 2000. STD Treatment Guidelines, 2002

Chlamydia

Chlamydia is *a bacterial infection that affects the reproductive organs of both males and females*. Forty percent of cases are reported in teens 15 to 19 years old. Chlamydia is asymptomatic, meaning there are no visible symptoms, in 75 percent of infected females and 50 percent of infected males. When symptoms are present, males may experience a discharge from the penis and burning upon urination. Females may have vaginal discharge, burning upon urination, or abdominal pain. Chlamydia is diagnosed by laboratory examination of secretions from the cervix in females and from the **urethra** in males. It can be treated with antibiotics, but no immunity develops, so a person can become infected again.

Because chlamydia is usually asymptomatic, it often goes undetected until serious complications occur. In females who are untreated, the infection can cause pelvic inflammatory disease (PID) and lead to chronic (long-term) pelvic pain or infertility. Untreated chlamydia also can lead to infertility in males. Chlamydia can cause premature birth, and infants born to infected females may develop eye disease or pneumonia.

Genital Herpes

Genital herpes is *an STD caused by the herpes simplex virus (HSV)*. There are two types of HSV:

▶ Type 1 usually causes cold sores.

▶ Type 2 usually causes genital sores.

However, both types can infect the mouth and the genitals. Nationwide, about 20 percent of the total adolescent population is infected with the virus. Genital herpes is twice as common in adults from 20 to 29 years old today as it was 20 years ago.

Most individuals who have genital herpes are asymptomatic and are not aware that they are infected. Those who do show symptoms typically have blisterlike sores in the genital area that occur periodically. It is not true that the virus can be spread only when blisters are present; the virus can spread in the absence of symptoms. Diagnosis is made through laboratory tests on the fluid from the blisters. Medication can relieve the symptoms but cannot cure herpes infection—once contracted, the virus remains in the body for life.

The herpes virus is potentially fatal for infants who contract the virus from their mothers at the time of delivery. The virus may also play a major role in the spread of HIV by making people who are infected with herpes more capable of transmitting or acquiring HIV.

Mothers have a responsibility to protect their infants from exposure to STDs during pregnancy as well as during breast-feeding. *Which STDs can be transmitted from a mother to her child during pregnancy and birth?*

Gonorrhea

Gonorrhea is *a bacterial STD that usually affects mucous membranes.* The highest rates of gonorrhea infection are found in females from 15 to 19 years old and in males from 20 to 24 years old. Symptoms in males include a discharge from the penis and painful urination. Diagnosis in males is made by staining and examining the discharge under a microscope. Approximately 50 percent of females with gonorrhea have no symptoms. Those who do may experience a vaginal discharge and pain or burning upon urination. Diagnosis in females is made by swabbing the cervix and growing the organisms in a laboratory. Gonorrhea can be treated with antibiotics. However, increased resistance to antibiotics can complicate treatment. A person can be reinfected if exposed again to the bacteria. If untreated, gonorrhea can lead to infertility in both males and females. The bacteria can also spread to the bloodstream and cause permanent damage to the joints. Females can pass the infection to their babies during childbirth. Infants born to mothers with gonorrhea can contract eye infections that cause blindness.

Trichomoniasis

Trichomoniasis is *an STD caused by a microscopic protozoan that results in infections of the vagina, urethra, and bladder.* About 7.4 million new cases of this disease are estimated to occur every year in the United States. Females may have no symptoms; however, the disease may result in **vaginitis,** an inflammation of the vagina characterized by discharge, odor, irritation, and itching. In females trichomoniasis is diagnosed by microscopic examination of the discharge. The organisms can sometimes be seen in a Pap test. Males usually show no symptoms. When symptoms do occur in males, they include mild urethral itching or discharge and burning after urination. Since the disease is difficult to diagnose in males, they are usually treated without laboratory testing if their partners are infected.

Syphilis

Syphilis is *an STD that attacks many parts of the body and is caused by a small bacterium called a spirochete.* The first sign of infection is a painless reddish sore called a chancre (SHAN-kuhr) at the site of infection. The sore will heal on its own, but if the infection is not treated, it spreads through the blood to other parts of the body. Eventually, the disease can damage internal organs, including the heart, liver, nervous system, and kidneys. If left untreated, the person is at risk of paralysis, convulsions, blindness, and heart disease. Syphilis can be transmitted from a pregnant female to her fetus. An infant infected with syphilis may have a damaged nervous system and can die from the effects.

Reading Check

Classify Which common STIs are viruses and which are bacterial?

STDs are caused by bacteria, viruses, and other pathogens. This single-celled protozoan causes trichomoniasis. *Why is it important for people to get tested if they think they may have an STD?*

FIGURE 25.2

OTHER COMMON STDs

Disease (cause)	Symptoms	Treatment	What Could Happen
Chancroid (bacteria)	Sores or bumps on the genitals	Antibiotics	Infection of lymph glands in groin area, sores
Bacterial vaginosis (bacteria)	Abnormal vaginal discharge, odor, pain, itching, or burning during urination	Antibiotics	In most cases no complications; can lead to PID and premature birth; risk of HIV and STDs
Hepatitis B (virus)	90% of victims are asymptomatic; nausea, vomiting, jaundice, loss of appetite	Antiviral drugs in some cases, but no cure	Chronic infection, cirrhosis of the liver, cancer of the liver
Hepatitis C (blood-borne infection)	Often asymptomatic	Antiviral drugs, but no cure	Liver damage, liver disease
Pubic lice (small insects)	Itching, presence of lice and eggs in pubic hair	Medicated soaps; washing all bedding, towels, and clothes	No lasting effects

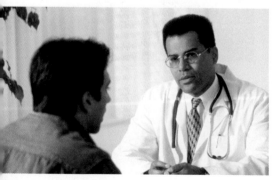

Early detection of STDs is important to avoid serious illness and further spread of the disease. *Why is it important for people not to treat an STD on their own?*

Seeking Treatment

Prevention of STDs is every individual's responsibility. Treatment is also an important personal responsibility. **Figure 25.2** above lists other common STDs, along with their symptoms and the treatment that is usually prescribed for each. As you have read, STDs can cause severe, long-term health problems. By law, information about these diseases is kept confidential. Only a health care professional can prescribe the correct treatment, including antibiotics, for some STDs.

Individuals also have a social obligation to prevent the spread of infection. Public health clinics sometimes help with contacting current and past partners to make sure they get any needed treatment. Ultimately, however, it is the responsibility of any person infected with an STD to notify everyone with whom he or she has had sexual contact. Informing someone else about the possibility of having an STD could save the person's life and shows that you understand how public health policies and government regulations influence health conditions.

Health Skills Activity

Refusal Skills: Lines of Defense

Juliana has been dating Kyle for several months. She has already explained to Kyle that she wants to remain abstinent, and until now he has respected her decision.

Kyle says, "Hey, Jules, let's skip the movie tonight and check out the party at my buddy's house. His folks are gone, and I hear there's going to be a band!"

Juliana responds, "It sounds like fun, but I don't know your buddy and it's pretty far away."

"No problem, I'll protect you!" Kyle laughs. "In fact, we'll finally have a chance to spend some time alone."

Juliana is worried about what might happen.

What Would You Do?

Apply the following refusal skills to write a response to Kyle. Use each refusal skill.

1. Say no in a firm voice.
2. Explain why you are refusing.
3. Suggest alternatives to the proposed activity.
4. Back up your words with body language.
5. Leave if necessary.

LESSON 2 **REVIEW**

Reviewing Facts and Vocabulary

1. Which STDs might not present noticeable symptoms?
2. Analyze and explain the harmful effects of two common STDs on fetuses and infants.
3. Where can a person go for treatment of an STD?

Thinking Critically

4. **Compare and Contrast.** Describe symptoms of gonorrhea and genital herpes for males and females.
5. **Analyzing.** Public policies enable health officials to locate and contact sexual partners of people who have been diagnosed with an STD. How do these policies help with the prevention and treatment of STDs?

Applying Health Skills

Refusal Skills. Construct a table similar to the one on page 656. Use this table to list reasons to say no to pressure to engage in sexual activity.

After You Read

Cause and Effect. Make a two-column chart. On the left side, list the common STDs (cause) and their symptoms. On the right side, list the corresponding treatments and lasting effects.

Visit **health.glencoe.com** for the Interactive Study Guide for Lesson 2.

Lesson 2 Common STIs **657**

HIV and AIDS

Guide to Reading

Building Vocabulary

As you read this lesson, write each new highlighted term and its definition in your notebook.

▶ acquired immune deficiency syndrome (AIDS) (p. 658)

▶ human immunodeficiency virus (HIV) (p. 658)

▶ opportunistic infection (p. 659)

Focusing on the Main Ideas

In this lesson, you will learn how to:

▶ Describe how HIV affects and destroys the immune system.

▶ Identify behaviors known to transmit HIV.

▶ Compare the relationships between unsafe behaviors, refusal skills, and the risk of HIV infection.

Reading Strategy

Predict

▶ Write a brief essay describing how HIV and AIDS are transmitted, based on your current knowledge.

Write a short paragraph describing what you know about the way your immune system protects your body from disease.

Health care workers wear goggles and disposable gloves whenever they may come in contact with body fluids. *Why are these precautions taken with all patients, not just those known to be infected with HIV?*

In July 1981 an outbreak of a rare form of skin cancer known as Kaposi's (KAY-puh-seez) sarcoma was reported. About a year later, the CDC labeled the disease **acquired immune deficiency syndrome**, or **AIDS**, *a disease in which the immune system of the patient is weakened*. That year more than 1,600 cases were reported and almost 700 deaths resulted from the newly identified disease. In 1983 the **human immunodeficiency virus**, or **HIV**, *a virus that attacks the immune system*, was confirmed as the cause. In 2003, AIDS was the sixth leading cause of death among adults from 25 to 44 years old.

Teens at Risk

In the United States the overall rate of new cases of HIV infection has fallen slightly since 1985, and new drug therapies help AIDS patients live longer. As a result, some people have a false sense that AIDS is no longer the problem it once was. However, data indicates that although new AIDS cases are declining among the population as a whole, there has been no decline in the number of diagnosed HIV infections among youth from 13 to 24 years old. In fact, teens have one of the fastest growing rates of HIV infection. Many young adults who are currently dying from AIDS were infected in their teens.

FIGURE 25.3

HOW HIV ATTACKS CELLS

1. HIV attaches to cell surface.
2. Virus core enters cell and goes to nucleus.
3. Virus makes a copy of its genetic material.
4. New virus assembles at cell surface.
5. New virus breaks away from host cell.

HIV doesn't survive well outside of the human body. *How does this characteristic of HIV affect its transmission?*

Infection with HIV can be prevented. Teens who choose abstinence from sexual activity and from injecting drugs greatly reduce their risk of HIV infection. Teens who refrain from these activities show that they know strategies when making decisions related to health needs and risks of young adults.

HIV and the Human Body

You may recall that lymphocytes are white blood cells that help your body fight pathogens. Your body contains billions of lymphocytes, which are produced in bone marrow and found in the blood, lymph nodes, appendix, tonsils, and adenoids. When HIV enters the blood, it invades certain cells of the immune system, including T cells, which help other lymphocytes identify and destroy pathogens. The viruses take over the cells and cause them to produce new copies of themselves. The newly produced viruses break out of the cells, destroying them. The new viruses infect other cells, and then the process repeats itself, as shown in **Figure 25.3.**

As the number of viruses increases and the number of T cells decreases, the immune system becomes less capable of preventing infections and cancer. The body becomes susceptible to common infections and to **opportunistic infections**, *infections that occur in individuals who do not have healthy immune systems.* These infections are difficult to treat. With a weakened immune system, the infected individual suffers one illness after another.

HIV infection is progressive; that is, it destroys the cells of the immune system over many months or years. Being infected with HIV does not necessarily mean that an individual has AIDS. AIDS is the advanced stage of HIV infection.

Reading Check

Explain What is the difference between AIDS and HIV?

Real-Life Application

AIDS in Teens

At least half of all new HIV infections in the United States occur in people under 25 years of age. Although more and more teens are protecting themselves against AIDS by abstaining from sexual activity, this age group still accounts for hundreds of new cases of HIV infection each year.

AIDS in 13- to 19-Year-Olds

Source: CDC, HIV/AIDS Surveillance in Adolescents, 2003
*In 1993 the CDC began using expanded reporting criteria, increasing numbers of reported cases.

ACTIVITY

Work with a small group. Brainstorm reasons that teens continue to become infected with HIV. For every reason, identify a potential solution. For example, if your group believes that using drugs is one reason, then you might identify more health education classes as a potential solution. Share your ideas with the rest of the class. Make a poster that portrays a health-promoting message drawn from this class discussion. Your poster should persuade teens to practice abstinence and emphasize that abstinence is the best way to prevent HIV infection.

How HIV Is Transmitted

The HIV organism lives inside cells and body fluids. However, it doesn't survive well in the air or on surfaces such as toilet seats or telephones. It cannot be transmitted through food. A person is not at risk of HIV infection by working next to or being in the same classroom as a person who is infected nor by merely touching an infected person.

HIV can be transmitted from an infected person to an uninfected person only in certain ways—through blood, semen, vaginal secretions, and breast milk. You can greatly reduce your chances of HIV infection by abstaining from sexual intercourse and avoiding the use of injected drugs.

▶ **Sexual intercourse.** HIV can be transmitted during any form of sexual intercourse. During intercourse, secretions containing HIV can enter a partner's blood through tiny cuts in the body. The risks of HIV infection increase with the number of people with whom a person is or has been sexually active. Having an STD that causes sores, including chlamydia, genital herpes, gonorrhea, or syphilis, increases the risk of HIV.

▶ **Sharing needles.** People who inject drugs and share needles are at high risk for contracting and spreading HIV. If a person who is infected with HIV injects drugs, the needle or syringe can become contaminated with that person's blood. Anyone who uses that same needle or syringe can inject HIV directly into his or her bloodstream. Injections under the skin or in the muscle also can spread HIV.

▶ **Mother to baby.** A pregnant female who is infected with HIV can pass the virus to her baby. HIV in the mother's blood can be transmitted through the umbilical cord and during delivery. Because breast milk can contain HIV, a baby can receive HIV while nursing.

Did You Know ❓

The manner in which HIV can be transmitted has been clearly identified through scientific investigations. Yet much false information still exists. HIV has NOT been shown to be spread through
- insect bites.
- sweat.
- sneezing.
- casual physical contact, such as shaking hands and hugging.

LESSON 3 REVIEW

Reviewing Facts and Vocabulary

1. Describe the HIV/AIDS epidemic in the teen population.
2. How does HIV attack the immune system?
3. How is HIV transmitted?

Thinking Critically

4. **Synthesizing.** Teens have a high rate of contracting HIV, yet more adults from 25 to 44 years old die from AIDS. What characteristic of HIV/AIDS causes this discrepancy?
5. **Analyzing.** Analyze the relationship between unsafe behaviors, refusal skills, and the risk of HIV.

Applying Health Skills

Advocacy. Prepare a script for a public service announcement on the epidemic of HIV/AIDS. Include statistics on numbers infected, diagnosis, and treatment. Be sure to include information on how people can protect themselves from getting HIV/AIDS.

After You Read

Analyze. Make a two-column chart. On one side, use Figure 25.3 to list the steps of the process by which HIV attacks cells. On the other side, list the ways that HIV is transmitted from an infected person to an uninfected person.

Treatment for HIV and AIDS

Guide to Reading

Building Vocabulary

As you read this lesson, write each new highlighted term and its definition in your notebook.

▶ asymptomatic stage (p. 662)

▶ symptomatic stage (p. 663)

▶ EIA (p. 663)

▶ Western blot (p. 664)

▶ pandemic (p. 665)

Focusing on the Main Ideas

In this lesson, you will learn how to:

▶ Examine how technology has impacted the health of persons with HIV.

▶ Identify world and community health services available for people living with HIV/AIDS.

▶ Develop refusal skills and ways to avoid unsafe situations.

Reading Strategy

Organize Information

▶ As you read, take notes on the stages of HIV infection and what tests are available to detect HIV.

Quick Write

Write a short paragraph describing what you might do to help a friend who is afraid he or she might have HIV.

Even though medicines can slow the progress of HIV infection, there is still no vaccine that prevents the disease.

Just as many STDs show no symptoms and many infected individuals don't seek treatment, the same is especially true for HIV. Infection can be ignored or overlooked for several years, during which time the virus can still be transmitted.

Stages of HIV Infection

The HIV infection develops in stages over the course of several years. A person is considered infectious immediately after contracting the virus. Approximately half of all persons develop symptoms about three to six weeks after becoming infected with HIV. These symptoms may include fever, rash, headache, body aches, and swollen glands. In general, these symptoms disappear within a week to a month and are often mistaken for another viral infection, such as the flu. After the flulike symptoms disappear, the person enters the **asymptomatic stage**, *a period of time during which a person infected with HIV has no symptoms*. A person may show no signs of illness for 6 months to 10 years or more. However, the viruses continue to grow and the infected person can still transmit the virus to others.

Symptomatic HIV Infection

During the asymptomatic stage, the immune system keeps pace with HIV infection by producing billions of new cells. Eventually, though, the number of cells in the immune system declines to the point where other infections start to take over. This marks the **symptomatic stage**, *the stage in which a person infected with HIV has symptoms as a result of a severe drop in immune cells*. The symptoms may include swollen glands, weight loss, and yeast infections.

AIDS

During the latter stage of HIV infection, more serious symptoms appear until the infection meets the official definition of AIDS. This includes the presence of HIV infection, a severely damaged immune system measured by numbers of helper T cells, and the appearance of one or more opportunistic infections or illnesses. By the time AIDS develops, HIV has often attacked brain cells, causing difficulty in thinking and remembering.

An EIA test is the first step in determining whether or not an individual is HIV positive. Anyone engaging in risk behaviors should be tested for HIV. *Why is it important for individuals who might be exposed to HIV to be tested even though they aren't experiencing symptoms?*

Detecting HIV

Individuals who think they may have been exposed to HIV should seek testing from a health care professional immediately. Testing to determine the presence of the virus can be done by a private physician or at a hospital, a health clinic, or a local health department. Most states have laws to protect the confidentiality of test results.

EIA Test

The first test usually performed is an ELISA, or **EIA**—*a test that screens for the presence of HIV antibodies in the blood*. The EIA reacts to even small numbers of HIV antibodies. However, the EIA may give inaccurate results. There are two reasons for this.

▶ **Developing antibodies takes time**—weeks or even months after initial infection. Before antibodies develop, the EIA may give a false negative result. This means the test is negative, but the person is positive; there aren't enough antibodies for the test to detect. Most infected people will test positive in three to four weeks, but some take up to six months to test positive.

▶ **Certain health conditions,** such as hemophilia, hepatitis, and pregnancy, can cause the EIA to give a false positive reading. This means that although the test was positive, the person actually does not have the infection.

How do opportunistic illnesses attack?
When the immune system is weakened by the HIV infection, diseases find an *opportunity* to attack the damaged system. There are over 30 common opportunistic illnesses, including Kaposi's sarcoma and pneumocystis carinii pneumonia (PCP)— a rare form of pneumonia.

Compare and Contrast
What is the difference between the asymptomatic stage and the symptomatic stage of HIV?

Western Blot Test

If the EIA test is positive, it can be repeated to make sure the results are accurate. If the repeat test is also positive, other confirmation tests will be done. The **Western blot**, or WB, is *the most common confirmation test for HIV in the United States*. If done properly, this test is 100 percent accurate. If the results of all three of these tests are positive, a person is determined to have HIV. Often these individuals are referred to as HIV-positive.

The Impact of the Availability of Health Services

When HIV was first identified in the early 1980s, there were no treatments for HIV and few treatments for the opportunistic infections associated with the virus. In the years since then, several medications have been developed to treat HIV and to treat and prevent the complications of opportunistic infections. More drugs and vaccines are being researched. For many people these new treatments have extended and improved the quality of life. None of the drugs, however, cures HIV/AIDS. One reason that a cure is so hard to find is that HIV infects the very cells that regulate the immune response. In addition, several new strains of the virus have emerged since it was first discovered, making it even harder to develop an effective treatment. Many treatments have side effects so severe that some people stop treatment or take medicines only once in a while. This can lead to the development of new, drug-resistant

FIGURE 25.4

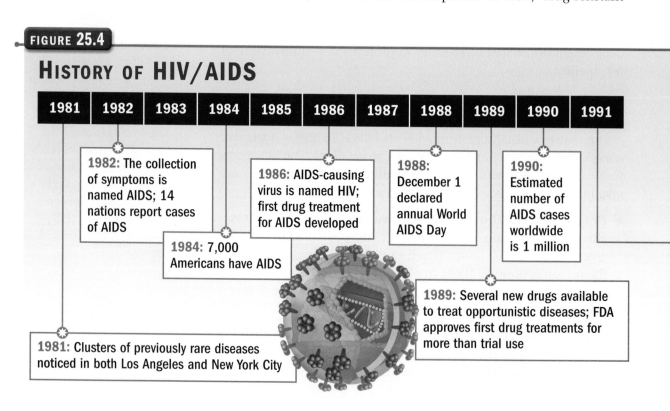

HISTORY OF HIV/AIDS

| 1981 | 1982 | 1983 | 1984 | 1985 | 1986 | 1987 | 1988 | 1989 | 1990 | 1991 |

1982: The collection of symptoms is named AIDS; 14 nations report cases of AIDS

1984: 7,000 Americans have AIDS

1986: AIDS-causing virus is named HIV; first drug treatment for AIDS developed

1988: December 1 declared annual World AIDS Day

1989: Several new drugs available to treat opportunistic diseases; FDA approves first drug treatments for more than trial use

1990: Estimated number of AIDS cases worldwide is 1 million

1981: Clusters of previously rare diseases noticed in both Los Angeles and New York City strains of the virus. Also, treatment can be costly, exceeding $1,000 a month. Worldwide, many infected individuals do not have access to treatment because of high costs and lack of availability. The time line shown in **Figure 25.4** summarizes some of the developments in HIV/AIDS research and treatment.

HIV/AIDS—A Continuing Problem

The number of newly reported AIDS cases in the industrialized world is decreasing. Much of this decrease in AIDS cases results from the success of drug cocktails—combinations of drugs—that slow the progression of HIV infection. However, research has identified new, drug-resistant strains of HIV. These strains do not respond to the drug cocktails currently used in the fight against AIDS. The combination of drug resistance and high-risk behaviors could result in HIV strains that are transmitted and spread even more widely. Despite the progress that has been made in the development of treatment options, HIV/AIDS is still a fatal disease for which there is no cure.

HIV/AIDS: THE GLOBAL PICTURE

At the end of 2002, an estimated 40 million people worldwide were infected with HIV/AIDS. This statistic means that HIV is now **pandemic**—*a global outbreak of infectious disease*. The number of people living with HIV is growing and is a health concern that requires collaborative decision making by health authorities worldwide. It is estimated that in 2002 alone, 5 million people became infected with HIV/AIDS worldwide.

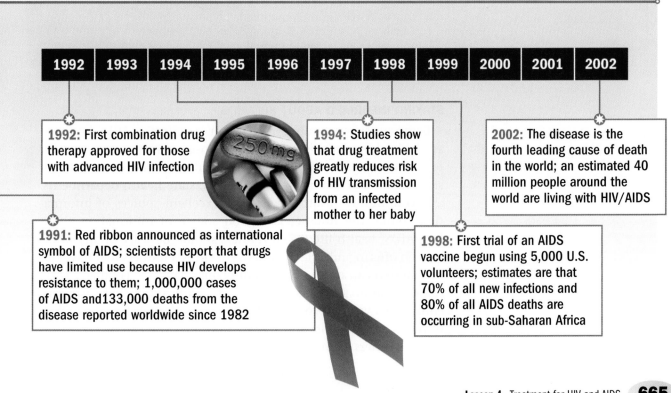

| 1992 | 1993 | 1994 | 1995 | 1996 | 1997 | 1998 | 1999 | 2000 | 2001 | 2002 |

1992: First combination drug therapy approved for those with advanced HIV infection

1994: Studies show that drug treatment greatly reduces risk of HIV transmission from an infected mother to her baby

2002: The disease is the fourth leading cause of death in the world; an estimated 40 million people around the world are living with HIV/AIDS

1991: Red ribbon announced as international symbol of AIDS; scientists report that drugs have limited use because HIV develops resistance to them; 1,000,000 cases of AIDS and 133,000 deaths from the disease reported worldwide since 1982

1998: First trial of an AIDS vaccine begun using 5,000 U.S. volunteers; estimates are that 70% of all new infections and 80% of all AIDS deaths are occurring in sub-Saharan Africa

Health Skills Activity

Helping Others

Mitch's high school class was looking for a service project when he learned that his older brother was HIV positive. He asked what he could do to help. Mitch's brother, Chris, said there was plenty he could do, "My doctor told me there are a lot of people who can't even get out and buy food."

Mitch suggested to his classmates that they consider a local service project. "We can help people closer to home," said Mitch. "We can deliver meals to people who are sick and can't get out of their homes to buy food." He suggested they volunteer for a local Meals on Wheels program. Some of the students were concerned about being in contact with sick people. Others worried about the time commitment. Another group of students mentioned that they didn't drive and wouldn't be able to deliver meals.

What Would You Do?

Apply these steps to help Mitch make a health-enhancing decision.

1. State the situation.
2. Obtain more information.
3. Weigh the possible outcomes.
4. Consider values.
5. Make a decision and act.
6. Evaluate the decision.

STAYING INFORMED ABOUT HIV/AIDS

Because neither a cure for AIDS nor an effective HIV vaccine is available, knowledge is the first defense against infection. New research can be found in newspapers and magazines and on television, radio, and the Internet. The CDC, state health departments, and community health services are excellent sources of information. While the Internet is a good source of information about HIV/AIDS, health-literate consumers should be wary of any information offering miracle treatments or cures. Products that have not been tested can harm or even kill people. The U.S. Food and Drug Administration sponsors a network of organizations that encourage consumer awareness to prevent fraud. By understanding the impact of high-risk behaviors and staying informed you can protect yourself and others from infection.

Abstinence and HIV/AIDS

During your teen years, you may feel pressure to experiment with new behaviors, such as engaging in sexual activity or using drugs. Consider that your actions today can change the entire course of your life. Choosing to remain abstinent shows that you are taking an active role in caring for your own health and acting responsibly by not jeopardizing the well-being of others. A person who remains aware of consequences knows various strategies when making decisions related to health needs and risks of young adults. Use of these refusal skills will help you avoid pressure to engage in sexual activity and use drugs:

▶ Avoid situations and events where drug use or the pressure to engage in sexual activity is likely to occur.

▶ Practice refusal skills. Be firm when you refuse to take part in drug use or sexual activity. Use body language as well as words to get your message across.

▶ Choose your relationships carefully. Avoid beginning a dating relationship with someone whom you know is sexually active with another person.

A Each of the more than 44,000 colorful panels in the AIDS Memorial Quilt memorializes the life of a person who died from AIDS. When the entire quilt was in Washington, D.C., it covered the National Mall. *How does the AIDS quilt help educate the public about HIV/AIDS?*

LESSON 4 REVIEW

Reviewing Facts and Vocabulary

1. What is asymptomatic HIV infection?
2. When is a Western blot test performed?
3. Explain how technologies such as new drug treatments have impacted the health status of individuals with HIV infection as well as people's attitudes toward the AIDS epidemic.

Thinking Critically

4. **Evaluating.** Why might people in the United States have better access to AIDS treatment than people in developing nations?
5. **Analyzing.** What is the relationship between the avoidance of unsafe situations and the use of refusal skills such as sexual abstinence?

Applying Health Skills

Accessing Information. Research new vaccines that are being developed for HIV/AIDS. Use several different sources of information in your search, such as Web sites, books, and newspaper and magazine articles. Evaluate the validity of your sources to make sure they are reliable and accurate. Then prepare a presentation analyzing the impact of the availability of these health services in the community and the world.

After You Read

Problems and Solutions. Fold your paper in half. On one side, list the reasons why HIV/AIDS is a continuing problem. On the other side, list current treatments for HIV and AIDS, including ways to detect HIV.

Changing the World

Meet one teen who knows he can make a difference.

Meet Nile Sandeen, 17. Nile's mission in life is to educate others about the realities of HIV/AIDS. TIME caught up with Nile in his hometown, Milwaukee, to find out more about this wonder teen:

TIME: When did you learn that you had AIDS, and how do you educate people about HIV?

NILE: I was born with HIV and diagnosed with AIDS when I was five. I'm a counselor at Camp Heartland, a summer camp for kids with HIV/AIDS. I also speak at schools nationwide about what it's like to live with the disease.

TIME: Did other kids treat you differently in school?

NILE: In kindergarten, word got out that I had AIDS. People freaked. It was very upsetting. Parents didn't want their kids to even sit near me.

TIME: What made you realize that you weren't alone?

NILE: Neil Willenson, a 22-year-old activist, heard about how badly I and other kids were being treated, so he started Camp Heartland in Willow River, Minnesota. I went there for 10 years, and it serves as a support group. We all have days where we think, "I don't even know how much more of life there will be."

TIME: Besides educating others about HIV, what do you do?

NILE: I'm more than the disease that I've got. At school I'm on the chess team, the debate team, I pitch for the baseball team and, yes, I frequently go on dates.

TIME: How will you change the world?

NILE: I know the more people I talk to, the less that others will be hurt by this disease. People will see we aren't so different. We may not see a cure in our lifetime, but as we continue to teach people to stay safe, we'll see less AIDS. ◢

TIME to THINK... About HIV

Nile was born with HIV. Brainstorm with the class all the ways that people have thought it possible to contract HIV. List them on the board. Then determine whether each is based on fact or fiction. Use your school's media center to research those you're unsure about.

1. **Advocacy.** Research groups that advocate teen abstinence from sexual activity. Find out what services these groups offer and how you can volunteer to help them. *(LESSON 1)*

2. **Accessing Information.** Identify community health services that help with prevention and treatment of STDs. Discover the types of educational materials they have for educating teens about the risks of STDs. Share your findings with the class. *(LESSON 2)*

3. **Advocacy.** Develop an HIV prevention program aimed at teens entering high school. Emphasize the relationship between unsafe behaviors, such as sexual contact and drug use, and the risk of HIV infection. *(LESSON 3)*

4. **Refusal Skills.** List two suggestions for practicing abstinence when pressured to engage in sexual activity or to use drugs. *(LESSON 4)*

CAREER Corner

Health Advocate

Do you like working with people? Can you synthesize information from a variety of sources to come up with innovative solutions to complex problems? If so, you may be interested in a career as a health advocate.

Health advocates work in a wide range of settings, but all health advocates work toward one goal: finding innovative ways to improve the delivery of health services.

Health advocates have several levels of certification. Two-year courses are available at some community colleges. Others become advocates through a Master of Arts program following college graduation. Find out more about this and other health careers by clicking on Career Corner at **health.glencoe.com.**

BEYOND *the* Classroom

Parent Involvement

Advocacy. With your parents, research ways that parents can help their children avoid risky behaviors that might lead to STDs. Work together with your parent or guardian to organize your research, and create guidelines for other parents. If you have access to the Internet, post the guidelines on a Web site.

School and Community

Finding Resources. Learn the names of organizations in your community that help people infected with HIV/AIDS. Make a list of these organizations, and describe the services each provides. Create a pamphlet containing the information you have gathered. Make the pamphlet available through the school health office.

After You Read

Use the notes you have taken in your Foldable to review what you have learned. Use the Internet or your school's media center to look for current research and statistics regarding teens and STDs. Report your findings on the back of your Foldable.

FOLDABLES™
Study Organizer

▶ **EXPLORING HEALTH TERMS** *Answer the following questions on a sheet of paper.*

Lesson 1 *Fill in the blanks with the correct term.*

abstinence	**sexually transmitted disease (STD)**
epidemic	**sexually transmitted infection (STI)**

1. An infection that spreads from person to person through sexual contact is called a(n) _____ or a(n) _____ .

2. When a community has a larger number of cases of an infectious disease than would be generally expected, the community is experiencing a(n) _____ .

3. The only 100 percent effective way to avoid STDs is to practice _____ .

Lesson 2 *Replace the underlined words with the correct term.*

chlamydia	**syphilis**
genital herpes	**trichomoniasis**
gonorrhea	**human papillomavirus (HPV)**

4. <u>Gonorrhea</u> can lead to pelvic pain and infertility.

5. <u>HPV</u> is an STD caused by the herpes simplex virus.

6. A bacterial STD that usually affects mucous membranes is <u>chlamydia</u>.

7. The first sign of <u>trichomoniasis</u> infection is a chancre at the site of infection.

Lesson 3 *Identify each statement as True or False. If false, replace the underlined term with the correct term.*

HIV	**AIDS**
opportunistic infections	

8. <u>AIDS</u> is the virus that attacks the immune system.

9. Being infected with <u>AIDS</u> does not necessarily mean a person has <u>HIV</u>.

10. <u>Opportunistic infections</u> are rare in a person with a normal immune system, but they easily invade the body of a person with a weakened immune system.

Lesson 4 *Match each definition with the correct term.*

EIA	**asymptomatic stage**
Western blot	**symptomatic stage**
pandemic	

11. A period of time during which a person infected with HIV has no symptoms.

12. The first test usually performed to screen for HIV antibodies in the blood.

13. The most common confirmation test for HIV in the United States.

▶ **RECALLING THE FACTS** *Use complete sentences to answer the following questions.*

1. Why are STDs in the United States considered a hidden epidemic?

2. Explain the relationship between alcohol and other drugs used by adolescents and the role these substances play in STDs.

3. What is the only method that is 100 percent effective in preventing STDs?

4. Which STDs stay in the body for life?

5. Why is early treatment of STDs important?

For more review questions for Chapter 25, go to **health.glencoe.com**.

6. Explain why an individual diagnosed with an STD should notify contacts.

7. Why is the risk of HIV infection low for a person whose coworker has tested positive for HIV?

8. Why does having multiple sexual contacts increase the risk of HIV infection?

9. List and describe the stages of HIV infection.

10. Relate the importance of tests to detect HIV and why early detection is important.

▶ WRITING CRITICALLY

1. **Persuasive.** Write an article for a health-related newsletter persuading teens to abstain from sexual activity. In your article, describe activities that place people at high risk for contracting a sexually transmitted disease (STD), and explain the consequences of STDs. Use supporting evidence giving logical reasons, examples, and quotes from experts.

2. **Descriptive.** Conduct research on a third world country that faces an HIV/AIDS epidemic but lacks the money and education to treat and prevent the disease. Write a descriptive article that could be published in a newspaper describing the AIDS epidemic in that particular country and how it affects its people. Make suggestions about possible solutions to the AIDS problem.

Standardized Test Practice

Read the paragraph below, look at the table, and then answer the questions.

According to the Centers for Disease Control, the number of reported AIDS cases was over 900,000 people as of December 2003. The statistics provided by the center are shown in several different forms. Cases can be grouped by age, location, race or ethnicity, or source of exposure. This table shows the ten states or territories that reported the highest total number of AIDS cases according to all figures received by December 2003.

State/ Territory	Total Number of AIDS Cases
New York	162,446
California	133,292
Florida	94,725
Texas	62,983
New Jersey	46,703
Illinois	30,139
Pennsylvania	29,988
Puerto Rico	28,301
Georgia	27,915
Maryland	26,918

1. What is the mean of the numerical data in the table?

   A about 27,000
   B 38,421
   C 64,341
   D 135,528

2. What is the median value of the numerical data in the table?

   F 26,918
   G 38,421
   H 64,341
   I 135,528

3. Does the fact that these nine states and one territory have the highest number of AIDS cases necessarily mean that they have the highest percentage of AIDS cases, based on the population of the state or territory? Explain your answer.

Noncommunicable Diseases and Disabilities

Eye ON THE Media — Prescription Drug Advertising

Prescription drug makers are required to follow Food and Drug Administration (FDA) guidelines for advertising. Advertisers must include the following specific information:

▶ **whether the drug will interact with another drug**

▶ **whether the drug might impair driving**

▶ **whether the drug is addictive**

Visit the Eye on the Media section at **health.glencoe.com** to learn more about FDA regulations for prescription drug advertising.

FOLDABLES™ Study Organizer

Before You Read

Make this Foldable to help you organize what you learn about cardiovascular disease. Begin with a sheet of notebook paper.

▶ **Step 1**

Fold a sheet of notebook paper in half along the long axis.

▶ **Step 2**

On the top fold, cut along every third line from the outside edge to the centerfold to form ten tabs.

▶ **Step 3**

Label the tabs as shown.

Circulatory System
CVD
Hypertension
Atherosclerosis
Angina Pectoris
Arrhythmias
Heart Attack
Congestive Heart Failure
Stroke
Risk Factors

As You Read

As you read and discuss the material in the chapter, use your Foldable to define terms, take notes, list statistics, and write descriptions pertaining to the chapter vocabulary terms.

SPOTLIGHT ON HEALTH

Using Visuals. Describe one lifestyle behavior that can reduce the risk of skin cancer.

Cardiovascular Diseases

Guide to Reading

Building Vocabulary

As you read this lesson, write each new highlighted term and its definition in your notebook.

▶ noncommunicable disease (p. 674)

▶ cardiovascular disease (p. 674)

▶ hypertension (p. 675)

▶ atherosclerosis (p. 675)

▶ angina pectoris (p. 677)

▶ arrhythmias (p. 677)

Focusing on the Main Ideas

In this lesson, you will learn how to:

▶ Describe the types of cardiovascular diseases.

▶ Discuss the importance of early detection.

▶ Identify risk behaviors and risk factors for cardiovascular diseases.

▶ Develop strategies related to the prevention of noncommunicable diseases.

Reading Strategy

Explain

▶ Write a brief essay answering the following question: Can heart disease affect young people? How?

 Quick Write

Make a list of habits that you think will benefit the health of your heart.

▼ Every day your heart pumps blood through the arteries to all the cells of your body. *Why should you establish and maintain healthful habits to care for your heart?*

A century ago communicable diseases were a leading cause of death in the United States. Since then, the average life span of Americans has nearly doubled, primarily because of public health efforts and new technologies. Today, however, major causes of death, such as heart disease and cancer, come from a different kind of disease. A **noncommunicable disease** is *a disease that is not transmitted by another person, a vector, or the environment.* In this lesson, you will learn the impact of personal health behaviors on body systems.

Cardiovascular Diseases

Your cardiovascular system transports blood to all parts of your body. Without oxygen and other materials that blood carries, your cells would die. Sometimes diseases interfere with the pumping action of the heart or the movement of blood through blood vessels. A **cardiovascular disease (CVD)** is *a disease that* *affects the heart or blood vessels.* Approximately 61 million Americans have some form of the disease. CVDs are responsible for more than 40 percent of all deaths in the United States, killing almost a million Americans each year.

Types of Cardiovascular Disease

The heart, blood, and blood vessels are the main parts of the circulatory system. When the parts work together properly, the cardiovascular system runs efficiently. When a problem affects one part, the entire system is threatened. As you read the description of each type of CVD, keep in mind that you can reduce your risk by avoiding tobacco; getting plenty of physical activity; maintaining a healthful weight; and following an eating plan low in saturated fat, cholesterol, and sodium.

Hypertension

Blood pressure is the force of blood created by the heart's contractions and the resistance of the vessel walls. Normal blood pressure varies with age, height, weight, and other factors. **Hypertension** is *high blood pressure*—pressure that is continually above the normal range for a particular person. If high blood pressure continues over a long period, the heart, blood vessels, and other body organs will be damaged. Hypertension is a major risk factor for other types of CVDs. Hypertension can occur at any age, but it is more common among people over the age of 35. Of Americans ages 20 to 74, 23 percent have hypertension. CVD, considered a "silent killer," often has no symptoms in its early stages, so it's important to get your blood pressure checked regularly. High blood pressure can be lowered with strategies such as medication, weight management, adequate physical activity, and proper nutrition.

Atherosclerosis

At birth, the lining of blood vessels is smooth and elastic. Over time, factors such as tobacco smoke, high blood pressure, and high cholesterol levels can damage the inner lining of the arteries. Fatty substances in the blood, called plaques, can build up on the artery walls, causing the arteries to thicken and lose their elasticity. *The process in which plaques accumulate on artery walls* is called **atherosclerosis** (a-thuh-roh-skluh-ROH-sis). This buildup is due mainly to food choices—specifically, a high intake of saturated fats and cholesterol. Sometimes, a blood clot forms in the area of plaque. The clot grows until it blocks the artery. If the affected artery feeds the heart or the brain, a heart attack or stroke may result.

The artery on the left is healthy. The one on the right shows evidence of atherosclerosis. *What effects can health behaviors have on body systems?*

Did You Know ?

Blood pressure is written as two numbers. The first number is the *systolic* number, which represents the pressure while the heart is beating. The second, or *diastolic*, number represents the pressure when the heart is resting between beats. For example, 122/76 represents a systolic pressure of 122 and a diastolic pressure of 76. High blood pressure in adults is defined as 140/90 or above.

Reading Check

Identify What are some of the tools that doctors use to diagnose diseases of the heart (Figure 26.1)?

Diseases of the Heart

Your **heart** pumps about 100,000 times a day *every* day to move blood to all parts of your body. Just like every other organ, your heart needs the oxygen from blood to function. When the blood supply to the heart is insufficient to provide enough oxygen, you may have a heart attack. The result can be damage to the heart muscle, or even sudden death due to cardiac arrest. Cardiac arrest and heart attacks are different. Heart attacks occur due to insufficient blood supply to the heart. Cardiac arrest occurs due to an electrical or rhythm problem with the heart. Methods for diagnosing and treating diseases of the heart and other CVDs are summarized in **Figure 26.1.**

FIGURE 26.1

DIAGNOSTIC TOOLS

EKG	MRI	Radionuclide Imaging	Angiography
An electrocardiogram (EKG) produces a graph of the electrical activity of the heart. It helps detect the nature of a heart attack and shows heart function.	Magnetic resonance imaging (MRI) uses powerful magnets to produce images of internal body organs. The images are used to identify heart damage and heart defects.	Radionuclides injected into the blood can be observed on a computer screen as they pass through the heart. This procedure is used to assess the heart's blood supply and to show heart function.	A thin, flexible tube is guided through blood vessels to the heart. Dye is injected, and motion X rays are taken to look for heart obstructions.

TREATMENT OPTIONS

Coronary Bypass	Angioplasty	Medications	Pacemaker
Often a healthy vein is removed from the leg or chest and placed elsewhere to create a detour around a blocked artery.	A tube with a balloon is inserted into a blocked artery. The balloon is inflated against the artery walls. Then it is deflated and removed. A metal structure may remain to keep the artery open.	Various medications are used to treat CVDs. These include diuretics to aid with the body's fluid balance, cholesterol-lowering drugs, and drugs that slow the blood's clotting mechanisms in order to reduce risk of stroke.	Pacemakers are used to treat an irregular heartbeat. The small device sends steady electrical impulses to the heart to make it beat regularly.

ANGINA PECTORIS

Angina pectoris (an-JY-nuh PEK-tuh-ruhs) is *chest pain that results when the heart does not get enough oxygen.* This pain, which usually lasts from a few seconds to minutes, is a warning sign that the heart is temporarily not getting enough blood. The most common cause of angina is atherosclerosis. Angina seldom causes permanent heart damage and sometimes can be treated with medication.

ARRHYTHMIAS

Arrhythmia is a change in the regular beat of the heart. The heart may seem to skip a beat or beat irregularly, very quickly, or very slowly. **Arrhythmias**, or *irregular heartbeats*, are common. They occur in millions of people who do not have underlying heart disease, and they usually don't cause problems. However, certain types of arrhythmias are serious. In one type of arrhythmia, called *ventricular fibrillation,* the electrical impulses regulating heart rhythm become rapid or irregular. This is the most common cause of sudden cardiac arrest, in which the heart stops beating without warning. Without immediate emergency help, death follows within minutes.

HEART ATTACK

Each year in the United States there are more than 1 million cases of heart attack, and more than 40 percent of those affected die. A heart attack is damage to the heart muscle caused by a reduced or blocked blood supply, usually because of atherosclerosis. Often ventricular fibrillation occurs seconds to hours or even days following a heart attack and can cause sudden death.

Many heart attacks are sudden and cause intense chest pain, but one in four produces no symptoms and is detected only when routine tests are done later. Most heart attacks start slowly with mild pain or discomfort, which is often mistaken for indigestion. Early detection of and immediate response to warning signs can often mean the difference between life and death.

CONGESTIVE HEART FAILURE

A heart attack is an immediate response to stress on the heart. Sometimes, however, the heart gradually weakens to the point that it cannot maintain its regular pumping rate and force. The result is a condition called congestive heart failure. This condition can be a result of high blood pressure, atherosclerosis, a heart valve defect, or other factors. Illegal drug use can also bring on this condition by increasing heart rate. Strategies for managing congestive heart failure include medication and the establishment of healthy lifestyle behaviors, such as good nutrition and adequate physical activity.

Heart Attack Warnings

These warning signs indicate that a heart attack may be happening and immediate medical attention is needed.

The warning signs of heart attack:

► Pressure, fullness, squeezing, or aching in the chest area

► Discomfort spreading to the arms, neck, jaw, upper abdomen, and back

► Chest discomfort with shortness of breath, lightheadedness, sweating, nausea, and vomiting

In many cases sudden cardiac arrest can be reversed if CPR or electric shock using a defibrillator is applied. *Why is it important to have defibrillators available in many different public places?*

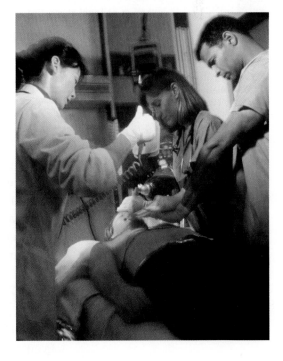

Hands-On Health ACTIVITY

Start a Healthy Habit

Working prevention strategies into your everyday life is the best way to reduce your risk of cardiovascular diseases. Take the quiz, and then complete the activity.

What You'll Need

- pen or pencil
- paper

What You'll Do

Number a sheet of paper from 1 to 10. Read each statement and write "always," "most of the time," "once in a while," or "never" for each item.

1. I avoid tobacco products and secondhand smoke.
2. I get 60 minutes of physical activity five or more days per week.
3. I get at least 30 minutes of moderate or 20 minutes of vigorous aerobic exercise at least three times a week.
4. I eat plenty of fruits, vegetables, and whole-grain foods.
5. I limit foods that are high in fat and cholesterol.
6. I limit my intake of salt and sodium.
7. I choose nutritious snacks.
8. I maintain a healthful weight.
9. I practice anger-management skills.
10. I practice stress-management skills.

Choose two habits you need to improve. In small groups, brainstorm a list of specific actions to help you practice these habits. Develop strategies to incorporate at least three healthy habits into your routine. Write a paragraph in which you describe your plan. After two weeks, evaluate what obstacles you faced, and identify what you are doing to improve.

Apply and Conclude

As a group, report on your successes in improving your lifestyle behaviors. Explain why the behaviors are healthful.

Stroke

When arterial blockage interrupts the flow of blood to the brain, a stroke may occur. Stroke can affect different parts of the body, depending on the part of the brain that is deprived of oxygen. Stroke also can occur as a result of a *cerebral hemorrhage*, a condition in which a blood vessel in the brain bursts, causing blood to spread into surrounding brain tissue.

Why Teens Are at Risk

The behaviors established during your teen years and early adult life determine, in large part, your risk of developing CVD. Even though the symptoms of CVD often don't show up until adulthood, the disease itself starts to develop in childhood, according to the American Heart Association. Autopsy results of adolescents who died from causes other than CVD have revealed that one in six already had evidence of CVD. Those who had a history of known risk factors, such as smoking or diabetes, were more likely to have blood-vessel damage. The health behaviors you practice *now* are affecting your cardiovascular system. An informed teen knows how to delay the onset of and reduce the risk for potential health problems during adulthood.

Risk Factors for Cardiovascular Disease

The American Heart Association has identified several factors, such as those listed in **Figure 26.2,** that increase the risk of heart disease and stroke.

Reading Check

Cause and Effect How does your behavior during the teen years affect your risk of developing CVD?

FIGURE 26.2

RISK FACTORS FOR CVDs YOU CAN CONTROL

Although you cannot control all risk factors, the ones listed below are the result of the daily decisions you make about your health and health habits.

Tobacco Use	• **Avoid the use of tobacco.** About 20 percent of the deaths from cardiovascular disease are smoking-related. Tobacco use is the biggest risk factor for teens. • **Avoid secondhand smoke.** Constant exposure to other people's smoke increases the risk of cardiovascular disease even for nonsmokers. About 40,000 nonsmokers exposed to environmental tobacco smoke die from CVDs each year.
High Blood Pressure	• **Have your blood pressure checked periodically.** Maintain normal blood pressure through a healthful diet, regular exercise, and proper weight. If your blood pressure is above normal, follow the advice of your physician to lower it.
High Cholesterol	• **Eat fewer high-fat foods.** High blood cholesterol can usually be controlled with medication and by practicing healthful lifestyle behaviors. Eat a diet low in cholesterol and saturated fats, and get regular physical activity. These behaviors help keep plaque from forming in your arteries.
Physical Inactivity	• **Get enough physical activity.** Physical inactivity can be a risk factor even if you aren't overweight. Get at least 30 to 60 minutes of physical activity each day. Regular physical activity strengthens your heart and helps you maintain a healthy weight.
Excess Weight	• **Maintain a healthy weight.** Excess weight increases the strain on the heart. It also raises blood pressure and the levels of blood cholesterol.
Stress	• **Reduce stress.** Constant stress can raise blood pressure. Practice stress-management techniques.
Drug and Alcohol Use	• **Avoid the use of alcohol and other drugs.** Drinking too much alcohol can raise blood pressure and cause heart failure or irregular heartbeat. Some illegal drugs increase the heart rate and blood pressure and can result in sudden death from heart failure.

RISK FACTORS THAT CANNOT BE CONTROLLED

Some risk factors for cardiovascular disease are out of your control, but you should be aware of them and know how they influence your health. These factors include:

▶ **Heredity.** Children whose parents have cardiovascular disease are more likely to develop CVD themselves.

▶ **Gender.** Men have a greater risk of developing cardiovascular disease earlier in life and a greater risk of having a heart attack than women do. However, research indicates that older women are less likely to survive a heart attack than men of the same age.

▶ **Age.** As people become older, they become more likely to develop CVD, as the risk increases with age. About 80 percent of people who die of cardiovascular disease are 65 or older.

Knowing the risk factors you can't control can help you make healthful decisions that protect your cardiovascular system. For example, if you have a family history of hypertension, you should be particularly careful to get the proper medical screenings and to practice preventive strategies, such as maintaining a healthful weight.

LESSON 1 REVIEW

Reviewing Facts and Vocabulary

1. What is *atherosclerosis*? How does it contribute to heart attacks?
2. Define *cardiovascular disease*. How does regular physical activity help prevent CVD?
3. What are five risk factors for CVD that you can control?

Thinking Critically

4. **Evaluating.** Which of the treatments in Figure 26.1 would most likely be used to treat atherosclerosis?
5. **Synthesizing.** How can practicing healthy lifestyle behaviors now help you avoid cardiovascular disease in the future?

Applying Health Skills

Practicing Healthful Behaviors. On a sheet of paper, design a table that lists five of your favorite snacks, and find out which ones are "heart-healthy." For each of the others, think of healthier alternatives that you would enjoy. Enter the alternatives in your table.

After You Read

Cause and Effect. Fold your paper in half. On one side, list the risk factors for cardiovascular diseases that you can control. On the other, list the types of cardiovascular disease.

Cancer

Guide to Reading

Building Vocabulary

As you read this lesson, write each new highlighted term and its definition in your notebook.

- cancer (p. 681)
- tumor (p. 681)
- benign (p. 681)
- malignant (p. 681)
- metastasis (p. 681)
- carcinogen (p. 682)
- biopsy (p. 686)
- remission (p. 687)

Focusing on the Main Ideas

In this lesson, you will learn how to:

- Describe the causes and types of cancer and the treatments for cancer.
- Discuss the importance of early detection and warning signs.
- Identify health behaviors that put you at risk for developing cancer.
- Develop strategies to prevent noncommunicable diseases.

Reading Strategy

Predict

- Scan the headings, subheadings, and photo captions. Write a list of questions about cancer that you think will be answered in the lesson.

Quick Write

Write a letter persuading someone to quit smoking based on the information you know about the cancer-related risk factors of tobacco use.

The body's cells are constantly growing and dividing. Most new cells are normal, but some are not. Sometimes these abnormal cells reproduce rapidly and uncontrollably, forming masses of abnormal cells inside otherwise normal tissue. This *uncontrollable growth of abnormal cells* is called **cancer**.

How Cancer Harms the Body

An abnormal mass of tissue that has no natural role in the body is called a **tumor**. Some tumors are **benign**, or *noncancerous*. Benign tumors grow slowly and are surrounded by membranes that prevent them from spreading from the original site. Although noncancerous tumors don't spread, they can be dangerous if they interfere with normal body functions. For example, a benign brain tumor may block the brain's blood supply.

Tumors that are **malignant**, or *cancerous*, spread to neighboring tissues and through the blood or lymph to other parts of the body. *The spread of cancer from the point where it originated to other parts of the body* is called **metastasis**. As cancer cells spread throughout the body, they divide and form new tumors.

Reduce your risk of skin cancer by protecting yourself from the sun's ultraviolet (UV) rays and reducing the amount of time you spend in the sun. *How does each item in the picture help protect you from UV rays?*

Many cancers harm the body because they kill normal cells when they compete with them for nutrients. Tumors put pressure on surrounding tissues and organs, interfering with body function. They can also block arteries, veins, and other passages in the body.

Types of Cancer

Cancer can develop in almost any part of the body and in different tissues of each part. **Figure 26.3** shows some types of cancers, grouped according to the body organs where they first develop. Cancers also can be classified according to the tissues they affect.

▶ *Lymphomas* are cancers of the **immune system.**

▶ *Leukemias* are cancers of the blood-forming organs.

▶ *Carcinomas* are cancers of the glands and body linings, including the skin and the linings of the digestive tract and lungs.

▶ *Sarcomas* are cancers of connective tissue, including bones, ligaments, and muscle.

Risk Factors for Cancer

Abnormal cells that have the potential to become cancer cells are produced every day and the immune system destroys most of them. If the immune system becomes weakened or the number of cancer cells becomes overwhelming, cancer may develop. In some cases normal cells change by themselves. In others a faulty gene may have been inherited; between 5 to 10 percent of cancers are hereditary.

The majority of cancers are caused by exposure to certain factors that increase the risk of cell damage. One factor is a **carcinogen** (car-SIN-uh-juhn), *a cancer-causing substance.* Examples of carcinogens are cigarette smoke and ultraviolet light. Several major risk factors for cancer are associated with lifestyle behaviors. It is estimated that about 60 percent of all cancers can be prevented through healthy lifestyle choices.

Tobacco Use

Tobacco use is the major cause of cancer deaths in the United States and the most preventable. Recent studies attribute nearly one in five deaths to smoking or exposure to **secondhand smoke.** About 87 percent of lung cancer deaths are caused by smoking. An additional 25 percent of females who smoke will die of other smoking-related diseases. Tobacco use also increases the risk of bladder, pancreas, and kidney cancers. At least 43 different carcinogens have been identified in tobacco and tobacco smoke.

FIGURE 26.3

TYPES OF CANCER

Organ Affected (new cases/year)	Some Risk Factors	Symptoms	Screening and Early Detection Methods
Skin (1 million) Most common type of cancer in the United States	Exposure to ultraviolet radiation from the sun, tanning beds, sun lamps, and other sources	Change on the skin, especially a new growth, a mole or freckle that changes, or a sore that won't heal	physical exam, biopsies
Breast (267,000) Second leading cause of cancer death for women	Genetic factors, obesity, alcohol use, physical inactivity	Unusual lump; nipple that thickens, changes shape, dimples, or has discharge	self-exam, mammogram
Prostate (232,090) Found mostly in men over age 55	Possible hereditary link, possible link to high-fat diet	Frequent or painful urination; inability to urinate; weak or interrupted flow of urine; blood in urine or semen; pain in lower back, hips, or upper thighs	blood test
Lung (173,770) Leading cause of cancer deaths in the United States	Exposure to cigarette smoke, radon, or asbestos	No initial symptoms; later symptoms include cough, shortness of breath, wheezing, coughing up blood, hoarseness	chest X ray
Colon/Rectum (146,940) Second leading cause of cancer deaths in the United States	Risk increases with age; closely related to colorectal cancer	Often no initial symptoms; later, blood in feces; frequent pain, aches, or cramps in stomach; change in bowel habits; weight loss	test for blood in the stool, sigmoidoscopy, colonoscopy
Mouth (30,000) Occurs mostly in people over 40	Use of tobacco, chewing tobacco, or alcohol	Sore or lump on mouth that doesn't heal; unusual bleeding; pain or numbness on lip, mouth, tongue, or throat; feeling that something is caught in the throat; pain with chewing or swallowing; change in voice	dental/oral exam
Cervix (10,520)	History of infection with HPV (human papillomavirus)	Usually no symptoms in early stages; later, abnormal vaginal bleeding, increased vaginal discharge	Pap test
Testicle (7,000) Most common cancer in men ages 15 to 34	Undescended testicle; family history of testicular cancer	Small, hard, painless lump on testicle; sudden accumulation of fluid in scrotum; pain in region between scrotum and anus	self-exam

Smokeless tobacco use is a major risk factor in the development of oral cancer, which affects the lips, mouth, and throat. Oral cancer kills roughly one person every hour. You can greatly reduce your risk of cancer by avoiding all forms of tobacco as well as secondhand smoke.

Sexually Transmitted Diseases

Some viruses, such as the human papillomavirus **(HPV)** and the **hepatitis B** virus, cause cervical and liver cancers, respectively. The risk of acquiring these pathogens can be reduced by abstinence from sexual activity and from injecting drugs through infected needles.

Dietary Factors

Approximately 30 percent of all cancer deaths are caused by dietary risk factors. A diet that is high in fat and low in fiber is often linked with cancer. Fats make colon cells more susceptible to carcinogens. Colon cells divide more rapidly if the diet is high in fat, increasing the chance that abnormal cells will form. Choosing foods low in fat and high in fiber reduces the risk of colon, breast, and prostate cancers. Dietary fiber speeds the movement of waste through the intestines, so carcinogens have less time to act on cells.

Reading Check

Identify What are the seven warning signs of cancer (Figure 26.4)?

FIGURE 26.4

A WORD OF CAUTION ABOUT CANCER

The American Cancer Society recommends that every individual should be alert to the seven warning signs of cancer. Note that their first letters, when combined, spell the word *caution*.

C hange in bowel habits (either loose stools or constipation)

A sore that does not heal

U nusual bleeding or discharge (as from the uterus, bladder, bowels, nipple, or with coughing)

T hickening or a lump in the breast or elsewhere (Let your health care provider decide what the lump means.)

I ndigestion or difficulty swallowing

O bvious change in a wart or mole

N agging cough or hoarseness

Other symptoms include fatigue and unexplained weight loss. The presence of these signs does not necessarily mean a person has cancer. If you experience any of these symptoms, contact a health care professional.

Radiation

Ultraviolet (UV) radiation from the sun is the main cause of **skin cancer.** Tanning beds and sunlamps also emit UV radiation, which is just as damaging as the sun's rays. A "tan" is the body's response to being injured by UV rays.

About 80 percent of skin cancers can be prevented. Reduce your exposure to UV light by avoiding tanning beds and sunlamps. Limit your time in the sun, especially between 10:00 A.M. and 4:00 P.M. When you must be in the sun, wear protective clothing and use a sunscreen that has an SPF (Sun Protection Factor) of at least 15 and that blocks all types of UV radiation. Pay attention to changes in moles on your skin, one of the seven warning signs of cancer listed in **Figure 26.4.**

Health-literate teens are able to analyze the causes, treatments, and prevention methods for cancers affecting body tissues and organs.

Reducing Your Risk

You can't control some risk factors for cancer, such as heredity, but you can reduce your risk by practicing the healthful behaviors listed in **Figure 26.5.**

FIGURE 26.5

HOW YOU CAN REDUCE YOUR RISK OF CANCER

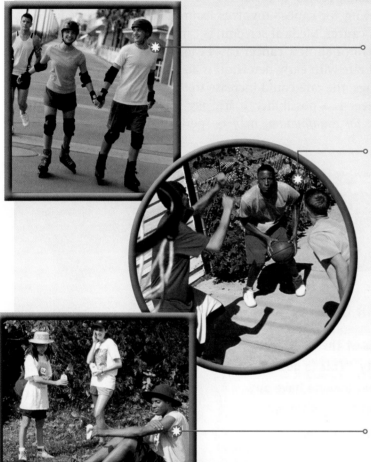

Practice abstinence from sexual activity to reduce the risk of sexually transmitted diseases. Hepatitis B can cause liver cancer, and HPV can cause cancers of the reproductive organs.

Be physically active.

Maintain a healthy weight.

Eat nutritious foods. Include 2–4 servings of fruits and 3–5 servings of vegetables every day. These foods are good sources of fiber, and some contain compounds that act against carcinogens.

Follow an eating plan that is low in saturated fat and high in fiber.

Protect your skin from ultraviolet radiation.

Avoid tobacco and alcohol. Tobacco is the single major cause of cancer death in the United States. Excess alcohol increases the risk of several types of cancer, including mouth and throat cancer.

Recognize the warning signs of cancer. Do regular self-exams to detect cancer early.

Detecting and Treating Cancer

Many advances have been made in the early detection and treatment of cancer through the use of new technologies. The survival rate for those with cancer depends on the type of cancer and how early it is detected.

Early detection, including self–examination and medical examination, is the most critical factor in successful cancer treatment. Many types of cancer can be detected through self-examination of the **breasts, testes,** and skin.

Screening for cancer involves examination or testing for early signs of cancer. Medical screenings can result in early detection of about half of all new cancer cases each year. The current five-year survival rate with early detection is about 80 percent. With regular screenings, the rate could increase to 95 percent.

If cancer is a possibility, a **biopsy**, *the removal of a small piece of tissue for examination*, may be performed. A biopsy is usually

Reading Check

Explain What are some of the ways to detect and treat cancer?

Health Skills Activity

Decision Making: Being Sun Smart

Amber rushes to meet her friends at the boat dock. "Sorry I'm late," she says breathlessly. "This is going to be great. I love to water-ski. Hey, does anyone have any sunscreen? I was in such a hurry that I forgot mine."

"I never use it. I don't burn," Taylor replies.

"I don't use it either. I like looking tan and healthy," Denise chimes in.

Amber knows that tan skin isn't healthy—it's damaged. "I always wear sunscreen," she says firmly. "I'll just run up the hill to that little corner store and buy some."

"Amber, the boat's in the water. We're ready to go," Denise protests.

What should Amber do?

What Would You Do?
Apply the six steps of the decision-making process to help Amber make a health-enhancing decision.
1. State the situation.
2. List the options.
3. Weigh the possible outcomes.
4. Consider values.
5. Make a decision and act.
6. Evaluate the decision.

necessary to determine whether cancer is present. X rays and other imaging techniques help determine a tumor's location and size. A health-literate individual understands the impact of technology on personal, family, and community health.

Treating Cancer

The methods used to treat cancer depend on several factors, such as the type of cancer and whether the tumor has spread. Treatment might include one or more of the following:

▶ **Surgery** removes some or all of the cancerous masses from the body.

▶ **Radiation therapy** aims rays from radioactive substances at cancerous cells. The radiation kills the cells and shrinks the cancerous mass.

▶ **Chemotherapy** uses chemicals to destroy cancer cells.

▶ **Immunotherapy** activates a person's immune system to recognize specific cancers and destroy them.

▶ **Hormone therapy** involves using medicines that interfere with the production of hormones. These treatments kill cancer cells or slow their growth.

Cancer that responds to treatment or is under control is said to be in **remission**, *a period of time when symptoms disappear.*

HEALTH Online

TOPIC **Cancer Research**

Go to **health.glencoe.com** to link to the American Cancer Society.

ACTIVITY Using the link, list five recent developments in cancer research.

LESSON **2** **REVIEW**

Reviewing Facts and Vocabulary

1. Define *cancer.* Name four risk factors for cancer.

2. What is the difference between a benign tumor and one that is malignant?

3. What are two important means of early cancer detection?

Thinking Critically

4. **Analyzing.** The physician of an adult family member has suggested that the person undergo a certain cancer screening procedure as part of a routine exam. The family member is afraid to have this procedure done. What would you tell this person?

5. **Evaluating.** Why do you think skin cancer is the most common cancer in the United States?

Applying Health Skills

Advocacy. Develop a cancer-awareness booklet that analyzes healthful strategies to reduce cancer risk and encourages people to develop these habits. Include information on technology and new treatments that impact the health status of people with cancer.

After You Read

Cause and Effect. Create a three-column chart. In the first column, list the risk factors for cancer. Next, list the types of cancer. Finally, list ways to reduce the risk of cancer.

 Visit **health.glencoe.com** for the Interactive Study Guide for Lesson 2.

Allergies, Asthma, Diabetes, and Arthritis

Guide to Reading

Building Vocabulary

As you read this lesson, write each new highlighted term and its definition in your notebook.

▶ allergy (p. 688)

▶ histamines (p. 689)

▶ asthma (p. 690)

▶ diabetes (p. 691)

▶ autoimmune disease (p. 691)

▶ arthritis (p. 693)

▶ osteoarthritis (p. 693)

▶ rheumatoid arthritis (p. 694)

Focusing on the Main Ideas

In this lesson, you will learn how to:

▶ **Describe** the characteristics, symptoms, causes, and treatments of noncommunicable diseases.

▶ **Examine** and implement health maintenance to prevent or manage noncommunicable diseases.

▶ **Develop** strategies related to the prevention and management of noncommunicable diseases.

Reading Strategy

Problems and Solutions

▶ Fold your paper into eight parts. On the left side, list the following: allergies, asthma, diabetes, and arthritis. List the appropriate symptoms with each title. On the right side, list treatments for each of the diseases.

Quick Write

Write a brief paragraph describing what you know about allergies, asthma, diabetes, and arthritis.

(A) An allergy to pollen, called hay fever, is one of the most common chronic diseases in the United States. Experts estimate that 35 million people suffer from hay fever.

Cardiovascular diseases and cancer are two of the most deadly noncommunicable diseases. Other noncommunicable diseases are chronic, meaning that they are present continuously or recur frequently over a long period time. Allergies, asthma, diabetes, and arthritis are chronic diseases that affect millions of people. Some, such as allergies, asthma, and certain types of diabetes, are caused by a response of the immune system. Others, such as osteoarthritis (ahs-tee-oh-ahr-THRY-tus), cause the breakdown of body cells and tissues.

Allergies

The sneezing and runny nose often associated with a cold are sometimes a response to substances in the air. An **allergy** is *a specific reaction of the immune system to a foreign and frequently harmless substance*. Allergies are among the common causes of illness and disability in the United States, affecting 40 to 50 million people.

Pollen, foods, dust, mold spores, chemicals, insect venom, and medicines are some of the more common *allergens*, substances that cause allergies. The body treats these allergens as foreign invaders. Antigens on the surface of allergens bind to special immune cells in the linings of the nasal passages. These cells release **histamines**, *chemicals that can stimulate mucus and fluid production in an area.*

Histamines produce the sneezing, itchy eyes, runny nose, and other symptoms that make a person with allergies uncomfortable. Some people have an allergic reaction that produces hives—itchy raised bumps on the skin. Others have serious reactions to allergens that can sometimes be life threatening. Severe symptoms include hives, itching or swelling of a stung area or the mouth, and difficulty breathing or swallowing. Other severe symptoms might be a raspy voice, swelling of the tongue, and a sharp drop in blood pressure, which can cause dizziness.

If someone you know experiences any of these symptoms after eating foods such as peanuts or shellfish or after being stung by a bee or wasp, seek medical attention immediately.

Diagnosing Allergies

Sometimes you can diagnose an allergy yourself. You may notice that when you are near certain kinds of plants you sneeze or that eating particular foods makes you break out in a rash. In some cases tests are required to determine the cause. Three common methods are used to identify the source of an allergic reaction—a blood test, a food elimination diet, and a skin test. During a skin test, the skin is scratched and small amounts of possible allergens are applied. If a person is allergic to any of the allergens, the skin in the area of the scratch swells and turns red because of the **inflammatory response.**

Treating Allergies

Sometimes allergy treatment can be as simple as avoiding the allergen. This is the best treatment for severe food and insect sting allergies. When avoidance is not possible, medicines, including *antihistamines* that help control the symptoms triggered by histamines, may be suggested. People with long-lasting or severe allergies should seek medical attention. Allergies can irritate the respiratory tract and lead to other health problems, such as asthma. People with severe allergies may receive *immunotherapy*, a series of shots that contain small amounts of the allergen to which the person is sensitive. The injections cause the immune system to become less sensitive to the allergens.

The body's response to allergens can cause a variety of symptoms. *What should you do if you or a family member experience more serious allergic reactions?*

Identify What are some of the more common allergens that trigger allergic reactions?

Experiencing an unpleasant reaction to something you eat does not necessarily mean that you have a food allergy. For instance, lactose intolerance is not an allergy. Because symptoms are similar, this is a common misconception. In reality, only a very small percentage of people actually have proven food allergies. For those who do, the main method of treatment is avoiding the food that causes the allergic reaction. This usually requires diligently reading ingredient lists.

Asthma

Some allergic reactions can lead to **asthma**, *an inflammatory condition in which the small airways in the lungs become narrowed, causing difficulty in breathing.* More than 17 million people in the United States have asthma, and each year more than 5,000 Americans die of this disease. Asthma can develop at any age; however, about one-third of those with asthma are under the age of 18.

The bronchial tubes of people with asthma are sensitive to certain substances called *triggers.* Common asthma triggers include air pollution, pet dander, and tobacco smoke, as well as microscopic mold, pollen, and dust mites, shown on this page. In an asthma attack, the asthma triggers cause the muscles of the bronchial walls to tighten and produce extra mucus. The respiratory passages narrow. The result can range from minor wheezing—breathing with a whistling sound—to severe difficulty breathing. In some cases the condition becomes life threatening.

Managing Asthma

Although asthma has no cure, most people with the condition can lead normal lives by behavior changes and the proper use of medication. People with asthma can lead normal, active lives with proper management that includes the following strategies:

▶ **Monitor the condition.** Recognize the warning signs of an attack: shortness of breath, chest tightness or pain, coughing or sneezing. Treating these symptoms quickly can help prevent attacks or keep an attack from worsening.

▶ **Manage the environment.** Reduce asthma triggers in the environment. Avoid exposure to tobacco smoke, eliminate carpets and rugs when possible, and wash bedding frequently.

▶ **Manage stress.** Stress can trigger an asthma attack. Relaxation and stress-management techniques can be helpful.

▶ **Take medication.** Medications can be used to relieve symptoms, prevent flare-ups, and make air passages less sensitive to asthma triggers. A *bronchodilator,* a type of medication taken with an inhaler, relaxes and widens respiratory passages.

People with asthma can be active at any age if they manage the disease and use proper precautions. *Why is it important for people of all ages with asthma to take responsibility for establishing and implementing health maintenance?*

Diabetes

Diabetes is *a chronic disease that affects the way body cells convert food into energy.* Each year approximately 1 million new cases are diagnosed. There is no cure for diabetes.

In a person with diabetes, the pancreas produces too little or no insulin, a hormone that helps glucose enter the body's cells. In some diabetics adequate insulin is produced, but cells don't respond normally to it. For the cells in the body to function, they need a constant source of energy—glucose—from foods. If glucose is not converted to energy, it builds up in the blood, and cells do not get the glucose they need to function. The only way to diagnose diabetes is through a blood test. Early detection of diabetes can prevent serious side effects, such as blindness. Diabetes is the main cause of kidney failure, limb amputations, and blindness in adults, as well as a major cause of heart disease and stroke. These effects, however, are not inevitable. If diagnosed, the disease can be successfully managed with medication, a healthful diet, and regular moderate exercise. In many cases, diabetes is preventable.

Type 1 Diabetes

Type 1 diabetes, which accounts for 5 to 10 percent of all diabetes cases, appears suddenly and progresses quickly. The body does not produce insulin, and glucose builds up in the blood, starving cells of the energy they need. Over time, the high blood-sugar level can cause damage to the eyes, kidneys, nerves, and heart.

The cause of type 1 diabetes is not clear. Some scientists suspect an environmental trigger—perhaps an as yet unidentified virus—that stimulates an immune response, destroying the insulin-producing cells of the pancreas in some individuals. For this reason, type 1 diabetes is known as an **autoimmune disease**, *a condition in which the immune system mistakenly attacks itself, targeting the cells, tissues, and organs of a person's own body.* People with type 1 diabetes must take daily doses of insulin, either through injections or through a special pump that is attached to the body by tubing or that is surgically implanted. Today, because of advanced treatment methods, many people with diabetes are able to live near-normal lives.

Type 2 Diabetes

Type 2 diabetes accounts for 90 to 95 percent of all cases of this disease. It most often appears after age 40. However, type 2 diabetes is now being found at younger ages and is even being diagnosed among children and teens. In this form of diabetes, the body is unable to make enough insulin or to use insulin properly. Buildup of glucose in the blood causes many of the same symptoms as type 1 diabetes.

Health Minute

Symptoms of Diabetes

According to the American Diabetes Association, of the estimated 17 million people in the United States who have diabetes, almost 6 million of them don't know it.

Symptoms of diabetes include:

► Frequent urination
► Excessive thirst
► Unexplained weight loss
► Extreme hunger
► Sudden vision changes
► Tingling in hands or feet
► Frequent fatigue
► Very dry skin
► Sores that are slow to heal
► More infections than usual

People with diabetes need to work closely with health care professionals to manage their condition. *Why is early detection of diabetes important?*

Type 2 diabetes is nearing epidemic proportions in the United States because of an increased number of older individuals in the population and a greater prevalence of obesity and inactive lifestyles. A diet high in fat, calories, and cholesterol increases the risk of diabetes. Thus, choosing lower-fat, lower-calorie alternatives can help reduce the risk of this disease. Increased physical activity also reduces risk because it helps control weight and lower blood cholesterol levels.

Treatment of type 2 diabetes includes weight management and regular physical activity. Individuals with this disease must

Real-Life Application

Raising Teen Awareness of Diabetes

Over the last decade diabetes and obesity have increased dramatically in both adults and teens. Examine the graph and answer the questions. Then use this information to create an advocacy message to encourage others to practice healthful behaviors to control their weight and reduce their risk of diabetes.

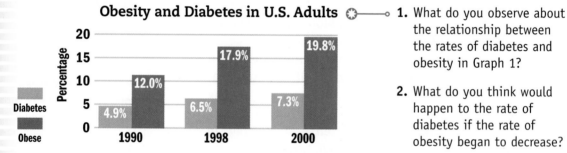

Obesity and Diabetes in U.S. Adults

Diabetes
Obese

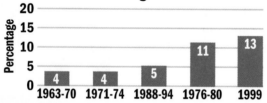

Prevalence of Overweight Among U.S. Adolescents

Source: CDC, Behavioral Risk Factor Surveillance System (1991–2000)

1. What do you observe about the relationship between the rates of diabetes and obesity in Graph 1?

2. What do you think would happen to the rate of diabetes if the rate of obesity began to decrease?

3. Look at Graph 2. What can you infer about the rate of diabetes in teens?

4. What are healthful eating habits and physical activity lifestyle behaviors that reduce the risk of diabetes?

ACTIVITY

In small groups, generate a list of lifestyle behaviors that people can practice to maintain a healthful weight and reduce their risk of diabetes. Create a 60-second public service announcement (PSA) to persuade teens to start good health habits early in life. Include at least one fact about diabetes and one lifestyle behavior that can reduce the risk of diabetes.

carefully monitor their diet in order to control their blood-sugar levels. In some cases oral medications or injections of insulin are required to manage the disease. Individuals who maintain a healthy weight understand the role of individual responsibility regarding risk behaviors.

Arthritis

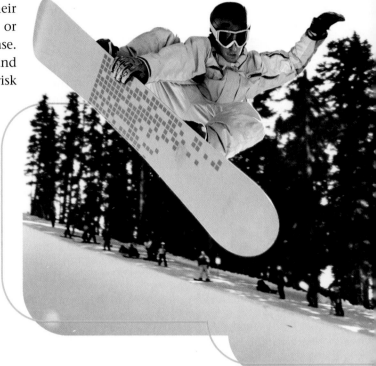

Arthritis is *a group of more than 100 different diseases that cause pain and loss of movement in the joints.* It is one of the most common medical problems in the world and the number one cause of disability in the United States. Arthritis is more common in older people, but it can affect anyone, including children and teens. In fact, 8.4 million people between the ages of 18 and 44 have arthritis, and millions of others are at risk for it.

Osteoarthritis

Osteoarthritis is *a disease of the joints in which cartilage breaks down.* Cartilage is the strong, flexible tissue that provides cushioning at the joints. In this disease the cartilage becomes pitted and frayed. In time it may wear away completely, and bones may rub against each other. Although osteoarthritis affects primarily the weight-bearing joints of the knees and hips, it can affect any joint—including those in the fingers, lower back, and feet—causing aches and soreness, especially when moving.

Osteoarthritis is one of the most common types of arthritis; in fact, it accounts for half of all arthritis cases. It affects about 20 million people in the United States and is most common in women and in people over the age of 45. Several strategies can reduce the risk of osteoarthritis:

▶ **Controlling weight.** Maintaining an appropriate weight reduces stress on joints by lessening wear and tear on cartilage.

▶ **Preventing sports injuries.** Warming up before exercising, adding strength training to your physical activities, and using appropriate equipment (including wrist guards and knee pads when necessary) help avoid joint injuries and damage to ligaments and cartilage, thus decreasing the risk of osteoarthritis. Let injuries heal completely before playing again.

▶ **Protecting against Lyme disease.** Lyme disease (which is spread by the bite of infected deer ticks), if left untreated, can result in a rare form of osteoarthritis. Using insect repellents, wearing long-sleeved shirts and pants when walking outdoors or in wooded areas, and being educated on tick recognition and removal can help reduce this risk factor.

 According to the Arthritis Foundation, an arthritis epidemic may result from the number of people who participate in adventure sports. *What can you do to reduce your risk of developing osteoarthritis?*

Compare and Contrast What are the similarities and differences between osteoarthritis and rheumatoid arthritis?

Rheumatoid Arthritis

Rheumatoid arthritis affects about 2.5 million people in the United States. It is three times more common in women than in men. Symptoms usually first appear between the ages of 20 and 50, but the disease also can affect young children. Juvenile rheumatoid arthritis is the most common form of arthritis in children.

Rheumatoid arthritis is *a disease characterized by the debilitating destruction of the joints due to inflammation.* Like type 1 diabetes, this type of arthritis is caused by an autoimmune disease for which there is no cure. Sufferers are likely to experience joint pain, inflammation, swelling, and stiffness. Eventually the joints may become deformed and cease to function normally. Rheumatoid arthritis affects mainly the joints in the hand, foot, elbow, shoulder, neck, knee, hip, and ankle. Other effects include fever, fatigue, and swollen lymph glands. The effects of this disease are usually symmetrical—both sides of the body develop the same symptoms at the same time and in the same pattern.

With the use of medication, the effects of the disease may be controlled. Treatment methods focus on relieving pain, reducing inflammation and swelling, and keeping the joints moving as normally as possible. A combination of exercise, rest, joint protection, and physical and occupational therapy also can help manage the disease.

LESSON 3 REVIEW

Reviewing Facts and Vocabulary

1. What are *histamines*, and what role do they play in allergies?
2. Define *asthma.* What are two strategies for managing this condition?
3. What is *osteoarthritis*? List two ways to reduce the risk of osteoarthritis.

Thinking Critically

4. **Synthesizing.** Why is it difficult to avoid many allergens?
5. **Analyzing.** Why is it important for individuals and family members with diabetes to take responsibility for establishing and implementing health maintenance?

Applying Health Skills

Practicing Healthful Behaviors. Make a table. In the first column, write the names of the noncommunicable diseases in this lesson. In the second column, identify risk factors for each disease. In the third column, describe and analyze strategies for healthful lifestyle behaviors that will reduce your risk for the disease.

After You Read

Problems and Solutions. Write an article for your school newspaper or a newsletter advocating for healthier food choices at school. What foods should be eliminated from school menus? Why?

Physical and Mental Challenges

Guide to Reading

Building Vocabulary

As you read this lesson, write each new highlighted term and its definition in your notebook.

▶ disability (p. 695)

▶ profound deafness (p. 696)

▶ mental retardation (p. 697)

▶ Americans with Disabilities Act (p. 699)

Focusing on the Main Ideas

In this lesson, you will learn how to:

▶ Examine the challenges faced by individuals with disabilities.

▶ Cite laws, policies, and practices on health-related issues for individuals with disabilities.

Reading Strategy

Organize Information

▶ Make a word web with the work *disability* in the center. List the types of disabilities in the spaces around it. As you read, record facts about each disability in the appropriate spaces.

Quick Write

Make a list of all the types of disabilities you are aware of, complete with descriptions.

 Computers are one of many devices that people with disabilities can use to meet their physical challenges. *Explain how technology has impacted the health status of individuals.*

Does your school have ramps and special restroom facilities to accommodate people in wheelchairs? Are there telephones for people who are hearing- or vision-impaired? Have you ever seen a closed-captioned television program? All these devices are designed to offset a **disability**, *any physical or mental impairment that limits normal activities, including seeing, hearing, walking, or speaking.* According to the latest U.S. Census Bureau statistics, almost 20 percent of the adult population has some type of disability. People with disabilities sometimes have difficulty doing things that others take for granted. The challenge may be physical, such as climbing stairs, seeing a sign, hearing a conversation, or holding a package, or it may be mental, such as understanding simple instructions. Health concerns such as these require collaborative decision making to aid those with impairments.

Physical Challenges

Most physical challenges can be classified as sight impairment, hearing impairment, or motor impairment.

Reading Check

Describe What are some common types of physical disability?

CHARACTER CHECK

Caring. Learning sign language can give you the ability to communicate with the hearing impaired. It is also a way of showing that you care about the needs of others. **Do some research to find organizations in your area that offer classes in sign language. Learn some simple signs so that you can communicate with people who are hearing impaired.**

▼ **Sign language enables many individuals with hearing impairments to enjoy concerts, plays, and other public events.**

Sight Impairment

Like other disabilities, sight impairment can be moderate, as for the more than 5 million Americans who are vision-impaired, or it can be severe, as for the 1.3 million people who are legally blind. In addition, an estimated 1.8 million people in the United States are unable to see words and letters in ordinary print even when wearing glasses or contact lenses. Although visual impairment is more common among older adults, nearly 1 in every 1,000 children has partial vision loss or is legally blind.

The leading cause of blindness is the result of complications of diabetes. Three other common causes of blindness are:

▶ **macular degeneration,** a disease in which the retina degenerates. It is the leading cause of blindness in individuals over 55.

▶ **glaucoma,** a disease that damages the optic nerve of the eye.

▶ **cataracts,** a clouding of the lens of the eye.

Regular eye exams are important for people of all ages. The early diagnosis of many conditions can help prevent blindness or slow its progress.

Hearing Impairment

About 20 million adults in the United States have disabilities that affect their ability to hear, and as many as 2 in every 1,000 children have a significant hearing impairment in both ears. Like sight impairment, hearing problems can range from minor to severe. **Profound deafness** is *a hearing loss so severe that a person affected cannot benefit from mechanical amplification, such as a hearing aid.*

One cause of deafness is heredity. Other causes are injury, disease, and obstructions, which can prevent sound waves from traveling to the inner ear. Obstructions may be caused by a buildup of wax, bone blockage, or something stuck in the ear. Some individuals are born with an inherited abnormal bone growth in the inner ear that may cause obstruction. Obstruction usually affects only one ear. Surgery can cure many of these cases.

Hearing impairments caused by nerve damage often occur with age but also can be the result of repeated exposure to loud noises—such as stereos, traffic, video games, and some machines. Going to one loud concert or blasting the stereo occasionally probably won't hurt your ears, but prolonged exposure to loud music can cause hearing loss. In fact, some experts think that hearing loss is occurring much earlier than it did just 30 years ago possibly because of the increase in environmental noise. This type of hearing impairment can be gradual, so if you have noticed that your hearing has changed, it may be time to visit an audiologist, a specialist in hearing problems.

Motor Impairment

Tasks that are simple for most people—tying a shoe, climbing the stairs, opening a jar, lifting a glass—can be a challenge for someone with a motor impairment. Motor impairments result when the body's range of motion and coordination are affected by an injury to the brain or a disorder of the nervous system.

Physical therapy often is used to help those with motor impairment. Through physical therapy, the joints are kept flexible and the muscles stretched, improving the individual's ability to move around. Physical therapists can teach people to use assistive devices. For example, people with limb amputations can be fitted with *prosthetics,* or artificial limbs. Motorized wheelchairs allow many people with motor impairments to get around without assistance. Computers can be adapted in many ways, such as with mouth sticks or head sticks for those unable to use their hands and arms.

Mental Challenges

Some challenges affect a person's ability to live independently in society. One such challenge is **mental retardation**, *the below-average intellectual ability present from birth or early childhood and associated with difficulties in learning and social adaptation.* This disability affects about 3 percent of the population, but many of those with this challenge are only mildly affected. Such individuals, who make up 75 percent of the mentally retarded population, cannot be outwardly distinguished from non-retarded people.

Several factors have been found to cause mental retardation, including injury, disease, and brain abnormality. Some factors are related to **genetic disorders** such as Down syndrome, PKU, Tay-Sachs, and Fragile X syndrome, the most common cause of genetically inherited developmental disability. Behaviors during pregnancy are another important factor. Pregnant women who use alcohol or other drugs greatly increase the risk that their babies will be born with mental retardation, low birth weight, or **fetal alcohol syndrome.** Another preventable risk factor during pregnancy is infection with rubella. Immunization against this disease either during childhood or within three months of becoming pregnant reduces the risk. A restricted supply of oxygen during birth can cause mental retardation. In older children, it can result from a head injury, stroke, and certain infections such as meningitis.

Advances in technology have benefited people who use assistive devices to perform daily activities. *Name one way your community is improving access and services for individuals with disabilities.*

Accommodating Differences

People with physical and mental challenges have the same needs and interests as do the rest of the population. They also have many of the same abilities. Historically, people with disabilities have been viewed as a separate population. Fortunately, in recent decades policies and practices have been put in place to help eliminate the barriers of stereotyping and prejudices. Passed by Congress in 1990, the **Americans with Disabilities Act** is *a law prohibiting discrimination against people with physical or mental disabilities in the workplace, transportation, public accommodations, and telecommunications.* The recent trends have resulted from advocacy efforts by individuals with physical and mental challenges and their supporters who have worked to establish the following important principles:

▶ Society should make certain changes, such as requiring wheelchair access to public transportation and building entrances that allow people with physical and mental disabilities to take part more readily in business and social activities.

▶ People should be evaluated on the basis of individual merit, not on stereotyped assumptions about disabilities.

▶ To the extent that each is able, people with disabilities should have the same opportunities as people who do not have physical or mental challenges.

 Guide dogs are trained to assist the visually impaired by safely navigating around obstacles such as curbs. *Why should you avoid touching or calling a working guide dog?*

Some provisions of the Americans with Disabilities Act require:

▶ employers with 15 or more employees to provide qualified individuals with disabilities an equal opportunity to benefit from employment-related opportunities available to others.

▶ state and local governments to follow specific architectural standards both in new construction and in the alteration of their buildings. They also must provide access in inaccessible older buildings and communicate effectively with people who have hearing, vision, or speech disabilities.

▶ telephone companies to establish telecommunications relay services (TRS) that enable callers with hearing and speech disabilities to communicate through a third-party communications assistant.

In addition, the Workforce Investment Act of 1998 ensures that any information posted to a Web site by a government agency must meet certain standards for accessibility by those who are disabled.

This ramp is one of many federally required accommodations for people who are disabled. *What other accommodations exist to help those with disabilities?*

LESSON 4 REVIEW

Reviewing Facts and Vocabulary

1. What is a *disability*?
2. List three common causes of blindness.
3. Discuss health-related issues, and list two laws that help integrate people with disabilities into society.

Thinking Critically

4. **Analyzing.** Identify several different ways that you use the senses of sight and hearing each day. For each item, identify challenges that might be associated with each task for someone with an impairment.
5. **Evaluating.** What loud noises are you subjected to each day? What might you do to reduce your exposure to the noise?

Applying Health Skills

Accessing Information. Go to **health.glencoe.com** to find a link to the National Information Center for Children and Youth with Disabilities Web site. Read about one type of disability, and summarize your findings in a one-page report.

After You Read

Explain. Write a skit showing how teens can get involved in activities that advocate for the disabled.

Visit **health.glencoe.com** for the Interactive Study Guide for Lesson 4.

Lesson 4 Physical and Mental Challenges **699**

Learning to
Learn

Think kids with learning disabilities aren't smart? The truth is, many are brighter than average. Meet one teen who outsmarted her classroom challenges.

Vanessa Flatley, 15, of New Jersey, discovered that she had dyslexia in the second grade. Dyslexia is a learning disability (LD) that involves a glitch in the brain's associative center—the area that allows people to recognize and comprehend written words. "With dyslexia, you picture things differently in your head," Vanessa says. "You get letters mixed up because you can't tell the difference between them."

Vanessa knew that she was smart—most kids with learning disabilities are—but she couldn't copy words written on a blackboard, and she also had trouble spotting and remembering patterns. This made it almost impossible for her to learn the alphabet and the multiplication tables.

A New Way of Learning

Vanessa left public school in third grade to attend the Learning Studio, a private, one-room school with two teachers. "I was more comfortable because the other kids there were like me," she says. "They didn't all have dyslexia, but they all had an LD." Even better, says Vanessa, she didn't feel dumb. It helped that teachers there knew that she and her classmates needed to get

information to their brains in different ways. Vanessa conquered the alphabet, for example, by handling letters covered in sandpaper.

Vanessa's proudest accomplishment was finally learning her multiplication tables. "I couldn't get them, even though I don't have trouble with algebra," she says. "My tutor was finally able to help me see the patterns."

What's next for Vanessa? "I'll be integrating into normal classes gradually," she explains. "I'm pretty nervous, but if I need extra help, I'll ask for it." Most important, years after being made to feel like the dumbest girl in the class, Vanessa is strong and confident. ◢

TIME to THINK... About Learning Disabilities

Did you know the list of celebrities with dyslexia includes Walt Disney, Thomas Edison, Whoopi Goldberg, and Tom Cruise? Choose one of these celebrities and investigate his or her life. Focus on how your subject dealt with dyslexia and managed to reach his or her dreams. Report your findings to the class.

1. **Practicing Healthful Behaviors.** Ask your parents about the history of cardiovascular disease in their families. Use this information to identify any potential risks you might have for developing cardiovascular disease. What steps can you take to reduce your risk? *(LESSON 1)*

2. **Analyzing Influences.** Look at product ads in a variety of magazines. Identify pictures that show people involved in behaviors that increase the risk of developing cancer. Describe how each of these behaviors puts a person at risk of developing cancer. Summarize your findings and report them to the class. *(LESSON 2)*

3. **Accessing Information.** Find out about the most common pollen allergens in your community. Gather information about when they are most prevalent and where you can get information about daily pollen counts. Display the information in the classroom. *(LESSON 3)*

4. **Advocacy.** Survey a local business to see how it might be made more accessible for individuals who have disabilities. Write a letter to the owner of the business making suggestions for improvement. *(LESSON 4)*

Oncologist

Are you interested in helping people who have cancer? If so, you might consider a career as an oncologist, a doctor who studies, diagnoses, and treats cancers. A person who wants to become an oncologist should be ready to deal with the emotional and psychological challenges associated with patients who may be terminally ill. Becoming an oncologist takes many years of formal training: a four-year college degree, a medical degree, a one-year internship, a four-year residency, and a fellowship in oncology. Find out about this and other careers in Career Corner at **health.glencoe.com.**

Parent Involvement

Advocacy. Find out about health fairs and other events in your community that support cancer education. Contact local chapters of the American Cancer Society to see how you and your parents can become involved.

School and Community

CPR Classes. Locate agencies in your community that teach CPR. Arrange for someone from the agency to teach CPR at your school. Help organize the event and prepare posters or flyers to let people know about it.

After You Read

Use the notes you have taken in your Foldable as a study guide. Review important terms, recall what you know about those terms, and check your responses by looking under the tabs.

FOLDABLES™
Study Organizer

➤ EXPLORING HEALTH TERMS
Answer the following questions on a sheet of paper.

Lesson 1 *Match each definition with the correct term.*

angina pectoris	cardiovascular disease
atherosclerosis	hypertension
arrhythmias	noncommunicable disease

1. Chest pain that results when the heart doesn't get enough oxygen.
2. A disease that is not transmitted by another person, a vector, or the environment.
3. High blood pressure.
4. Irregular heartbeats.

Lesson 2 *Fill in the blank with the correct term.*

benign	malignant
biopsy	metastasis
cancer	remission
carcinogen	tumor

5. An abnormal mass of tissue that has no natural role in the body is a _____.
6. The spread of cancer from where it originates is called _____.
7. Cigarette smoke and UV radiation are two examples of a _____.
8. A laboratory analysis of a section of tissue taken from a site where abnormal cell growth is suspected is a _____.

Lesson 3 *Match each definition with the correct term.*

allergy	diabetes
autoimmune disease	histamines
arthritis	osteoarthritis
asthma	rheumatoid arthritis

9. A specific reaction of the immune system to a foreign and frequently harmless substance.
10. A chronic disease that affects the way body cells convert food into energy.
11. A disease characterized by the debilitating destruction of the joints due to inflammation.

Lesson 4 *Replace the underlined words with the correct term.*

Americans with Disabilities Act
disability
mental retardation
profound deafness

12. Disability is hearing loss so severe that a hearing aid doesn't help.
13. Profound deafness is the below-average intellectual ability present from birth or early childhood.
14. Mental retardation is a law prohibiting discrimination against people with physical or mental disabilities.

➤ RECALLING THE FACTS
Use complete sentences to answer the following questions.

1. Why is hypertension considered a "silent killer"?
2. How does plaque affect arteries?
3. What are the warning signs of a heart attack?
4. How does a high-fat diet increase the risk of cancer?

For more review questions for Chapter 26, go to **health.glencoe.com**.

5. Why should people with long-lasting or severe allergies seek medical attention?

6. What are two major ways that people can reduce the risk of type 2 diabetes?

7. How does an autoimmune disease harm the body?

8. What are two of the provisions of the Americans with Disabilities Act?

➤ WRITING CRITICALLY

1. **Persuasive.** Write a public service announcement that encourages teens to develop healthful habits to reduce their risk of cardiovascular disease or cancer later in life. Persuade teens that their behaviors today will affect their health in the future.

2. **Narrative.** Write a one-page script about a disabled teen and his or her friend. In your script, show how the teen and his or her friend worked together to overcome a challenging situation, such as developing a physical activity program, auditioning for a part in a school play, or learning to drive a car.

Standardized Test Practice

 The purpose of expository writing is to explain, define, or tell how to do something by giving information. The *Writing Situation* presents the topic: community accessibility for people with disabilities. The *Directions for Writing* suggests that you think about ways that your community can improve its accessibility for people with disabilities, and why such changes are good for everyone.

PROMPT

Writing Situation: Most communities have made many changes to make buildings, parks, and playgrounds more accessible to people with disabilities. But, there is still more work to be done.

Directions for Writing: Think about some places you feel still need changing in order to make them more accessible. Describe what needs to be done and how you would do it.

Now explain why such changes benefit everyone in a community.

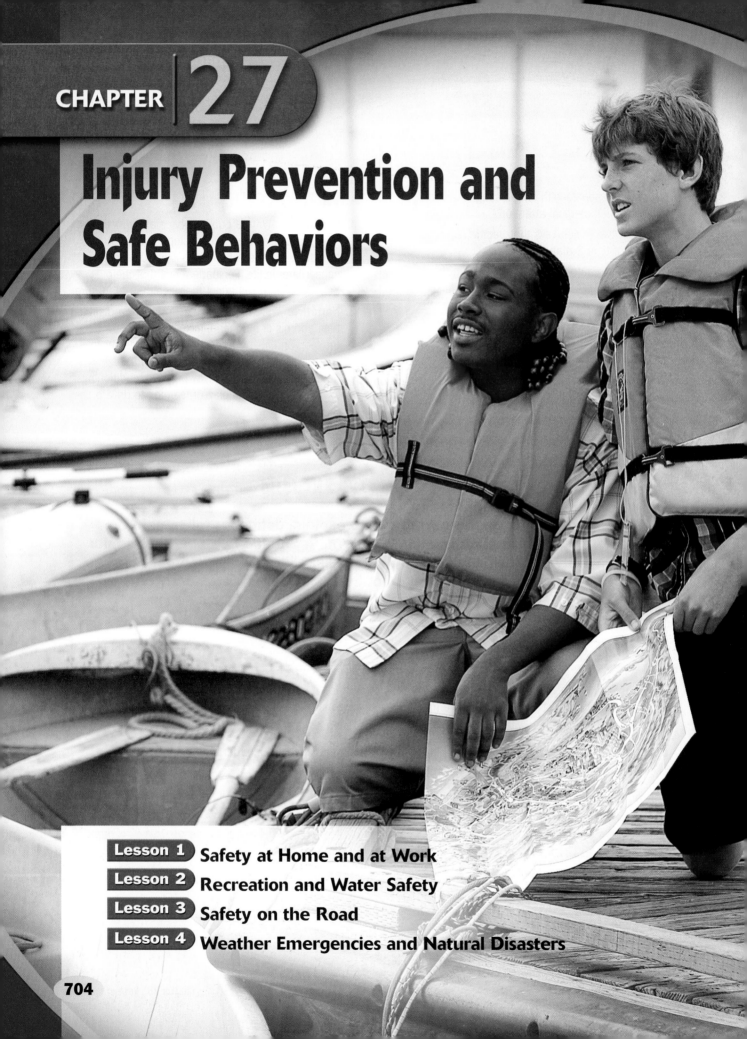

Injury Prevention and Safe Behaviors

Middle School Safe-Behaviors Project

People of different ages prefer different types of media. Media outlets use this information to target messages to specific age groups. Some methods for conveying information include

► music,

► video games and television, and

► comic books.

Visit the Eye on the Media section at **health.glencoe.com** to learn more about targeted media campaigns.

FOLDABLES™
Study Organizer

Before You Read

Make this Foldable chart to help you organize what you learn about safety at home and at work. Begin with a sheet of 8½" x 11" paper or a sheet of notebook paper.

► Step 1

Fold a sheet of paper in half along the long axis.

► Step 2

Open the sheet of paper. Fold ½" from the top of the paper. Fold again 1" from the top of the paper.

► Step 3

Unfold. Draw lines along the fold lines and label as shown.

Safety	
Home	Work

As You Read

As you read and discuss the material in the chapter, use your Foldable to define terms, outline safety suggestions, and record main ideas.

SPOTLIGHT ON HEALTH

Using Visuals. Safe behaviors can prevent many unintentional injuries. What are some behaviors that can reduce your risk of unintentional injury while hiking with friends?

Safety at Home and at Work

Guide to Reading

Building Vocabulary

As you read this lesson, write each new highlighted term and its definition in your notebook.

▶ unintentional injury (p. 706)

▶ accident chain (p. 706)

▶ smoke alarm (p. 708)

▶ fire extinguisher (p. 708)

▶ Occupational Safety and Health Administration (OSHA) (p. 713)

Focusing on the Main Ideas

In this lesson, you will learn how to:

▶ Develop strategies for preventing accidental injuries at home and at work.

▶ Examine proper training and procedures to prevent accidental injuries.

Reading Strategy

Cause and Effect

▶ Make a T chart. On one side, list the causes of accidental injuries. On the other side of the chart, list safety precautions.

Describe some of the things you can do to help reduce the risk of accidental injury at home.

▲ Many accidental injuries can be prevented by taking precautions such as wiping up spills. *How can this behavior help prevent an accidental injury?*

The National Safety Council reports that a fatal home injury occurs every 18 minutes and a disabling home injury occurs every 4 seconds. One goal of *Healthy People 2010* is to reduce the number of deaths caused by unintentional or accidental injuries.

Accidental Injuries

There are two types of injuries—intentional and unintentional, or accidental. An intentional injury is the result of a deliberate attempt to cause harm. An **unintentional injury** is *an injury resulting from an unexpected event, or accident.* There are many actions you can take to prevent such injuries.

Strategies for Preventing Accidental Injuries

Although accidental injuries often seem to be random events, experts have observed an **accident chain**, or *a sequence of events that leads to an unintentional injury.* Health-literate consumers know injury-prevention and injury-management strategies for personal, family, and community health. Most accidental injuries include five steps that are connected, much like the links in a chain. **Figure 27.1** shows these steps.

FIGURE 27.1

PREVENTING ACCIDENTS AND UNINTENTIONAL INJURIES: THE ACCIDENT CHAIN

1. The Situation. Mark has overslept and has to rush to get ready for school.

2. The Unsafe Habit. Mark often leaves his books on the stairs.

3. The Unsafe Action. Mark isn't looking where he is going as he races down the stairs.

4. The Accident. Mark trips over his books and falls down the stairs.

5. The Result. When he falls, Mark sprains his wrist. He's also late for school.

Safety at Home

Taking precautions and planning ahead are strategies to help prevent injuries from fire, falls, electrical shock, and poisonings.

Preventing Fires

Most household fires are caused by heating equipment, appliances, electrical wiring, and smoking. Three elements—fuel, heat, and oxygen—must be present for a fire to occur. Fuel can be carelessly stored rags, wood, gasoline, or paper. A heat source can be a lighted match, a damaged electrical wire, a smoldering cigarette, or a pilot light. The oxygen in the air feeds and fans the flames. Removing one element will prevent a fire from starting. To avoid unintentional fire injuries:

► Never leave a candle burning unattended.

► Store matches and lighters out of the reach of children.

► Make sure that a person doesn't fall asleep while smoking.

► Keep stoves and ovens clean.

► Replace frayed electrical cords.

Reading Check

Identify What are the steps of the accident chain?

Creating a Fire-Safety Plan

In this activity you will create a home fire-safety plan with a poster showing escape routes.

What You'll Need

- ruler (optional)
- poster paper and art supplies

What You'll Do

1. Draw a floor plan of your home on poster paper, including doors, hallways, windows, and stairways.

2. Use arrows to point out the fastest way to escape from every room.

3. Identify an alternate escape route for each room in case the first route is blocked by flames or smoke.

4. Indicate the location of smoke alarms and fire extinguishers.

5. Designate a place for your family to meet outside your home and mark it on the escape plan.

6. At the bottom of your plan, write:
   - When escaping, stay low to the floor.
   - Call 911 or the fire department.
   - Never go back inside to retrieve something.

Apply and Conclude

Share the plan with your family, and post it in a prominent place in your home. Schedule a home fire drill at least once a month with all family members.

FIRE-SAFETY EQUIPMENT

To increase your chances of survival in case of fire, there are two life-saving devices that should be present in every home.

▶ A **smoke alarm** is *an alarm that is triggered by the presence of smoke.* Safety experts recommend that one smoke alarm be located on every floor of a home, preferably outside a sleeping area and near the kitchen. They also advise that the alarm be tested once a month and that batteries be replaced at least once a year.

▶ A **fire extinguisher** is *a portable device that puts out small fires by ejecting fire-extinguishing chemicals.* If your home has a fire extinguisher, check the dial on the equipment periodically to ensure that it still has enough pressure to work in an emergency. When using an extinguisher, stand away from the flames; aim at the source of the fire, not at the flames; and move the spray from side to side. If you are unsure of your ability to put out the fire, forget the extinguisher, get out of the house, and call the fire department.

Preventing Falls

According to the National Safety Council, one-fifth of injuries that require treatment in an emergency room are the result of falls. A few simple precautions can help reduce the risk of injuries from falls:

▶ Keep stairways well lit, in good repair, free of clutter, and equipped with sturdy handrails and nonskid stair strips.

▶ Keep the floor clean. Mop up any spills immediately.

▶ Use nonskid throw rugs, or place nonskid mats under rugs.

▶ Make sure bathtubs and showers have safety rails and nonskid mats.

▶ Do not run electrical or telephone cords across areas where people walk.

▶ If there are small children in the home, install adjustable safety latches so that windows will open only a few inches. This is especially important for windows above the first floor. Make sure the windows can be opened in case of fire or other emergency.

▶ Use a sturdy step stool when reaching for items in high places.

Preventing Electrical Shock

Electricity can be dangerous if not used correctly. Improper use or maintenance of electrical appliances, wiring, and outlets can cause severe electrical shock. Follow these safety precautions when using electrical appliances to help reduce the risk of injury:

▶ Unplug an electrical appliance immediately if anything seems to be wrong. Always pull on the plug, not the cord.

▶ Inspect cords periodically for signs of cracked insulation. If the cord is frayed, replace it immediately.

▶ Do not run cords under carpets or rugs; the cords can be damaged when walked on.

▶ Never use an electrical appliance or power tool if your body, clothing, or the floor is wet.

▶ Check outlets and extension cords to make sure they aren't overloaded.

▶ In homes with small children, cover unused outlets with plastic protectors.

 Prevent electrical shocks by using extension cords and electrical outlets correctly. *Why might an overloaded outlet cause a problem?*

CHARACTER CHECK

Citizenship. Keep your eyes open for potential safety hazards at school. Notice any frayed electrical wires, overloaded outlets, or extension cords stretched across areas where people walk. **Do your part to help make your school a safe environment—report any unsafe situation to the custodian or a teacher.**

Preventing Poisoning

According to the Centers for Disease Control and Prevention (CDC), nearly 900,000 emergency room visits each year are associated with poisonings. About 90 percent of poisonings occur in the home, and more than half involve children under six years of age. Most potentially poisonous products—detergents, disinfectants, paints, polishes, and insecticides—are typically found in the kitchen, bathroom, utility closet, basement, and garage. It is important that you learn to identify hazardous and life-threatening situations and their consequences. Here are a few guidelines for preventing poisoning:

▶ Keep medications and other potentially poisonous substances in childproof containers. Store them out of the reach of children. Dispose of any expired medications.

▶ Store all household chemicals in their original containers. Never store them in food or drink containers.

▶ Never mix household chemicals. Many household cleaners contain ammonia or bleach, which give off toxic gases when combined.

▶ Use products that give off fumes, such as ammonia, bleach, petroleum products, and paints, only in well-ventilated areas.

▶ Make sure there is adequate ventilation when using fuel-burning appliances. These appliances give off carbon monoxide gas while in use. Inhaling this poisonous gas can damage body tissues and cause death from lack of oxygen.

Figure 27.2 summarizes strategies for staying safe in and around your home. Putting these strategies into practice will decrease the likelihood of unintentional injuries.

Firearm Safety

Up to 40 percent of homes in the United States contain firearms. Firearm injuries are one of the top ten causes of death in the United States, and the number of nonfatal firearm injuries is considerable—over 200,000 per year. Following these recommendations can help reduce the risk of injury from firearms:

▶ Never point a firearm at anyone for any reason.

▶ Treat all firearms as if they are loaded. If you find a firearm, leave the area and tell an adult.

▶ Store firearms unloaded, and store the ammunition separately. Both should be in locked cabinets that are well out of the reach of children.

A Use proper safety precautions for storing household chemicals and medicines, especially if there are small children in the home. *How should medications be stored?*

Reading Check

Explain What are some of the safety strategies you can practice to help prevent accidental injuries?

FIGURE 27.2

SAFETY AT HOME

Practice these safety strategies to help prevent injuries at home.

Test smoke alarms once a month, and change the batteries at least once a year.

Make sure your body and the floor are dry before using electrical appliances such as hair dryers and curling irons.

Store gasoline and other flammable liquids away from hot water heaters or other sources of flames or sparks.

Be sure stairs and hallways are well lit.

Store household products in a secure place, out of the reach of children.

Always turn the handles of pots and pans away from the front of the stove so that they cannot be accidentally knocked or pulled off.

Make sure there is good ventilation when you use chemical products to avoid being overcome by fumes.

Store propane cylinders outdoors to prevent an explosion or a fire.

▶ Prolonged typing on the computer keyboard and clicking the mouse can cause repetitive motion injuries (RMIs). RMIs start when the same task is performed repeatedly, straining tissues in the affected area. If these tissues don't get a chance to heal, the damage adds up. Symptoms include pain and tingling. Taking frequent breaks and making sure you're positioned properly at the computer can help prevent RMIs.

Computer and Video Game Safety

Computer tasks often require you to sit in one place for long periods of time and make repetitive motions while staring at the screen. This can cause eyestrain and sore muscles and may even lead to wrist, hand, or arm injuries. To help reduce the risk of injury, take a 10-minute break every hour or so. If you are working intensely for a long period of time, occasionally give your eyes a rest by looking up and focusing on objects that are far away.

Your work area should be a comfortable and healthy place to work. **Figure 27.3** shows the correct way to sit at a computer. Determine whether your computer and chair are adjusted correctly. Here are some other things to consider when setting up a work area:

▶ **Lighting.** Lighting for a computer should be indirect and not too bright. Avoid creating a glare on your computer screen.

▶ **Adjustability.** Chairs, computer monitors, and desks or other work surfaces should be adjustable for the comfort of each user. This is especially important if people of different heights use the same work area.

FIGURE 27.3

COMPUTER WORKSTATION DESIGN

Making your workstation comfortable will reduce fatigue; eyestrain; blurred vision; headaches; and back, neck, and arm cramps.

Use indirect lighting to avoid glare. Arrange the computer so that it is at right angles to windows and other light sources.

Adjust your chair to keep your back straight. This will help keep your body aligned, which reduces muscle strain.

Adjust the height and angle of the monitor so that it is at or slightly lower than eye level. The distance between your eyes and the monitor should be 18–30 inches.

Adjust the chair so that your feet can rest flat on the floor. Use a footrest if the chair is not adjustable. Your forearms, wrists, and hands should be straight when you are using the mouse or keyboard.

Adjust the height of the computer table so that the keyboard is comfortable, usually slightly higher than waist level. Your forearms should be parallel to the floor when you are using the keyboard.

Safety on the Job

Many teens have part-time or full-time jobs. In fact, the U.S. Department of Labor says that more than 3 million teens earn paychecks during summer vacations alone; others work part-time jobs during the school year. Unfortunately, about 500 of these workers are injured every day. Many of these accidental injuries could have been avoided if training had been provided before machinery and equipment were used. Teens are permitted to perform certain tasks on the job but prohibited from performing others. The Department of Labor prohibits anyone under 18 from doing certain jobs, including roofing and construction work, demolition, driving a forklift and any vehicle, operating power-driven machinery, and handling explosives and radioactive materials.

Both employees and employers must follow safety rules issued by the **Occupational Safety and Health Administration (OSHA)**, *the agency in the federal government that is responsible for promoting safe and healthful conditions in the workplace.* Because many people spend about one-third of the day on the job, it's everyone's responsibility to take steps to ensure a healthful and injury-free workplace.

The U.S. Department of Labor regulates the types of tasks that teens are allowed to perform on the job. *List two types of jobs that the Department of Labor prohibits teens under 18 from doing.*

LESSON 1 — REVIEW

Reviewing Facts and Vocabulary

1. What are the five steps in the accident chain?
2. What three elements must be present for a fire to start?
3. Define the term *smoke alarm.*

Thinking Critically

4. **Analyzing.** Why should people always treat a firearm as though it were loaded?
5. **Synthesizing.** Think of a specific job that a teen might have. Analyze strategies for preventing accidental injuries on that job, and develop a checklist that features these strategies.

Applying Health Skills

Advocacy. Make a poster that encourages family members to practice safety habits. Your poster should include specific safety precautions that family members can take to stay safe in the home. Display your poster at home, and discuss with your family any steps that might be taken to improve safety.

After You Read

Explain. Draw a poster showing safety precautions at home or at school. Visually show how to avoid injury.

Visit **health.glencoe.com** for the Interactive Study Guide for Lesson 1.

Lesson 1 Safety at Home and at Work **713**

Recreation and Water Safety

Guide to Reading

Building Vocabulary

As you read this lesson, write each new highlighted term and its definition in your notebook.

▶ heat exhaustion (p. 715)

▶ hypothermia (p. 715)

Focusing on the Main Ideas

In this lesson, you will learn how to:

▶ **Develop** strategies for preventing accidental injuries that occur during recreational activities.

▶ **Examine** the consequences of risk-taking during recreational activities.

Reading Strategy

Predict

▶ Scan the headings, subheadings, and photo captions. Write a short sunmmary predicting the lesson content.

Write a short paragraph describing the supplies and safety gear you would take on a hike.

Packing the right supplies will help guarantee that outdoor activities are safe and fun. *With what consequence might you associate the risk-taking activity of engaging in outdoor activities without the proper supplies?*

Common sense and caution can minimize the risk of accidental injuries during recreational activities. Health-literate individuals understand the role of individual responsibility regarding personal risk behavior.

Recreational Safety

Outdoor activities are enjoyable and can help you stay fit. To stay healthy and safe during outdoor activities:

▶ **Know your limits.** Stick with tasks that match your level of ability.

▶ **Bring supplies.** Take plenty of safe drinking water with you. Plan simple meals and take supplies to store foods safely.

▶ **Wear protective clothing.** The proper clothing can protect against the weather and poisonous plants and insects.

▶ **Tell people your plans.** Let them know where you're going and when you plan to return. If possible, carry a cell phone in case of emergencies.

▶ **Plan ahead for the weather.** Warm days may turn into cold nights and storms may occur suddenly. Before planning any outdoor activities, check the local weather and plan your trip according to those conditions. Bring enough clothes that you can add layers or remove layers according to the weather. To avoid heat exhaustion, stay in the shade in hot weather and drink plenty of water. **Heat exhaustion** is *an overheating of the body that results in cold, clammy skin and symptoms of shock.* Use sunscreen to protect the skin from UV rays. A health-literate individual understands how the environmental conditions of the community influence the health of individuals.

Safety While Camping and Hiking

To prevent injuries when camping and hiking:

▶ Stay in specified campsites, and hike only in approved areas. Never hike or camp alone.

▶ Be knowledgeable about poisonous plants, insects, and snakes. If you'll be in grassy areas, wear socks and long pants tucked into socks or boots to help protect against ticks and mosquitoes.

▶ Be cautious around wildlife. Do not store food in your tent. Store food where animals cannot get to it, such as in a vehicle or suspended from a high tree branch.

▶ Be careful around campfires and observe fire safety rules. Never cook inside a tent. Smother all campfires with dirt and water.

▶ Never drink water from lakes, rivers, or streams; they may contain disease-causing pathogens.

Winter Sport Safety

When skiing, snowboarding, or participating in other winter sports, dress in layers. This can prevent **hypothermia**, *a condition in which body temperature becomes dangerously low.* Make sure the outermost layer is waterproof, and wear a hat. Don't forget to put on sunscreen, especially in high elevations. Always wear the appropriate safety equipment, and make sure it's in good working order and is sized correctly for you.

Reading ✓ Check

Describe What is the difference between heat exhaustion and hypothermia?

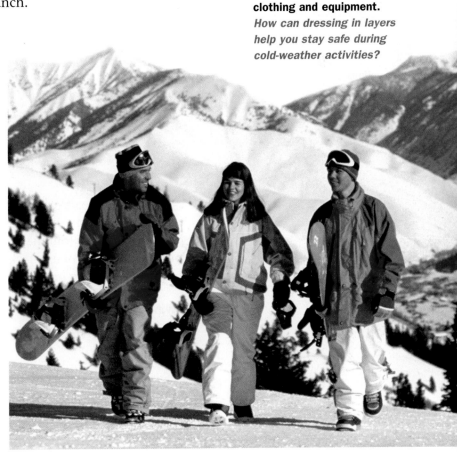

Ⓥ **Safe participation in winter sports requires proper clothing and equipment.** *How can dressing in layers help you stay safe during cold-weather activities?*

Real-Life Application

Breaking the Accident Chain

Local Teen Injured in Diving Accident

A Summitville teen is in critical condition after he was recovered from the bottom of a pool Saturday night. Jon Franklin was at the party of a friend where more than 30 people were present. Franklin was found in about six feet of water. The pool had no depth indicators and the area was poorly lit. No one present had training in water safety. Witnesses say alcohol may have been a factor in the accident. A hospital spokesperson has confirmed that Franklin suffered a severe spinal cord injury and that his prognosis is uncertain.

Diving accidents cause more than 850 spinal cord injuries each year. Many of these injuries result in the paralysis of all four limbs. Read the article, and answer the questions below to increase your understanding of how "links" in the accident chain lead to injuries:

- What was the situation?
- What were the unsafe habits that contributed to this accident?
- What was the unsafe action?
- What was the accident?
- What was the result?

ACTIVITY

As a class, discuss the answers to the questions. Individually, bring in a newspaper clipping about a recreational accident. In small groups, identify the situation, the unsafe habits and actions, the accident itself, and the result. Write a paragraph describing how the accident chain could have been broken. Post your clippings and paragraphs on the bulletin board.

Water Safety

Swimming, boating, and other water sports are great summer activities. However, drowning is the second leading cause of injury-related death. The four major causes of drowning are failure to wear a life jacket, alcohol use, lack of swimming skill, and hypothermia. Follow these safety precautions for water-related activities.

SWIMMING

► Learn how to swim. Know your abilities, and always swim with a buddy.

► Swim only in designated areas where a lifeguard is present.

► If you get a muscle cramp, relax, float, and press and squeeze the muscle until it relaxes.

DIVING

▶ Learn the proper diving technique. Always check water depth before diving. The American Red Cross recommends a minimum depth of nine feet.

▶ Never dive in unfamiliar areas or into dark or shallow water. Make sure the area is clear of swimmers and floating objects.

BOATING AND PERSONAL WATERCRAFT

▶ Learn how to handle a boat or personal watercraft (PWC) correctly, and know the laws governing their use.

▶ Always wear approved personal flotation devices on boats and PWC.

▶ At the first indication of bad weather, return to shore.

▶ Never ride in a boat or PWC with an operator who has been using alcohol or other drugs.

Figure 27.4 shows survival techniques you can use if you fall into deep water.

Ⓐ **Always wear a Coast Guard–approved personal flotation device when boating or using a personal watercraft.**

FIGURE 27.4

DROWNING PREVENTION

If you fall into cold water while boating, assume one of these positions. They can help you stay afloat and reduce the risk of hypothermia until help arrives.

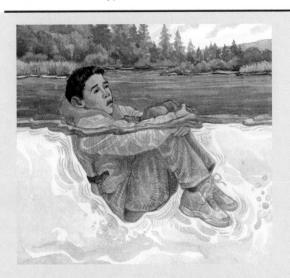

A. Lessen heat loss by drawing your knees up to your chest and keeping your upper arms close to the sides of your body. You lose a lot of heat through your head, so try to keep it out of the water.

B. If you are with one or more people, huddle close together in a circle to preserve body heat. A child or smaller person who loses heat faster should be placed in the center of the circle.

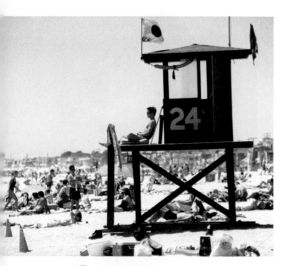

Always stay within designated swimming areas that are supervised by a lifeguard.

Lake, River, and Ocean Safety

Swimming in lakes, rivers, or the ocean presents added safety concerns. Keep these precautions in mind:

▶ **Swim in supervised areas only.** Select an area that is clean and well maintained.

▶ **Enter feet first.** Hidden objects, unexpected drop-offs, and aquatic life may be lurking beneath the surface.

▶ **Watch for marine warnings.** Check to see whether the warning flag is up, or ask the lifeguard whether the water is safe for swimming. If you are at the ocean, check the tides and surf conditions before entering the water. Don't enter the water in an area marked "No Swimming."

▶ **Be aware of surroundings.** Be sure rafts and docks are in good condition. Stay away from piers, pilings, and diving platforms when in the water. Never swim under a raft or dock.

▶ **Plan ahead.** Always make sure that you have enough energy to swim back to shore. If you are pulled offshore by rapid currents or undertows, swim gradually out of the current by swimming across it, often parallel to the shore.

LESSON 2 REVIEW

Reviewing Facts and Vocabulary

1. Why is it risky to drink from lakes, rivers, and streams?
2. Analyze and identify three strategies for preventing accidental injuries while camping or hiking.
3. Define the term *hypothermia*.

Thinking Critically

4. **Synthesizing.** You and your family are taking a boat out on the lake for the afternoon. What supplies and safety equipment should you bring with you?
5. **Analyzing.** You and your friend Jake are skiing. He suggests that you try the advanced slope, even though both of you are beginners. What negative consequences are associated with this risk-taking?

Applying Health Skills

Practicing Healthful Behaviors. Choose a sport that you would like to learn, and make a list of the proper equipment and safety precautions associated with that sport. Be sure to incorporate all safety precautions, wear the proper clothing, and use safety equipment.

After You Read

Compare and Contrast. Draw three circles that slightly overlap each other. In the first circle, list safety tips for camping and hiking. In the next circle, list safety tips for winter sports. In the last, list water safety tips. In the part that overlaps all three circles, list the safety tips common to all outdoor activities.

Safety on the Road

Guide to Reading

Building Vocabulary

As you read this lesson, write each new highlighted term and its definition in your notebook.

▶ vehicular safety (p. 719)

▶ graduated driver's license (p. 720)

▶ road rage (p. 722)

▶ defensive driver (p. 722)

Focusing on the Main Ideas

In this lesson, you will learn how to:

▶ Develop strategies to prevent accidental injuries while driving or riding in a car or other vehicle.

▶ Examine the consequences of risk-taking such as drinking and driving.

Reading Strategy

Predict

▶ Scan the headings and captions. Write three questions you think will be answered in this lesson.

Quick Write

Make a list of all the safety measures you think would prevent an unintentional injury while driving a car.

Ⓐ Automobile safety begins even before you start the car—buckle up!

According to the CDC, motor vehicle crashes are the leading cause of death among teens—more than 5,700 teens died on the road in 2001. The fatality rate for teen drivers is about four times higher than the rate for drivers from 25 to 65 years old. The percentages are staggering:

▶ 14 percent of *all* drivers involved in fatal crashes were between the ages of 15 and 20.

▶ 21 percent of these drivers had been drinking and driving.

▶ 80 percent of these drivers were not wearing safety belts.

Automobile Safety

When teens are entrusted with driving a car, they have a responsibility to themselves, their families, their passengers, and the people in other vehicles. Behaving responsibly means practicing **vehicular safety**—*obeying the rules of the road, as well as using or exercising common sense and good judgment.* That means driving within the speed limit, yielding the right-of-way when indicated, and observing local traffic regulations. A conscientious teen understands the role of individual responsibility regarding personal risk behaviors.

Reading ✓ Check

Explain What are some of the ways you can exercise common sense and good judgment as a driver?

Being supervised by an experienced driver can help a teen improve his or her driving skills. *What are three of the common-sense rules of vehicular safety?*

To exercise common sense and good judgment as a driver:

▶ **Pay attention to your vehicle.** Before you start the car, adjust the mirrors and seat to positions that are best for you. Buckle your safety belt. Adjust other items such as the radio, heater, and air conditioner before the car starts moving.

▶ **Pay attention to other drivers.** A popular TV public service announcement sponsored by the National Safety Council advised drivers to "watch out for the other guy." This advice is still sound. At night or when inclement weather reduces visibility, turn on your headlights so that other drivers can see you. In general, drive as though the other driver is going to act irresponsibly. If you do this, you will always be prepared for the unexpected.

▶ **Pay attention to road conditions.** This includes reducing your speed when the road is icy or wet, when a lane narrows, and when there is construction or congestion.

▶ **Pay attention to your physical state.** Don't drive when you are sleepy. If you are tired, do something to refresh yourself, such as rolling down the window or turning on the radio. If you are extremely tired, pull over at the nearest rest stop and call home.

▶ **Pay attention to your emotional state.** If you are angry or feeling other strong emotions, don't drive. Your mental state can affect your judgment and reaction time as much as your physical state can.

Teen Driving Safety

The National Center for Statistics and Analysis reports that 8,155 drivers between 15 and 20 years old were killed in automobile accidents in the year 2000. According to the CDC, teen drivers are more likely than older drivers to speed, run red lights, make illegal turns, ride with an intoxicated driver, and drive after using alcohol or drugs. Teens are also more likely than older drivers to underestimate the dangers in hazardous situations, and they have less experience adjusting to these situations. In an effort to reduce the number of teen deaths in car crashes, some states have adopted a graduated driver's licensing program. A **graduated driver's license (GDL)** is *a licensing program that gradually increases a new driver's driving privileges over time as experience and skill are gained.* This system allows a new driver to improve his or her driving skills while under the supervision of an older driver. Over time, a teen driver gains more skill, and the driving restrictions are lifted.

Resilient TEENS

Erika Altepeter and her younger brother were like twins. "He was my best friend," says Erika. "We went everywhere and did everything together." Then in August of 2004, the unthinkable happened. The car her brother was riding in crashed, killing him instantly.

At the time, Erika was still recovering from a near fatal accident of her own. "I was really sad and couldn't understand why this happened," says Erika. But then letters from the people who had received her brother's organs began to arrive in the mail. "My brother helped 40 people all together," says Erika, "and that feels really good."

"My brother's death taught me some important things," says Erika. "For example, you never know when someone might die, so don't forget to tell them how much you love them. Oh, and never hold grudges."

"My brother helped 40 people all together, and that feels really good."

 Reading Check **Explain** What helped Erika through the grieving process when her brother died?

Being a Responsible Driver

As you learn to drive and make decisions behind the wheel, be considerate. Follow these safety tips:

▶ Always signal when you are about to make a turn or change lanes. Turn the signal off after the maneuver is complete.

▶ Follow all traffic signals and signs, including speed limits.

▶ Don't tailgate. Following too closely can cause an accident. Other drivers may view tailgating as a hostile act.

▶ Let other drivers merge safely into traffic. Cutting them off or not allowing them to merge is unsafe for you and others.

 Reading Check

Describe What are some of the precautions you can take to reduce the risk of injury in an automobile?

▼ When caught in a traffic slowdown, allow other drivers to merge. Such actions diminish the risks of road rage. *Identify three other actions that could help defuse road rage.*

ROAD RAGE

Sometimes people who are otherwise emotionally stable become enraged in certain driving situations. **Road rage** is *a practice of endangering drivers by using a vehicle as a weapon.* It can be triggered by a variety of acts, including disputes over a parking space, obscene gestures, loud music, overuse of the horn, and slow driving. A driver consumed with road rage may run red lights, tailgate, or pass on a shoulder. Some enraged drivers have been known to use guns or other weapons. If you see someone who is truly a danger on the road, keep your distance. Get the vehicle's license plate number, and report it promptly to the police.

Other Preventive Strategies

Safety belts save lives. Yet according to the CDC's statistics on teen driving, one in five high school students report that they rarely or never wear safety belts when riding with someone else. Drivers and passengers who fail to use safety belts are more likely to be thrown from the vehicle in a crash. Make sure everyone in the car is buckled up, and take these precautions:

- ▶ Never engage in high-risk driving behavior such as speeding, drag racing, or daredevil stunts.

- ▶ Alcohol and other drugs impair judgment, coordination, and reaction time. *Never* use these substances and drive—the consequences could be fatal.

- ▶ Don't let distractions such as eating or adjusting the radio or CD player take your attention away from the road. Don't use cell phones while driving.

- ▶ Realize that you have no control over what other drivers are doing, so for the sake of your safety, drive defensively. A **defensive driver** is *a driver who is aware of potential hazards and reacts to avoid them.* A defensive driver acquires driving skills and knowledge to stay safe on the road.

Safety on Wheels

It is important to use proper safety equipment and common sense when bicycling; skateboarding; riding a scooter; or operating a motorcycle, off-road vehicle, or moped. Almost half of the motorcycle drivers who were killed in the year 2000 were not wearing helmets. Even helmet-wearing drivers of motorcycles and mopeds had a fatality rate 18 times higher than drivers of passenger cars.

BICYCLE SAFETY

Bicycles are a main form of transportation in many nations around the world. Their popularity in the United States has grown dramatically in recent years because cycling is a great way to stay fit. For safe cycling:

▶ Always wear a safety-approved, hard-shell helmet that fits properly.

▶ Ride with traffic. Always yield the right-of-way—you will not win against a car or truck.

▶ Watch for cars pulling into traffic and for car doors that swing open suddenly in your path.

▶ Obey the same rules as drivers, such as signaling before you turn and stopping for red lights and stop signs.

▶ Learn to use the hand signals for making turns and stopping.

▶ Except when signaling, keep both hands on the handlebars.

▶ Make sure your bike has a bright headlight and a red rear light and reflector for night riding.

▶ Wear reflective, or at least light-colored, clothing when riding at dawn, dusk, after dark, or in the rain.

SKATING SAFETY

Skateboarding and in-line skating can be a lot of fun. Follow these tips to help keep these activities safe:

▶ Wear protective equipment—wrist guards, elbow and knee pads, and a safety-approved, hard-shell helmet.

▶ Watch for pedestrians and keep your speed under control.

▶ If you begin to fall, curl up into a ball and roll, staying loose.

▶ Do not hold anything in your hand, such as a portable radio. Doing so will not allow you to fall properly.

By behaving safely and using proper safety equipment, you can avoid injury while riding a scooter, skateboarding, or in-line skating.

MOTORCYCLES AND ALL-TERRAIN VEHICLES

Motorcycles and mopeds are subject to the same traffic laws as cars. All-terrain vehicles (ATVs) are driven off-road. A driver's license is not required to operate an ATV, but operators still need to use common sense and know the rules of the road. Cyclists and ATV operators can also reduce the likelihood of injury by following these safety tips:

▶ Be aware of potential hazards, such as a car door opening or the presence of pedestrians.

▶ Wear a helmet and proper clothing, including eye protection.

▶ Be cautious in wet weather when tire traction is poor.

▶ Do not carry an additional rider unless you have a second seat and an additional set of safety equipment, including a helmet.

▶ Do not grab onto objects or other vehicles while moving.

▶ Do not use ATVs on paved roads or streets. Ride four-wheeled ATVs only; they are less likely to flip than three-wheeled ones.

When riding ATVs in unfamiliar areas, be alert for wires, fences, and downed trees, which can cause serious accidents.

LESSON 3 REVIEW

Reviewing Facts and Vocabulary

1. Define the term *vehicular safety*.

2. Analyze and identify three strategies for preventing accidental injuries while driving a car.

3. What is a *defensive driver*?

Thinking Critically

4. **Evaluating.** What does the saying "it's better to be alive than right" mean when it comes to vehicular safety?

5. **Synthesizing.** Drinking and driving can have serious consequences. Associate this risk-taking with three consequences.

Applying Health Skills

Advocacy. Choose a type of vehicle you learned about in this lesson. Think of ways to teach teens about the safety rules and equipment that a person must use to operate that vehicle safely. With classmates, create a video, public service announcement, or comic book that encourages teens to stay safe by following the tips in your presentation.

After You Read

Cause and Effect. List three ways you might be at risk while in a car, on a bicycle, or skating. Write a brief paragraph describing how your behavior can add to your risk, and what you can do to minimize those risks.

Weather Emergencies and Natural Disasters

Guide to Reading

Building Vocabulary

As you read this lesson, write each new highlighted term and its definition in your notebook.

▶ severe weather (p. 725)

▶ emergency survival kit (p. 726)

▶ hurricane (p. 727)

▶ flash flood (p. 727)

▶ tornado (p. 728)

▶ blizzard (p. 728)

▶ earthquake (p. 729)

Focusing on the Main Ideas

In this lesson, you will learn how to:

▶ Develop strategies to prevent accidental injuries during severe weather and natural disasters.

▶ Examine the ways in which technology can increase the survival rate during a severe weather event.

▶ Identify safety procedures that should be followed during a severe weather event or natural disaster.

Reading Strategy

Predict

▶ Scan the headings and captions in this lesson. Write a brief summary describing what you know about preparing for severe weather or natural disasters that affect your area.

Quick Write

Prepare a list of safety precautions you should have in place in case of an emergency.

The sky turns dark, and an ominous funnel appears on the horizon. You're driving home when a sudden thunderstorm strikes, and visibility is drastically reduced. Situations like this can occur without warning. Knowing how the environmental conditions of the community influence the health of individuals can help you stay safe.

Severe Weather

Severe weather refers to *harsh or dangerous weather conditions*. Some types of severe weather, such as tornadoes, hurricanes, and blizzards, usually occur in certain regions and at certain times of the year. When severe weather threatens, the National Weather Service (NWS) uses the media to issue watches and warnings. A *watch* means that the weather conditions are right for a specific weather event to occur. A *warning* means that severe weather has been sighted and is heading toward your area.

Severe weather warnings are broadcast on television and radio stations. *What other technologies have impacted the ability of communities to stay safe during severe weather?*

Emergency Survival Preparation

Discuss with your family where to go during an emergency, where to meet if family members get separated, and whom to contact if help is needed. Prepare an **emergency survival kit**—*a group of items that can be used for a short time until an emergency situation has stabilized.* Here are some supplies to collect before disaster strikes:

▶ **Water and food.** Plan on 1 gallon of water per person per day. Store canned and ready-to-eat foods, and a can opener.

▶ **Phone, radio, lighting, and blankets.** A charged cell phone is helpful when phone service is disrupted. Keep a battery-operated radio, flashlights, and extra batteries for each on hand. Blankets can be used for both warmth and shelter.

▶ **Other supplies.** Items such as medications and money may need to be added to your kit at the last minute.

Reading Check

Compare and Contrast
What is the difference between a National Weather Service watch and a warning?

Health Skills Activity

Goal Setting: Preparing an Emergency Survival Kit

Dean and his sister Tara are watching the news about a recent flood in a nearby town.

"I'm glad that's not us!" exclaims Tara. "I'd hate to have our house full of mud. It would ruin my CDs."

"That would be the least of our worries," Dean says. "It wouldn't be safe to drink water from the tap. We wouldn't have food, lights, or a place to sleep."

Tara replies, "I hadn't thought about that. I don't even know Mom's work number without looking it up. Do you?" Tara asks.

"We aren't very prepared, are we? I think we need to put together a survival kit for emergencies," Dean says.

What Would You Do?
Apply the five goal-setting steps to Dean and Tara's situation.

1. Identify a specific goal and write it down.
2. List the steps you will take to reach your goal.
3. Identify potential problems and ways to get help and support from others.
4. Set up checkpoints to evaluate your progress.
5. Reward yourself when you have achieved your goal.

Hurricanes

A **hurricane** is *a powerful storm that originates at sea, characterized by winds of at least 74 miles per hour, heavy rains, flooding, and sometimes tornadoes.* Hurricanes strike mainly on the eastern and southern coasts of the United States and usually occur from June through November, with the peak months being August and September. The NWS tracks hurricanes and issues warnings when they are approaching. If a hurricane watch is issued, secure your property. Bring in items from outside that may blow away in strong winds, such as lawn furniture, children's toys, bicycles, and trash cans. Board up windows and doors, and tape any glass you are unable to cover. If a hurricane warning is issued, seek shelter. Evacuate if the NWS instructs you to do so. The farther inland you go, the safer you will be.

 Floods are one type of natural disaster. *Why do you need to drink only bottled water in the event of a flood?*

Floods

Floods occur throughout the United States and can happen at any time of year. Flooding is often the result of severe rains that accompany hurricanes. If a flood is likely to occur, move valuables and furniture to a safe location or to higher ground. Listen to radio bulletins while you watch for rising water, and be prepared to evacuate. Before leaving, turn off the utilities in your home. Never walk, swim, ride a bike, or drive a car through flood waters. Both drowning and electrocution are risks in flooded areas. Drink only bottled water because floods can pollute the water supply. Learn under what conditions to abandon your home and when it is safer to stay put until help arrives.

FLASH FLOODS

A **flash flood** is *a flood with great volume and of short duration that is usually caused by heavy rainfall.* If you are in an area that is under a flash-flood warning, leave low-lying areas immediately. Do not attempt to drive through floodwaters or to cross police barricades. Stay away from streams, creeks, storm drains, and irrigation ditches, all of which become treacherous during flash floods.

Severe Thunderstorms

Thunderstorms can occur anywhere in the United States. Most thunderstorms include heavy rains, strong winds, lightning, and sometimes hail. Storm clouds and darkening skies indicate that a

Q & A

Can lightning strike twice in the same place?

Yes! The saying, "Lightning never strikes the same place twice" is a myth. Tall buildings are often hit repeatedly in successive storms. Even the same bolt of lightning can strike the same place multiple times. The flickering effect you sometimes see in a lightning bolt is actually multiple strokes of lightning following the same path.

If a tornado warning is issued, seek shelter immediately. *Where is the best place in your community to seek shelter if a tornado warning is issued?*

HEALTH *Online*

TOPIC **Natural Disasters**

Go to **health.glencoe.com** to link to the American Red Cross Web site.

ACTIVITY Using the information at this site, make a list of ways to prepare for natural disasters and another of ways to stay safe during them. What items do the two lists have in common?

thunderstorm is approaching. If you are on the water, go to shore. If you are outdoors, get inside. If you can't get inside, take shelter to avoid being struck by lightning. However, stay away from tall structures and trees, because lightning is attracted to tall objects. As a safety precaution, do not use computers, telephones, or televisions during a severe thunderstorm.

Tornadoes

Tornadoes have occurred in every state and can occur at any time of year. The peak months for tornadoes are March through August. A **tornado** is *a whirling, funnel-shaped windstorm that drops from the sky to the ground and produces a narrow path of destruction on land.* Tornadoes are often associated with severe thunderstorms. The winds of a tornado can reach speeds of up to 200 miles per hour, destroying everything in their path. Health-literate teens are able to identify hazardous and life-threatening situations and their consequences. If a tornado approaches, take these precautions:

▶ If you are outside or in a car, seek shelter inside a sturdy building, not a tent or mobile home. If you cannot get to a shelter, lie down in a ditch or low-lying area. Cover yourself with bulky clothing or a blanket. Protect your head with your hands.

▶ If you are indoors, stay away from windows. A storm cellar, basement, or crawl space is the safest place to be. If such an area is not available, go to an interior room, such as a bathroom, hallway, or closet. Cover yourself and protect your head with a mattress or blanket. As a last resort, get under a piece of heavy furniture and hold onto it.

Winter Storms

A severe winter storm called a **blizzard**, *a snowstorm with winds of at least 35 miles per hour,* is common in the northern areas of the United States. To protect yourself during blizzards and other winter storms, follow these steps:

▶ **Stay inside.** The safest place to be during a blizzard is indoors.

▶ **Wear protective clothing.** If you must go outside, prepare for the extremely cold temperatures and the blowing snow. Put on several layers of loose-fitting, lightweight clothing. Air that gets trapped between layers will help keep you warm. Choose an outer layer that is wind- and water-resistant. Use a scarf to protect your mouth and neck. Wear a hat, and wear mittens or gloves to protect your hands and fingers. Wear insulated, water-resistant boots to keep your feet warm and dry.

▶ **Avoid getting lost.** Use landmarks to find your way, or stay where you are until help arrives.

Earthquakes

An **earthquake** is *a violent shaking movement of the earth's surface*. Earthquakes can occur in all parts of the United States, but they are most common west of the Rocky Mountains. California alone averages almost 5,000 weak but detectable quakes each year. Most casualties during earthquakes are caused by falling objects or collapsing structures. If you live in an area prone to earthquakes, make sure bookcases and other tall or heavy furniture are bolted to the wall. Follow these safety procedures in the event of an earthquake:

▶ If you are inside a building, stand or crouch in a strongly supported doorway, brace yourself in an inside corner of the building, or get under a piece of sturdy furniture. Cover your head with your arms or a pillow.

▶ If you are outdoors when the earthquake hits, stay away from buildings, trees, and power lines.

▶ Use caution after the tremors have stopped. Stay out of damaged buildings. Be aware that utilities such as electrical or gas lines may be damaged and hazardous. Be prepared for aftershocks— smaller quakes that occur after the main earthquake.

The hazards of an earthquake continue after the shaking has stopped. *Identify measures established in your community to prepare for disasters.*

LESSON 4 REVIEW

Reviewing Facts and Vocabulary

1. Define *severe weather*, and list three examples.
2. What is an *emergency survival kit?*
3. How does a hurricane differ from a tornado?

Thinking Critically

4. **Analyzing.** Imagine that a tornado is approaching your home. What strategies can help prevent accidental injuries during this severe weather event?

5. **Evaluating.** Explain how technology and the media have impacted the health status of communities by improving the chances of surviving a severe weather event. What suggestions might you make to further improve their ability to reach a wide range of the population?

Applying Health Skills

Accessing Information. Use online or print resources to obtain a recommended list of items that should be included in an earthquake emergency kit. Write a PSA detailing the items in the kit. Post the information on a public display board.

After You Read

Explain. Prepare a disaster plan for your family. What items should you have ready in case of an emergency? Where will family members meet? Share the plan with your family and post it at home in a prominent place.

Cruise Control

New teen driving restrictions put parents in the rear window.

Anne Rekerdres likes to call it "the everlasting punishment." When the 17-year-old North Dallas senior came home with a speeding ticket, her dad, Randy, slapped the back bumper of her beloved car with a sticker that read: "How's my driving? 1-866-2-TELLMOM." "It was humiliating," says Anne. Still, there was nothing she could do. Recalls Randy, "I told her, 'If the sticker comes off, there go your keys.'"

Tattletale bumper stickers, which publicize where to call to notify parents about bad driving, are a trend that won't end soon. Besides the Web site on which Anne's dad bought hers, two other services—the San Diego–based Dad's Eyes (877-DADS-EYES) and 800-4-MYTEEN of Arlington, Texas—also allow strangers to report on teen driving. The stickers have even become popular in Texas's municipal court system, where several judges regularly sentence speeding teens to six months with the embarrassing banners.

Do the stickers actually make teens drive more safely? Stephanie Collins, 16, from Green Bay, Wisconsin, thinks so. "I always think about the sticker when I'm driving. When other drivers do something stupid, sometimes I feel like I want to cut them off, but then I remember the sticker is there, and I stay calm."

Anne's dad agrees. "As long as she perceives she can be reported," says Randy, "it works." His attitude doesn't make Anne happy, but she's learning to accept her punishment.

From Mesquite, Texas, Amanda Holmes, 16, offers this advice to other teens who might be thinking about driving carelessly: "I wouldn't recommend speeding if this sticker is the punishment. They make your car stand out because they are bright orange like the one I have." ▮

How's My Driving?
Tell-My-Mom.com
1-866-2-TELLMOM

TIME to THINK... About Traffic Violations

The sticker described in the article is one way to deter teens from speeding or breaking other traffic laws. With a group, think up other ways that might also be effective. Devise public service ads promoting one of your ideas. Include catchy headlines and create pictures that will make the ads dramatic.

Health Skills Application

1. **Advocacy.** Write a letter that stresses the importance of on-the-job training for teen workers in your community. Research your local and state laws, and include them in your letter. Submit your letter to your school or local newspaper for publication. *(LESSON 1)*

2. **Refusal Skills.** Mary is excited to be invited out on a boat for a day of water-skiing and swimming. However, when she arrives at the boat, Mary learns that the driver of the boat has been drinking alcohol. What should Mary do? *(LESSON 2)*

3. **Decision Making.** Imagine that you attended a party that lasted longer than you had planned. Because your license is graduated, you are not allowed to drive your car at this time of night. Use the decision-making steps to determine what to do. *(LESSON 3)*

4. **Practicing Healthful Behaviors.** Create an informative poster on how to stay safe during severe weather events. Make your poster available to other teens in your school. *(LESSON 4)*

CAREER Corner

Paramedic

Are you interested in helping other people in emergency situations? Paramedics are trained to give immediate and skilled care to people in all types of medical emergencies. These emergencies range from car crashes, heart attacks, and drownings to helping with childbirth. Lives depend upon the quick and competent care of paramedics as they provide assistance to and transport sick or injured people.

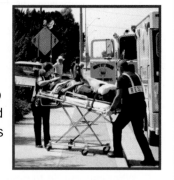

Would you like to study to be a paramedic? To enter this profession, you'll need emergency medical training. Find out more about this and other health careers by clicking on Career Corner at **health.glencoe.com.**

BEYOND *the* Classroom

Parent Involvement

Accessing Information.
Learning to swim can save your life. Research recreation and water-safety programs in your community. With your parents, find out how your family can become involved in these educational programs. If programs do not already exist in your community, find out how you can bring them to your community.

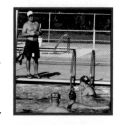

School and Community

American Red Cross. The American Red Cross helps communities during and immediately after a weather emergency or natural disaster. It also offers first-aid, recreation, and water-safety education classes. Contact the agency and find out what volunteer positions are available. Share your findings with the rest of the class.

After You Read

Use the notes you have taken in your Foldable to review what you have learned. On the back of your Foldable, write a brief narrative about an experience you have had that relates to injury prevention and safe behaviors.

▶ **EXPLORING HEALTH TERMS** *Answer the following questions on a sheet of paper.*

Lesson 1 *Match each definition with the correct term.*

unintentional injury	Occupational Safety
smoke alarm	and Health
fire extinguisher	Administration
accident chain	(OSHA)

1. A sequence of events that leads to an unintentional injury.

2. A portable device that puts out small fires by ejecting fire-extinguishing chemicals.

3. An injury resulting from an unexpected event, or accident.

4. The agency in the federal government that is responsible for promoting safe and healthful conditions in the workplace.

Lesson 2 *Identify each statement as True or False. If false, replace the underlined term with the correct term.*

hypothermia	heat exhaustion

5. An overheating of the body that results in cold, clammy skin and symptoms of shock is known as <u>hypothermia</u>.

6. <u>Heat exhaustion</u> is a condition in which body temperature becomes dangerously low.

Lesson 3 *Match each definition with the correct term.*

vehicular safety	defensive driver
graduated driver's license	road rage

7. A driver who is aware of potential hazards and reacts to avoid them.

8. A practice of endangering drivers by using a vehicle as a weapon.

9. A licensing program that gradually increases a new driver's driving privileges over time as experience and skill are gained.

Lesson 4 *Replace the underlined words with the correct term.*

severe weather	hurricane	tornado
emergency survival kit	flash flood	blizzard
earthquake		

10. A <u>flash flood</u> is a violent shaking movement of the earth's surface.

11. A <u>hurricane</u> is a flood with great volume and of short duration that is caused by heavy rainfall.

12. A <u>tornado</u> is a snowstorm with winds of at least 35 miles per hour.

▶ **RECALLING THE FACTS** *Use complete sentences to answer the following questions.*

1. Explain why the pattern of events that can lead to an unintentional injury is known as the "accident chain."

2. Why should every home be equipped with smoke alarms and a fire extinguisher?

3. Why is mixing household chemicals an unsafe procedure?

4. Why should everyone learn to swim?

5. What can you do to protect yourself from heat exhaustion?

6. Why are some states adopting a graduated driver's license program?

7. Why is it important to be aware of your emotional state when driving?

8. What are two safety behaviors that can keep you safe on a skateboard?

For more review questions for Chapter 27, go to **health.glencoe.com**.

9. What precautions should you take if a hurricane watch is issued for your area?

10. Where is the safest place to be during a blizzard?

11. Where do earthquakes occur most often in the United States?

▶ WRITING CRITICALLY

1. **Descriptive.** Write two paragraphs. In the first paragraph, provide a step-by-step description of a situation that led to an accident. In the second paragraph, describe the precautions that could have been taken to prevent the accident.

2. **Narrative.** Write a one-page story about a teen and his or her family and what they do to survive a natural disaster, such as a tornado, earthquake, or flood. Briefly describe the disaster and how they safely respond to the situation.

Standardized Test Practice

 Read the passage below and then answer the questions.

Storm Surges

Which is the deadliest aspect of a hurricane: high winds, flying debris, or a storm surge? If you guessed storm surge, you're correct. Storm surges are responsible for 9 out of 10 hurricane-related deaths.

Storm *surge* is the amount of water pushed toward shore by hurricane winds. Areas with shallow slopes off the coastlines are particularly susceptible to storm surges because wind-driven water can travel easily up the slope. Water is very heavy—approximately 1,700 pounds per cubic yard. Storm surges are often made up of thousands of tons of water. It's not hard to imagine what a repeated pounding by such heavy waves can do to most buildings.

1. Which phrase in the second paragraph helps you understand the meaning of the word *susceptible*?

   A It's not hard to imagine
   B Areas with shallow slopes off the coastline
   C Water is very heavy
   D water can travel easily up the slope

2. What is the writer's purpose in writing this passage?

   F to inform readers how heavy water is
   G to provide advice about how to design coastal buildings
   H to warn readers about the dangers of storm surges
   I to help readers understand the dangers of flying debris

3. Design a brochure that uses words and pictures to get across the ideas in the passage above to a middle school audience.

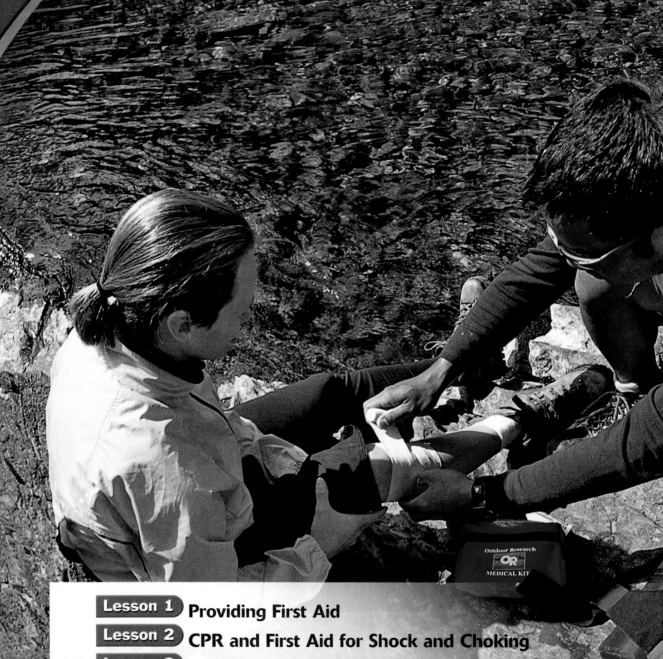

CHAPTER 28

First Aid and Emergencies

Eye ON THE Media

Emergency and Rescue Workers in the Media

Emergency and rescue workers have been featured in the media after such events as natural disasters. These stories highlight characteristics that are highly valued:

► **bravery**

► **selflessness**

► **empathy**

Visit the Eye on the Media section at **health.glencoe.com** to learn more about how the media represents emergency and rescue workers.

FOLDABLES™
Study Organizer

Before You Read

Make this Foldable to help you organize what you learn about providing first aid. Begin with a sheet of 8½″ x 11″ paper or notebook paper.

► **Step 1**

Fold a sheet of paper in half along the long axis.

► **Step 2**

Fold into thirds.

► **Step 3**

Cut the top layer along both folds. Label as shown.

Check *Call* *Care*

As You Read

As you read and discuss the material in the chapter, use your Foldable to record what you learn about the three Cs, the first steps to take in an emergency situation.

SPOTLIGHT ON HEALTH

Using Visuals. In what specific ways do you think providing the correct first-aid techniques will help the recovery of an injured person?

Providing First Aid

Guide to Reading

Building Vocabulary

As you read this lesson, write each new highlighted term and its definition in your notebook.

▶ first aid (p. 736)

▶ universal precautions (p. 737)

Focusing on the Main Ideas

In this lesson, you will learn how to:

▶ **Examine** the nation's goals for individual, family, and community health and appropriate first aid procedures.

▶ **Discuss** the importance of learning first aid.

▶ **Develop** strategies for responding to accidental injuries.

Reading Strategy

Organize Information

▶ Draw a chart with five columns. As you read take notes, placing comments for each main heading in one column.

Write a paragraph explaining the importance of learning first-aid procedures.

ⓥ **Universal precautions protect both the caregiver and the victim from coming into contact with blood and other body fluids that may contain pathogens.**

Suppose that you are in the school lunchroom and your best friend begins to choke. Do you know what to do in this situation? Your response to an accident or an emergency can minimize injury and might even save a life. A health-literate individual knows injury-prevention and injury-management strategies for personal, family, and community health.

First Aid

First aid is *the immediate, temporary care given to an ill or injured person until professional medical care can be provided.* First aid is administered in the seconds and minutes following an emergency in which someone becomes ill or injured. Learning first-aid procedures is an important step in meeting the nation's health goals and objectives for individuals, family, and communities described in *Healthy People 2010.* Using the proper first-aid procedures can reduce the number of people who sustain further injury or die in the absence of early and effective treatment.

Take the Health Inventory for Chapter 28 at **health.glencoe.com**.

Universal Precautions

Some infectious agents, such as the HIV and hepatitis B viruses, can be transmitted through contact with blood and other body fluids. Because of this risk, it is important that you use universal precautions when you administer first aid. **Universal precautions** are *actions taken to prevent the spread of disease by treating all blood and other body fluids as if they contained pathogens.* Universal precautions include strategies such as wearing protective gloves when there is a possibility of touching blood or other body fluids, using a mouthpiece or other protective ventilation devices for breathing emergencies, and washing your hands before and after providing first aid.

Reading Check

Describe What are the first steps to take when responding to an emergency?

Responding to an Emergency

Recognizing an emergency is the first step in responding to it. Common indicators of an emergency include unusual sights, sounds, odors, and behaviors. If you find yourself at the scene of an emergency, remain calm and follow the steps in **Figure 28.1,** which were developed by the American Red Cross.

FIGURE 28.1

CHECK, CALL, CARE

These are the first steps to take in an emergency situation.

1. **Check the scene and the victim.**
   Look around to be sure that the scene is safe. Be alert for dangers such as spilled chemicals, traffic, fire, escaping steam, downed electrical lines, and smoke. Determine the number of victims. If no immediate danger is evident, do not move the victim. Move the victim only if his or her life is threatened.

2. **Call for help.**
   Call the local emergency number or 911. Answer all of the dispatcher's questions. Do not hang up until the dispatcher does. If possible, have someone else make the call so that you can stay with the victim. If you are the one calling for help, finish the call as quickly as possible, and return to the victim.

3. **Provide care for the victim.**
   If possible, get the victim's permission before giving first aid. Always address life-threatening emergencies first. Take care of anyone who is unconscious; who is not breathing or is having trouble breathing; who shows no signs of circulation, such as moving or coughing; or who is bleeding severely. If you aren't sure that the victim is conscious, tap him or her on the shoulder and ask, "Are you okay?"

Types of Injuries

Not all injuries are emergencies. Splinters and scrapes, for example, are relatively minor injuries, and the first-aid treatment for them is usually quick and simple. Other injuries are severe enough to endanger life or cause serious physical damage.

Open Wounds

Open wounds are one type of injury. Treatment depends on the severity and type of wound:

▶ **Abrasion.** If the skin is scraped against a hard surface, tiny blood vessels in the outer layers of the skin break, resulting in an abrasion. Because of the way the injury occurs, dirt and bacteria can easily enter the site. Therefore, it's especially important to clean the wound to prevent infection and speed healing.

▶ **Laceration.** A laceration is a cut caused by a sharp object, such as a knife or broken glass, slicing through the layers of skin. This type of laceration usually has smooth edges. A hard blow from a blunt instrument or tearing the skin may cause lacerations with jagged edges. All lacerations are accompanied by bleeding. Deep lacerations can result in heavy bleeding, as well as damage to nerves, large blood vessels, and soft tissues. Infection may also occur.

▶ **Puncture.** A puncture wound is a small but deep hole caused by a pin, nail, fang, or other object that pierces the skin. Puncture wounds do not usually cause heavy external bleeding, but they may cause internal bleeding if the penetrating object damages major blood vessels or internal organs. Puncture wounds carry a high risk of infection, including tetanus.

▶ **Avulsion.** An avulsion results when tissue is partially or completely separated from the body. A partially avulsed piece of skin may remain attached, but it hangs like a flap. Heavy bleeding is common. Sometimes a body part, such as a finger, may be severed. With today's medical technology, severed body parts can sometimes be reattached surgically. Pack the severed part in ice or ice water, if possible, to preserve the tissue. Immediately call for professional medical assistance.

Knives and other sharp objects can cause lacerations. When using any sharp tool, pay attention to what you are doing. *What other strategies can you apply to reduce the risk of lacerations?*

Health Skills Activity

How to Handle a Puncture Wound

Jamie, 16, is looking after Jason, her 7-year-old neighbor, for the afternoon. They are in the backyard playing with toy cars and trucks. After a while, Jason gets up and walks over to the toolshed.

"Jason," Jamie calls, "you're not supposed to go over there. Come back here and pull out my car with your tow truck. I'm stuck in the mud."

Jason starts to walk back, and suddenly starts screaming and holding his foot.

"Oh, my gosh!" Jamie cries. She looks at Jason's foot.

Jason has stepped on a nail, which has punctured his foot. Jamie notes that the wound looks deep but doesn't appear to be bleeding heavily.

What should Jamie do?

What Would You Do?
Describe in detail how you would apply these first-aid steps to Jamie's situation.

1. Protect yourself from infections spread by contact with blood.
2. Control any bleeding.
3. Clean the wound.
4. Protect the wound.
5. Get medical attention if necessary.

First Aid for Bleeding

To stop blood flow from an open wound, first put on clean protective gloves, if possible. Wash a minor wound with mild soap and running water to remove dirt and debris. Do not attempt to clean a severe injury such as an avulsion. Always wash your hands before and after providing care, even if you wear gloves.

To control bleeding:

▶ Cover the wound with sterile gauze or a clean cloth and press firmly.

▶ If possible, elevate the wound above the level of the heart.

▶ Cover the gauze or cloth dressing with a sterile bandage.

▶ If necessary, cover the dressing with a pressure bandage and/or use pressure point bleeding control (see next page).

▶ Call for help or have someone else do so.

 Applying pressure to a wound will often stop the flow of blood. *What precautions should you take before assisting someone with an open wound?*

A pressure bandage may be used to maintain continuous pressure on a wound. *Identify a situation that would require the use of a pressure bandage.*

How to Apply a Pressure Bandage

Roller bandages can be used to maintain continuous pressure on a wound and control bleeding. A bandage applied snugly to the injured area will hold the dressing in place and facilitate blood clotting. To use a roller bandage:

▶ Place a dressing over the wound.

▶ Secure the roller bandage over the dressing.

▶ Using overlapping turns, cover the dressing completely, as shown in the diagram at the left.

▶ Secure the roller bandage in place by splitting its end into two strips. Tie the split bandage ends tightly over the wound.

▶ Make sure that the bandage is not so tight that it cuts off circulation. It should be just tight enough to maintain pressure on the wound.

Pressure Point Bleeding Control

If elevating the wound and applying a pressure bandage do not stop the bleeding, pressure point bleeding control must be used. This procedure involves pressing the main artery against a bone to stop blood supply to the injured area. Because this technique stops normal blood circulation, it should be used only when absolutely necessary. The diagram at the left shows the location of the points at which pressure should be applied when using this technique.

A person who requires pressure point bleeding control is seriously injured and possibly in shock. Professional medical assistance is necessary and should be consulted before this procedure is applied.

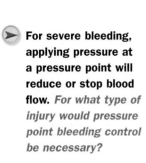

For severe bleeding, applying pressure at a pressure point will reduce or stop blood flow. *For what type of injury would pressure point bleeding control be necessary?*

Burns

Heat, radiation from the sun, certain chemicals, and electricity can all burn the skin and soft tissues of the body. Burns caused by heat are the most common. Those caused by chemicals or electricity require special first-aid procedures—for information on treating these types of burns, contact the American Red Cross.

Burns are classified according to depth: first-degree burns are superficial, and second- and third-degree burns are deep. Minor burns can be treated at home. Severe burns, however, require professional medical care. **Figure 28.2** shows the three classifications of burns and the treatment for each.

FIGURE 28.2

TYPES OF BURNS AND TREATMENT

The severity of the burn determines the type of burn and treatment.

First-degree burn	Second-degree burn	Third-degree burn
In a **first-degree burn,** only the outer layer of skin is burned and turns red. Cool the burn with cold running water or by immersing it in cold water (not ice) for 10 minutes. A clean, cold, wet towel will help reduce pain. Pat the area dry, and cover it with a sterile bandage.	A **second-degree burn** is one in which the top several layers of skin are damaged. The skin will have blisters and appear blotchy. Cool the burn with cold water (not ice), and elevate the burned area. Wrap the area loosely with a sterile, dry dressing. Do not pop blisters or peel loose skin. Seek professional medical attention.	A **third-degree burn** is a serious burn in which deeper layers of skin and possibly fat, muscle, nerves, and bone are damaged. Call for professional medical help immediately. Cool the burn with large amounts of cold water (not ice). Cover the area with a dry, sterile dressing or clean cloth.

LESSON 1 REVIEW

Reviewing Facts and Vocabulary

1. Define *first aid*.
2. Relate the nation's health goals and objectives to individual, family, and community health: Explain why knowing first-aid procedures can help achieve the goals of *Healthy People 2010*.
3. Why is it necessary to use universal precautions when giving first aid to a person who is bleeding?

Thinking Critically

4. **Synthesizing.** Analyze and develop a strategy for responding to an accidental injury such as a minor laceration.
5. **Analyzing.** Describe a strategy for responding to an accidental injury such as a second-degree burn.

Applying Health Skills

Communication Skills. What would you say to a teen who isn't sure why he or she should learn first aid? Write a dialogue in which you use effective communication skills to explain to the teen the importance of knowing first aid.

After You Read

Explain. Write a one-page summary describing the difference between the three types of burns. How would you identify a first-, second-, or third-degree burn? Include step-by-step information on what treatment you can provide someone who has been burned.

CPR and First Aid for Shock and Choking

Guide to Reading

Building Vocabulary

As you read this lesson, write each new highlighted term and its definition in your notebook.

▶ chain of survival (p. 742)

▶ defibrillator (p. 742)

▶ cardiopulmonary resuscitation (CPR) (p. 743)

▶ shock (p. 747)

Focusing on the Main Ideas

In this lesson, you will learn how to:

▶ Describe the steps for responding to life-threatening emergencies.

▶ Demonstrate strategies for responding to an emergency situation requiring CPR.

▶ Identify strategies for responding to a shock or choking victim.

Reading Strategy

Organize Information

▶ Make a three-column chart. In the first column, list the steps of CPR for adults and CPR for infants and children. In the second column, list the steps of first aid for shock. In the last column, list the steps of first aid for choking.

Quick Write

Write a paragraph describing what you know about CPR.

⚠ The increased availability of AEDs has led to improved survival rates for heart-attack victims.

In an emergency you need to act quickly—the first few minutes after a medical crisis are usually the most critical. The key is knowing what to do, remaining calm, and making a decision to act.

Life-Threatening Emergencies

If the victim in an emergency is unresponsive, you must begin immediately the **chain of survival**, *a sequence of actions that maximize the victim's chances of survival.* If the victim is an adult, you can begin the first two links in the chain: call 911 and begin CPR. The next two links, early defibrillation and transfer to advanced care, are usually the responsibility of the emergency medical personnel when they arrive. A **defibrillator** is *a device that delivers an electric shock to the heart to restore its normal rhythm.* An automated external defibrillator (AED) is a handheld device that almost anyone can be trained to use. AEDs have not been approved for use on children who are younger than eight years old or who weigh under 55 pounds.

CPR

A person whose breathing and heartbeat have stopped may need CPR. **Cardiopulmonary resuscitation (CPR)** is *a life-saving first-aid procedure that combines rescue breaths with chest compressions, supplying oxygen to the body until normal body functions can resume.* You must be properly trained by a professional and certified before administering CPR.

CPR for Adults

If an adult victim is unresponsive, tap him or her and ask in a loud voice, "Are you okay?" If the victim doesn't respond, start the chain of survival. First, call 911 or have someone else do so. Then kneel beside the victim and follow the steps developed by the American Heart Association, which are shown in **Figures 28.3** and **28.4** on page 744.

Reading Check

Define What is the chain of survival?

FIGURE 28.3

ADULT CPR

Check the airway. Look inside the victim's mouth. Remove anything you see blocking the airway. If you don't suspect head or neck injuries, lay the person flat on a firm surface. Gently tilt the head back by lifting the chin with one hand while pushing down on the forehead with the other. If you suspect head or neck injuries, do not move the victim. Open his or her airway by lifting the jaw instead.

Check breathing. Look, listen, and feel for breathing. *Look* for chest movement. *Listen* at the victim's mouth for breathing. *Feel* for exhaled air on your cheek. If the victim is not breathing normally, begin rescue breathing:

1. Keeping the victim's head in the proper position, pinch the nostrils shut.

2. Place your mouth over the victim's mouth, forming a seal. Give two slow breaths, each about 2 seconds long. The victim's chest should rise with each breath.

Begin chest compressions. A person trained in CPR should begin chest compressions immediately (see **Figure 28.4**). If the victim responds (coughs or moves, for example) but is still not breathing normally, give one rescue breath every 5 seconds.

FIGURE 28.4

ADULT CPR CYCLES

1 **Position your hands.** To begin chest compressions, find a spot on the lower half of the victim's breastbone, right between the nipples. Place the heel of one hand on that point, and interlock your fingers with the fingers of the other hand. Don't allow your fingers to rest on the victim's ribs.

2 **Begin chest compressions and rescue breathing.** Lean over the victim so that your shoulders are directly above your arms and hands. Lock your elbows and press straight down quickly and firmly at a rate of about 100 compressions per minute. Allow the chest to spring back between compressions. After every 30 compressions, give two rescue breaths. If the victim begins to respond, stop chest compressions. If the victim coughs or moves but is still not breathing, give one rescue breath every 5 seconds until help arrives. If the victim begins breathing normally, turn the victim onto his or her side and wait for professional medical help.

Resilient TEENS

When Mark Van Es was 15, his school counselor called him into her office for a talk. "She heard I was smoking and drinking," says Mark, "'Decide where you want to go in life and how you're going to get there,' she said. That really made me think."

Shortly thereafter, Mark became a First Responder. "I saw an entire family killed by a drunk driver who got up and walked away unhurt. That's when I realized that smoking and drinking were not for me."

"Decide where you want to go in life and how you're going to get there."

These days, Mark dreams of becoming the governor of his state. His parents have different political beliefs, but he's learned to listen carefully to both sides. "I'm always stuck in the middle," says Mark with a laugh. "Both my parents try to win me over. I just try to have an open mind."

To achieve his goals, Mark joined FCCLA, a nonprofit national organization that is teaching him valuable skills like team building and public speaking. "I'm seen as a little different around here," he says, "but that's okay. I've got a goal, and I know I'm gonna get there."

Reading Check

Explain How did focusing on the future help Mark avoid risky behaviors?

CPR for Infants and Children

Infants and children in life-threatening emergencies aren't treated in exactly the same way that adults are. For example, you shouldn't use an AED on an infant or a child. Likewise, you can't use the same amount of force in chest compressions. **Figures 28.5** and **28.6** on the next page show how to perform CPR on infants and children. These steps were developed by the American Heart Association. For an infant or a child, provide about one minute of CPR *before* calling 911 for help.

Reading Check

Compare and Contrast What are some of the differences in CPR treatment for adults, children, and infants?

FIGURE 28.5

THE ABCs OF INFANT AND CHILD CPR

A Airway. Look inside the victim's mouth. Remove anything you see blocking the airway. If you don't suspect head or neck injuries, lay the victim flat on a firm surface. Gently tilt the head back by lifting the chin with one hand while pushing down on the forehead with the other. If you suspect head or neck injuries, do not move the victim. Instead, open his or her airway by lifting the jaw.

B Breathing. Look, listen, and feel for breathing. *Look* for chest movement. *Listen* at the victim's mouth for breathing. *Feel* for exhaled air on your cheek. If the victim is not breathing, begin rescue breathing:

Keep the victim's head in position. For a child, pinch the nostrils shut and seal your mouth over the victim's mouth. For an infant, seal your mouth over the mouth and nose. Give two slow breaths, each about 1 to 1½ seconds long. The chest should rise with each breath.

C Circulation. Check for signs of circulation, such as breathing, coughing, or movement. If there are no signs of circulation, a person trained in CPR should begin chest compressions immediately (see **Figure 28.6**). If the victim responds (coughs or moves, for example) but is still not breathing normally, give two rescue breaths every 3 seconds for either a child or an infant.

FIGURE 28.6

INFANT AND CHILD CPR CYCLES

1 Position your hands. With one hand, keep the victim's head tilted, unless you suspect head or neck injury. For a child, place the heel of your other hand on the lower half of the breastbone and position your shoulder directly over your straightened arm and hand. For an infant, imagine a line drawn between the nipples. Place two or three fingers of your hand on the lower half of the infant's breastbone, about one finger's width below the imaginary nipple line.

2 Begin chest compressions and rescue breathing. Compress the victim's chest downward approximately one-third to one-half the depth of the chest at a rate of *about* 100 times per minute for a child, and *at least* 100 times per minute for an infant. Release pressure completely between compressions. After every 30 compressions, give two rescue breaths (see **Figure 28.5**). Complete 20 continuous cycles (just over 1 minute) of CPR. If the victim shows signs of circulation, stop chest compressions and continue rescue breathing if necessary (one rescue breath every 3 seconds).

First Aid for Shock

When something happens to reduce blood flow throughout the body, limiting the amount of oxygen carried to the cells, shock may occur. **Shock** is *a failure of the cardiovascular system to keep an adequate supply of blood circulating to the vital organs of the body.* This life-threatening emergency requires immediate medical attention. Common symptoms of shock include restlessness or irritability; altered consciousness; nausea; pale or ashen appearance; cool, moist skin; and rapid breathing and pulse. Knowing how to recognize shock, and what to do if shock occurs, shows that you know injury-prevention and injury-management strategies for personal, family, and community health.

If you suspect a head or spinal injury, don't move the victim. Otherwise, have the victim lie down if he or she has not already done so. This position often minimizes pain and keeps the victim calm. You should also:

▶ phone 911 or the local emergency number.

▶ control any external bleeding.

▶ elevate the legs about 12 inches, unless you suspect head or back injury or broken bones involving the legs or hips. If you aren't sure, leave the victim lying flat. This helps the blood return to the heart.

▶ never give the victim anything to eat or drink. Eating or drinking could cause vomiting.

▶ reassure the victim.

First Aid for Choking

Choking occurs when a person's airway becomes blocked by food or object. If the obstruction is not removed, the victim can die from lack of oxygen within a few minutes.

To help someone who is choking, you must first recognize the signs. A person may clutch his or her throat with one or both hands, which is the universal sign for choking. The victim may also cough weakly, make high-pitched sounds, or turn blue in the face. If someone appears to be choking but can cough forcefully or speak, do not attempt first aid. A strong cough can expel the object from the airway.

If you suspect that someone is choking, ask, "Are you choking?" and look for the universal choking sign. Then ask, "Can you speak?" If the person cannot speak in reply, the airway is completely blocked and the victim needs immediate first aid.

Did You Know

➤ An *In Case of Emergency,* or ICE, entry in your cell phone contact list can help emergency medical workers identify your next of kin in an emergency. Include the letters **ICE** before the name of a parent or guardian in your cell phone contact list to identify that person as your emergency contact.

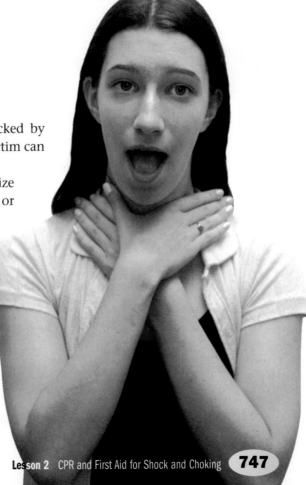

Ⓨ **Be alert for the universal choking sign.**

Use abdominal thrusts on a choking adult, but never on a choking infant. Use back blows alternating with chest thrusts for an infant. *Why do you think different methods are used for adults and infants?*

If the choking victim is an adult or a child, use abdominal thrusts—quick inward and upward pulls to the diaphragm—to force the obstruction out of the airway. To perform this procedure, stand behind the victim and place your arms around him or her. Make a fist with one hand, and grasp it with your other hand. Pull inward and upward just under the rib cage.

If you begin to choke while you are alone, use your own fist and hand to perform the procedure on yourself. You can also try pressing your abdomen forcefully against the back of a chair.

If the choking victim is an infant, hold the baby face down on your forearm. Support the infant's head and neck with your hand and point the head downward so that it is lower than the chest. With the heel of your hand, give the infant five blows between the shoulder blades. If the object is not dislodged, turn the infant over and perform five chest thrusts as described in the CPR section. Alternate the five blows between the shoulders with five chest thrusts until the object is dislodged or the infant begins to breathe or cough. Call 911 if the object is not dislodged within one minute. If the infant loses consciousness, phone 911 and begin CPR if you are trained and certified in the procedure.

LESSON 2 REVIEW

Reviewing Facts and Vocabulary

1. Define *cardiopulmonary resuscitation*.
2. Why should you never give a shock victim anything to eat or drink?
3. What is the universal sign for choking?

Thinking Critically

4. **Evaluating.** Explain why it's important to check the airway before beginning CPR.
5. **Analyzing.** Compare the strategy for responding to a choking adult with the strategy for responding to a choking infant.

Applying Health Skills

Advocacy. Make a video encouraging teens to learn basic first-aid techniques for choking and shock. Make the video available to your class.

After You Read

Problems and Solutions. Write a one-page skit showing what to do if a life-threatening emergency occurred at school or home. Include at least two characters and explain how your character identified the problem and what steps he or she took to help the victim.

Responding to Common Emergencies

Guide to Reading

Building Vocabulary

As you read this lesson, write each new highlighted term and its definition in your notebook.

▶ fracture (p. 750)

▶ unconsciousness (p. 751)

▶ concussion (p. 752)

Focusing on the Main Ideas

In this lesson, you will learn how to:

▶ Identify strategies for responding to muscle, joint, and bone injuries.

▶ Identify strategies for responding to injuries resulting in unconsciousness.

▶ Examine strategies for responding to injuries such as animal bites, nosebleeds, and foreign objects in the eye.

Reading Strategy

Problems and Solutions

▶ Make a T chart. On one side of the chart, list the five types of common emergencies. On the other side of the chart, list the solutions or strategies that can help prevent further injury for each type of emergency.

Quick Write

Write a paragraph describing how you would respond if a friend had a severe nosebleed.

Suppose that you and a friend are out jogging when your friend falls and sprains an ankle. How can you be sure that the injury is a sprain and not a fracture? Knowing the proper response strategies can help prevent further injury or complications. A health-literate individual also knows how to analyze situations requiring professional health services.

 Bone, muscle, and joint injuries can be serious, but they are usually not life threatening.

Muscle, Joint, and Bone Injuries

When too much stress is put on an area of the body, an injury may occur. These injuries vary in severity and can affect the bones, muscles, tendons, or ligaments. Some injuries, such as muscle strain, will usually feel better in a few days. Other injuries, such as a broken bone, may take several weeks to heal and require professional medical treatment for a full recovery to occur.

Applying ice to a sprain reduces swelling and eases pain. *Why is it a good idea to see a health care professional if you suspect that you have a sprain?*

Reading Check

Describe What is the P.R.I.C.E. procedure?

Muscle Cramps

A muscle cramp is the sudden and painful tightening of a muscle. Muscle cramps can occur when you are physically active or at rest. Some medications can also cause them. If a muscle cramp occurs:

▶ Stretch out the affected muscle to counteract the cramp.

▶ Massage the cramped muscle firmly.

▶ Apply moist heat to the area.

▶ Get medical help if the cramp persists.

Strains and Sprains

A strain is an injury to a muscle, usually resulting from overuse. The symptoms of a strain include pain, swelling, bruising, and loss of movement caused by small tears in the muscle. A sprain is an injury to a ligament. Sprains usually result from a sudden twisting force. Sprains also cause pain and swelling from badly stretched or torn ligaments. Minor sprains and strains may be treated with the **P.R.I.C.E.** procedure:

▶ **P**rotection—Protect the area from further injury.

▶ **R**est—Avoid any movements and activities that cause pain, including any use of the affected muscle or joint. Help the victim find a comfortable position.

▶ **I**ce—Ice helps reduce pain and swelling. Place ice cubes in a plastic bag, and wrap a towel or cloth around the bag. Hold the bag on the affected area for 20 minutes, remove it for 20 minutes, and then reapply it. Repeat this process every 3 waking hours over the course of 72 hours.

▶ **C**ompression—Light pressure from wearing an elastic wrap or bandage can help reduce swelling. The wrap should be firm but not uncomfortable.

▶ **E**levation—Raising the affected limb above the level of the heart helps reduce pain and swelling.

Fractures and Dislocations

Fractures and dislocations are similar. A **fracture** is *a break in the bone.* If a joint is under extreme stress, it may dislocate, or disconnect. First-aid procedures are the same for both fractures and dislocations. If possible, keep the victim still and call 911. If the victim must be moved, keep the fractured area immobilized by securing a splint to the body part with clean lengths of cloth. You can fashion a splint from everyday materials such as rolled newspapers and heavy cardboard. Seek professional medical care immediately.

Unconsciousness

Unconsciousness is *a condition in which a person is not alert and aware of his or her surroundings.* There are different levels of unconsciousness, ranging from drowsiness to coma. An unconscious victim can choke to death because of his or her inability to cough, clear the throat, or react to a blocked airway. The primary goal when providing first aid to an unconscious victim is to prevent choking until professional medical help arrives. If the victim is unconscious, place him or her in the recovery position shown in **Figure 28.7** and seek professional medical help immediately.

Fainting

Fainting occurs when the blood supply to the brain is temporarily inadequate. Loss of consciousness is usually brief. Although fainting doesn't always indicate a medical problem, it might be symptomatic of a serious disorder. Treat fainting as a medical emergency until the symptoms are relieved and the cause is known.

If you feel faint, lie down or sit down and place your head between your knees. If someone else faints, position the person on his or her back with legs elevated 8 to 12 inches above the heart unless you suspect head or neck injury. Do not place a pillow under the person's head. This can block airflow. Loosen any tight clothing. Sponge the person's face with water. Do not splash water on the face; this may cause the person to choke. If the person vomits, quickly roll him or her into the recovery position shown in **Figure 28.7** to prevent choking. If the person fails to revive promptly, seek medical help.

CHARACTER CHECK

Citizenship. If you see someone who has just suffered an injury, don't assume that someone else will stop and help. Everyone else might be making that same assumption. **Be a responsible member of your community. If you see someone who needs medical assistance, do what you can to help, even if all you can do is call 911.**

FIGURE 28.7

THE RECOVERY POSITION

The recovery position is the safest placement for an unconscious person because the airway is protected. Put the person in the recovery position only if no spinal or head injury is suspected.

This position helps an unconscious person breathe and allows fluids such as blood and vomit to drain. Do not move a person if you suspect spinal or head injuries. Movement can worsen these injuries.

Reading Check

Explain Why is the recovery position the safest placement for an unconscious person (Figure 28.7)?

Concussion

A **concussion** is *a jarring injury to the brain that affects normal brain function.* Even if there are no external signs of injury, the brain can strike the inside of the skull and be damaged. To avoid causing spinal injury, do not move an unconscious victim if you suspect a head injury or concussion. Check the person's airway, breathing, and circulation, and get professional medical help immediately. If you suspect that a person has a concussion:

▶ Have a conscious victim lie down.

▶ Use first aid for any bleeding.

▶ If the victim is unconscious and you do not suspect head or neck injury, place him or her in the recovery position, as shown in **Figure 28.7** on page 751. Call 911 immediately.

Animal Bites

One of the most serious possible consequences of an animal bite is rabies, a viral disease of the nervous system that if left untreated eventually causes paralysis and death. There is no cure for rabies after symptoms develop. However, if a person is vaccinated promptly after being bitten, he or she can develop immunity before symptoms appear.

When someone is bitten, report the incident to your community health department or animal control department. It's important to determine whether the animal has rabies. If you find the animal, do not try to capture it. Give its description and location to the proper authorities or the police. The animal will be captured for testing and observation.

Animal bites also carry the risk of infection, including tetanus, an often fatal disease. Although tetanus can be treated, the treatment is long, difficult, and often unsuccessful. Tetanus can be prevented, however, by keeping your immunizations up to date. First aid strategies for animal bites includes the following:

▶ Wash the bite area with mild soap and warm water for five minutes to remove saliva and any other foreign matter.

▶ Use direct pressure or pressure point bleeding control to stop any bleeding.

▶ If the wound is swollen, apply ice wrapped in a towel for 10 minutes.

▶ Cover the wound with a clean dressing or bandage.

Never approach a strange dog. Always ask the owner's permission before approaching or touching a dog that you do not know. *What two diseases are associated with animal bites?*

Nosebleeds

Nosebleeds often occur if the nose is struck or if the mucous membranes in the nose dry out from breathing dry air. Seek professional medical attention if nosebleeds occur often.

To treat a nosebleed, keep the person quiet. Walking, talking, and blowing the nose may increase bleeding. Tell the person to breathe through his or her mouth. Have the person sit down and lean forward. Do not tilt the person's head back—doing so may cause the person to choke as blood runs down the back of the throat. Using a protective barrier, press on the bleeding nostril. Maintain pressure for 15 minutes. If the person's nose is still bleeding after 15 minutes, repeat the procedure. If bleeding continues, seek professional medical help.

Applying direct pressure to a nosebleed usually stops the bleeding. *Why might dry air cause a nosebleed?*

Hands-On Health ACTIVITY

First-Aid Stations

In this activity you will set up learning stations for common emergencies and rotate through them.

What You'll Need

- pen or pencil and notebook paper
- poster board and markers
- props (optional)

What You'll Do

1. In small groups, research the following information for the emergency assigned by your teacher:
   - how to recognize it
   - appropriate steps to take in the correct sequence
   - what to do after first aid has been provided

2. Decide on a creative way to present your material at a learning station, such as a poster, a board game, a quiz show, a puzzle, a news story, or demonstrations with props such as bandages.

3. Each group will set up a learning station. One person in each group coordinates the activities at each learning station while all other students rotate through the stations. Group members take turns supervising their station.

Apply and Conclude

Write a script for a skit about a teen or a group of teens who encounter a medical emergency. The script should show one teen experiencing the emergency while the others administer proper first aid.

Object in the Eye

Foreign objects such as dirt, sand, and slivers of wood or metal that enter the eye are irritating and can cause damage. Encourage the victim not to rub the eye, an action that may scratch the cornea, but to blink several times. If blinking does not dislodge the object, try to find it in the eye. First, wash your hands. Gently pull the lower eyelid down while the person looks up. If you don't see anything, hold the upper lid open and examine the eye while the person looks down. If you see the object on the surface of the eye, lightly touch it with a moistened cotton swab or the corner of a clean cloth.

You can also flush the eye with sterile saline solution or tap water. If the person is wearing contact lenses, do not remove the lens before flushing the eye. To flush the eye, tilt the person's head to the side so that the affected eye is lower than the unaffected eye. Gently hold the eye open with one hand. With the other hand, pour a steady stream of cool water into the eye, from the inside corner toward the outside corner. The water should wash over the surface of the eye. Seek professional medical help if the object is not removed.

▼ **To flush an object out of your own eye, gently pour water from a small clean glass into the eye.**

LESSON 3 REVIEW

Reviewing Facts and Vocabulary

1. What is a *fracture?*
2. What is the primary goal when providing first aid to an unconscious person?
3. What are two common causes of nosebleeds?

Thinking Critically

4. **Analyzing.** While hiking with you, a friend stumbles on a tree root and falls. By the time you get home, her ankle is badly swollen and she can't walk without leaning on you. Analyze and describe the strategy you would use to respond to this accidental injury.
5. **Evaluating.** Why should you seek professional medical care if a sprain or strain doesn't improve or if you suspect that the injury might be a fracture?

Applying Health Skills

Accessing Information. Use online and print resources to find additional information about rabies. Using the information you have obtained, write a newspaper article about giving first aid to someone who has been bitten by an animal, including how to prevent rabies.

After You Read

Problems and Solutions. Draw a poster or create a brochure showing what to do if a muscle, bone, or joint injury occurs. Include step-by-step instructions describing how to help the injured person. Include information describing when it's advised to seek medical attention.

Visit **health.glencoe.com** for the Interactive Study Guide for Lesson 3.

Treatment for Poisonings

Guide to Reading

Building Vocabulary

As you read this lesson, write each new highlighted term and its definition in your notebook.

▶ poison (p. 755)

▶ venom (p. 755)

▶ poison control center (p. 755)

Focusing on the Main Ideas

In this lesson, you will learn how to:

▶ Examine strategies for responding to injuries such as poisonings.

▶ Identify strategies for responding to injuries such as bites and stings.

▶ Identify strategies for responding to injuries caused by contact with poisonous plants.

Reading Strategy

Predict

▶ Scan the headings, subheadings, and photo captions. Write a summary describing what you currently know about the dangers of poisons in the home.

Quick Write

Write a paragraph describing what you would do if you were hiking and came into contact with a poisonous plant.

Knowing how to respond to accidental poisoning injuries is an important part of first aid. A **poison** is *any substance—solid, liquid, or gas—that causes injury, illness, or death when introduced into the body.* Approximately 90 percent of poisonings occur in the home, and more than half of these poisonings involve children under the age of six.

Types of Poisoning

Poisoning results when substances that are not meant to enter the body do so. The substance could be a chemical that is swallowed, a pesticide that is absorbed through the skin, or **venom**, *a poisonous substance secreted by a snake, spider, or other creature,* that is injected into the body through a sting or bite. Even certain plants and foods can be poisonous. Gases or vapors may also be poisonous, such as carbon monoxide from hot water heaters and furnaces, exhaust fumes from automobiles, and fumes from gas- or oil-burning stoves. Your poison control center can tell you the correct procedure to follow in the event of a poisoning. A **poison control center** is *a 24-hour hot line that provides emergency medical advice on treating poisoning victims.*

Many household products become poisons if they are used incorrectly.
Where can you find information about the toxicity of various household products?

Poison can enter the body in four ways: ingestion, inhalation, absorption, and injection. *What can you do to prevent accidental poisonings?*

First Aid for Poisoning

Proper treatment of poisoning requires professional guidance. The best resource in handling poison emergencies is the local poison control center. Have the phone number of your poison control center posted near your phone.

Time is critical when a poisoning has occurred. Some poisoning situations require quick action to minimize the amount of damage to the victim or to prevent death. First, call 911 for help. Then practice these first-aid strategies for poisonings.

▶ **Swallowed poisons** vary in their first-aid treatment because the substances that can be swallowed affect the body differently. Quickly try to determine what was swallowed, and call your poison control center. Follow the instructions given to you. It is important that you call the poison control center first. You may be instructed to give the victim something that dilutes the poison, such as milk or water, or you may be directed to induce vomiting. Do not try to induce vomiting unless you are told to do so. Some poisons can be aspirated into the lungs and cause even more damage; others can burn the esophagus if the victim vomits.

▶ **Inhaled poison** is serious because of the damage that can be done to the lungs and other organs of the respiratory system. Quickly get the person to fresh air. Do not breathe in the fumes. If the victim is not breathing, start rescue breathing.

▶ **Poison on the skin** must be removed as quickly as possible to limit the exposure to the body. Remove contaminated clothing. Rinse skin continuously with water for 15 minutes. Then rinse the skin with mild soap and water. Rinse again with fresh water. If possible, have someone call 911 while you are rinsing the skin.

▶ **Poison in the eye** is absorbed quickly. Immediately start flushing the eye with lukewarm water and continue for 15 minutes. Have the victim blink the eye as much as possible while flooding the eye. Do not force the eye open, and do not rub the eye. Have someone call 911 while you are rinsing the eye.

When you call the poison control center:

▶ Be prepared to give your name, location, and telephone number.

▶ Provide the name of the substance, when it was ingested, and the amount involved. If possible, give the brand name of the product and a list of the ingredients.

▶ Describe the state of the victim, as well as his or her age and weight.

▶ Be prepared to follow instructions and answer any questions.

Real-Life Application

Contacting a Poison Control Center

Poisonous products often display warning labels that provide instructions on what to do if someone swallows, inhales, or has skin or eye contact with the product. For cases of poisoning in which the specific product is known, use this information when you contact the poison control center.

The WORKS Toilet Bowl Cleaner

WARNING: KEEP OUT OF REACH OF CHILDREN
CONTAINS: HYDROXYACETIC ACID ✦

FIRST AID:
If in eyes: Hold eye open and rinse slowly and gently with water for 15–20 minutes.
Remove contact lenses, if present, after the first five minutes, ✦ and then continue rinsing eye.
If on skin or clothing: Remove contaminated clothing. ✦
Rinse skin immediately with plenty of water for 15–20 minutes.
If swallowed: Have person sip a glass of water if he or she is able to swallow.
Do not induce vomiting unless told to do so by a poison control center. ✦
Do not give anything by mouth to an unconscious person. ✦

Why is it important for a poison control center to know the specific poison?

Why should you remove contact lenses if a chemical has entered the eye?

Why must contaminated clothing be removed at once?

What is a poison control center? Where is the one nearest you?

Why is it dangerous to give an unconscious person something to drink?

ACTIVITY

With a partner, role-play a scenario that involves contacting a poison control center when a child has ingested the product shown above. Write your dialogue, and then practice asking and giving information clearly and calmly. One of you will be the caller; the other will be a health professional at the poison control center. The latter will ask for the caller's name and telephone number, as well as questions about

- the child's condition, age, and weight.
- the suspected poison and what instructions/warnings/ingredients appear on the label.
- the time the poisoning may have occurred.
- what first aid the caller may have already provided.

Conclude the role-play with what you think the health professional might tell the caller to do. Then switch roles and repeat the role-play.

FIGURE 28.8

FIRST AID FOR SNAKEBITE

Use the following steps to administer first aid to a snakebite victim:

- Get the victim to a hospital. This is the most important step. Keep the victim calm and in a reclining position, if possible. The more the victim moves, the greater the risk that venom will circulate throughout the body.

- Keep the bitten area at or below the level of the heart. If the bitten area is on a limb, immobilize that limb.

- Call 911, or have someone else do so. Follow any instructions that are given.

- Do not apply ice or heat. Applying heat will diffuse the venom more rapidly. Applying ice will cause tissue damage. Also, do not give the victim aspirin or other drugs. Some substances can interact dangerously with the venom or thin the blood, causing the venom to spread more rapidly into tissues.

- Maintain breathing and prevent aggravation of the wound. If you are the victim of a snakebite and are alone, walk slowly and rest periodically to help minimize blood circulation.

First Aid for Poisonous Bites and Stings

Insect and animal stings and bites are among the most common sources of injected poisonings. A poisonous bite or sting can come from several sources, including insects, spiders, ticks, scorpions, snakes, marine life, and other animals.

Snakebite

There are about 20 species of venomous snakes in the United States. Most are rattlesnakes, copperheads, coral snakes, and water moccasins (also called cottonmouths). Usually, the bite of a venomous snake is not fatal; however, a bite can cause severe pain, loss of function, and, in rare situations, loss of a limb. The first-aid procedures for snakebite are found in **Figure 28.8.**

Insect Bites and Stings

Some insects, such as the bee, hornet, yellow jacket, wasp, and fire ant, cause painful stings that can produce a strong allergic reaction. For people who are highly allergic to the venom of these insects even one sting can cause a life-threatening condition. These people need immediate medical attention if they are stung. It's important to develop and identify the priorities in responding to medical emergencies. However, for most people, insect bites are uncomfortable but not life threatening. Follow these first-aid procedures for insect bites and stings:

Reading Check

Define What is poison?

- Move to a safe area to avoid further harm. Try to remove the stinger by scraping it off with a firm, sharp-edged object such as a credit card or fingernail.

- Wash the area with mild soap and water to help prevent infection. To reduce pain and swelling, apply a cold compress. Apply hydrocortisone cream, calamine lotion, or a baking soda paste to the area several times a day until the pain is gone.

- If the victim was bitten by a venomous spider or scorpion and begins to have trouble breathing or shows other signs of a severe reaction, call 911 immediately.

These are common poisonous plants.

Poison Oak

Poison Ivy

Poison Sumac

First Aid for Poisonous Plants

About 85 percent of Americans will develop an allergic skin reaction if exposed to poison ivy, poison oak, or poison sumac. Symptoms include blistering, swelling, burning, and itching at the point of contact, and the person may develop fever.

The first defense against poisonous plants is to recognize and avoid them. If you come into contact with a poisonous plant, remove contaminated clothing. Flush affected areas with water, and then wash thoroughly with soap and water. Certain over-the-counter preparations can be used to wash the affected areas. If a rash develops, use calamine lotion to relieve the itching. For severe discomfort or pain, seek medical attention.

LESSON 4 REVIEW

Reviewing Facts and Vocabulary

1. Define the terms *poison* and *venom.*

2. What information should you have ready when you call a poison control center?

3. Analyze and describe the strategy for responding to accidental injuries such as insect bites and stings.

Thinking Critically

4. **Analyzing.** Analyze and describe a strategy for preventing an accidental poisoning injury in your kitchen.

5. **Synthesizing.** Develop a list of items needed to administer first aid to a bee-sting victim who is not allergic to bee venom.

Applying Health Skills

Practicing Healthful Behaviors. Prepare a pamphlet that shows the first-aid procedures for responding to poisonings. Include each type of poisoning mentioned in this lesson. Make your pamphlet available to other students in your school.

After You Read

Problems and Solutions. Make a T chart. Label one side Problem, and list the types of poisoning. Label the other side Solution, and list the strategies for responding to the types of poisoning.

Visit **health.glencoe.com** for the Interactive Study Guide for Lesson 4.

Lesson 4 Treatment for Poisonings **759**

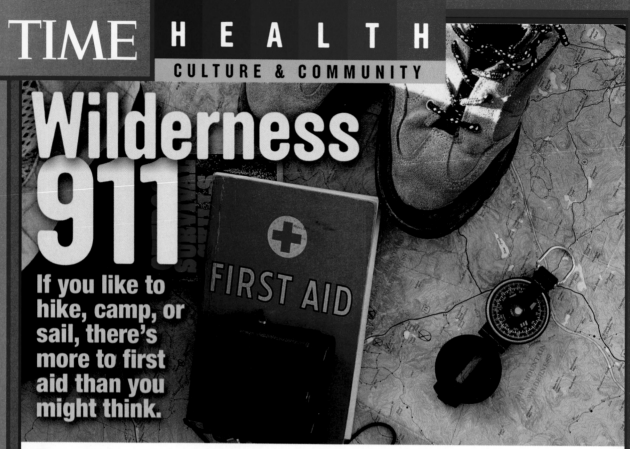

TIME HEALTH

CULTURE & COMMUNITY

Wilderness 911

If you like to hike, camp, or sail, there's more to first aid than you might think.

For many teens, camping is a great way to relax and have fun with family and friends. While the nearby state park may not be back-country, medical help isn't always nearby. So a quick class on wilderness first aid might be what the doctor ordered—especially when the nearest hospital is more than an hour away.

Why "an hour or more"? Doctors have identified a "golden hour" just after accidents, heart attacks, and other emergencies in which they can do the most to save lives.

Learning the Rules

Practicing wilderness first aid ensures that at least some of the benefits of treatment within the golden hour are not lost. In urban first aid, for example, you're taught to splint a suspected sprain, strain, or fracture as close as you can to the position you found it in. Under wilderness conditions, you need to be alert to the possibility that nerves or the blood supply in the affected limb may have been cut off. For that reason, you must pull gently and straighten out the limb before splinting to restore circulation and

sensation. Otherwise, the accident victim could permanently lose use of that arm or leg. As a rule, if you're not seriously injured and you know your way back and can move under your own power, it's better to hike out than wait for rescue.

A good first-aid class will stress prevention. For example, make sure to carry plenty of food, water, and extra clothes—even if you're just out for the afternoon. A sudden change in the weather or a broken leg could turn your stroll into an uncomfortable night outdoors. That's why you should take something to insulate you from the ground and prevent hypothermia. ◼

TIME to THINK... | About Wilderness Safety

The article mentions the condition *hypothermia*. Create a first-aid pamphlet with the class that describes symptoms, prevention, and treatment of hypothermia. Make sure you include specific information. Would you feel confident in giving the pamphlet to a friend who was going camping?

Health Skills Application

ADVOCACY

1. Advocacy. Prepare a talk that encourages younger students in your community to learn first aid. Compile lists of local emergency telephone numbers for distribution. *(LESSON 1)*

ANALYZING INFLUENCES

2. Analyzing Influences. Evaluate the effect of technology on first aid. For example, what techniques and capabilities are available today that were not available 50 years ago? *(LESSON 2)*

ACCESSING INFORMATION

3. Accessing Information. Research to learn whether your state has a high incidence of rabies and what measures are taken to keep the disease under control. *(LESSON 3)*

PRACTICING HEALTHFUL BEHAVIORS

4. Practicing Healthful Behaviors. Find out which poisonous plants are in your area, how they can be recognized, and what to do in case of exposure to them. Use what you have learned to create a teaching tool, such as a poster or a comic book, for elementary school children. *(LESSON 4)*

CAREER Corner

Emergency Physician

Can you make fast and accurate decisions? As an emergency physician, you often have to make quick diagnoses under extreme conditions. You also need to be able to communicate.

To become an emergency physician, you need a four-year college degree and a medical degree. After finishing medical school, you'll need one year of internship and two to three years of residency. Find out more about this and other health careers by clicking on Career Corner at **health.glencoe.com.**

BEYOND *the* Classroom

Parent Involvement

Accessing Information. Learn more about where members of your community can become certified in CPR. With your parents, find out how your family can become involved in promoting CPR certification for everyone. If classes are not available in your community, find out how you can arrange for someone to provide classes in your community.

School and Community

CPR Certification. Train to become certified in CPR. Then research to find out how you can volunteer to help teach others the life-saving techniques of CPR.

After You Read

Use the notes you have taken in your Foldable to review what you have learned about the three Cs. On the back of your Foldable, record what you have learned about different types of injuries.

FOLDABLES ™
Study Organizer

► EXPLORING HEALTH TERMS
Answer the following questions on a sheet of paper.

Lesson 1 *Match each definition with the correct term.*

universal precautions   first aid

1. The immediate, temporary care given to an ill or injured person until professional medical care can be provided.

2. Actions taken to prevent the spread of disease by treating all blood and other body fluids as though they contained pathogens.

Lesson 2 *Match each definition with the correct term.*

defibrillator   shock
chain of survival
cardiopulmonary resuscitation

3. A failure of the cardiovascular system to keep an adequate supply of blood circulating to the vital organs of the body.

4. A device that delivers an electric shock to the heart to restore its normal rhythm.

5. A sequence of actions that maximize the victim's chances of survival.

Lesson 3 *Fill in the blanks with the correct term.*

concussion   unconsciousness
fracture

A blow to the head can cause a (**_6_**), which is a jarring injury to the brain, without actually causing (**_7_**). If the blow is hard enough, it can cause a skull (**_8_**).

Lesson 4 *Fill in the blanks with the correct term.*

venom   poison
poison control center

A (**_9_**) provides emergency medical advice on treating poisoning victims. Snake (**_10_**) is a (**_11_**) when it is introduced into the human body.

► RECALLING THE FACTS
Use complete sentences to answer the following questions.

1. What are two universal precautions that a person should follow when giving first aid to another person?

2. What are the first three things you should do when you recognize an emergency situation?

3. What are the four types of open wounds?

4. What is the chain of survival for adults?

5. What are the ABCs of CPR?

6. What are the symptoms of shock?

7. What is the first-aid procedure for a person who has a muscle cramp?

8. What is the first-aid procedure for a person who has fainted?

9. Why is the recovery position the safest position for a person who is unconscious?

10. What is the first-aid procedure for a person who has inhaled poison?

11. What is the first-aid procedure for poison in the eye?

12. Why is it important to wash a poisonous bite or sting with mild soap and water?

---

762 **Chapter 28** Review

For more review questions for Chapter 28, go to **health.glencoe.com**.

► WRITING CRITICALLY

1. Descriptive. Write a one-page summary describing a situation in which a teen must administer first aid to another person who is bleeding. Describe the steps the teen must take to care for the injury.

2. Narrative. Write a one-page story about a young child who may have swallowed a poisonous substance. Describe the steps that should be taken to respond to the situation. In your story, be sure to present interesting characters, and include a setting, a plot, and dialogue.

Standardized Test Practice

 Read the passage below and then answer the questions.

Tornado Hits School

BROWNWOOD, TEXAS — At South Elementary today, a tornado touched down, injuring a teacher. The tornado also broke windows and damaged trees. Later, it touched down about one mile from the school. A convenience store and several homes were damaged.

When the twister touched down near the elementary school, it injured a teacher who was standing outside the building. Thirty children under the supervision of the physical education teacher were outside on a playground adjacent to the building. Because the playground was next to the building, the instructor rushed the children into the building as soon as she heard the tornado alarm. The kids hurried to hallways in the center of the building before the tornado hit. The storm broke the school's front door and most of its windows.

"We are thankful that no students were injured in the storm," said Principal Jennifer Rodriguez.

The teacher, Tyrone Rasco, was not so lucky. According to witnesses, the storm swirled him nearly 10 feet into the air, then dropped him suddenly. He was covered in mud and was bleeding from a small cut on his head. According to Ms. Rodriguez, he is listed in satisfactory condition at Regional Hospital. "We hope he can return to school soon," she said.

"Counselors are available to students who need to talk about today's event," added the principal.

1. What was the author's purpose in writing this article?

(A) to describe the damage that a tornado caused at a school
(B) to report about the actions of the physical education teacher
(C) to explain why all people should stay inside during tornados
(D) to inform the public that tornado warning systems are important

2. Which word or phrase has the same meaning as the words *adjacent to* in this sentence from the article?

Thirty children under the supervision of the physical education teacher were outside on a playground adjacent to the building.

(F) next to
(G) nearby
(H) far from
(I) underneath

3. Write an article that focuses on an aspect of the tornado that the first article does not.

Environmental Health

Environmental Health in the News

Different print media sources may vary in the way a story is covered. The information in two articles on the same topic may differ for the following reasons:

► Different sources were interviewed.

► The writer or editor may be biased.

► The regional versus national perspective may differ.

Visit the Eye on the Media section at health.glencoe.com to learn more about differences in reporting environmental health news.

Study Organizer

Before You Read

Make this Foldable study guide to record and collect information on air quality and types of pollution. Begin with a sheet of 11" x 17" paper.

► **Step 1**

Fold a sheet of paper into thirds.

► **Step 2**

Unfold. Fold 2" of the bottom side of the paper upward. Glue or staple the sides of the fold to form pockets.

► **Step 3**

Label as shown. Place 3" x 5" notecards or pieces of paper inside the pockets.

Air Pollution	Indoor Air Pollution	Noise Pollution

As You Read

As you read and discuss the material in the chapter, use your Foldable to record and define terms, identify and explain each type of pollution, and list possible causes and effects.

SPOTLIGHT ON HEALTH

Using Visuals. Taking care of the environment is everyone's responsibility. In what specific ways do you and your family actively take part in protecting the environment?

Air Quality

Guide to Reading

Building Vocabulary

As you read this lesson, write each new highlighted term and its definition in your notebook.

► air pollution (p. 766)
► smog (p. 767)
► Air Quality Index (AQI) (p. 768)
► asbestos (p. 769)
► radon (p. 769)
► noise pollution (p. 770)
► decibel (p. 770)

Focusing on the Main Ideas

In this lesson, you will learn how to:

► Analyze the nation's environmental health goals and objectives.
► Identify sources of air pollution and strategies for reducing it.
► Examine information relating to a variety of critical environmental health issues.

Reading Strategy

Cause and Effect

► Use your Foldable at the start of the chapter to organize the material in the chapter into three parts. Identify each type of pollution, and list the causes and effects for each.

Write a paragraph explaining how you think breathing polluted air could negatively affect your health.

 Air quality affects all living organisms, including humans. *Why is it important to alert the public when air pollution levels are extremely high?*

Modern technology has improved our lives. However, the pollution of air, land, and water that may result from technological advances can harm the environment and individual health. An informed individual understands the impact of technology on personal, family, and community health.

Air Pollution

Air pollution is linked to an estimated 50,000 to 120,000 premature deaths each year. One goal of *Healthy People 2010* is to reduce the proportion of persons exposed to air that does not meet the U.S. Environmental Protection Agency's (EPA) health-based standards for ozone, a major component of air pollution.

Air pollution is *the contamination of the earth's atmosphere by substances that pose a health threat to living things.* The EPA monitors air quality and sets U.S. air quality standards. The agency has identified five major air pollutants whose levels need to be regulated in order to have cleaner air nationwide. These pollutants are described in **Figure 29.1.**

Take the Health Inventory for Chapter 29 at **health.glencoe.com.**

FIGURE 29.1

FIVE COMMON AIR POLLUTANTS

The EPA has set national air quality standards for these pollutants.

Air Pollutant	Sources	Primary Health Concerns
Ozone (O_3) is a gas composed of three oxygen atoms. Ground-level ozone is a major component of **smog**, *a yellow-brown haze that forms when sunlight reacts with air pollution.*	O_3 forms from a chemical reaction between nitrogen oxide compounds and volatile organic compounds (VOCs). Motor vehicle exhaust, industrial emissions, gasoline vapors, and chemical solvents are the primary sources of nitrogen oxides and VOCs.	O_3 can irritate and inflame lung airways. It is linked to aggravated asthma, reduced lung capacity, and increased susceptibility to respiratory illnesses such as pneumonia and bronchitis.
Particulate Matter (PM) is a general term for particles such as dust, dirt, soot, smoke, mold, and liquid droplets that are found in the air.	PM may be emitted directly into the air from sources such as motor vehicle exhaust and factories. PM may also form in the air through chemical reactions between gases.	PM is linked to aggravated asthma, chronic bronchitis, decreased lung function, and premature death.
Carbon Monoxide (CO) is a colorless, odorless gas that contains carbon and oxygen. It is formed when carbon in fuel is not burned completely.	Outdoor sources of CO include motor vehicle exhaust and industrial processes. Indoor sources include gas stoves, cigarette smoke, and unvented gas and kerosene space heaters.	CO is poisonous. It prevents the body from receiving the oxygen it needs. It affects people with heart disease and can harm the central nervous system. Large quantities are fatal.
Sulfur Dioxide (SO_2) is a gas made up of sulfur and oxygen. It dissolves in water to form an acid, and it reacts with other gases in the air to form sulfates and other harmful particles.	SO_2 is formed when fuel that contains sulfur (such as coal and oil) is burned, when gasoline is extracted from oil, and when metals are extracted from their ores.	SO_2 contributes to respiratory illnesses and aggravates existing heart and lung diseases.
Nitrogen Oxides (NO_X) is a general term for a group of highly reactive gases that contain varying amounts of nitrogen and oxygen.	These substances form when fuel is burned at high temperatures. Primary sources include motor vehicles and electric utilities.	Nitrogen oxides help form ground-level ozone. They form particles that cause or trigger serious respiratory problems.

Reducing Air Pollution

The Clean Air Act of 1990 regulates the five pollutants described in Figure 29.1. Even with such laws in place, air quality can vary. The **Air Quality Index (AQI)**, developed by the EPA, is *an index for reporting daily air quality.* Shown in **Figure 29.2,** the AQI informs the public about local air quality and whether air pollution levels pose health risks. A health-literate individual understands how public health policies and government regulations influence health conditions.

You and your family can take the following actions to help reduce air pollution.

▶ **Reduce car use.** Walk or bicycle, take public transportation, or carpool to your destination.

▶ **Conserve energy.** Turn off lights when not in use. Set the air conditioner at a higher temperature. Put on extra layers of clothing instead of turning up the heat.

▶ **Use air-friendly machinery.** Small motors such as those found on mowers, chain saws, and leaf blowers emit pollutants. Use manual machinery when possible.

Reading Check

Describe What are some of the actions you and your family can take to reduce air pollution?

FIGURE 29.2

AIR QUALITY INDEX (AQI)

The AQI alerts people to possible health effects of breathing polluted air.

Range	Air Quality	Color Code
0 to 50	**Good:** There is little or no health risk.	Green
51 to 100	**Moderate:** Some pollutants may pose a health concern for a small number of individuals.	Yellow
101 to 150	**Unhealthy for Sensitive Groups:** Unless a person has specific health concerns, pollution levels in this range are not likely to cause health problems.	Orange
151 to 200	**Unhealthy:** All individuals may experience some minor negative effects.	Red
201 to 300	**Very Unhealthy:** More serious effects may be felt by all individuals.	Purple
301 to 500	**Hazardous:** Entire population is at risk.	Maroon

Indoor Air Pollution

Most people spend about 90 percent of their time indoors. EPA studies indicate that indoor levels of certain pollutants may be 2 to 5 times—and on occasion more than 100 times—higher than outdoor levels. Sources of indoor air pollution include building and furnishing materials such as carpeting and furniture made of certain pressed woods. Another source is old insulation containing **asbestos** (as-BES-tuhs), *a fibrous mineral that has fireproof properties*. When materials containing asbestos deteriorate, tiny fibers of the mineral are released into the air. Household cleaning products and other chemicals also contribute to indoor air pollution. Another major source is the particles and gases that form as a result of combustion. Stoves, furnaces, fireplaces, heaters, and tobacco smoke can all contaminate indoor air. Inadequate ventilation increases the problem. Energy-efficient homes may have so little air exchange that pollutants build up to dangerous levels.

Health Concerns of Indoor Air Pollution

The effects of indoor air pollution depend on the contaminant and the length of exposure. Immediate health concerns include irritation of the eyes, nose, and throat; headaches; dizziness; and fatigue. Long-term exposure to some pollutants can cause asthma. Exposure to lead, especially in children, can damage the kidneys, liver, brain, and nerves. Asbestos has been linked to lung cancer, especially in people who smoke. High levels of carbon monoxide can cause death.

The EPA estimates that **radon**, *an odorless, radioactive gas,* causes at least 14,000 lung cancer deaths per year. Radon is produced during the natural breakdown of the element uranium in soil, rocks, and water. It can seep into a house through cracks in the foundation. Home testing is the only way to assess exposure to radon. Homes with high levels of radon require increased indoor-outdoor air exchange. Some may need structural work to reduce radon levels.

Managing Indoor Air Pollution

To manage indoor air pollution, you must first identify the contaminants. Often, removing or replacing an object or appliance and providing sufficient indoor-outdoor air exchange will solve the problem. Make sure that hot water heaters and furnaces are properly vented and operating efficiently to avoid a buildup of carbon monoxide. Many families have installed carbon monoxide detectors to warn of a toxic buildup. Similar detectors are available for radon. Homeowners who discover the presence of asbestos or lead should seek professional help in removing these contaminants.

What is sick building syndrome?

The term *sick building syndrome* (SBS) refers to a situation in which the occupants of a building experience health problems that seem to be linked to the atmosphere within the building. Symptoms of SBS include headache; itchy and irritated eyes, throat, or nose; dizziness and nausea; fatigue; inability to concentrate; and a sensitivity to odors. SBS sufferers often report relief soon after leaving the building.

HEALTH Online

TOPIC Indoor Air Pollution

Go to **health.glencoe.com** and click on Web Links for information on ways to minimize indoor air pollution.

ACTIVITY List five ways a person can help minimize indoor air pollution. Share your findings with the class.

Real-Life Application

Indoor Air Pollution and Asthma: What You Can Do

The incidence of asthma in people of all ages is increasing. Indoor air pollution has been identified as a major contributor to this increase. Study the graph, answer the questions on the right, and then complete the activity.

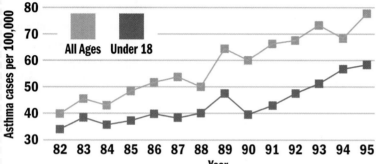

Estimated Number of Asthma Cases

All Ages   Under 18

Asthma cases per 100,000

80
70
60
50
40
30

82 83 84 85 86 87 88 89 90 91 92 93 94 95

Year

Source: National Center for Health Statistics, National Health Survey, 1982–1995

Work with a small group. Use reliable library and online sources to investigate additional measures that can improve indoor air quality. Cite your sources, and provide an explanation of why each source is reliable.

What can be done to reduce the levels of such triggers as dust and pet dander in the home?

In the 1960s children and teens were outside at least three hours each day. Today, they are outside less than two hours each day. How might these facts relate to the increase in asthma?

Today's homes allow less air to circulate. How might this contribute to the increase in asthma? What can be done to increase ventilation?

Tobacco smoke is one of the leading contributors to asthma attacks. How can exposure to tobacco smoke be limited or prevented?

Reading Check

Define What is noise pollution?

Noise Pollution

Traffic, loud music, and power tools such as mowers and construction equipment are all sources of noise pollution. **Noise pollution** is *harmful and unwanted sound of sufficient intensity to damage hearing.* Hearing impairment caused by noise rarely leads to total deafness; however, the hearing loss is permanent, and hearing aids often do not compensate for the damage.

A **decibel** is *a unit used to express the relative intensity of loudness of sound.* Normal conversation is about 65 decibels. Exposure to noise levels of 85 decibels and above can result in temporary hearing loss, often accompanied by ringing in the ears. Normal hearing will usually return, but continued exposure can lead to permanent hearing loss. **Figure 29.3** shows the decibel levels of various sounds.

FIGURE 29.3

DECIBEL LEVELS OF COMMON SOUNDS

Weakest sound heard by the average ear

Constant exposure at 85 decibels or greater may cause hearing loss.

Tractor, motorcycle, snowmobile

Rocket launch

Ambulance siren, amplified music

Normal conversation

Hair dryer, power lawn mower

Chain saw

Jet engine at takeoff

0   60   85   90   100   110   120   140   180

Reducing Noise Pollution

There are several ways to reduce noise pollution in your environment. Be sure to keep the volume down on stereos, radios, and television sets. Avoid unnecessary use of the car horn. When possible, use manual tools instead of power tools.

LESSON 1 REVIEW

Reviewing Facts and Vocabulary

1. Define *air pollution* and *noise pollution*.
2. Describe the EPA's role in monitoring air quality.
3. List two actions you can take to help reduce noise pollution.

Thinking Critically

4. **Evaluation.** Relate the nation's environmental health goals and objectives in *Healthy People 2010* to individual, family, and community health.
5. **Analyzing.** Imagine that the media has reported an AQI of 175. Paul, who has asthma, can't decide whether he wants to go in-line skating outdoors or play basketball in the air-conditioned gym. Determine which choice is healthier for Paul, and explain your decision.

Applying Health Skills

Accessing Information. Think of a specific critical health issue related to air pollution. Find information on this topic, and develop strategies to evaluate this information and information relating to a variety of critical health issues. Make a list of these strategies.

After You Read

Describe. Write a one-page summary describing two to three things you can do to protect the environment and your health. Show how taking action to protect the environment is linked to good health.

Protecting Land and Water

Guide to Reading

Building Vocabulary

As you read this lesson, write each new highlighted term and its definition in your notebook.

▶ biodegradable (p. 772)

▶ landfill (p. 772)

▶ hazardous waste (p. 773)

▶ deforestation (p. 774)

▶ urban sprawl (p. 774)

▶ wastewater (p. 775)

Focusing on the Main Ideas

In this lesson, you will learn how to:

▶ **Identify** the sources of land and water pollution.

▶ **Examine** the impact of population on community and world health.

▶ **Discuss** the influence of laws on health-related environmental issues.

▶ **Identify** strategies for reducing land and water pollution.

Reading Strategy

Explain

▶ Write a brief summary outlining what you know about waste disposal. List any questions you have.

Write a brief paragraph describing how you can help keep lakes and rivers free of pollution.

Most wastes are disposed of in landfills and covered with soil to prevent the spread of disease by insects and rodents.

The wastes generated by human activity can pollute both land and water. However, there are many actions people can take to reduce pollution and help preserve land and water resources.

Waste Disposal

Many wastes are **biodegradable**, or *able to be broken down by microorganisms in the environment*. However, when biodegradable materials are discarded in quantities too large for nature to handle, or when materials are not biodegradable, other waste-disposal solutions must be found.

Solid Waste

Much solid waste ends up in landfills. A **landfill** is *an area that has been safeguarded to prevent disposed wastes from contaminating groundwater*. Landfills must be located away from certain areas to protect groundwater (water that collects under the earth's surface) and must be lined with special materials to prevent leakage. Landfill operators must follow practices that reduce odor and control disease-carrying insects and rodents.

FIGURE 29.4

HAZARDOUS WASTES

Source/Activity That Generates Waste	Type of Waste Produced
Arts and crafts (e.g., painting, building models)	Solvents, paints, adhesives
Dry cleaning	Solvents
Construction	Oils, solvents, paints
Vehicle maintenance	Solvents, paints, ignitable wastes, used oil and batteries
Yardwork and gardening	Pesticides, herbicides, solvents
Household tasks	Solvents, oils, cleaning materials, paints, paint thinner

Hazardous Waste

A **hazardous waste** is *a substance that is explosive, corrosive, highly reactive, or toxic to humans or other life forms.* Industrial processes generate some hazardous wastes. Others are generated by common activities, including those described in **Figure 29.4.** Household products such as batteries are also considered hazardous wastes. Many of these wastes are banned from landfills and must be disposed of at special collection sites so that they don't contaminate the environment.

Nuclear wastes, a collection of radioactive materials that pose serious hazards to humans and other life forms, are a type of hazardous waste. Exposure to radiation can increase the risk of cancer. It can also alter a person's sex cells, causing genetic abnormalities to be passed on to offspring. Because of the long decay rates of some radioactive materials, these materials must be isolated in secure facilities for thousands of years.

Reading Check

Describe What is the difference between biodegradable and nonbiodegradable waste?

Expansion and Development

Throughout history population growth has been accelerating. It took half a million years for humankind to reach a population size of 1 billion, but the next billion people were born in a span of only 80 years, and close to 1½ billion more have been born since 1975. In certain U.S. communities and world regions, population growth impacts include a low quality of life and much human suffering. Rapid population growth also leads to swift deterioration of the land and to a severe drain on resources such as water.

Urban development can also have a dramatic impact on the land. As new cities are built, room for them must be cleared. This clearing has been at the expense of wilderness areas and rain forests.

Using public transportation instead of driving reduces pollution and helps conserve resources. *How might an efficient public transportation system improve community health?*

Reading Check

Analyze Why are certain developing countries at risk for deforestation?

Disappearing Forests

Developing nations in Central America, Africa, and Southeast Asia are rapidly expanding in agriculture and industry. These nations have been clearing tropical forests on a massive scale for fuel and to make way for farms and ranch land. This **deforestation**, or *destruction of forests,* has upset the fragile balance of nature.

Aside from providing a home to countless plant and animal species, the world's great forests play a vital part in controlling soil erosion, flooding, and sediment buildup in rivers, lakes, and reservoirs. Deforestation interferes with these processes. It can also change regional patterns of rainfall as a result of altered rates of evaporation, transpiration (vapor exhaled from the surface of green plants), and runoff. Without trees, precipitation declines and the region grows hotter and drier. Ultimately, desertlike conditions prevail where there were once rich, tropical grasslands.

Urban Sprawl

The spreading of city development (houses, shopping centers, businesses, and schools) onto undeveloped land is called **urban sprawl**. As the land surrounding cities becomes developed, environmental problems can occur. Runoff from parking lots and fertilized lawns may contaminate the drinking water supply. Air quality worsens as increased automobile and lawnmower usage adds more engine exhaust to the air.

To help address the problem of urban sprawl, city planners are rethinking the way suburbs are organized to help reduce consumption of natural resources and decrease the amount of pollution. In planned communities, schools and businesses are located within walking distance of homes, and sidewalks are required. Walking the short distances from home to work, school, or shopping provides physical activity for pedestrians, saves resources, and reduces pollution. The inclusion of efficient public transportation in these communities helps reduce the number of people driving to work. Consequently, fewer vehicles are on the highways, reducing both the level of pollution and the number of injuries and deaths caused by traffic accidents.

Water Supplies and Pollution

The EPA requires water suppliers to monitor and test water before sending it through municipal and community water systems. If the water is contaminated, the supplier must shut down the system and fix the problem. No agencies monitor the quality of water coming from private wells, however. Water treatment and purity depend on actions taken by those who use the well.

All drinking water is susceptible to pollution. Because the water can come from large sources such as rivers, lakes, and aquifers (water-bearing layers of rock, sand, or gravel) that underlie several counties or states, the pollution source can be far away from where the water is used. A health-literate consumer understands how the environmental conditions of the community influence the health of individuals.

Polluted Runoff

Water pollution is sometimes caused by illegal dumping of industrial chemical wastes, but a greater contamination problem is created by pollution that comes from many sources throughout the environment. Most surface water contamination is caused by polluted runoff—rainwater or snowmelt that runs over the land, picking up such contaminants as pesticides, fertilizers, and wastes. Polluted runoff can also contaminate groundwater, the primary source of drinking water for millions of people in the United States.

Wastewater

Wastewater, *used water that comes from homes, communities, farms, and businesses,* is another source of water pollution. Along with sewage, wastewater includes water that is generated and discharged from industries, feedlots, and many other sources. Wastewater contains harmful substances such as human and animal wastes, metals, and pathogens. Some wastewater must be treated by cooling in order to prevent thermal pollution. Thermal pollution occurs when the temperature of discharged water is higher than the temperature of a body of water in the environment. Because this hot water can disrupt aquatic ecosystems, it must be cooled before it enters the environment. The EPA regulates the treatment and discharge of wastewater under the Clean Water Act. Treated water that is released back into the environment must be safe for humans and other living organisms.

Other Sources of Water Pollution

Other sources of water pollution include:

▶ **Sediment.** Sediment from land erosion can destroy aquatic ecosystems and clog lakes, stream channels, and harbors.

▶ **Oil.** Some oil contamination comes from the cleaning of oil tankers and the release of oil from offshore drilling rigs. Problems can also occur when people dump used motor oil and household chemicals down household and storm drains.

Health Minute

Strategies for Protecting Water Supplies

There are actions you can take to help prevent the contamination of drinking water.

To protect drinking water:

▶ **Recycle engine oil.** Just 1 quart of oil can contaminate up to 2 million gallons of drinking water.

▶ **Be careful about what you put down the drain.** In areas that use septic systems, harmful chemicals may end up in your drinking water.

▶ **Keep cars, boats, and watercraft maintained.** Prevent fuel and lubricant leaks by keeping engines well tuned.

▼ Polluted runoff is a major source of water pollution in the United States.

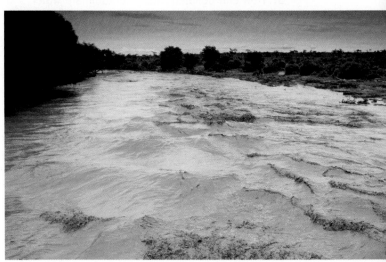

Reducing the Risks

You and your family can take steps to help keep our land and water clean.

▶ Recycle materials whenever possible to reduce the amount of waste going to landfills. You'll learn more about reducing solid wastes in Lesson 3.

▶ Dispose of all materials properly. Don't put oil paints, paint solvents, or batteries into the trash. Don't pour household chemicals or motor oil down the drain or onto the ground. Instead, take these and other hazardous materials to the appropriate collection sites.

▶ Follow directions when using chemicals such as cleaning products, fertilizers, and pesticides, and don't overuse them.

▶ Reduce water usage. Repair leaky faucets. Follow the recommendations for landscape watering that apply to your area. Reducing water usage decreases the amount of water that must be treated.

CHARACTER CHECK

Citizenship. When you dispose of hazardous household materials properly, you are demonstrating good citizenship and respect for the environment. **Make a pledge to always dispose of hazardous materials in a responsible manner. Share your knowledge about the dangers of hazardous materials with others, and encourage them to make responsible decisions.**

LESSON 2 REVIEW

Reviewing Facts and Vocabulary

1. What is a *landfill*?
2. Assess the impact of population on community and world health.
3. How can polluted runoff contaminate water supplies?

Thinking Critically

4. **Applying.** Analyze the influence of laws like the Clean Water Act on health-related issues.
5. **Analyzing.** You have probably heard the saying, "Water, water everywhere, but not a drop to drink." Explain this statement in terms of available drinking water.

Applying Health Skills

Advocacy. Create a comic book about a superhero named Captain Cleanup and his or her adventures cleaning up land and water pollution. The comic book should be targeted to elementary school students and contain a strong message about what young people can do to reduce land and water pollution.

After You Read

Compare and Contrast. Draw a circle. Draw another circle that overlaps the first. In the first circle, list the facts about solid-waste disposal. In the other circle, list facts about liquid-waste disposal. In the center overlap, list the steps you can take to help keep our land and water clean.

Visit **health.glencoe.com** for the Interactive Study Guide for Lesson 2.

Advocating for a Healthy Environment

Building Vocabulary

As you read this lesson, write each new highlighted term and its definition in your notebook.

▶ conservation (p. 777)

▶ precycling (p. 779)

▶ recycling (p. 779)

Quick Write

Explain how the environment would benefit from your participation in a recycling program.

Focusing on the Main Ideas

In this lesson, you will learn how to:

▶ Define the terms *conserving resources, precycling,* and *recycling.*

▶ Develop strategies for protecting the environment.

▶ Identify a variety of community and world environmental protection programs.

Reading Strategy

Organize Information

▶ Make a word web with *healthy environment* in the center. Surround the center with circles labeled Conservation, Precycling, Recycling, and Community Action. As you read, record facts in the appropriate spaces.

Many of today's environmental problems result from the lifestyle and consumer choices we make. In this lesson you'll learn about strategies to protect the health of the environment, both in your community and worldwide. Health-literate teens know how the environmental conditions of the community influence the health of individuals.

Conserving Resources

Most natural resources don't exist in an endless supply. The coal, natural gas, and petroleum we use for fuel took millions of years to form. It takes about 20 years for a tree to become large enough to cut for use as paper. These examples illustrate the need to conserve our natural resources. **Conservation** is *the protection and preservation of the environment by managing natural resources to prevent abuse, destruction, and neglect.* The actions that you and your family take at home have an impact on the environment. Some actions you can take to conserve natural resources are featured on the next page.

Planting trees helps replenish this natural resource. *How do trees benefit the environment?*

Putting on an extra layer of clothing instead of turning up the heat helps conserve natural resources. *Why is it important to conserve natural resources?*

Turning off lights saves electricity. *How else can you reduce electricity use in your home?*

Heating and Cooling

▶ Seal leaks around doors, windows, and electrical sockets to prevent heated or cooled air from escaping. Keep doors and windows shut, and close fireplace vents when the fireplace is not in use to keep cooled or heated air inside the home.

▶ During heating season, wear an extra layer of clothing instead of turning up the thermostat. Keep the thermostat at about 68°F. For further conservation, turn the thermostat down at bedtime.

▶ Keep the thermostat at about 78°F during air-conditioning season. Use a fan to keep air circulating—this will make the area feel cooler.

Water Conservation

▶ Wash clothes in warm or cold, not hot, water. Accumulate a full load before washing laundry or running the dishwasher.

▶ Fix leaky faucets, and never let water run unnecessarily. Turning off the water while brushing your teeth or shaving can save 4.5 gallons of water per minute.

▶ If you have a large-capacity toilet tank, fill plastic bottles with water, seal them, and place them in the tank. The bottles will keep the tank from filling completely, which will save up to a gallon of water per flush.

Lighting and Appliances

▶ Replace traditional lightbulbs with compact fluorescent bulbs, which use less energy and last longer.

▶ Switch off lights when you leave a room.

▶ Turn off televisions, radios, computers, and other appliances when they are not in use.

▶ Use a microwave or toaster oven instead of a conventional oven when cooking a small amount of food.

▶ Don't preheat a conventional oven for longer than necessary. Avoid opening the oven door unnecessarily while the appliance is in use.

Precycling and Recycling Programs

The easiest, most cost-efficient way of conserving natural resources is reducing the quantity of waste. Precycling and recycling are two ways of accomplishing this goal.

Precycling

Precycling—*reducing waste before it is generated*—means purchasing and using products wisely. How can you precycle? Reduce your use of products that are used once and then discarded. For example, try using cloth napkins instead of paper ones. Purchase products in bulk or in the largest package appropriate for your use to reduce excess packaging. Buying products such as laundry detergent or fruit juice as concentrates also reduces packaging. Choose products designed to be recycled. For example, look for the code on plastic packages. Those that carry a 1, 2, or 3 are most easily recycled.

Precycling also involves reusing materials. Reusing paper or plastic shopping bags or carrying your own cloth bags is a form of precycling. So is donating unneeded household goods or clothing to charities instead of discarding them.

Recycling

Recycling is *the processing of waste materials so that they can be used again.* Recycling has several benefits:

▶ **Recycling conserves resources.** Both energy and raw materials are conserved by recycling. For example, making a can from recycled aluminum takes only 10 percent of the energy needed to make a new can from raw materials.

▶ **Recycling reduces reliance on landfills.** Landfill space is limited, and it cannot keep up with increasing demands. Because of this, it is important to reduce the amount of waste that gets deposited in landfills.

▶ **Recycling protects environmental health.** Recycling utilizes materials that might otherwise harm the environment if disposed of in landfills. Thus recycling efforts lead to a cleaner and more healthful environment.

Reading Check

Define What is conservation?

Carrying your own cloth bags instead of using paper or plastic ones is one way to precycle. *What is another example of precycling?*

Hands-On Health ACTIVITY

One Planet—Your Role

In this activity you will create a chart that demonstrates the need to conserve resources.

What You'll Need

- pen or pencil and notebook paper
- poster board or construction paper
- markers

What You'll Do

1. Divide a sheet of paper into three columns. Label the columns "Items I Throw Away Every Week," "Ways of Precycling or Recycling," and "Why It Matters."
2. List at least five items in the first column, and complete the other two columns for those items.
3. Work in a small group. Combine the best ideas and create a poster-sized chart, similar to the one on your sheet of paper, that includes several ways to precycle or recycle commonly used items. Use persuasive language, and illustrate your group's chart.
4. Present the chart to the class. Then display it in the classroom or in a school hallway.

Apply and Conclude

Find statistics on how precycling and recycling help reduce waste and pollution. Be sure to relate the data to the actions described in your poster.

Manufacturers put codes on plastic containers to give consumers information on how to recycle.

TIPS FOR RECYCLING AND REDUCING WASTE

More than 80 percent of household waste can be recycled. The following are some guidelines for specific recyclable materials.

▶ **Aluminum.** Rinse cans and other aluminum items such as pie pans and frozen food trays. Crush them to save space.

▶ **Cardboard.** Flatten cardboard boxes and tie them together.

▶ **Glass.** Rinse all glass containers. Recycle metal lids separately.

▶ **Plastics.** Look for the code on the container. Most recyclers take plastics marked with a 1, 2, or 3.

▶ **Newspaper.** Stack newspapers and tie the bundles with string or rope, or place the papers in paper shopping bags for easy handling.

▶ **Glossy Paper.** Contact services that help you remove your name from mailing lists. Find out whether a local retirement or community center can use discarded magazines. What you can't eliminate or redistribute, recycle.

Protecting the Environment

Here are some practical suggestions for becoming involved in protecting the environment:

▶ **Become an informed consumer.** Evaluate products with regard to their impact on natural resources. Give feedback to companies on ways they can help protect the environment.

▶ **Contact organizations that promote the conservation of resources and educate people on environmental issues.** Ask for ideas on how to conserve natural resources. Consider joining an environmental organization. Most of these organizations can give you information on current environmental issues. They can also suggest ways to promote the health of the environment. A health advocate knows methods for working cooperatively with others to advocate for healthy communities.

▶ **Take action against local polluters.** The environmental problems in your community directly affect your health. Join with others to inform elected officials of your concerns.

Much of the waste generated in a typical American home can be recycled. *What materials are recycled in your community?*

LESSON 3 REVIEW

Reviewing Facts and Vocabulary

1. Define the term *conservation.*
2. What is the difference between *precycling* and *recycling?*
3. List three environmental benefits of recycling.

Thinking Critically

4. **Analyzing.** How does conserving resources protect the health of the environment?
5. **Applying.** Develop strategies to conserve natural resources in your home. List three strategies not included in this lesson that your family can undertake to conserve resources.

Applying Health Skills

Accessing Information. Research and describe a variety of community and world environmental protection programs. Create a chart to display the information that you obtain. Include the name of the community or country, the name of the program, and a brief description of the program's mission.

After You Read

Cause and Effect. Pick one of the following topics: Conserving Resources, Precycling and Recycling Programs, or Protecting the Environment. Write a newspaper opinion piece designed to convince your readers why it is important to conserve resources, precycle or recycle, or protect the environment. Focus on the health reasons for conservation.

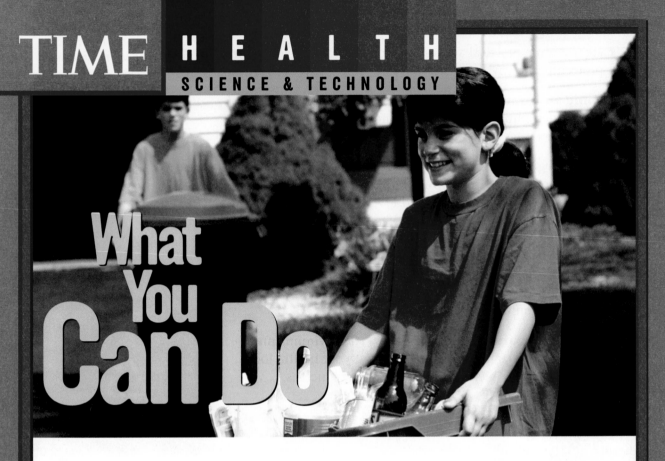

What You Can Do

People in the United States produce an average of 20,000 pounds of carbon dioxide (CO_2) a year. Decreasing that number would make us healthier (by making the atmosphere cleaner and slowing down global warming) and wealthier (by lowering bills for electricity, heating fuels, and gas). To reduce the amount of CO_2 in the air, follow these tips from Environmental Defense and the World Wildlife Fund.

1. Get It Just Right

Don't overheat or overcool rooms. Set the thermostat lower in winter and higher in summer.

Average annual CO_2 reduction: approximately 500 pounds for each 2°F adjustment

2. Pitch In

Reduce waste and promote energy-efficient measures at your school. Help set up community recycling programs.

Average CO_2 reduction: 4 pounds for every pound of office paper recycled

3. Get Smart on Wash Day

Wash laundry in warm or cold water, not hot.

Average annual CO_2 reduction: as much as 500 pounds for two loads a week

4. Home Improvement

Plant trees next to your house, and paint your house a light color if you live in a warm climate or a dark color in a cold climate.

Average annual CO_2 reduction: approximately 5,000 pounds

5. Don't Bag It

Buy minimally packaged goods and reusable products. Recycle.

Average annual CO_2 reduction: 1,000 pounds for 25 percent less garbage. ◼

TIME to THINK... About CO_2

The tips above describe great ways to reduce CO_2. What is CO_2? Create a flow chart with the class that shows how CO_2 contributes to global warming. Is there anything that you do daily that makes you part of the flow chart?

1. Accessing Information. Choose one of the five air pollutants tracked by the EPA. Research whether that pollutant is present in the air in your community. Write a brief report summarizing your findings. *(LESSON 1)*

2. Advocacy. Polluted runoff may occur as a result of heavy rains that wash fertilizers and pesticides from lawns. Write a public service announcement encouraging people to carefully follow application instructions for these products. *(LESSON 2)*

3. Goal Setting. Talk with your family about ways to conserve natural resources. Then use the goal-setting steps to choose and work toward a family conservation goal. As part of the goal-setting process, have each family member sign a pledge to do his or her part to conserve resources. *(LESSON 3)*

CAREER Corner

Environmental Engineering Technician

Would you like to improve the quality of the environment? If so, you might enjoy a career as an environmental engineering technician.

Environmental engineering technicians work closely with environmental engineers and scientists in developing methods and devices used in the prevention, control, and correction of environmental hazards.

To become an environmental engineering technician, you will need a two-year associate's degree or extensive on-the-job training. Find out more about this and other health careers by clicking on Career Corner at **health.glencoe.com.**

BEYOND the Classroom

Parent Involvement

Accessing Information. Find out what materials are recycled in your community. Work with a parent or other adult family member to interview managers of several recycling centers or hazardous waste collection sites. Put together an informative pamphlet that describes local waste-management and recycling services. Make your pamphlet available to other families in your neighborhood.

School and Community

Volunteering Opportunities. Locate a recycling center or charitable organization in your community that collects donated items for resale. Contact the agency to find out what volunteer positions are available. Share what you have learned with your classmates.

After You Read

Use the notes you have taken in your Foldable to review what you have learned about air quality and the types of pollution.

► EXPLORING HEALTH TERMS *Answer the following questions on a sheet of paper.*

Lesson 1 *Match each definition with the correct term.*

air pollution	noise pollution
asbestos	radon
decibel	smog
Air Quality Index (AQI)	

1. A yellow-brown haze that forms when sunlight reacts with air pollution.

2. An index for reporting daily air quality.

3. A fibrous mineral that has fireproof properties.

4. An odorless, radioactive gas that can cause cancer.

5. A unit used to express the relative intensity of loudness of sound.

Lesson 2 *Fill in the blanks with the correct term.*

landfill	biodegradable
deforestation	urban sprawl
hazardous waste	wastewater

6. _____ wastes can be broken down by microorganisms in the environment.

7. A substance that is explosive, corrosive, highly reactive, or toxic to humans and other life forms is known as _____ .

8. The destruction of forests is known as _____ .

9. The spreading of city development onto undeveloped land is called _____ .

10. _____ is used water that comes from homes, communities, farms, and businesses.

Lesson 3 *Replace the underlined words with the correct term.*

precycling	conservation
recycling	

11. <u>Recycling</u> is the protection and preservation of the environment by managing natural resources.

12. <u>Conservation</u> involves making decisions about products *before* you purchase them in order to reduce waste.

13. The processing of materials so that they can be used again in some form is <u>precycling</u>.

► RECALLING THE FACTS *Use complete sentences to answer the following questions.*

1. Name five common air pollutants.

2. List two strategies for managing indoor air pollution.

3. Temporary hearing loss may occur when a person is exposed to noise levels at or above what decibel level?

4. If many wastes are biodegradable, why are landfills necessary?

5. What is nuclear waste?

6. List three sources of water pollution and two ways of reducing this type of pollution.

7. Name three ways to conserve natural resources.

8. List three precycling strategies.

9. What are three practical ways to become involved in protecting the environment?

For more review questions for Chapter 29, go to **health.glencoe.com**.

► WRITING CRITICALLY

1. **Descriptive.** Write a half-page summary describing your vision of a rainforest. What colors are seen in a rainforest? What kind of wildlife lives there? What is the climate like? Use the other half of the paper to describe what the same area would look like if it was destroyed by deforestation. How does deforestation impact the environment?

2. **Persuasive.** Write an article that could be published in a newspaper persuading others to take actions to protect the environment. In your article, inform others on how they can conserve natural resources. Provide ideas of things that everyone can do to help the environment. Give logical reasons that explain why conservation is necessary for the earth.

Standardized Test Practice

 Read the passage below and then answer the questions.

Why Recycle?

(1) Did you know that the typical American family throws away more than 1,000 pounds of trash per year? (2) Much of that garbage ends up in landfills. (3) Soon, these landfills will be full and we are running out of places to put new ones. (4) How can we reduce these mountains of garbage? (5) We can do it by recycling.

(6) Some people worry that recycling costs too much, but it actually saves money because it means less solid-waste disposal. (7) Others say that people are too lazy to separate trash and wash out cans and bottles. (8) This is not true.

(9) The greatest thing about recycling is that it is something each of us can do to help our planet. (10) No matter what our age, size, economic or education level, we can all take part. (11) Earth is where we all are living and so we should care.

1. Which sentence should be added after sentence (8) to help support the topic?

   A It's very difficult to peel the labels off of jars.
   B It's good to give things away instead of throwing them away.
   C Across the country, people have been willing to recycle.
   D My school recently started a recycling program.

2. What is the most effective way to rewrite the last sentence?

   F Everyone can do something, no matter what their age.
   G Why is it that some people do not seem to care about recycling?
   H Earth is our home, and we should keep it safe and healthy.
   I Many people think that our planet is beautiful from space.

3. Write a paragraph using persuasive techniques urging sports arenas and stadiums to recycle bottles and cans.

Appendix Table of Contents

HEALTH SKILLS		NATIONAL HEALTH EDUCATION STANDARDS
	Comprehending Concepts	Students will comprehend concepts related to health promotion and disease prevention.
ACCESSING INFORMATION	Accessing Information	Students will demonstrate the ability to access valid health information and health-promoting products and services.
PRACTICING HEALTHFUL BEHAVIORS / STRESS MANAGEMENT	Practicing Healthful Behaviors Stress Management	Students will demonstrate the ability to practice health-enhancing behaviors and reduce health risks.
ANALYZING INFLUENCES	Analyzing Influences	Students will analyze the influence of culture, media, technology, and other factors on health.
COMMUNICATION SKILLS / CONFLICT RESOLUTION / REFUSAL SKILLS	Communication Skills Conflict Resolution Refusal Skills	Students will demonstrate the ability to use interpersonal communication skills to enhance health.
DECISION MAKING / GOAL SETTING	Decision Making Goal Setting	Students will demonstrate the ability to use goal-setting and decision-making skills to enhance health.
ADVOCACY	Advocacy	Students will demonstrate the ability to advocate for personal, family, and community health.

Healthy People 2010

Healthy People 2010 is a set of 28 health objectives established for the nation to achieve over the first decade of the new century. The objectives, listed on these pages, were created after the Surgeon General's Report in 2000 identified specific National Health Promotion and Disease Prevention goals. The chapters and lessons in *Glencoe Health* provide strategies for addressing many of the objectives of *Healthy People 2010.*

1. **Access to Quality Health Services** Improve access to comprehensive, high-quality health care services.

2. **Arthritis, Osteoporosis, and Chronic Back Conditions** Prevent illness and disability related to arthritis and other rheumatic conditions, osteoporosis, and chronic back conditions.

3. **Cancer** Reduce the number of new cancer cases as well as the illness, disability, and death caused by cancer.

4. **Chronic Kidney Disease** Reduce new cases of chronic kidney disease and its complications, disability, death, and economic costs.

5. **Diabetes** Through prevention programs, reduce the disease and economic burden of diabetes, and improve the quality of life for all persons who have or are at risk for diabetes.

6. **Disability and Secondary Conditions** Promote the health of people with disabilities, prevent secondary conditions, and eliminate disparities between people with and without disabilities in the U.S. population.

7. **Educational and Community-Based Programs** Increase the quality, availability, and effectiveness of educational and community-based programs designed to prevent disease and improve health and quality of life.

8. **Environmental Health** Promote health for all through a healthy environment.

9. **Family Planning** Includes preventing unintended pregnancy.

10. **Food Safety** Reduce foodborne illnesses.

11. **Health Communication** Use communication strategically to improve health.

12. **Heart Disease and Stroke** Improve cardiovascular health and quality of life through the prevention, detection, and treatment of risk factors; early identification and treatment of heart attacks and strokes; and prevention of recurrent cardiovascular events.

13. **HIV** Prevent human immunodeficiency virus (HIV) infection and its related illness and death.

14. Immunization and Infectious Diseases Prevent disease, disability, and death from infectious diseases, including vaccine-preventable diseases.

15. Injury and Violence Prevention Reduce injuries, disabilities, and deaths due to unintentional injuries and violence.

16. Maternal, Infant, and Child Health Improve the health and well-being of women, infants, children, and families.

17. Medical Product Safety Ensure the safe and effective use of medical products.

18. Mental Health and Mental Disorders Improve mental health and ensure access to appropriate, quality mental health services.

19. Nutrition and Overweight Promote health and reduce chronic disease associated with diet and weight.

20. Occupational Safety and Health Promote the health and safety of people at work through prevention and early intervention.

21. Oral Health Prevent and control oral and craniofacial diseases, conditions, and injuries, and improve access to related services.

22. Physical Activity and Fitness Improve health, fitness, and quality of life through daily physical activity.

23. Public Health Infrastructure Ensure that federal, tribal, state, and local health agencies have the infrastructure to provide essential public health services effectively.

24. Respiratory Diseases Promote respiratory health through better prevention, detection, treatment, and education efforts.

25. Sexually Transmitted Diseases Promote responsible sexual behaviors, strengthen community capacity, and increase access to quality services to prevent sexually transmitted diseases (STDs) and their complications.

26. Substance Abuse Reduce substance abuse to protect the health, safety, and quality of life for all, especially children.

27. Tobacco Reduce illness, disability, and death related to tobacco use and exposure to secondhand smoke.

28. Vision and Hearing Improve the visual and hearing health of the nation through prevention, early detection, treatment, and rehabilitation.

40 Developmental Assets

Search Institute has identified the following building blocks of healthy development that help young people grow up healthy, caring, and responsible.

External Assets

Support

1. **Family Support**—Family life provides high levels of love and support.
2. **Positive Family Communication**—Young person and her or his parent(s) communicate positively, and young person is willing to seek advice and counsel from parents.
3. **Other Adult Relationships**—Young person receives support from three or more nonparent adults.
4. **Caring Neighborhood**—Young person experiences caring neighbors.
5. **Caring School Climate**—School provides a caring, encouraging environment.
6. **Parent Involvement in Schooling**—Parent(s) are actively involved in helping young person succeed in school.

Empowerment

7. **Community Values Youth**—Young person perceives that adults in the community value youth.
8. **Youth as Resources**—Young people are given useful roles in the community.
9. **Service to Others**—Young person serves in the community one hour or more per week.
10. **Safety**—Young person feels safe at home, school, and in the neighborhood.

Boundaries and Expectations

11. **Family Boundaries**—Family has clear rules and consequences and monitors the young person's whereabouts.
12. **School Boundaries**—School provides clear rules and consequences.
13. **Neighborhood Boundaries**—Neighbors take responsibility for monitoring young people's behavior.
14. **Adult Role Models**—Parent(s) and other adults model positive, responsible behavior.
15. **Positive Peer Influence**—Young person's best friends model responsible behavior.
16. **High Expectations**—Both parent(s) and teachers encourage the young person to do well.

Constructive Use of Time

17. **Creative Activities**—Young person spends three or more hours per week in lessons or practice in music, theater, or other arts.
18. **Youth Programs**—Young person spends three or more hours per week in sports, clubs, or organizations at school and/or in the community.
19. **Religious Community**—Young person spends one or more hours per week in activities in a religious institution.
20. **Time at Home**—Young person is out with friends "with nothing special to do" two or fewer nights per week.

Internal Assets

Commitment to Learning

21. **Achievement Motivation**—Young person is motivated to do well in school.
22. **School Engagement**—Young person is actively engaged in learning.
23. **Homework**—Young person reports doing at least one hour of homework every school day.
24. **Bonding to School**—Young person cares about her or his school.
25. **Reading for Pleasure**—Young person reads for pleasure three or more hours per week.

Positive Values

26. **Caring**—Young person places high value on helping other people.
27. **Equality and Social Justice**—Young person places high value on promoting equality and reducing hunger and poverty.
28. **Integrity**—Young person acts on convictions and stands up for her or his beliefs.
29. **Honesty**—Young person "tells the truth even when it is not easy."
30. **Responsibility**—Young person accepts and takes personal responsibility.
31. **Restraint**—Young person believes it is important not to be sexually active or to use alcohol or other drugs.

Social Competencies

32. **Planning and Decision Making**—Young person knows how to plan ahead and make choices.
33. **Interpersonal Competence**—Young person has empathy, sensitivity, and friendship skills.
34. **Cultural Competence**—Young person has knowledge of and comfort with people of different cultural/racial/ethnic backgrounds.
35. **Resistance Skills**—Young person can resist negative peer pressure and dangerous situations.
36. **Peaceful Conflict Resolution**—Young person seeks to resolve conflict nonviolently.

Positive Identity

37. **Personal Power**—Young person feels he or she has control over the "things that happen to me."
38. **Self-Esteem**—Young person reports having a high self-esteem.
39. **Sense of Purpose**—Young person reports that "my life has a purpose."
40. **Positive View of Personal Future**—Young person is optimistic about her or his personal future.

PHYSICAL ACTIVITY AND FITNESS GUIDELINES

The Surgeon General's Report on Physical Activity and Health, along with the President's Council on Physical Fitness and Sports, identified fitness as a major public health concern. The Physical Fitness Objectives from *Healthy People 2010* for children and adolescents appear below.

Physical Activity in Children and Adolescents

- Increase the proportion of adolescents who engage in moderate physical activity for at least 30 minutes on 5 or more of the previous 7 days.

- Increase the proportion of adolescents who engage in vigorous physical activity that promotes cardiorespiratory fitness 3 or more days per week for 20 or more minutes per occasion.

- Increase the proportion of the nation's public and private schools that require daily physical education for all students.

- Increase the proportion of adolescents who participate in daily school physical education.

- Increase the proportion of adolescents who spend at least 50 percent of school physical education class time being physically active.

- Increase the proportion of adolescents who view television 2 or fewer hours on a school day.

PHYSICAL FITNESS GUIDELINES

Regular physical activity performed on a daily basis reduces the risk of developing illness or disease. Moderate physical activity can be achieved in a variety of ways, and the Centers for Disease Control and Prevention have developed this list of examples showing moderate amounts of activity that can contribute to an individual's health.

Physical Activities Arranged by Energy Level and Time

- Washing and waxing a car for 45–60 minutes
- Washing windows or floors for 45–60 minutes
- Playing volleyball for 45 minutes
- Playing touch football for 30–45 minutes
- Gardening for 30–45 minutes
- Wheeling self in wheelchair for 30–40 minutes
- Walking 1 ¾ miles in 35 minutes (20 min/mile)
- Basketball (shooting baskets) for 30 minutes
- Bicycling 5 miles in 30 minutes
- Dancing fast (social) for 30 minutes
- Pushing a stroller 1 ½ miles in 30 minutes

- Raking leaves for 30 minutes
- Walking 2 miles in 30 minutes (15 min/mile)
- Water aerobics for 30 minutes
- Swimming laps for 20 minutes
- Wheelchair basketball for 20 minutes
- Basketball (playing a game) for 15–20 minutes
- Bicycling 4 miles in 15 minutes
- Jumping rope for 15 minutes
- Running 1 ½ miles in 15 minutes (10 min/mile)
- Shoveling snow for 15 minutes
- Stair walking for 15 minutes

Source: CDC, Physical Activity and Health, A Report of the Surgeon General

Glossary

A

Absorption The passage of digested food from the digestive tract into the cardiovascular system (Ch. 17, 442)

Abstinence A deliberate decision to avoid harmful behaviors, including sexual activity before marriage and the use of tobacco, alcohol, and other drugs (Ch. 1, 20; Ch. 12, 318; Ch. 25, 649)

Abuse Physical, mental/emotional, or sexual mistreatment of one person by another (Ch. 13, 348)

Accident chain A sequence of events that leads to an unintentional injury (Ch. 27, 706)

Acquired immune deficiency syndrome (AIDS) A disease in which the immune system of the patient is weakened (Ch. 25, 658)

Action plan A multistep strategy to identify and achieve your goals (Ch. 2, 36)

Active immunity Immunity your body develops to protect you from disease (Ch. 24, 631)

Active listening Paying close attention to what someone is saying and communicating (Ch. 10, 256)

Addiction A physiological or psychological dependence on a drug (Ch. 23, 595)

Addictive drug A substance that causes physiological or psychological dependence (Ch. 21, 540)

Additive interaction Medicines working together in a positive way (Ch. 23, 589)

Adolescence The period from childhood to adulthood (Ch. 20, 514)

Adoption The legal process of taking a child of other parents as one's own (Ch. 20, 527)

Adrenal glands Glands that help the body recover from stress and respond to emergencies (Ch. 18, 466)

Advertising A written or spoken media message designed to interest consumers in purchasing a product or service (Ch. 3, 49)

Advocacy Taking action to influence others to address a health-related concern or to support a health-related belief (Ch. 2, 32)

Aerobic exercise Any activity that uses large muscle groups, is rhythmic in nature, and can be maintained continuously for at least 10 minutes three times a day or for 20 to 30 minutes at one time (Ch. 4, 83)

Affection A feeling of fondness for someone (Ch. 12, 313)

Affirmation Positive feedback that helps others feel appreciated and supported (Ch. 11, 278)

Aggressive Overly forceful, pushy, hostile, or otherwise attacking in their approach (Ch. 12, 312)

Air pollution The contamination of the earth's atmosphere by substances that pose a health threat to living things (Ch. 29, 766)

Air Quality Index (AQI) An index for reporting daily air quality (Ch. 29, 768)

Alcohol abuse The excessive use of alcohol (Ch. 22, 565)

Alcohol poisoning A severe and potentially fatal physical reaction to an alcohol overdose (Ch. 22, 571)

Alcoholic An addict who is dependent on alcohol (Ch. 22, 576)

Alcoholism A disease in which a person has a physical or psychological dependence on drinks that contain alcohol (Ch. 22, 576)

Alienation Feeling isolated and separated from everyone else (Ch. 9, 230)

Allergy A specific reaction of the immune system to a foreign and frequently harmless substance (Ch. 26, 688)

Americans with Disabilities Act A law prohibiting discrimination against people with physical or mental disabilities in the workplace, transportation, public accommodations, and telecommunications (Ch. 26, 699)

Amniocentesis A procedure in which a syringe is inserted through a pregnant female's abdominal wall into the amniotic fluid surrounding the developing fetus (Ch. 19, 501)

Amniotic sac A thin, fluid-filled membrane that surrounds and protects the developing embryo (Ch. 19, 487)

Anabolic-androgenic steroids Synthetic substances similar to the male hormone testosterone (Ch. 4, 94; Ch. 23, 601)

Anaerobic exercise Intense short bursts of activity in which the muscles work so hard that they produce energy without using oxygen (Ch. 4, 84)

Analgesics Pain relievers (Ch. 23, 588)

Anemia A condition in which the ability of the blood to carry oxygen is reduced (Ch. 16, 426)

Angina pectoris Chest pain that results when the heart doesn't get enough oxygen (Ch. 26, 677)

Anorexia nervosa A disorder in which the irrational fear of becoming obese results in severe weight loss from self-imposed starvation (Ch. 6, 154)

Antagonistic interaction Occurs when the effect of one medicine is canceled or reduced when taken with another medicine (Ch. 23, 589)

Antibody A protein that acts against a specific antigen (Ch. 24, 631)

Antigen A substance that is capable of triggering an immune response (Ch. 24, 630)

Anxiety The condition of feeling uneasy or worried about what may happen (Ch. 8, 210)

Anxiety disorder A condition in which real or imagined fears are difficult to control (Ch. 9, 225)

Appendicitis Inflammation of the appendix (Ch. 17, 450)

Appendicular skeleton The 126 bones of the upper and lower limbs, shoulders, and hips (Ch. 15, 387)

Appetite A desire, rather than a need, to eat (Ch. 5, 111)

Arrhythmia Irregular heartbeats (Ch. 26, 677)

Arteries Blood vessels that carry blood away from the heart (Ch. 16, 419)

Arthritis A group of more than 100 different diseases that cause pain and loss of movement in the joints (Ch. 26, 693)

Asbestos A fibrous mineral that has fireproof properties, once widely used as an insulator (Ch. 29, 769)

Assailant A person who commits a violent act against another (Ch. 13, 341)

Assault An unlawful attack on a person with the intent to harm or kill (Ch. 13, 344)

Assertive Standing up for your rights and beliefs in firm but positive ways (Ch. 12, 310; Ch. 13, 332)

Asthma An inflammatory condition in which the trachea, bronchi, and bronchioles become narrowed, causing difficulty in breathing (Ch. 16, 434; Ch. 26, 690)

Asymptomatic stage A period of time during which a person infected with HIV has no symptoms (Ch. 25, 662)

Atherosclerosis The process in which plaques accumulate on artery walls (Ch. 26, 675)

Auditory ossicles Three small bones linked together that connect the eardrum to the inner ear (Ch. 14, 377)

Autoimmune disease A condition in which the immune system mistakenly attacks itself, targeting the cells, tissues, and organs of a person's own body (Ch. 26, 691)

Autonomy The confidence that a person can control his or her own body, impulses, and environment (Ch. 19, 505)

Axial skeleton The 80 bones of the skull, spine, ribs, vertebrae, and sternum, or breastbone (Ch. 15, 387)

─────── **B** ───────

Bacteria Single-celled microorganisms (Ch. 24, 623)

Behavior therapy A treatment process that focuses on changing unwanted behaviors through rewards and reinforcements (Ch. 9, 237)

Benign Noncancerous (Ch. 26, 681)

Bile A yellow-green, bitter fluid important in the breakdown and absorption of fats (Ch. 17, 445)

Binge drinking Drinking five or more alcoholic drinks at one sitting (Ch. 22, 571)

Binge eating disorder A disorder characterized by compulsive overeating (Ch. 6, 155)

Biodegradable Able to be broken down by microorganisms in the environment (Ch. 29, 772)

Biomedical therapy The use of certain medications to treat or reduce the symptoms of a mental disorder (Ch. 9, 237)

Biopsy The removal of a small piece of tissue for examination (Ch. 26, 686)

Birthing center A facility in which females with low-risk pregnancies can deliver their babies in a homelike setting (Ch. 19, 492)

Bladder A hollow muscular organ that acts as a reservoir for urine (Ch. 17, 455)

Blizzard A snowstorm with winds of at least 35 miles per hour (Ch. 27, 728)

Blood alcohol concentration (BAC) The amount of alcohol in a person's blood expressed as a percentage (Ch. 22, 570)

Blood pressure A measure of the amount of force that the blood places on the walls of blood vessels, particularly large arteries, as it is pumped through the body (Ch. 16, 424)

Body composition The ratio of body fat to lean body tissue, including muscle, bone, water, and connective tissue such as ligaments, cartilage, and tendons (Ch. 4, 81)

Body image The way you see your body (Ch. 6, 144)

Body language Nonverbal communication through gestures, facial expressions, behaviors, and posture (Ch. 10, 258; Ch. 13, 332)

Body mass index (BMI) A ratio that allows you to assess your body size in relation to your height and weight (Ch. 6, 145)

Brain stem A 3-inch-long stalk of nerve cells and fibers that connects the spinal cord to the rest of the brain (Ch. 15, 403)

Bronchi The airways that connect the trachea and the lungs (Ch. 16, 431)

Bronchitis An inflammation of the bronchi caused by infection or exposure to irritants such as tobacco smoke or air pollution (Ch. 16, 433)

Bulimia nervosa A disorder in which some form of purging or clearing of the digestive tract follows cycles of overeating (Ch. 6, 154)

Bullying The act of seeking power or attention through the psychological, emotional, or physical abuse of another person (Ch. 13, 336)

─────── **C** ───────

Calories Units of heat that measure the energy used by the body and the energy that foods supply to the body (Ch. 5, 110)

Cancer Uncontrollable growth of abnormal cells (Ch. 26, 681)

Capillaries Small vessels that carry blood between arterioles and small vessels called venules (Ch. 16, 419)

Carbohydrates The starches and sugars present in foods (Ch. 5, 114)

Carbon monoxide A colorless, odorless, and poisonous gas (Ch. 21, 541)

Carcinogen A cancer-causing substance (Ch. 21, 541; Ch. 26, 682)

Cardiac muscle A type of striated muscle that forms the wall of the heart (Ch. 15, 395)

Cardiopulmonary resuscitation (CPR) A life-saving first-aid procedure that combines rescue breaths with chest compressions, supplying oxygen to the body until normal body functions can resume (Ch. 28, 743)

Cardiorespiratory endurance The ability of the heart, lungs, and blood vessels to use and send fuel and oxygen to the body's tissues during long periods of moderate-to-vigorous activity (Ch. 4, 80)

Cardiovascular disease (CVD) A disease that affects the heart or blood vessels (Ch. 26, 674)

Cartilage A strong, flexible connective tissue (Ch. 15, 387)

Cerebellum The second largest part of the brain (Ch. 15, 403)

Cerebral palsy A group of nonprogressive neurological disorders that are the result of damage to the brain before, during, or just after birth or in early childhood (Ch. 15, 409)

Cerebrum The largest and most complex part of the brain (Ch. 15, 402)

Cervix The opening to the uterus (Ch. 18, 476)

Chain of survival A sequence of actions that maximize the victim's chances of survival (Ch. 28, 742)

Character Those distinctive qualities that describe how a person thinks, feels, and behaves (Ch. 2, 37)

Child abuse Domestic abuse directed at a child (Ch. 11, 288)

Chlamydia A bacterial infection that affects the reproductive organs of both males and females (Ch. 25, 654)

Chorionic villi sampling (CVS) A procedure in which a small piece of membrane is removed from the chorion, a layer of tissue that develops into the placenta (Ch. 19, 501)

Choroid A thin structure that lines the inside of the sclera (Ch. 14, 372)

Chromosomes Threadlike structures found within the nucleus of a cell that carry the codes for inherited traits (Ch. 19, 499)

Chronic stress Stress associated with long-term problems that are beyond a person's control (Ch. 8, 204)

Chyme A creamy, fluid mixture of food and gastric juices (Ch. 17, 444)

Citizenship The way you conduct yourself as a member of the community (Ch. 10, 249)

Clique A small circle of friends, usually with similar backgrounds or tastes, who exclude people viewed as outsiders (Ch. 12, 304)

Club drugs Drugs associated with concerts, dance clubs, and all-night parties called raves (Ch. 23, 606)

Cluster suicides A series of suicides occurring within a short period of time and involving several people in the same school or community (Ch. 9, 233)

Cognition The ability to reason and think out abstract solutions (Ch. 20, 516)

Cognitive therapy A treatment method designed to identify and correct distorted thinking patterns that can lead to feelings and behaviors that may be troublesome, self-defeating, or self-destructive (Ch. 9, 237)

Commitment A promise or a pledge (Ch. 20, 524)

Communicable disease A disease that is spread from one living thing to another or through the environment (Ch. 24, 622)

Communication The ways in which you send messages to and receive messages from others (Ch. 10, 250)

Comparison shopping A method of judging the benefits of different products by comparing several factors, such as quality, features, and cost (Ch. 3, 50)

Compromise A problem-solving method that involves each participant's giving up something to reach a solution that satisfies everyone (Ch. 10, 251)

Concussion A jarring injury to the brain that affects normal brain function (Ch. 28, 752)

Conduct disorder A pattern of behavior in which the rights of others or basic social rules are violated (Ch. 9, 228)

Confidentiality Respecting the privacy of another and keeping details secret (Ch. 10, 267)

Conflict Any disagreement, struggle, or fight (Ch. 10, 262)

Conflict resolution The process of ending a conflict through cooperation and problem solving (Ch. 2, 30; Ch. 10, 264)

Congenital A condition that is present at birth (Ch. 16, 425)

Conservation The protection and preservation of the environment by managing natural resources to prevent abuse, destruction, and neglect (Ch. 29, 777)

Constructive criticism Nonhostile comments that point out problems and encourage improvement (Ch. 7, 183; Ch. 10, 260)

Consumer advocate People or groups whose sole purpose is to take on regional, national, and even international consumer issues (Ch. 3, 63)

Cool-down An activity that prepares the muscles to return to a resting state (Ch. 4, 91)

Cooperation Working together for the good of all (Ch. 10, 250)

Coping Dealing successfully with difficult changes in your life (Ch. 9, 239)

Cornea A transparent tissue that bends and focuses light before it enters the lens (Ch. 14, 372)

Crisis center A facility that handles emergencies and provides referrals to an individual needing help (Ch. 11, 291)

Cross-contamination The spreading of bacteria or other pathogens from one food to another (Ch. 5, 136)

Culture The collective beliefs, customs, and behaviors of a group (Ch. 1, 14)

Cumulative risks Related risks that increase in effect with each added risk (Ch. 1, 19)

Curfew A set time at which you must be home at night (Ch. 12, 317)

Custody A legal decision about who has the right to make decisions affecting the children in a family and who has the responsibility of physically caring for them (Ch. 11, 281)

Cycle of violence Pattern of repeating violent or abusive behaviors from one generation to the next (Ch. 11, 289)

Cystitis An inflammation of the bladder (Ch. 17, 456)

─────────── **D** ───────────

Dandruff A condition that can occur if the scalp becomes too dry and dead skin cells are shed as sticky, white flakes (Ch. 14, 365)

Date rape When one person in a dating relationship forces the other person to participate in sexual intercourse (Ch. 13, 350)

Decibel A unit used to express the relative intensity of loudness of sound (Ch. 29, 770)

Decision-making skills Steps that enable you to make a healthful decision (Ch. 2, 33)

Defense mechanisms Mental processes that protect individuals from strong or stressful emotions and situations (Ch. 7, 189)

Defensive driver A driver who is aware of potential hazards and reacts to avoid them (Ch. 27, 722)

Defibrillator A device that delivers an electric shock to the heart to restore its normal rhythm (Ch. 28, 742)

Deforestation Destruction of forests (Ch. 29, 774)

Depressants Drugs that tend to slow the central nervous system (Ch. 22, 563; Ch. 23, 606)

Depression A prolonged feeling of helplessness, hopelessness, and sadness (Ch. 8, 211)

Dermis The thicker layer of the skin beneath the epidermis that is made up of connective tissue and contains blood vessels and nerves (Ch. 14, 360)

Designer drugs Synthetic substances meant to imitate the effects of hallucinogens and other dangerous drugs (Ch. 23, 610)

Detoxification A process in which the body adjusts to functioning without alcohol (Ch. 22, 578)

Developmental assets Building blocks of development that help young people grow up as healthy, caring, and responsible individuals (Ch. 7, 179)

Developmental task An event that needs to happen in order for a person to continue growing toward becoming a healthy, mature adult (Ch. 19, 504)

Diabetes A chronic disease that affects the way body cells convert food into energy (Ch. 26, 691)

Diaphragm The muscle that separates the chest from the abdominal cavity (Ch. 16, 429)

Dietary Guidelines for Americans A set of recommendations for healthful eating and active living (Ch. 5, 122)

Dietary supplement A nonfood form of one or more nutrients (Ch. 6, 161)

Digestion The mechanical and chemical breakdown of foods for use by the body's cells (Ch. 17, 442)

Disability Any physical or mental impairment that limits normal activities, including seeing, hearing, walking, or speaking (Ch. 26, 695)

Divorce A legal end to a marriage contract (Ch. 11, 281)

DNA (deoxyribonucleic acid) The chemical unit that makes up chromosomes (Ch. 19, 499)

Domestic violence Any act of violence involving family members (Ch. 11, 286)

Drug watches Organized community efforts by neighborhood residents to patrol, monitor, report, and otherwise try to stop drug deals and drug abuse (Ch. 23, 612)

Drug-free school zone An area within 1,000 feet of a school and designated by signs, within which people caught selling drugs receive especially severe penalties (Ch. 23, 612)

Drugs Substances other than food that change the structure or function of the body or mind (Ch. 23, 586)

─────────── **E** ───────────

Earthquake A violent shaking movement of the earth's surface (Ch. 27, 729)

Eating disorder An extreme, harmful eating behavior that can cause serious illness or even death (Ch. 6, 153)

EIA A test that screens for the presence of HIV antibodies in the blood (Ch. 25, 663)

Electrolytes Minerals that help maintain the body's fluid balance (Ch. 6, 158)

Elimination The expulsion of undigested food or body wastes (Ch. 17, 442)

Embryo The cluster of cells that develops between the third and eighth weeks of pregnancy (Ch. 19, 486)

Emergency survival kit A group of items that can be used for a short time until an emergency situation has stabilized (Ch. 27, 726)

Emerging infection A communicable disease whose incidence in humans has increased within the past two decades or threatens to increase in the near future (Ch. 24, 640)

Emotional abuse A pattern of behavior that attacks the emotional development and sense of worth of an individual (Ch. 11, 287)

Emotional intimacy Ability to experience a caring, loving relationship with another person with whom you can share your innermost feelings (Ch. 20, 523)

Emotional maturity State at which the mental and emotional capabilities of an individual are fully developed (Ch. 20, 520)

Emotions Signals that tell your mind and body how to react (Ch. 7, 184)

Empathy The ability to imagine and understand how someone else feels (Ch. 7, 186)

Emphysema A disease that progressively destroys the walls of the alveoli (Ch. 16, 435)

Empty-nest syndrome Feelings of sadness or loneliness that accompany children's leaving home and entering adulthood (Ch. 20, 531)

Endocrine glands Ductless—or tubeless—organs or group of cells that secrete hormones directly into the bloodstream (Ch. 18, 464)

Environment The sum of your surroundings (Ch. 1, 13)

Environmental tobacco smoke (ETS) Air that has been contaminated by tobacco smoke (Ch. 21, 551)

Epidemics Occurrences of diseases in which many people in the same place at the same time are affected (Ch. 25, 648)

Epidemiology The scientific study of patterns of disease in a population (Ch. 3, 65)

Epidermis The outer, thinner layer of the skin that is composed of living and dead cells (Ch. 14, 360)

Epilepsy A disorder of the nervous system that is characterized by recurrent seizures—sudden episodes of uncontrolled electrical activity in the brain (Ch. 15, 409)

Ethanol The type of alcohol in alcoholic beverages (Ch. 22, 562)

Euphoria A feeling of intense well-being or elation (Ch. 23, 605)

Exercise Purposeful physical activity that is planned, structured, and repetitive and that improves or maintains personal fitness (Ch. 4, 81)

Extended family Your immediate family and other relatives such as grandparents, aunts, uncles, and cousins (Ch. 11, 277)

Extensor The muscle that opens a joint (Ch. 15, 395)

External auditory canal A passageway about 1 inch long that leads to the remaining portion of the outer ear, the eardrum (Ch. 14, 376)

F

Fad diets Weight-loss plans that are popular for only a short time (Ch. 6, 151)

Fallopian tubes A pair of tubes with fingerlike projections that draw in the ovum (Ch. 18, 475)

Family The basic unit of society (Ch. 11, 274)

Family counseling Therapy to restore healthy relationships in a family (Ch. 11, 294)

Fermentation The chemical action of yeast on sugars (Ch. 22, 562)

Fertilization Union of a male sperm cell and a female egg cell (Ch. 19, 486)

Fetal alcohol syndrome (FAS) A group of alcohol-related birth defects that includes both physical and mental problems (Ch. 19, 494; Ch. 22, 576)

Fetus Developing embryo in the uterus (Ch. 19, 486)

Fiber An indigestible complex carbohydrate (Ch. 5, 115)

Fire extinguisher A portable device that puts out small fires by ejecting fire-extinguishing chemicals (Ch. 27, 708)

First aid The immediate, temporary care given to an ill or injured person until professional medical care can be provided (Ch. 28, 736)

F.I.T.T. Frequency, intensity, time/duration, and type of activity (Ch. 4, 90)

Flash flood A flood with great volume and of short duration that is usually caused by heavy rainfall (Ch. 27, 727)

Flexibility The ability to move a body part through a full range of motion (Ch. 4, 81)

Flexor The muscle that closes a joint (Ch. 15, 395)

Food additives Substances intentionally added to food to produce a desired effect (Ch. 5, 131)

Food allergy A condition in which the body's immune system reacts to substances in some foods (Ch. 5, 133)

Food intolerance A negative reaction to a food or part of food caused by a metabolic problem, such as the inability to digest parts of certain foods or food components (Ch. 5, 134)

Foodborne illness Food poisoning (Ch. 5, 134)

Foster care A temporary arrangement in which a child is placed under the guidance and supervision of a family or an adult who is not related to the child by birth (Ch. 11, 292)

Fracture A break in the bone (Ch. 28, 750)

Fraud Deliberate deceit or trickery (Ch. 3, 61)

Friendship A significant relationship between two people that is based on caring, trust, and consideration (Ch. 10, 249; Ch. 12, 303)

Frostbite A condition that results when body tissues become frozen (Ch. 4, 100)

G

Gametes Reproductive cells (Ch. 20, 515)

Gang A group of people who associate with one another to take part in criminal activity (Ch. 13, 337)

Gastric juices Secretions from the stomach lining that contain hydrochloric acid and pepsin, an enzyme that digests protein (Ch. 17, 444)

Gene therapy The process of inserting normal genes into human cells to correct genetic disorders (Ch. 19, 503)

Genes The basic units of heredity (Ch. 19, 499)

Genetic disorder A disorder caused partly or completely by a defect in genes (Ch. 19, 500)

Genital herpes An STD caused by the herpes simplex virus (HSV) (Ch. 25, 654)

Goal Something you aim for that takes planning and work (Ch. 2, 34)

Gonads The ovaries and testes (Ch. 18, 466)

Gonorrhea A bacterial STD that usually affects mucous membranes (Ch. 25, 655)

Graduated driver's license A licensing program that gradually increases a new driver's driving privileges over time as experience and skill are gained (Ch. 27, 720)

Grief The sorrow caused by the loss of a loved one (Ch. 11, 282)

Grief response An individual's total response to a major loss (Ch. 9, 239)

Group therapy Treating a group of people who have similar problems and who meet regularly with a trained counselor (Ch. 9, 237)

H

Hair follicle A structure that surrounds the root of a hair (Ch. 14, 365)

Hallucinogens Drugs that alter moods, thoughts, and sense perceptions including vision, hearing, smell, and touch (Ch. 23, 609)

Harassment Persistently annoying others (Ch. 12, 308)

Hazardous waste A substance that is explosive, corrosive, highly reactive, or toxic to humans or other life-forms (Ch. 29, 773)

Health The combination of physical, mental/emotional, and social well-being (Ch. 1, 4)

Health care system All the medical care available to a nation's people, the way they receive care, and the method of payment (Ch. 3, 54)

Health consumer Anyone who purchases or uses health products or services (Ch. 3, 48)

Health education The providing of accurate health information to help people make healthy choices (Ch. 1, 7)

Health fraud Sale of worthless products or services claimed to prevent diseases or cure other health problems (Ch. 3, 61)

Health insurance A plan in which private companies or government programs pay for part or all of a person's medical costs (Ch. 3, 57)

Health literacy A person's capacity to learn about and understand basic health information and services and use these resources to promote his or her health and wellness (Ch. 1, 8)

Health screening A search or check for diseases or disorders that an individual would otherwise not have knowledge of or seek help for (Ch. 4, 95)

Health skills Specific tools and strategies that help you maintain, protect, and improve all aspects of your health (Ch. 2, 28)

Healthy People 2010 A nationwide health promotion and disease prevention plan designed to serve as a guide for improving the health of all people in the United States (Ch. 1, 7)

Heartburn A burning sensation in the center of the chest that may rise from the bottom, or tip, of the breastbone up to the throat (Ch. 17, 448)

Heat cramps Muscle spasms that result from a loss of large amounts of salt and water through perspiration (Ch. 4, 99)

Heat exhaustion An overheating of the body that results in cold, clammy skin and symptoms of shock (Ch. 27, 715)

Heatstroke A condition in which the body loses the ability to rid itself of excessive heat through perspiration (Ch. 4, 99)

Hemodialysis A technique in which an artificial kidney machine removes waste products from the blood (Ch. 17, 457)

Hemoglobin The oxygen-carrying protein in blood (Ch. 16, 418)

Herbal supplement A chemical substance from plants that may be sold as a dietary supplement (Ch. 6, 161)

Heredity All the traits that are biologically passed from parents to their children (Ch. 1, 12; Ch. 19, 498)

Hernia When an organ or tissue protrudes through an area of weak muscle (Ch. 15, 398)

Hiatal hernia A condition in which part of the stomach pushes through an opening in the diaphragm (Ch. 17, 448)

Hierarchy of needs A ranked list of those needs essential to human growth and development, presented in ascending order starting with basic needs and building toward the need for reaching your highest potential (Ch. 7, 172)

Histamines Chemicals that can stimulate mucous and fluid production in an area (Ch. 26, 689)

Hodgkin's disease A type of cancer that affects the lymph tissue (Ch. 16, 427)

Homicide The willful killing of one human being by another (Ch. 13, 344)

Hormones Chemical substances that are produced in glands and help regulate many of your body's functions (Ch. 7, 185; Ch. 18, 464; Ch. 20, 514)

Hostility The intentional use of unfriendly or offensive behavior (Ch. 7, 187)

Human immunodeficiency virus (HIV) A virus that attacks the immune system (Ch. 25, 658)

Human papillomavirus (HPV) A virus that can cause genital warts or asymptomatic infection (Ch. 25, 652)

Hunger A natural physical drive that protects you from starvation (Ch. 5, 111)

Hurricane A powerful storm that originates at sea, characterized by winds of at least 74 miles per hour, heavy rains, flooding, and sometimes tornadoes (Ch. 27, 727)

Hydration Taking in fluids so that the body functions properly (Ch. 4, 94)

Hypertension High blood pressure (Ch. 26, 675)

Hypothermia A condition in which body temperature becomes dangerously low (Ch. 4, 101; Ch. 27, 715)

────────── I ──────────

Illegal drugs Chemical substances that people of any age may not lawfully manufacture, possess, buy, or sell (Ch. 23, 592)

Illicit drug use The use or sale of any substance that is illegal or otherwise not permitted (Ch. 23, 592)

"I" message A statement in which a person describes how he or she feels by using the pronoun "I" (Ch.10, 256)

Immune system A network of cells, tissues, organs, and chemicals that fights pathogens (Ch. 24, 627)

Immunity The state of being protected against a particular disease (Ch. 24, 630)

Implantation The attachment of the zygote to the uterine wall (Ch. 19, 486)

Indigestion A feeling of discomfort in the upper abdomen (Ch. 17, 448)

Infatuation Exaggerated feelings of passion for another person (Ch. 12, 313)

Infection A condition that occurs when pathogens enter the body, multiply, and damage body cells (Ch. 24, 622)

Infertility The inability to conceive a child (Ch. 18, 478)

Inflammatory response A reaction to tissue damage caused by injury or infection (Ch. 24, 628)

Inhalants Substances whose fumes are sniffed and inhaled to achieve a mind-altering effect (Ch. 23, 600)

Integrity A firm adherence to a moral code (Ch. 20, 532)

Interpersonal communication The exchange of thoughts, feelings, and beliefs between two or more people (Ch. 2, 28)

Interpersonal conflict Disagreement between groups of any size, from two people to entire nations (Ch. 10, 262)

Intoxication The state in which the body is poisoned by alcohol or another substance and the person's physical and mental control is significantly reduced (Ch. 22, 563)

────────── J ──────────

Jaundice A yellowing of the skin and eyes (Ch. 24, 638)

────────── L ──────────

Labor The final stage of pregnancy in which the uterus contracts and pushes the baby out of the mother's body (Ch. 19, 490)

Labyrinth The inner ear (Ch. 14, 377)

Lacrimal gland The gland that secretes tears into ducts that empty into the eye (Ch. 14, 371)

Landfill An area that has been safeguarded to prevent disposed wastes from contaminating groundwater (Ch. 29, 772)

Larynx Voice box (Ch. 16, 431)

Leukemia A form of cancer in which any one of the different types of white blood cells is produced excessively and abnormally (Ch. 16, 426)

Leukoplakia Thickened, white, leathery-looking spots on the inside of the mouth that can develop into oral cancer (Ch. 21, 542)

Ligament A band of fibrous, slightly elastic connective tissue that attaches bone to bone (Ch. 15, 389)

Lipid A fatty substance that does not dissolve in water (Ch. 5, 117)

Long-term goal A goal that you plan to reach over an extended period of time (Ch. 2, 35)

Lymph The clear fluid that fills the spaces around body cells (Ch. 16, 421)

Lymphocytes Specialized white blood cells that provide the body with immunity (Ch. 16, 421; Ch. 24, 630)

────────── M ──────────

Mainstream smoke The smoke exhaled from the lungs of a smoker (Ch. 21, 551)

Malignant Cancerous (Ch. 26, 681)

Malpractice Failure by a health professional to meet accepted standards (Ch. 3, 61)

Manipulation An indirect, dishonest way to control or influence others (Ch. 12, 308)

Marijuana Plant whose leaves, buds, and flowers are usually smoked for their intoxicating effects (Ch. 23, 598)

Marital adjustment How well a person adjusts to marriage and to his or her spouse (Ch. 20, 525)

Mastication The process of chewing (Ch. 17, 443)

Media The various methods of communicating information (Ch. 1, 15; Ch. 3, 49)

Mediation A process in which specially trained people help others resolve their conflicts peacefully (Ch. 10, 267)

Mediator A person who helps others resolve issues to the satisfaction of both parties (Ch. 11, 294)

Medical history Complete and comprehensive information about your immunizations and any health problems you have had to date (Ch. 3, 58)

Medicines Drugs that are used to treat or prevent diseases or other conditions (Ch. 23, 586)

Megadose Very large amount of a dietary supplement (Ch. 6, 161)

Melanin A pigment that gives the skin, hair, and iris of the eyes their color (Ch. 14, 361)

Melanoma The most serious form of skin cancer (Ch. 14, 364)

Menopause The end of the reproductive years for a female (Ch. 18, 476)

Menstruation Shedding of the uterine lining (Ch. 18, 476)

Mental disorder An illness of the mind that can affect the thoughts, feelings, and behaviors of a person, preventing him or her from leading a happy, healthful, and productive life (Ch. 9, 224)

Mental retardation The below-average intellectual ability present from birth or early childhood and associated with difficulties in learning and social adaptation (Ch. 26, 697)

Mental/emotional health The ability to accept yourself and others, adapt to and manage emotions, and deal with the demands and challenges you meet in life (Ch. 7, 170)

Metabolism The process by which the body breaks down substances and gets energy from food (Ch. 4, 78; Ch. 22, 569)

Metastasis Spread of cancer from the point where it originated to other parts of the body (Ch. 26, 681)

Minerals Substances that the body cannot manufacture but that are needed for forming healthy bones and teeth and for regulating many vital body processes (Ch. 5, 120)

Miscarriage The spontaneous expulsion of a fetus that occurs before the twentieth week of a pregnancy (Ch. 19, 496)

Modeling Observing and learning from the behaviors of those around you (Ch. 7, 175)

Mood disorder An illness, often with an organic cause, that involves mood extremes that interfere with everyday living (Ch. 9, 226)

Mourning The act of showing sorrow or grief (Ch. 9, 240)

Muscle cramp A spasm or sudden tightening of a muscle (Ch. 4, 102)

Muscle tone The natural tension in the fibers of a muscle (Ch. 15, 396)

Muscular endurance The ability of the muscles to perform physical tasks over a period of time without becoming fatigued (Ch. 4, 80)

Muscular strength The amount of force a muscle can exert (Ch. 4, 80)

MyPyramid A guide for making healthful daily food choices (Ch. 5, 124)

N

Narcotics Specific drugs that are obtainable only by prescription and are used to relieve pain (Ch. 23, 608)

Neglect Failure to provide for a child's physical or emotional needs (Ch. 11, 288)

Negotiation The use of communication and often compromise to settle a disagreement (Ch. 10, 266)

Nephrons The functional units of the kidneys (Ch. 17, 454)

Neurons Nerve cells (Ch. 15, 400)

Nicotine The addictive drug found in tobacco leaves (Ch. 21, 541)

Nicotine substitute A product that delivers small amounts of nicotine into the user's system while he or she is trying to give up the tobacco habit (Ch. 21, 549)

Nicotine withdrawal The process that occurs in the body when nicotine, an addictive drug, is no longer used (Ch. 21, 548)

Noise pollution Harmful and unwanted sound of sufficient intensity to damage hearing (Ch. 29, 770)

Noncommunicable disease A disease that is not transmitted by another person, a vector, or from the environment (Ch. 26, 674)

Nutrient-dense foods Foods that are high in nutrients as compared with their calorie content (Ch. 6, 148)

Nutrients Substances in food that your body needs to grow, to repair itself, and to supply you with energy (Ch. 5, 110)

Nutrition The process by which the body takes in and uses food (Ch. 5, 110)

O

Obesity Having an excess amount of body fat (Ch. 6, 146)

Occupational Safety and Health Administration (OSHA) The agency in the federal government that is responsible for promoting safe and healthful conditions in the workplace (Ch. 27, 713)

Online shopping Using the Internet to buy products and services (Ch. 3, 52)

Opportunistic infection An infection that occurs in an individual who does not have a healthy immune system (Ch. 25, 659)

Ossification The process by which bone is formed, renewed, and repaired (Ch. 15, 387)

Osteoarthritis A disease of the joints in which cartilage breaks down (Ch. 26, 693)

Osteoporosis A condition in which there is the progressive loss of bone tissue (Ch., 4, 78; Ch. 15, 391)

Ova Female reproductive cells (Ch. 18, 474)

Ovaries The female sex glands that store the ova and produce female sex hormones (Ch. 18, 474)

Overdose A strong, sometimes fatal reaction to taking a large amount of a drug (Ch. 23, 594)

Overexertion Overworking the body (Ch. 4, 99)

Overload Working the body harder than it is normally worked (Ch. 4, 90)

Over-the-counter (OTC) medicines Medicines that you can buy without a prescription (Ch. 23, 590)

Overweight A condition in which a person is heavier than the standard weight range for his or her height (Ch. 6, 146)

Ovulation The process of releasing a mature ovum into the fallopian tube each month (Ch. 18, 474)

——————— **P** ———————

Pancreas Gland that serves two systems—the digestive and the endocrine systems (Ch. 18, 465)

Pandemic A global outbreak of infectious disease (Ch. 25, 665)

Paranoia Irrational suspiciousness or distrust of others (Ch. 23, 600)

Parathyroid glands Glands that produce a hormone that regulates the body's calcium and phosphorus balance (Ch. 18, 465)

Passive A tendency to give up, give in, or back down without standing up for rights and needs (Ch. 12, 312)

Passive immunity Temporary immunity received from another person or from antibodies (Ch. 24, 631)

Pasteurization The process of treating a substance with heat to destroy or slow the growth of pathogens (Ch. 5, 135)

Pathogen An organism that causes disease (Ch. 24, 622)

Peer mediation A process in which trained students help other students find fair ways to resolve conflict and settle their differences (Ch. 13, 339)

Peer mediators Students trained to help other students find fair resolutions to conflicts and disagreements (Ch. 10, 267)

Peer pressure The influence that people your age may have on you (Ch. 12, 307)

Peers People of similar age who share similar interests (Ch. 1, 13; Ch. 12, 302)

Penis A tube-shaped organ that extends from the trunk of the body just above the testes (Ch. 18, 469)

Peptic ulcer A sore in the lining of the digestive tract (Ch. 17, 451)

Perception The act of becoming aware through the senses (Ch. 8, 198)

Periodontal disease An inflammation of the periodontal structures (Ch. 14, 370)

Periodontium The area immediately around the teeth (Ch. 14, 367)

Peristalsis A series of involuntary muscle contractions that move food through the digestive tract (Ch. 17, 443)

Personal identity Your sense of yourself as a unique individual (Ch. 7, 178)

Personality A complex set of characteristics that makes you unique (Ch. 7, 175)

Phagocyte A white blood cell that attacks invading pathogens (Ch. 24, 629)

Pharynx Throat (Ch. 16, 431)

Physical abuse The intentional infliction of bodily harm or injury on another person (Ch. 11, 287; Ch. 13, 349)

Physical activity Any form of movement that causes your body to use energy (Ch. 4, 74)

Physical fitness The ability to carry out daily tasks easily and have enough reserve energy to respond to unexpected demands (Ch. 4, 74)

Physical maturity State at which the physical body and all its organs are fully developed (Ch. 20, 520)

Physiological dependence A condition in which the user has a chemical need for a drug (Ch. 23, 595)

Pituitary gland Regulates and controls the activities of all other endocrine glands (Ch. 18, 465)

Placenta A thick, blood-rich tissue that lines the walls of the uterus during pregnancy and nourishes the embryo (Ch. 19, 487)

Plaque A sticky, colorless film that acts on sugar to form acids that destroy tooth enamel and irritate gums (Ch. 14, 368)

Plasma The fluid in which other parts of the blood are suspended (Ch. 16, 418)

Platelets Cells that prevent the body's loss of blood (Ch. 16, 420)

Platonic friendship A friendship with a member of the opposite gender in which there is affection, but the two people are not considered a couple (Ch. 12, 303)

Pleurisy An inflammation of the lining of the lungs and chest cavity (Ch. 16, 433)

Pneumonia An inflammation of the lungs commonly caused by a bacterial or viral infection (Ch. 16, 433; Ch. 24, 636)

Poison Any substance—solid, liquid, or gas—that causes injury, illness, or death when introduced into the body (Ch. 28, 755)

Poison control center A 24-hour hot line that provides emergency medical advice on treating poisoning victims (Ch. 28, 755)

Post-traumatic stress disorder A condition that may develop after a person's exposure to a terrifying event that threatened or caused physical harm (Ch. 9, 226)

Precycling Reducing waste before it is generated (Ch. 29, 779)

Prejudice An unfair opinion or judgment of a particular group of people (Ch. 10, 260; Ch. 13, 342)

Prenatal care Steps that a pregnant female can take to provide for her own health and for the health of her baby (Ch. 19, 492)

Prescription medicine Medicines that cannot be used without the written approval of a licensed physician (Ch. 23, 590)

Prevention Practicing health and safety habits to remain free of disease and injury (Ch. 1, 6)

Preventive care Actions that prevent the onset of disease or injury (Ch. 3, 55)

Primary care physician Medical doctor who provides physical checkups and general care (Ch. 3, 54)

Priorities Those goals, tasks, and activities that you judge to be more important than others (Ch. 12, 319)

Profound deafness A hearing loss so severe that a person affected cannot benefit from mechanical amplification, such as a hearing aid (Ch. 26, 696)

Progression The gradual increase in overload necessary to achieve higher levels of fitness (Ch. 4, 90)

Protective factors Conditions that shield individuals from the negative consequences of exposure to risk (Ch. 8, 216)

Proteins Nutrients that help build and maintain body cells and tissues (Ch. 5, 116)

Psychoactive drugs Chemicals that affect the central nervous system and alter activity in the brain (Ch. 23, 603)

Psychological dependence Condition in which a person believes that a drug is needed in order to feel good or to function normally (Ch. 23, 595)

Psychosomatic response A physical reaction that results from stress rather than from an injury or illness (Ch. 8, 202)

Psychotherapy An ongoing dialogue between a patient and a mental health professional (Ch. 9, 237)

Puberty The time when a person begins to develop certain traits of adults of his or her own gender (Ch. 20, 514)

Public health A community-wide effort to monitor and promote the welfare of the population (Ch. 3, 64)

Pulp The tissue that contains the blood vessels and nerves of a tooth (Ch. 14, 368)

R

Radon An odorless, radioactive gas (Ch. 29, 769)

Random violence Violence committed for no particular reason (Ch. 13, 344)

Rape Any form of sexual intercourse that takes place against a person's will (Ch. 13, 346)

Recovery The process of learning to live an alcohol-free life (Ch. 22, 578)

Recycling The processing of waste materials so that they can be used again in some form (Ch. 29, 779)

Reflex A spontaneous response of the body to a stimulus (Ch. 15, 404)

Refusal skills Communication strategies that can help you say no when you are urged to take part in behaviors that are unsafe, unhealthful, or that go against your values (Ch. 2, 30; Ch. 12, 310)

Rehydration Restoring lost body fluids (Ch. 6, 158)

Relationship A bond or connection you have with other people (Ch. 10, 248)

Relaxation response A state of calm that can be reached if one or more relaxation techniques are practiced regularly (Ch. 8, 209)

Remission A period of time when symptoms disappear (Ch. 26, 687)

Repetitive motion injury Damage to tissues caused by prolonged, repeated movements (Ch. 15, 393)

Reproductive system The system of organs involved in producing offspring (Ch. 18, 468)

Resiliency The ability to adapt effectively and recover from disappointment, difficulty, or crisis (Ch. 8, 214; Ch. 11, 285)

Respiration The exchange of gases between the body and the environment (Ch. 16, 428)

Resting heart rate The number of times your heart beats in one minute when you are not active (Ch. 4, 92)

Retina The light-sensitive membrane on which images are cast by the cornea (Ch. 14, 372)

Rheumatoid arthritis A disease characterized by the debilitating destruction of the joints due to inflammation (Ch. 26, 694)

Risk behaviors Actions that can potentially threaten your health or the health of others (Ch. 1, 17)

Road rage A practice of endangering drivers by using a vehicle as a weapon (Ch. 27, 722)

Role A part you play in a relationship (Ch. 10, 250)

Role model Someone whose success or behavior serves as an example for others (Ch. 2, 40)

S

Sclera The white part of the eye (Ch. 14, 372)

Scoliosis An abnormal lateral, or side-to-side, curvature of the spine (Ch. 15, 391; Ch. 19, 507)

Scrotum An external skin sac that extends outside the body and contains the testes (Ch. 18, 469)

Sebaceous glands Structures within the skin that produce an oily secretion called sebum (Ch. 14, 361)

Sedentary lifestyle A way of life that involves little physical activity (Ch. 4, 77)

Self-actualization The striving to become the best you can be (Ch. 7, 174)

Self-control A person's ability to use responsibility to override emotions (Ch. 12, 319)

Self-defense Any strategy for protecting oneself from harm (Ch. 13, 332)

Self-directed Able to make correct decisions about behavior when adults are not present to enforce rules (Ch. 20, 528)

Semen A thick fluid containing sperm and other secretions from the male reproductive system (Ch. 18, 469)

Separation A decision between married individuals to live apart from each other (Ch. 11, 281)

Severe weather Harsh or dangerous weather conditions (Ch. 27, 725)

Sex characteristics The traits related to a person's gender (Ch. 20, 515)

Sexual abuse Any sexual contact that is forced upon a person against his or her will (Ch. 11, 287)

Sexual assault Any intentional sexual attack against another person (Ch. 13, 346)

Sexual harassment Uninvited and unwelcome sexual conduct directed at another person (Ch. 13, 336)

Sexual violence Any form of unwelcome sexual conduct directed at an individual, including sexual harassment, sexual assault, and rape (Ch. 13, 345)

Sexually transmitted diseases (STDs) Infectious diseases spread from person to person through sexual contact (Ch. 12, 318; Ch. 25, 648)

Sexually transmitted infections (STIs) Infectious diseases spread from person to person through sexual contact (Ch. 25, 648)

Shock A failure of the cardiovascular system to keep an adequate supply of blood circulating to the vital organs of the body (Ch. 28, 747)

Short-term goal A goal that you can reach in a short length of time (Ch. 2, 35)

Sibling A brother or sister (Ch. 11, 278)

Side effects Reactions to medicine other than the one intended (Ch. 23, 589)

Sidestream smoke The smoke from the burning end of a cigarette, pipe, or cigar (Ch. 21, 551)

Sinusitis Inflammation of the tissues that line the sinuses (Ch. 16, 435)

Skeletal muscles Muscles that are attached to bone and cause body movements (Ch. 15, 395)

Smog A yellow-brown haze that forms when sunlight reacts with air pollution (Ch. 29, 767)

Smoke alarm An alarm that is triggered by the presence of smoke (Ch. 27, 708)

Smokeless tobacco Tobacco that is sniffed through the nose, held in the mouth, or chewed (Ch. 21, 542)

Smooth muscles Muscles that act on the lining of passageways and internal organs (Ch. 15, 395)

Sobriety Living without alcohol (Ch. 22, 578)

Specialist Medical doctor trained to handle particular kinds of patients or medical conditions (Ch. 3, 54)

Specificity Particular exercises and activities that improve particular areas of health-related fitness (Ch. 4, 90)

Sperm Male reproductive cells (Ch. 18, 468)

Spousal abuse Domestic violence directed at a spouse (Ch. 11, 287)

Sprain An injury to the ligament surrounding a joint (Ch. 4, 102)

Stalking The repeated following, harassment, or threatening of an individual to frighten or cause him or her harm (Ch. 13, 349)

Stereotype An exaggerated and oversimplified belief about an entire group of people, such as an ethnic or religious group, or a gender (Ch. 12, 305)

Sterility The inability to reproduce (Ch. 18, 472)

Stillbirth A dead fetus expelled from the body after the twentieth week of pregnancy (Ch. 19, 496)

Stimulant A drug that increases the action of the central nervous system, the heart, and other organs (Ch. 21, 541; Ch. 23, 605)

Strain A condition resulting from damaging a muscle or tendon (Ch. 4, 102)

Stress The reaction of the body and mind to everyday challenges and demands (Ch. 8, 198)

Stress management Ways to deal with or overcome the negative effects of stress (Ch. 2, 31)

Stress-management skills Skills that help an individual handle stress in a healthful, effective way (Ch. 8, 208)

Stressor Anything that causes stress (Ch. 8, 199)

Stroke A condition where an arterial blockage interrupts the flow of blood to the brain (Ch. 26, 678)

Substance abuse Any unnecessary or improper use of chemical substances for nonmedical purposes (Ch. 23, 592)

Suicide The act of intentionally taking one's own life (Ch. 9, 230)

Suppression Holding back or restraining (Ch. 7, 189)

Sweat glands Structures within the dermis that secrete perspiration through ducts to pores on the skin's surface (Ch. 14, 361)

Symptomatic stage The stage in which a person infected with HIV has symptoms as a result of a severe drop in immune cells (Ch. 25, 663)

Synergistic effect Interaction of two or more medicines that results in a greater effect than when the medicines are taken alone (Ch. 23, 589)

Syphilis An STD that attacks many parts of the body and is caused by a small bacterium called a spirochete (Ch. 25, 655)

T

Tar A thick, sticky, dark fluid produced when tobacco burns (Ch. 21, 541)

Tartar The hard, crustlike substance formed when plaque hardens (Ch. 14, 370)

Tendon A fibrous cord that attaches muscle to the bone (Ch. 15, 389)

Tendonitis The inflammation of a tendon (Ch. 15, 398)

Testes Two small glands that produce sperm (Ch. 19, 469)

Testosterone Male sex hormone (Ch. 18, 469)

Thyroid gland Produces hormones that regulate metabolism, body heat, and bone growth (Ch. 18, 465)

Tinnitus A condition in which a ringing, buzzing, whistling, roaring, hissing, or other sound is heard in the ear in the absence of external sound (Ch. 14, 379)

Tolerance The ability to accept others' differences and allow them to be who they are without expressing disapproval (Ch. 10, 260)

Tolerance A condition in which the body becomes used to the effects of a medicine (Ch. 23, 589)

Tornado A whirling, funnel-shaped windstorm that drops from the sky to the ground and produces a narrow path of destruction on land (Ch. 27, 728)

Toxin A substance that kills cells or interferes with their functions (Ch. 24, 623)

Trachea Windpipe (Ch. 16, 431)

Training program A program of formalized physical preparation for involvement in a sport or another physical activity (Ch. 4, 93)

Transitions Critical changes that occur at all stages of life (Ch. 20, 529)

Trichomoniasis An STD caused by a microscopic protozoan that results in infections of the vagina, urethra, and bladder (Ch. 25, 655)

Tuberculosis A contagious bacterial infection that usually affects the lungs (Ch. 16, 435)

Tumor An abnormal mass of tissue that has no natural role in the body (Ch. 26, 681)

U

Umbilical cord A ropelike structure that connects the embryo and the mother's placenta (Ch. 19, 487)

Unconditional love Love without limitation or qualification (Ch. 20, 528)

Unconsciousness A condition in which a person is not alert and aware of his or her surroundings (Ch. 28, 751)

Underweight A condition in which a person is less than the standard weight range for his or her height (Ch. 6, 147)

Unintentional injury An injury resulting from an unexpected event, or accident (Ch. 27, 706)

Universal precautions Actions taken to prevent the spread of disease by treating all blood and other body fluids as if they contained pathogens (Ch. 28, 737)

Urban sprawl The spreading of city development (houses, shopping centers, businesses, and schools) onto undeveloped land (Ch. 29, 774)

Ureters Tubes that connect the kidneys to the bladder (Ch. 17, 454)

Urethra The tube that leads from the bladder to the outside of the body (Ch. 17, 455)

Urethritis The inflammation of the urethra (Ch. 17, 456)

Urine Liquid waste material (Ch. 17, 453)

Uterus A hollow, muscular, pear-shaped organ inside a female's body (Ch. 18, 474)

V

Vaccine A preparation of dead or weakened pathogens that are introduced into the body to stimulate an immune response (Ch. 23, 587; Ch. 24, 631)

Vagina A muscular, elastic passageway that extends from the uterus to the outside of the body (Ch. 18, 475)

Values The ideas, beliefs, and attitudes about what is important that help guide the way you live (Ch. 2, 34)

Vector An organism, such as a tick, that carries and transmits pathogens to humans or other animals (Ch. 24, 625)

Vegan Vegetarians who eat only foods of plant origin (Ch. 6, 160)

Vegetarian A person who eats mostly or only foods that come from plant sources (Ch. 6, 159)

Vehicular safety Obeying the rules of the road, as well as exercising common sense and good judgment (Ch. 27, 719)

Veins Blood vessels that return blood to the heart (Ch. 16, 419)

Venom A poisonous substance secreted by a snake, spider, or other creature (Ch. 28, 755)

Verbal abuse Using words to mistreat or injure another person (Ch. 13, 349)

Violence Threatened or actual use of physical force or power to harm another person or to damage property (Ch. 13, 335)

Virus A form of genetic material that invades living cells to reproduce (Ch. 24, 623)

Vitamins Compounds that help regulate many vital body processes, including the digestion, absorption, and metabolism of other nutrients (Ch. 5, 119)

W

Warm-up An activity that prepares the muscles for work (Ch. 4, 90)

Warranty A company's or a store's written agreement to repair a product or refund your money should the product not function properly (Ch. 3, 50)

Wastewater Used water that comes from homes, communities, farms, and businesses (Ch. 29, 775)

Weight cycling The repeated pattern of loss and regain of body weight (Ch. 6, 152)

Wellness An overall state of well-being, or total health (Ch. 1, 5)

Western blot (WB) The most common confirmation test for HIV in the United States (Ch. 25, 664)

Withdrawal A condition that occurs when a person stops using a medicine on which he or she has a chemical dependency (Ch 23. 589)

Workout The part of an exercise program when the activity is performed at its highest peak (Ch. 4, 90)

A

Absorption/absorción Proceso mediante el cual la comida digerida pasa desde el aparato digestivo al sistema cardiovascular.

Abstinence/abstinencia Una decisión deliberada de evitar una conducta considerada arriesgada o dañina como la actividad sexual prematrimonial, el consumo de tabaco, alcohol, y otras drogas.

Abuse/abuso El maltrato físico, mental/emocional o sexual de una persona por otra.

Accident chain/cadena de accidentes Una serie de sucesos que generan una herida sin intención.

Acquired immune deficiency syndrome (AIDS)/síndrome de inmunodeficiencia adquirida (SIDA) Enfermedad en la cual el sistema inmunológico del paciente se encuentra debilitado.

Action plan/plan de acción Una estrategia que ayuda a identificar y lograr metas.

Active immunity/inmunidad activa La inmunidad que desarrolla el cuerpo para protegerse de enfermedades.

Active listening/audición activa Escuchar atentamente lo que alguien dice o comunica.

Addiction/adicción La dependencia psicológica o fisiológica a las drogas.

Addictive drug/droga adictiva Una substancia que causa la dependencia psicológica o fisiológica.

Additive interaction/interacción aditiva Medicinas que trabajan en conjunto de una manera positiva.

Adolescence/adolescencia La etapa entre la infancia y la edad adulta.

Adoption/adopción Proceso legal para tener como hijo un niño de otros padres.

Adrenal glands/glándulas suprarrenales Glándulas que ayudan al cuerpo a recuperarse del estrés y a actuar ante emergencias.

Advertising/publicidad Un mensaje, oral o escrito, diseñado para incentivar a los consumidores a comprar un producto o servicio.

Advocacy/apoya Apoyar o defender acciones que tienen como objetivo influenciar a otras personas para que respalden asuntos o creencias relacionadas con la salud.

Aerobic exercise/ejercicio aeróbico Cualquier actividad física que sea rítmica, que implique el uso de grupos de músculos grandes y que pueda ser mantenida por al menos 10 minutos tres veces al día o por 20 a 30 minutos en una acción continua.

Affection/afecto El sentimiento de cariño por otra persona.

Affirmation/afirmación Una reacción positiva que ayuda a que otras personas se sientan apreciadas y respaldadas.

Aggressive/agresivo Excesivamente fuerte, insistente, hostil, o de predisposición belicosa.

Air pollution/contaminación atmosférica La contaminación de la atmósfera de la tierra por sustancias que presentan peligro a la salud de los seres vivos.

Air Quality Index (AQI)/índice de calidad del aire Un indicador para informar sobre la calidad del aire diario.

Alcohol abuse/abuso de alcohol Uso excesivo de alcohol.

Alcohol poisoning/envenenamiento alcohólico Una reacción física severa y algunas veces fatal a una sobredosis de alcohol.

Alcoholic/alcohólico Una persona que es adicta al alcohol.

Alcoholism/alcoholismo Enfermedad en que la persona es adicta física o psicológicamente a bebidas alcohólicas.

Alienation/alienación Sentirse solo y separado de todo el mundo.

Allergy/alergia Una reacción específica del sistema inmunológico a una substancia extraña que es usualmente inofensiva.

Americans with Disabilities Act/Ley para Americanos Incapacidados Una ley que prohíbe la discriminación de personas discapacitadas por parte de los lugares de trabajo, transporte, lugares públicos y telecomunicaciones.

Amniocentesis/amniocentesis Un procedimiento en la cual se inserta una jeringa a través de la pared abdominal de una mujer embarazada hasta llegar al líquido amniótico alrededor del embrión en desarrollo.

Amniotic sac/saco amniótico Una membrana delgada llena de líquido que envuelve y protege al embrión.

Anabolic-androgenic steroids/esteroides anabolizantes-androgénicos Substancias sintéticas semejantes a la testosterona, la hormona masculina.

Anaerobic exercise/ejercicio anaeróbico Períodos cortos de actividad física intensiva en la cual los músculos trabajan tan fuerte que producen energía sin usar oxígeno.

Analgesics/analgésicos Medicamentos que alivian el dolor.

Anemia/anemia Condición en la cual la habilidad de la sangre de transportar oxígeno disminuye.

Angina pectoris/angina de pecho Un dolor en el pecho que es causado porque el corazón no está recibiendo suficiente oxígeno.

Anorexia nervosa/anorexia nerviosa Un desorden de alimentación en el cual el miedo irracional a convertirse obeso/a resulta en la pérdida extrema de peso por una dieta de hambre autoimpuesta.

Antagonistic interaction/interacción antagónica Situación en la cual el efecto de un medicamento se elimina o reduce por tomar otro medicamento.

Antibody/anticuerpo Una proteína que ataca antígenos específicos.

Antigen/antígeno Una substancia que es capaz de liberar un agente inmune.

Anxiety/ansiedad La condición de sentirse abrumado o preocupado acerca de lo que que pasará.

Anxiety disorder/trastorno de ansiedad Una condición en la cual el miedo, ya sea real o imaginado, es difícil de controlar.

Appendicitis/apendicitis La inflamación del apéndice.

Appendicular skeleton/esqueleto apendicular Los 126 huesos de las extremidades superiores e inferiores, los hombros, y las caderas.

Appetite/apetito El deseo, mas que la necesidad, de comer.

Arrhythmia/arritmia Palpitaciones irregulares del corazón.

Arteries/arterias Vasos sanguíneos que llevan la sangre desde el corazón a otras partes del cuerpo humano.

Arthritis/artritis Un grupo de mas de 100 condiciones que causan dolor y la pérdida de movimiento en las articulaciones.

Asbestos/asbesto Una fibra mineral que tiene propiedades contra combustión y que fue comúnmente usada como aislante.

Assailant/agresor Una persona que comete un acto violento contra otra persona.

Assault/asalto Un ataque ilegal contra una persona con la intención de hacerle daño o matarla.

Assertive/firme Sostener de manera positiva los derechos y creencias propios.

Asthma/asma Una condición inflamatoria en que la traquea, los bronquios y los bronquiolos se estrechan provocando dificultad para respirar.

Asymptomatic stage/Etapa sin síntomas Un período de tiempo durante el cuál una persona infectada por el VIH no tiene síntomas.

Atherosclerosis/artereosclerosis El proceso en el cual depósitos se acumulan en las paredes de las arterias.

Auditory ossicles/huesecillos auditorios Tres pequeños huesos que se encuentran unidos y conectan el tímpano con el oído.

Autoimmune disease/enfermedad autoinmunológica Una condición en la cuál el sistema inmune se ataca a sí mismo por error, afectando a las células, los tejidos, y los órganos del cuerpo de la misma persona.

Autonomy/autonomía La capacidad que una persona tiene para controlar su propio cuerpo, impulsos y medio ambiente.

Axial skeleton/esqueleto axial Los 80 huesos del cráneo, la columna vertebral, el esternón.

— **B** —

Bacteria/bacteria Microorganismos compuestos de una sola célula.

Behavior therapy/terapia de comportamiento Un terapia cuyo objetivo es cambiar conductas indeseadas a través de recompensas y refuerzos.

Benign/benigno No canceroso.

Bile/bilis Un líquido amargo de color amarillo-verde que es importante para la descomposición y absorción de las grasas.

Binge drinking/borrachera El consumo de cinco o más bebidas alcohólicas en un corto plazo.

Binge eating disorder/trastorno de la alimentación excesiva Un desorden de alimentación caracterizado por comer demasiado y de manera compulsiva.

Biodegradable/biodegradable Algo que se descompone por los microorganismos del medio ambiente.

Biomedical therapy/terapia biomédica El uso de ciertos medicamentos para tratar o reducir los síntomas de un desorden mental.

Biopsy/biopsia La extirpación diagnóstica de una pequeña muestra de tejido.

Birthing center/centro de partos Un lugar en el cual mujeres con un embarazo de bajo riesgo pueden dar a luz en un ambiente hogareño.

Bladder/vejiga Un órgano muscular hueco que actúa como recipiente para la orina.

Blizzard/ventisca Una tormenta de nieve con vientos que superan las 35 millas por hora.

Blood alcohol concentration (BAC)/concentración de alcohol en la sangre La cantidad de alcohol contenida en la sangre expresada como un porcentaje.

Blood pressure/tensión arterial Una medida de la presión que la sangre genera en las paredes de los vasos sanguíneos, especialmente en las arterias grandes, cuando la sangre es impulsada por el cuerpo.

Body composition/composición del cuerpo La proporción entre tejido graso y tejido magro incluyendo los músculos, los huesos, el agua, y los tejidos conjuntivos tales como ligamentos, cartílagos y tendones.

Body image/imagen corpora La forma en que uno se ve a su propio cuerpo.

Body language/lenguaje del cuerpo Comunicación no-verbal a través de gestos, expresiones faciales, comportamientos y postura.

Body mass index (BMI)/índice de masa corporal Una medida que permite la evaluación del tamaño de un cuerpo en relación con su peso y estatura.

Brain stem/vástago del cerebro Un ramificación de neuronas y fibras de tres pulgadas de largo que conecta la médula espinal al resto del cerebro.

Bronchi/bronquios Los pasajes que conectan la traquea con los pulmones.

Bronchitis/bronquitis Una inflamación de los bronquios causada por la infección o exposición a irritantes como el humo de tabaco o contaminación ambiental.

Bulimia nervosa/bulimia nerviosa Un trastorno de episodios de comer con exceso seguidos de alguna forma de auto-purgación o limpieza del aparato digestivo.

Bullying/intimidación Buscar poder o atraer atención por abuso psicológico, emocional o físico de otra persona.

---------------- **C** ----------------

Calories/calorías Unidades de calor que miden la energía que usa el cuerpo y la energía que la comida proporciona al cuerpo.

Cancer/cáncer El crecimiento incontrolable de células anormales.

Capillaries/capilares Vasos muy pequeños que transportan la sangre entre las arteriolas y las vénulas.

Carbohydrate/carbohidrato Las féculas y azúcares contenidos en los alimentos.

Carbon monoxide/monóxido de carbono Un gas sin color, inodoro, y venenoso.

Carcinogen/cancerígeno Un substancia que produce cáncer.

Cardiac muscle/músculo cardiaco Un tipo de músculo estriado que forma las paredes del corazón.

Cardiopulmonary resuscitation (CPR)/resucitación cardiopulmonar Un procedimiento de primeros auxilios que combina la respiración artificial con presiones en el pecho, proveyendo oxígeno hasta que las funciones vitales puedan resumir.

Cardiorespiratory endurance/resistencia cardio-respiratoria La habilidad que tienen el corazón, los pulmones y los vasos sanguíneos de utilizar y enviar energía y oxígeno a los tejidos del cuerpo durante largos períodos de tiempo con actividad moderada hasta enérgica.

Cardiovascular disease (CVD)/enfermedad cardio-vascular Una enfermedad que afecta el corazón o los vasos sanguíneos.

Cartilage/cartílago Tejido conjuntivo que es fuerte y flexible.

Cerebellum/cerebelo La segunda parte más grande del cerebro.

Cerebral palsy/parálisis cerebral Un grupo de desordenes neurológicos no progresivos y que son el resultado de daños al cerebro antes, durante, o justo después del nacimiento o durante la niñez temprana.

Cerebrum/cerebro La parte más grande y compleja del cerebro.

Cervix/cuello del útero La entrada del útero.

Chain of survival/cadena de supervivencia Una secuencia de acciones que tiene como objetivo maximizar las posibilidades de supervivencia de una víctima.

Character/carácter Las características distintivas que describen como una persona piensa, siente y actúa.

Child abuse/maltrato infantil Abuso doméstico dirigido hacia los niños.

Chlamydia/clamidia Una infección bacteriana que afecta los órganos reproductores de los hombres y mujeres.

Chorionic villi sampling (CVS)/biopsia de vellosidades coriónicas Un procedimiento mediante el cual se remueve una pequeña muestra de membrana de una capa de tejido que se desarrolla en la placenta llamada corión.

Choroid/coroides Una estructura delgada que cubre la parte interna de la esclerótica.

Chromosomes/cromosomas Estructuras parecidas a hilos encontradas dentro del núcleo de una célula y que cargan los códigos para rasgos heredados.

Chronic stress/estrés crónico El estrés relacionado con problemas de largo plazo y fuera del control de una persona.

Chyme/chyme Una mezcla cremosa y líquida de alimento y jugos gástricos.

Citizenship/ciudadanía La manera de comportarse como miembro de la comunidad.

Clique/pandilla Un grupo pequeño de amigos generalmente con gustos y experiencias similares que excluyen a otras personas vistas como ajenas a ellos.

Club drugs/drogas de club Drogas asociadas con conciertos, clubes de baile, y fiestas nocturnas conocidas como "raves".

Cluster suicides/serie de suicidios Una serie de suicidios que ocurren en un período de tiempo corto que involucran a varias personas de un mismo colegio o comunidad.

Cognition/cognición La habilidad de razonar y pensar con soluciones abstractas.

Cognitive therapy/terapia cognoscitiva Una terapia diseñada para identificar y corregir modelos de pensamientos los cuales pueden generar comportamientos que sean problemáticos, contraproducentes, o destructivos para sí mismo.

Commitment/compromiso Una promesa u obligación.

Communicable disease/enfermedad contagiosa Una enfermedad que se puede transmitir de un ser vivo a otro o a través del medio ambiente.

Communication/comunicación Las maneras de enviar los mensajes a otros y de recibir mensajes enviados por otros.

Comparison shopping/compras comparadas Evaluar los beneficios de diferentes productos comparando factores tales como calidad, características y precio.

Compromise/acuerdo Un método para resolver problemas en que cada participante debe sacrificar algo con el fin de solucionar el problema.

Concussion/conmoción cerebral Una situación que es el resultado de un golpe en el cerebro y que afecta su normal funcionamiento.

Conduct disorder/desorden de conducta Un patrón de comportamiento en el cual los derechos de otros o las reglas sociales básicas son violados.

Confidentiality/confidencialidad Respetar la vida privada de otros y guardar detalles secretos.

Conflict/conflicto Cualquier desacuerdo, pelea o enojo.

Conflict resolution/resolución de conflicto Proceso de resolver un desacuerdo a través de la cooperación y solución de problemas.

Congenital/congénito Una condición que se presenta al nacimiento.

Conservation/conservación La protección y preservación del medio ambiente a través de la prevención de abusos, destrucción e incorrecto uso de los recursos naturales.

Constructive criticism/crítica constructiva Comentarios no hostiles acerca del problema que tienen como objetivo mejorar un comportamiento o situación.

Consumer advocate/defensor del consumidor Gente o grupos cuyo único propósito es confrontar los problemas regionales, nacionales, y hasta internacionales del consumidor.

Cool-down/enfriamiento Una actividad que prepara los músculos para volver a un estado de relajación.

Cooperation/cooperación Trabajar juntos para el beneficio de todos.

Coping/hacer frente a Ocuparse exitosamente de los cambios difíciles de la vida.

Cornea/córnea Un tejido transparente que refracta y enfoca la luz antes de pasar al cristalino.

Crisis center/centro para crisis Un plante que maneja emergencias y envía a un individuo que necesita ayuda a especialistas.

Cross-contamination/traspasar la contaminación La dispersión de bacteria u otros microbios patogénicos de una comida a otra.

Culture/cultura Las creencias, costumbres y comportamiento colectivos de un grupo de personas.

Cumulative risks/riesgos acumulados Riesgos relacionados que aumentan en efecto con cada riesgo más.

Curfew/toque de queda Un período de tiempo de restricción en casa nocturno.

Custody/custodia Una decisión legal acerca de quién tiene el derecho de tomar las decisiones que afectarán a un niño, y quién tiene la responsabilidad de hacerse cargo de él.

Cycle of violence/ciclo de violencia Patrón de comportamiento violento o abusivo repetido de una generación a la próxima.

Cystitis/cistitis La inflamación de la vejiga.

───────── **D** ─────────

Dandruff/caspa Una condición que puede resultar si el cuero cabelludo se seca y las células muertas de la piel se desprenden como partículas blancas pegajosas.

Date rape/violación Cuando una persona que se encuentra en una cita obliga a la otra a participar en una actividad sexual.

Decibel/decibelios Una medida que se usa para expresar la intensidad relativa del volumen del sonido.

Decision-making skills/habilidades para tomar decisiones Los pasos necesarios para tomar una correcta decisión.

Defense mechanisms/mecanismos de defensa Procesos mentales que protegen a individuos de emociones y situaciones fuertes o estresantes.

Defensive driver/manejo defensivo Un conductor consciente de peligros posibles que reacciona para evitarlos.

Defibrillator/máqina de defibrilación Un aparato que proporciona choques eléctricos al corazón para restaurar su ritmo normal.

Deforestation/desforestación Destrucción de los bosques.

Depressants/sedantes Sustancias que tienden a disminuir la función del sistema nervioso central.

Depression/depresión Un sentimiento prolongado de soledad, desesperación y tristeza.

Dermis/dermis La capa más gruesa de la piel que se encuentra debajo de la epidermis que está compuesta de tejidos conectivos y contiene vasos sanguíneos y nervios.

Designer drugs/droga de diseño Sustancias sintéticas que tratan de imitar los efectos de los alucinógenos y otras drogas peligrosas.

Detoxification/desintoxicación Un proceso mediante el cual el cuerpo se ajusta para funcionar sin alcohol.

Developmental assets/recursos para el desarrollo Componentes básicos del desarrollo que ayudan a que los jóvenes crecen saludables, afectuosos, y responsables.

Developmental task/tareas requeridas para el desarrollo Sucesos necesarios para que una persona continúe creciendo y se convierta en un adulto saludable y maduro.

Diabetes/diabetes Una enfermedad crónica que afecta el modo en que las células del cuerpo conviertan los alimentos en energía.

Diaphragm/diafragma El músculo que separa los pulmones de la cavidad abdominal.

***Dietary Guidelines for Americans*/Pautas alimenticias para los estadounidenses** Una serie de recomendaciones para la alimentación saludable y la vida activa de los estadounidenses.

Dietary supplement/suplemento alimenticio Uno o más alimentos nutritivos que no son comida.

Digestion/digestión La descomposición mecánica y química de la comida para uso por las células corporales.

Disability/incapacidad Cualquier impedimento físico o mental que limita el desarrollo de actividades normales inclusive ver, oír, caminar o hablar.

Divorce/divorcio Un fin legal de un contrato de matrimonio.

DNA (deoxyribonucleic acid)/ADN (acido desoxirribonucleico La unidad química que compone los cromosomas.

Domestic violence/violencia doméstica Cualquier acto de violencia que incluya a los miembros de una familia.

Drug watches/vigilantes de la droga Un grupo de personas de un vecindario organizadas para espiar, seguir, denunciar o directamente frenar el abuso y venta de drogas.

Drug-free school zone/zona de escuela libre de drogas Un área que comprende 1,000 pies alrededor de una escuela y se encuentra señalizada, en la cual las personas que son atrapadas vendiendo drogas son severamente penalizadas o castigadas, más que lo usual.

Drugs/drogas Sustancias, excepto alimentos, que cambian la estructura o funcionamiento del cuerpo o mente de las personas.

–––––––––––––––––––– **E** ––––––––––––––––––––

Earthquake/terremoto Un temblor que mueve fuertemente la superficie de la tierra.

Eating disorder/desorden alimenticio Un comportamiento que se caracteriza por comer en forma extrema y dañina causando que la persona se pueda enfermar o morir.

EIA/ensayo inmunoenzimático de enzimas Un análisis que estudia la presencia de VIH en la sangre.

Electrolytes/electrolitos Minerales que ayudan a mantener el equilibrio de los fluidos del cuerpo.

Elimination/eliminación La expulsión de comida no digerida o desechos del cuerpo.

Embryo/embrión El grupo de células que se desarrolla entre la tercera y la octava semanas del embarazo.

Emergency survival kit/botiquín de primeros auxilios Un grupo de artículos que pueden ser utilizados por un corto plazo hasta que la situación de emergencia se haya estabilizado.

Emerging infection/infección emergente Una enfermedad infecciosa cuya incidencia en humanos ha aumentado durante las últimas dos décadas o que amenaza con incrementar en el futuro cercano.

Emotional abuse/abuso emocional Un comportamiento que ataca el desarrollo emocional y la estima de un individuo.

Emotional intimacy/intimidad emocional La habilidad de experimentar una relación de amor y cuidado con otra persona con la cual también se pueden compartir los sentimientos más íntimos.

Emotional maturity/madurez emocional Un estado en el cual las capacidades mentales y emocionales de una persona se encuentran totalmente desarrolladas.

Emotions/emociones Señales que le comunican a la mente y el cuerpo como actuar.

Empathy/empatía La habilidad para imaginar y entender como otra persona siente.

Emphysema/enfisema Una enfermedad que destruye progresivamente las paredes de los alveolos.

Empty-nest syndrome/síndrome del nido vacío Sentimiento de tristeza y soledad que ocurre cuando los hijos, quienes ya se convirtieron en adultos, se van de la casa de sus padres.

Endocrine glands/glándulas endocrinas Órganos o grupos de células sin conductos o tubos que secretan directamente en el flujo sanguíneo.

Environment/medio ambiente Todo lo que nos rodea.

Environmental tobacco smoke (ETS)/ambiente con humo de cigarro Aire que ha sido contaminado por el humo de cigarrillos.

Epidemic/epidemia Una situación en la cual mucha gente contrae una enfermedad al mismo tiempo y en el mismo lugar.

Epidemiology/epidemiología El estudio científico de los patrones de las enfermedades en una población.

Epidermis/epidermis La capa más fina y externa de la piel la cual se encuentra compuesta de células vivas y muertas.

Epilepsy/epilepsia Un desorden del sistema nervioso caracterizado por convulsiones continuas —repentinos episodios de incontrolable actividad eléctrica del cerebro.

Ethanol/etanol El alcohol que se encuentra en las bebidas alcohólicas.

Euphoria/euforia El sentimiento de un intenso bienestar o alegría.

Exercise/ejercicio Actividad física que es planeada, estructurada y repetitiva, y que tiene como objetivo el mantenimiento o el mejoramiento del estado físico de una persona.

Extended family/familia extensa La familia inmediata (padres y hermanos) y otros parientes, como por ejemplo tíos, tías, primos y abuelos.

Extensor/extensor Un músculo que abra una articulación.

External auditory canal/canal auditivo externo Un pasaje de cerca de una pulgada de largo el cual conecta el oído externo con el tímpano.

–––––––––––––––––––– **F** ––––––––––––––––––––

Fad diets/dietas de moda Planes para perder peso que son populares por un corto plazo.

Fallopian tubes/trompas de Falapio Un par de conductos con terminaciones en forma de dedos que ayudan al óvulo en su camino hacia el útero.

Family/familia La unidad básica de una sociedad.

Family counseling/terapia familiar Terapia que ayuda a restaurar las relaciones entre los miembros de una familia.

Fermentation/fermentación La reacción química de la levadura en el azúcar.

Fertilization/fertilización La unión del espermatozoide y el óvulo.

Fetal alcohol syndrome (FAS)/síndrome de alcoholismo fetal Un grupo de defectos de nacimiento causados por el alcohol y que incluyen problemas físicos y mentales.

Fetus/feto El embrión en desarrollo que se encuentra dentro del útero.

Fiber/fibra Un carbohidrato que no es digerible.

Fire extinguisher/extintor de incendios Un aparato portátil que ayuda a apagar incendios a través de la aplicación de químicos extinguidores de fuego.

First aid/primeros auxilios La atención inmediata y temporal que se le proporciona a una persona enferma o herida hasta que una atención medica profesional pueda ser proporcionada.

F.I.T.T./F.I.T.A. Frecuencia, intensidad, tiempo/duración, y tipo de actividad.

Flash flood/inundación repentina Una inundación de gran volumen y corta duración que es comúnmente causada por fuertes lluvias.

Flexibility/flexibilidad La habilidad de mover una parte del cuerpo fácilmente y en muchas direcciones.

Flexor/músculo flexor Los músculos que cierran las articulaciones.

Food additives/aditivos alimentarios Substancias que son adicionadas a los alimentos en forma intencional para generar un efecto deseado.

Food allergy/alergia a comida Una condición en la cuál el sistema inmunológico del cuerpo reacciona a substancias contenidas en algunos alimentos.

Food intolerance/intolerancia a la comida Una reacción negativa a los alimentos (o un elemento particular del alimento) causado por un problema metabólico, como por ejemplo la inhabilidad de digerir ciertos alimentos o algunos de sus componentes.

Foodborne illness/enfermedad alimenticia Intoxicación alimenticia.

Foster care/custodia temporal Un arreglo temporal en el cual un niño es entregado a una familia o adulto no emparentado para que lo guíe y supervise.

Fracture/fractura La rotura de un hueso.

Fraud/fraude Engaño deliberado.

Friendship/amistad Una relación importante entre dos personas que esta basada en solidaridad, confianza y consideración.

Frostbite/congelación Una condición en la cual los tejidos del cuerpo se congelan.

————————— **G** —————————

Gametes/gametos Células reproductoras.

Gang/banda criminal Un grupo de personas quienes se encuentran vinculados por haber participado en una actividad criminal.

Gastric juices/jugos gástricos La secreciones que provienen del revestimiento del estómago y que contienen ácido clorhídrico y pepsina, una enzima que digiere la proteína.

Gene therapy/terapia genética Un proceso que consiste en introducir genes normales en las células humanas para corregir trastornos genéticos.

Genes/genes Las unidades básicas de la herencia.

Genetic disorder/trastorno genético Un trastorno causado parcial o completamente por defectos en los genes.

Genital herpes/herpes genital Infección de transmisión sexual causada por el virus herpes simple.

Goal/objetivo Algo que una persona desea y para el cual hace planes y trabaja.

Gonads/gónadas Los ovarios y los testículos.

Gonorrhea/gonorrea Una infección bacteriana de transmisión sexual que comúnmente afecta a las membranas mucosas.

Graduated driver's license/licencia de manejar graduada Un programa de licencias que incrementa los privilegios de los conductores nuevos con el tiempo como premio a la experiencia y habilidad.

Grief/aflicción La pena causada por la pérdida de un ser querido.

Grief response/aflicción La respuesta de un individuo a una gran pérdida.

Group therapy/terapia de grupo Tratamiento de un grupo de personas quienes tienen problemas similares.

————————— **H** —————————

Hair follicle/folículo de pelo Una estructura que rodea la raíz de un pelo.

Hallucinogens/alucinógenos Drogas que alteran el estado de ánimo, el pensamiento, y la percepción, incluso la vista, oído, olfato y tacto.

Harassment/acoso Molestar persistentemente a otra persona.

Hazardous waste/desechos peligrosos Substancia que es explosiva, corrosiva, altamente reactiva, o tóxica para los seres humanos o otras formas de vida.

Health/salud La combinación de bienestar físico, mental/emocional y social.

Health care system/sistema de asistencia médica Toda la asistencia médica disponible para la población de una nación, la forma en que la atención es recibida y la forma en que se paga.

Health consumer/consumidor de servicios de salud Cualquier persona que consume o usa productos o servicios de salud.

Health education/educación de la salud Proveer a las personas con información adecuada de tal manera que puedan tomar decisiones que sean saludables.

Health fraud/engaño sobre la salud La venta de productos o servicios inútiles que supuestamente sirven para prevenir enfermedades o mejorar otros problemas de la salud.

Health insurance/seguro de salud Un plan mediante el cual compañías privadas o el gobierno pagan parte o todos los gastos médicos de una persona.

Health literacy/instrucción sobre la salud La capacidad que tiene una persona para aprender y comprender información básica acerca de la salud y los servicios relacionados, y de usar esos conocimientos para mejorar su propia salud y bienestar.

Health screening/diagnóstico de la salud Estudiar o chequear la salud de una persona con el objetivo de detectar anticipadamente enfermedades u otros problemas de salud.

Health skills/habilidades de la salud Herramientas y estrategias que ayudan a mantener, proteger, y mejorar todos los aspectos de la salud.

Healthy People 2010/Gente saludable 2010 Un plan nacional de salud y prevención de enfermedades que fue diseñado para promover el mejoramiento de la salud de todas las personas en los Estados Unidos.

Heartburn/acidez Una sensación de quemadura en el centro del pecho que puede subir desde la parte inferior del esternón hasta la garganta.

Heat cramps/calambre debido al calor Espasmos musculares que son el resultado de la pérdida de grandes cantidades de sal y agua a través del sudor.

Heat exhaustion/agotamiento debido al calor Un sobrecalentamiento del cuerpo que produce síntomas de un estado de choque y que hace que la piel se ponga helada y húmeda.

Heatstroke/insolación Una condición en la cuál el cuerpo pierde la habilidad para deshacerse del calor excesivo a través del sudor.

Hemodialysis/hemodiálisis Una técnica a través de la cual una máquina de diálisis limpia los desechos de la sangre.

Hemoglobin/hemoglobina La proteína que lleva el oxígeno en la sangre.

Herbal supplement/suplemento herbario Una substancia química de hierbas las cuales se pueden vender como suplemento nutritivo.

Heredity/herencia Todos los rasgos que biológicamente son transferidos de los padres a los hijos.

Hernia/hernia Cuando un órgano o tejido sobresale en un área de músculos débiles.

Hiatal hernia/hernia de hiato Una condición en la cuál una parte del estómago se sale por una abertura en el diafragma.

Hierarchy of needs/pirámides de las necesidades Una graduación de tales necesidades esenciales al crecimiento y desarrollo humano, presentadas en orden ascendiente desde las necesidades más básicas hasta la realización personal.

Histamines/histaminas Substancias químicas que pueden estimular la mucosa y la producción de fluidos en una área del cuerpo.

Hodgkin's disease/enfermedad de Hodgkin Un tipo de cáncer que afecta el tejido linfático.

Homicide/homicidio Cuando una persona mata a otra.

Hormones/hormonas Substancias químicas producidas por las glándulas y que ayudan a regular muchas funciones del cuerpo humano.

Hostility/hostilidad Un comportamiento intencional que es antipático, desagradable u ofensivo.

Human immunodeficiency virus (HIV)/virus de inmunodeficiencia humana (VIH) Un virus que ataca al sistema inmunológico.

Human papillomavirus (HPV)/papovavirus humano (HPV) Un virus que puede causar verrugas genitales o infecciones asintomáticas.

Hunger/hambre La necesidad física y natural de alimentos que nos protege de la inanición.

Hurricane/huracán Una tormenta muy fuerte que se origina en el mar, y que se caracteriza por vientos de al menos 74 millas por hora, fuertes lluvias, inundaciones, y algunas veces tornados.

Hydration/hidratación Tomar los líquidos necesarios para mantener las funciones corporales normales.

Hypertension/hipertensión Presión arterial alta.

Hypothermia/hipotermia Una condición en la cual la temperatura del cuerpo baja demasiado.

I

Illegal drugs/drogas ilegales Substancias químicas que ninguna persona, cualquiera sea su edad, puede legalmente producir, poseer, comprar o vender.

Illicit drug use/uso ilegal de drogas El uso o venta de cualquier substancia que es ilegal o no permitida.

"I" message/mensaje "YO" Una declaración en la cual una persona describe como él o ella se siente usando el pronombre "yo."

Immune system/sistema de defensas Una combinación de células, tejidos, órganos, y substancias químicas que combaten agentes patógenos.

Immunity/inmunidad El estado de estar protegido contra una enfermedad en particular.

Implantation/implantación La fijación del zigoto en la pared del útero.

Indigestion/indigestión Un sentimiento de molestia en la parte superior del abdomen.

Infatuation/adoración Los sentimientos de pasión exagerados por otra persona.

Infection/infección Una condición que ocurre cuando agentes patógenos entran al cuerpo, se multiplican y dañan las células.

Infertility/infertilidad La incapacidad de poder concebir un hijo.

Inflammatory response/respuesta inflamatoria Una reacción al daño a los tejidos causada por una lesión o infección.

Inhalants/inhalantes Substancias cuyos gases se aspiran o inhalan para alcanzar un estado alucinante.

Integrity/integridad Una adherencia firme al código moral.

Interpersonal communication/comunicación entre personas El intercambio de pensamientos, sentimientos y creencias entre dos o más personas.

Interpersonal conflict/conflicto entre personas Desacuerdo entre dos o más personas.

Intoxication/Intoxicación Un estado en el cual el cuerpo se encuentra embriagado por alcohol u otra substancia, y el control físico y mental de la persona se encuentra reducido significativamente.

—————— J ——————

Jaundice/ictericia Estado en el cual la piel y los ojos se ponen de color amarillo.

—————— L ——————

Labor/parto El estado final del embarazo en el cual el útero se contrae y empuja el bebé hacia afuera del cuerpo de la madre.

Labyrinth/laberinto Oído interno.

Lacrimal gland/glándula lagrimal La glándula que produce las lágrimas y que las libera por los canales que se vacían en el ojo.

Landfill/terraplenes sanitarios Un área en donde se deposita la basura y que garantiza que no contaminará el medio ambiente.

Larynx/laringe Lugar donde se encuentran las cuerdas vocales.

Leukemia/leucemia Un tipo de cáncer en el cual los glóbulos blancos de la sangre se reproducen excesiva y anormalmente.

Leukoplakia/leucoplaquia Granos con apariencia de piel blanca dura y espesa que se encuentran dentro de la boca y que pueden llegar a producir un cáncer oral.

Ligament/ligamento Un tejido fuerte y elástico que une los huesos.

Lipid/lípido Una substancia grasosa que no se disuelve en el agua.

Long-term goal/objetivo de largo plazo Un objetivo que se planea alcanzar en un periodo largo de tiempo.

Lymph/linfa Un líquido claro que llena los espacios entre las células del cuerpo.

Lymphocytes/linfocitos Células blancas de la sangre que son especialistas en proporcionar la inmunidad al cuerpo humano.

—————— M ——————

Mainstream smoke/humo directo El humo exhalado por los pulmones de un fumador.

Malignant/maligno Canceroso.

Malpractice/mala práctica médica Condición en la que un profesional de la salud no cumple con los estándares aceptados.

Manipulation/manipulación Controlar o influenciar a otros de manera indirecta y desonesta.

Marijuana/marihuana Una planta cuyas hojas, brotes y flores son generalmente fumadas para su efecto embriagador.

Marital adjustment/adaptación matrimonial La manera como una persona se ajusta al matrimonio y a su esposo o esposa.

Mastication/masticación El proceso de masticar.

Media/medios de comunicación Los métodos diferentes usados para comunicar información.

Mediation/mediación Proceso mediante el cual la gente especializada ayuda a resolver conflictos de manera pacífica.

Mediator/mediador Una persona quien ayuda a otros a resolver problemas de manera que las dos partes queden satisfechas.

Medical history/historia médica La información completa acerca de las vacunas y problemas de salud que una persona ha tenido a lo largo de su vida.

Medicines/medicamentos Drogas que son tomadas para terminar o prevenir una enfermedad u otra condición de la salud.

Megadose/megadosis Una cantidad grande de suplemento alimenticio.

Melanin/melanina El pigmento que da el color a la piel, cabello y el iris del ojo.

Melanoma/melanoma El cáncer de la piel más grave de todos.

Menopause/menopausia La época que marca el fin de la vida reproductora de una mujer.

Menstruation/menstruación La eliminación de materia procedente del útero.

Mental disorder/desorden mental Una enfermedad mental que afecta la manera de pensar, el comportamiento y los sentimientos de una persona, y que le impide tener una vida feliz, saludable y productiva.

Mental retardation/retardo mental La habilidad intelectual inferior al promedio que se presenta desde el nacimiento o niñez y que se relaciona con dificultades de aprendizaje y adaptación social.

Mental/emotional health/salud mental/emocional La habilidad de aceptarse a sí mismo y a otras personas, y de adaptarse y hacer frente a las emociones, cambios y nuevas demandas de la vida.

Metabolism/metabolismo Proceso mediante el cual el cuerpo procesa y obtiene energía de los alimentos.

Metastasis/metástasis La extensión del cáncer desde el punto de origen a otras partes del cuerpo.

Minerals/minerales Substancias no producidas por el cuerpo pero que son necesarias para la formación de huesos y dientes saludables, y para regular otros procesos vitales del cuerpo.

Miscarriage/aborto (natural) La expulsión espontánea del feto que ocurre antes de la semana número veinte del embarazo.

Modeling/modelando El proceso de observar y aprender del comportamiento de las personas de alrededor.

Mood disorder/desorden del carácter Una enfermedad, comúnmente de causa orgánica, que se caracteriza por cambios extremos del humor de una persona y que afecta la vida diaria.

Mourning/luto El acto de mostrar pena o dolor.

Muscle cramp/calambre muscular El espasmo o endurecimiento repentino de un músculo.

Muscle tone/tono muscular La tensión natural de los tejidos de los músculos.

Muscular endurance/resistencia muscular La habilidad de los músculos para hacer actividades físicas sin fatigarse.

Muscular strength/fuerza muscular La fuerza que un músculo puede ejercer.

MyPyramid Una guía para hacer las elecciones diarias saludables de alimento.

N

Narcotics/narcóticos Drogas específicas que se usan para aliviar el dolor y que sólo se pueden obtener con receta médica.

Neglect/abandono La no-satisfacción de las necesidades físicas y emocionales de un niño.

Negotiation/negociación El uso de comunicación y compromiso para resolver un desacuerdo.

Nephron/nefrona La unidad de funcionamiento de los riñones.

Neurons/neuronas Células nerviosas.

Nicotine/nicotina Una droga adictiva que se encuentra en las hojas del tabaco.

Nicotine substitute/substituto de nicotina Un producto que libera una pequeña cantidad de nicotina en el cuerpo de una persona que está tratando de dejar de fumar.

Nicotine withdrawal/reacción al retiro de nicotina El proceso que ocurre en el cuerpo cuando la nicotina, una droga adictiva, deja de ser consumida.

Noise pollution/contaminación auditiva Un nivel de ruido no deseado que es lo suficientemente alto para dañar la audición de las personas.

Noncommunicable disease/enfermedad no contagiosa Una enfermedad que no se transmite entre las personas o por un vector, y que tampoco proviene del medio ambiente.

Nutrient-dense foods/alimentos fuertes en elementos nutritivos Alimentos que proporcionan una alta cantidad de elementos nutritivos comparados con las calorías contenidas.

Nutrients/nutrientes Substancias contenidas en los alimentos y que el cuerpo necesita para crecer, mantener un buen estado de salud y generar energía.

Nutrition/nutrición Proceso mediante el cual el cuerpo absorbe y usa los alimentos.

O

Obesity/obesidad El exceso de gordura en el cuerpo.

Occupational Safety and Health Administration (OSHA)/Agencia de Seguridad y Salud Ocupacional Agencia del gobierno federal que es responsable de promover el uso de condiciones de trabajo seguras y saludables.

Online shopping/compras en Internet Comprar bienes o servicios vía Internet.

Opportunistic infection/infección oportunista Una infección que ataca a un individuo con sistema inmunológico debilitado.

Ossification/osificación El proceso mediante el cual el hueso se forma, renueva y repara.

Osteoarthritis/osteoartritis Una enfermedad de las articulaciones en la cual el cartílago se deteriora.

Osteoporosis/osteoporosis Una condición que se caracteriza por la pérdida progresiva de los tejidos de los huesos.

Ova/óvulos Células reproductoras femeninas.

Ovaries/ovarios Las glándulas sexuales femeninas que contienen los óvulos y producen hormonas sexuales.

Overdose/sobredosis Una reacción fuerte, y algunas veces fatal, al consumo de una gran cantidad de drogas.

Overexertion/sobresfuerzo Cuando el cuerpo trabaja demasiado.

Overload/sobrecarga Hacer trabajar el cuerpo más fuerte de lo normal.

Over-the-counter (OTC) medicines/medicamento sin receta Medicamentos que pueden ser comprados sin una receta médica.

Overweight/sobrepeso Una condición en la cual una persona pesa más de lo apropiado para su estatura.

Ovulation/ovulación Proceso mensual en que se desprende un óvulo maduro que baja al útero.

P

Pancreas/páncreas Una glándula que ayuda al funcionamiento de los sistemas digestivo y endocrino.

Pandemic/pandemia La transmisión global de una enfermedad infecciosa.

Paranoia/paranoia La sospecha o desconfianza irracional acerca de otras personas.

Parathyroid glands/glándulas paratiroides Glándulas que producen una hormona que regula el equilibrio de calcio y fósforo en el cuerpo.

Passive/pasivo Una tendencia a entregarse, rendirse, o echarse atrás sin defender sus derechos ni necesidades.

Passive immunity/inmunidad pasiva La inmunidad temporal recibida por medio de otra persona o anticuerpos.

Pasteurization/pasteurización Proceso mediante el cual una substancia es tratada con calor para destruir o reducir agentes patógenos.

Pathogen/patógeno Un organismo que causa enfermedades.

Peer mediation/mediación por contemporáneos Un proceso mediante el cual estudiantes entrenados ayudan a otros estudiantes a encontrar el camino para resolver un conflicto y a terminar con sus diferencias.

Peer mediators/mediadores contemporáneos Estudiantes entrenados que ayudan a otros estudiantes a encontrar una manera justa de resolver conflictos y desacuerdos.

Peer pressure/presión de los contemporáneos La influencia que gente de tu misma edad puede tener en ti.

Peers/contemporáneos Gente cuya edad e intereses son similares a los tuyos.

Penis/pene Un órgano con forma de tubo que se extiende del tronco del cuerpo y justo arriba de los testículos.

Peptic ulcer/úlcera péptica Una llaga en el revestimiento del aparato digestivo.

Perception/percepción El acto de darse cuenta de algo a través de los sentidos.

Periodontal disease/enfermedad periodontal La inflamación de la estructura de soporte dental.

Periodontium/membrana periodontal El área inmediatamente alrededor de los dientes.

Peristalsis/movimientos peristálticos Una serie de contracciones musculares involuntarias que mueven la comida a través del aparato digestivo.

Personal identity/identidad personal El sentirse como un individuo único.

Personality/personalidad Un conjunto complejo de características que hacen que una persona ser única.

Phagocyte/fagocito Un glóbulo blanco de la sangre que ataca la invasión de patógenos.

Pharynx/faringe Garganta.

Physical abuse/abuso físico El acto intencional de dañar o herir el cuerpo de otra persona.

Physical activity/actividad física Cualquier forma de movimiento que provoque que el cuerpo consuma energía.

Physical fitness/buena condición física La habilidad de responder fácilmente a tareas diarias y tener suficiente energía para responder a demandas inesperadas.

Physical maturity/madurez física Un estado en el cual el cuerpo físico y todos sus organismos se encuentran totalmente desarrollados.

Physiological dependence/dependencia fisiológica Cuando un drogadicto o consumidor de drogas tiene una necesidad química de éstas.

Pituitary gland/glándula pituitaria Glándula que regula o controla las actividades de todas las glándulas endocrinas.

Placenta/placenta El tejido espeso y rico en sangre que cubre las paredes del útero durante el periodo de embarazo y que alimenta al feto.

Plaque/placa Una película blanda e incolora que actúa a través del azúcar para formar los ácidos que destruyen el esmalte de los dientes e irritan las encías.

Plasma/plasma Un fluido en el cual los otros componentes de la sangre se encuentran suspendidos.

Platelets/plaquetas Células que previenen la pérdida de sangre del cuerpo.

Platonic friendship/amistad platónica Una amistad con una persona del sexo opuesto en la cual hay sentimientos mutuos de afecto, pero los amigos no son considerados una pareja.

Pleurisy/pleuritis Una inflamación de la pleura, la membrana que recubre los pulmones, y de la cavidad del pecho.

Pneumonia/pulmonía Una inflamación de los revestimientos de los pulmones y pecho.

Poison/veneno Cualquier substancia—sólida, líquida o gaseosa—que al entrar en el cuerpo causa una herida, una enfermedad o la muerte.

Poison control center/Centro para el control de envenenamientos Una línea telefónica que funciona las 24 horas del día para dar consejo sobre el tratamiento de envenenamiento para víctimas.

Post-traumatic stress disorder/Desorden de estrés post-traumático Una condición que se puede desarrollar después que una persona ha sido expuesta a un evento aterrador que lo amenaza o causa daño físico.

Precycling/prereciclage Reducir la basura antes de generarla.

Prejudice/prejuicio Una opinión o juicio injusto acerca de un grupo particular de personas.

Prenatal care/cuidado prenatal Todas las medidas que una mujer embarazada puede tomar para cuidar su propia salud y la de su bebé.

Prescription medicine/medicinas recetadas Medicinas que no pueden ser usadas sin la aprobación escrita de un médico.

Prevention/prevención La práctica de hábitos saludables y seguros que permiten evitar enfermedades y daños.

Preventive care/cuidado preventivo Las acciones que previenen el comienzo de una enfermedad o lesión.

Primary care physician/médico general Un médico que proporciona chequeos y el cuidado general de sus pacientes.

Priorities/prioridades Los objetivos, tareas y actividades que son consideradas más importantes que otras.

Profound deafness/sordera profunda Una pérdida severa de la audición y la cual no puede ser tratada con amplificación mecánica como por ejemplo un audífono.

Progression/progresión El aumento gradual en la sobrecarga necesaria para lograr mejor condición física.

Protective factors/factores protectores Condiciones que protegen a una persona de las consecuencias negativas de una exposición a situaciones arriesgadas.

Proteins/proteínas Elementos nutritivos que ayudan a construir y mantener las células y tejidos.

Psychoactive drugs/drogas psico-activas Substancias químicas que afectan el sistema central nervioso y alteran la actividad del cerebro.

Psychological dependence/dependencia psicológica Una condición en la cual una persona cree que se necesita una droga para sentirse bien o funcionar normalmente.

Psychosomatic response/respuesta psicosomática Una reacción física que es resultado del estrés en vez de una enfermedad o herida.

Psychotherapy/psicoterapia Una terapia a través del diálogo entre el paciente y un profesional de la salud mental.

Puberty/pubertad El periodo de tiempo en el cual una persona comienza a desarrollar ciertos rasgos que son característicos de su sexo.

Public health/salud pública Un esfuerzo comunitario para la protección y el fomento de la salud de la población.

Pulp/pulpa Un tejido que contiene los vasos sanguíneos y los nervios de un diente.

━━━━━━━━ **R** ━━━━━━━━

Radon/radón Un gas inodoro y radioactivo.

Random violence/violencia aleatoria Violencia cometida sin una razón en especial.

Rape/violación Cualquier tipo de acto sexual que tiene lugar contra la voluntad de una persona.

Recovery/recuperación El proceso de aprender a vivir una vida sin alcohol.

Recycling/reciclar El procesamiento de la basura de tal manera que pueda ser utilizada nuevamente en alguna forma.

Reflex/reflejo La respuesta espontánea del cuerpo a estímulos.

Refusal skills/habilidad de negarse Estrategias de comunicación que ayudan a decir no cuando uno está a punto de participar en actividades arriesgadas, no saludables o que van en contra de sus valores.

Rehydration/rehidración La restauración de líquidos perdidos por el cuerpo.

Relationship/relaciones Las conexiones que una persona tiene con otros.

Relaxation response/respuesta de relajamiento Un estado de calma que puede ser alcanzado cuando una o varias técnicas de relajación son practicadas regularmente.

Remission/remisión El periodo de tiempo cuando los síntomas desaparecen.

Repetitive motion injury/Daño por movimiento repetido El daño a los tejidos causado por movimientos prolongados y repetitivos.

Reproductive system/aparato reproductor El conjunto de órganos que permiten la reproducción.

Resiliency/fuerza moral La habilidad de adaptarse eficazmente y recuperarse después de una decepción, dificultad o crisis.

Respiration/respiración El intercambio de gases entre el cuerpo humano y el medio ambiente.

Resting heart rate/ritmo cardíaco en descanso El número de latidos del corazón que se producen cuando la persona se encuentra en estado pasivo.

Retina/retina Membrana sensitiva a la luz y en la cual las imágenes son proyectadas por la córnea.

Rheumatoid arthritis/artritis reumatoide Una enfermedad caracterizada por la destrucción debilitadora de las articulaciones debido a la inflamación.

Risk behaviors/comportamiento arriesgado Acciones que pueden poner en peligro su salud o la de otras personas.

Road rage/violencia al conducir Acciones causadas cuando un conductor maneja en forma peligrosa usando su vehículo como un arma.

Role/función La participación de una persona en una relación.

Role model/modelo de conducta Alguien cuyo éxito o comportamiento sirve de ejemplo para otros.

━━━━━━━━ **S** ━━━━━━━━

Sclera/esclerótica La parte blanca del ojo.

Scoliosis/escoliosis Una desviación lateral, o de lado a lado, de la columna.

Scrotum/escroto Un saco externo de piel que se extiende afuera del cuerpo y que contiene los testículos.

Sebaceous glands/glándulas sebáceas Estructuras dentro de la piel que producen una secreción aceitosa llamada sebo.

Sedentary lifestyle/estilo de vida sedentario Un estilo de vida que incluye poca actividad física.

Self-actualization/realización personal El esfuerzo realizado para lograr lo mejor de uno mismo.

Self-control/dominio de sí mismo La habilidad de una persona para controlar sus emociones.

Self-defense/defensa propia Cualquier estrategia para protegerse a sí misma de un daño.

Self-directed/auto-dirigido La habilidad para tomar decisiones correctas acerca de su comportamiento en la ausencia de adultos para imponer las reglas.

Semen/semen Un líquido espeso que contiene los espermatozoides y otras secreciones del aparato reproductor masculino.

Separation/separación Cuando una pareja de personas casadas decide vivir aparte uno del otro.

Severe weather/clima severo Condiciones climáticas severas o peligrosas.

Sex characteristics/características sexuales Los rasgos relacionados con el sexo de una persona.

Sexual abuse/abuso sexual Cualquier contacto sexual que es realizado a la fuerza o contra el consentimiento de una persona.

Sexual assault/agresión sexual Cualquier ataque sexual intencional en contra de otra persona.

Sexual harassment/acoso sexual Cualquier conducta sexual no solicitada y desagradable que se dirige a otra persona.

Sexual violence/violencia sexual Cualquier acto sexual no solicitado que es dirigido a una persona y que incluye acoso sexual, agresión sexual y violación.

Sexually transmitted diseases (STDs)/enfermedades transmitidas sexualmente Enfermedades que se transmiten a través del contacto sexual entre dos personas.

Sexually transmitted infections (STIs)/infecciones transmitidas sexualmente Infecciones que se transmiten a través del contacto sexual entre dos personas.

Shock/choque Una falla en el sistema cardiovascular que no permite una circulación suficiente de sangre a los órganos vitales del cuerpo.

Short-term goal/Objetivo de corto plazo Un objetivo que se puede alcanzar en un corto periodo de tiempo.

Sibling/hermano Un hermano o hermana.

Side effects/efecto secundario Cualquier reacción inesperada a una medicina.

Sidestream smoke/humo indirecto El humo que proviene de una colilla de cigarrillo, pipa o cigarro.

Sinusitis/sinusitis La inflamación de los tejidos nasales.

Skeletal muscles/músculos del esqueleto Músculos unidos a los huesos y que producen el movimiento del cuerpo.

Smog/smog Una neblina de color amarillo-café que se produce cuando la luz solar reacciona con la contaminación ambiental.

Smoke alarm/alarma de humo Una alarma que se active por la presencia del humo.

Smokeless tobacco/tabaco sin humo Tabaco que es olfateado a través de la nariz, mantenido en la boca, y masticado.

Smooth muscles/músculos lisos Músculos que actúan sobre el forro de los tubos y órganos internos.

Sobriety/sobriedad Vivir sin consumir alcohol.

Specialist/especialista Un médico entrenado para tratar una determinada clase de pacientes y condiciones médicas.

Specificity/especificidad Una clase especial de actividades y ejercicios para mejoran partes especiales de la condición física que están relacionadas con la salud.

Sperm/espermatozoides Células reproductoras masculinas.

Spousal abuse/abuso conyugal Violencia doméstica dirigida hacia el esposo o esposa.

Sprain/torcedura El daño a los ligamentos que circundan una articulación.

Stalking/acecho El seguimiento, acoso, o amenaza repetido que un individuo hace a otro para atemorizarlo o dañarlo.

Stereotype/estereotipo Una creencia exagerada y sobresimplificada que se extiende a todo un grupo, como un grupo étnico o religioso o a un sexo.

Sterility/esterilidad La incapacidad de reproducirse.

Stillbirth/aborto La expulsión de un feto muerto por el cuerpo de la madre después de la semana número veinte.

Stimulant/estimulante Una droga que acelera el funcionamiento del sistema central nervioso, el corazón y otros órganos.

Strain/esguince Una condición resultante del daño de un músculo o tendón.

Stress/estrés La reacción del cuerpo o la mente a los cambios y demandas de la vida diaria.

Stress management/manejo del estrés Los medios para hacer frente o superar los efectos negativos del estrés.

Stress-management skills/habilidades para superar el estrés Habilidades que ayudan a una persona a manejar el estrés de una manera saludable y efectiva.

Stressor/estresante Cualquier cosa que produce el estrés.

Stroke/accidente cerebrovascular Una condición en la cual un vaso sanguíneo se bloquea impidiendo el flujo de la sangre al cerebro.

Substance abuse/abuso de substancias Cualquier uso inapropiado o excesivo de substancias químicas con propósitos no médicos.

Suicide/suicidio El acto de tomar su propia vida.

Suppression/supresión El acto de restringirse o retenerse.

Sweat glands/glándulas sudoríparas Estructuras dentro de la dermis que secretan el sudor por conductos hasta los poros en la superficie de la piel.

Symptomatic stage/estado sintomático El estado en el cual una persona afectada por el VIH presenta síntomas resultantes de una reducción severa de las células inmunológicas.

Synergistic effect/efecto sinergénico La interacción entre dos medicinas que resultan en un efecto más fuerte que si se toman por separado.

Syphilis/sífilis Una enfermedad de transmisión sexual bacteriana que ataca muchas partes del cuerpo y es causada por una bacteria llamada espiroqueta.

T

Tar/alquitrán Un líquido espeso, pegajoso y oscuro que se forma al quemarse el tabaco.

Tartar/sarro La substancia dura y con forma de corteza que se forma en los dientes cuando la placa se endurece.

Tendon/tendón Un tejido fuerte que une los músculos a los huesos.

Tendonitis/tendinitis La inflamación de un tendón.

Testes/testículos Dos glándulas pequeñas que producen los espermatozoides.

Testosterone/testosterona Hormona sexual masculina.

Thyroid gland/tiroides Glándula que produce las hormonas que regulan el metabolismo, el calor del cuerpo, y el crecimiento de los huesos.

Tinnitus/acúfeno Una condición en que se oye un timbre, un zumbido, un silbido, un bisbiseo, un rugido, u otro sonido en el oído en la ausencia de sonido externo.

Tolerance/tolerancia La habilidad de aceptar puntos de vista diferentes y permitir que otras personas se expresen sin mostrar desaprobación.

Tolerance/tolerancia Una condición en la que el cuerpo se acostumbra a los efectos de los medicamentos.

Tornado/tornado Una tormenta en forma de torbellino que cae desde el cielo a la tierra y que produce la destrucción al pasar.

Toxin/toxina Una substancia que mata células o que interfiere con su funcionamiento.

Trachea/traquea Vía respiratoria.

Training program/programa de entrenamiento Un programa formal de preparación física para participación en un deporte o cualquier otra actividad física.

Transitions/transiciones Cambios críticos que ocurren en todas las etapas de la vida.

Trichomoniasis/tricomoniasis Una enfermedad de transmisión sexual causada por un protozoo microscópico que tiene como resultado las infecciones de la vagina, de la uretra, y de la vejiga.

Tuberculosis/tuberculosis Una infección bacteriana contagiosa que comúnmente afecta los pulmones.

Tumor/tumor Una masa de tejidos anormales que no tiene ningún papel natural en el cuerpo.

U

Umbilical cord/cordón umbilical Una estructura igual a una soga que conecta el embrión a la placenta de la madre.

Unconditional love/amor incondicional Amor sin limitaciones ni exigencias.

Unconsciousness/inconsciencia Una condición en la cual una persona no esta consciente del ambiente que lo rodea.

Underweight/bajo peso Una condición en la que una persona pesa menos de lo que debería pesar de acuerdo con su estatura.

Unintentional injury/daños no intencionales Daños que resultan de situaciones inesperadas o accidentes.

Universal precautions/precauciones universales Acciones tomadas para prevenir la expansión de enfermedades, tratando la sangre o cualquier otro líquido corporal como si estuviera contaminado.

Urban sprawl/expansión urbana La expansión de la ciudad (casas, centros comerciales, negocios, y escuelas) a tierras no urbanizadas.

Ureters/uréter Cada uno de los dos canales que conjuntan los riñones y la vejiga.

Urethra/uretra El canal que conduce desde la vejiga hasta afuera del cuerpo.

Urethritis/uretritis La inflamación de la uretra.

Urine/orina Líquido compuesto de desechos.

Uterus/útero Un órgano muscular y con forma de pera dentro del cuerpo femenino.

V

Vaccine/vacuna Una preparación de agentes patógenos muertos o debilitados introducidos en el cuerpo para estimular el sistema de defensas.

Vagina/vagina Un conducto muscular y elástica que va desde el útero hasta la parte externa del cuerpo de una mujer.

Values/valores Las ideas, creencias y actitudes consideradas importantes que guían la vida de una persona.

Vector/vector Un organismo, como por ejemplo un insecto, que lleva y transmite agentes patógenos a personas y otros animales.

Vegan/vegetariano estricto Vegetariano quien come exclusivamente alimentos de origen vegetal.

Vegetarian/vegetariano Una persona que come principalmente o solamente alimentos que provienen de las plantas.

Vehicular safety/seguridad vehicular Usar el sentido común, un buen criterio y obedecer las reglas de la carretera.

Veins/venas Vasos sanguíneos que llevan la sangre al corazón.

Venom/veneno Una substancia venenosa secretada por serpientes, arañas u otra criatura viviente.

Verbal abuse/abuso verbal Usar palabras para maltratar o dañar a otras personas.

Violence/violencia Cualquier amenaza o acto físico para dañar o maltratar a una persona o propiedad.

Virus/virus Material genético que invade las células vivas para reproducirse.

Vitamins/vitaminas Substancias que ayudan a regular las funciones vitales del cuerpo inclusive la digestión, la absorción de líquidos y el metabolismo de otros elementos nutritivos.

W

Warm-up/precalentamiento Una actividad que prepara los músculos para el ejercicio.

Warranty/garantía Una promesa escrita, en la cual una empresa o compañía se compromete a reparar un producto o devolver el dinero si éste no funciona bien.

Wastewater/agua de desperdicio Agua sucia que proviene de casas, comunidades, granjas, e industrias.

Weight cycling/ciclo de peso La situación repetida de subir y bajar de peso corporal.

Wellness/bienestar El estado de buena salud.

Western blot (WB)/Western Blot La prueba para confirmar el SIDA mas usada en los Estados Unidos.

Withdrawal/síndrome de abstinencia Es una condición en alguien con farmacodependencia que se presenta al quitársele el medicamento.

Workout/entrenamiento La parte de un programa de actividad física en la que los ejercicios se realizan al más alto nivel.

Note: Page numbers in italic type refer to a picture or feature only.

Malignant tumors, 681
Malocclusion, 370
Malpractice, 61
Managed care plans, 57
Manic-depressive disorder, 227
Manipulation, 308, *309*
March of Dimes, 64
Marijuana, *425*, 598–600
Marital adjustment, 525
Marriage, 524–526
Maslow, Abraham, 172
Maslow's hierarchy of needs, 172–174
Mastication, 443
Maturity, 520, 525
MDMA, 610
Meals on Wheels, 139
Measles, *640*
Media, 9, 15–16, 49, 50, 343, 563, 594
Mediation, 267, 294
Medical history, 58
Medical laboratory technician, 437
Medical records, accessing, 58
Medical records technician, 617
Medicines, 59, 495, 586–591
Medulla oblongata, 403
Megadoses, 161
Melanin, 361, 362
Melanoma, 364, *365*
Memory lymphocytes, 631
Meninges, 401, 402
Meningitis, *640*
Menstrual cramps, 477
Menstruation, 476
Mental changes
    during adolescence, 516
    in middle adulthood, 531
Mental disorders, 224–230, 234
Mental/emotional health, 11, 170–177
    abuse and, 287, 349
    balance of physical/social health
        and, 12
    behavior and, 15
    benefits of physical activity to,
        75–76
    coping with losses and crises,
        238–241
    drug use and, 594
    effects of sexual activity on, 321
    getting help with, 234–237
    good, characteristics of, 170–171
    hierarchy of needs, 172–174
    managing emotions, 188–191
    marijuana use and, 600
    meeting needs, 174
    mental disorders, 224–229
    personal identity and, 182
    personality, 175, 177
    positive self-esteem and, *170*, 171
    promoting, 177
    stress and, 203
    suicide, 230–233
    understanding emotions, 184–187
    violent behavior and, 343
Mental health professionals, 235–237
Mental needs, 276
Mental retardation, 697
Metabolism, 78–79, 569
Metastasis, 681
Methamphetamine, 606
Midbrain, 403
Migraine headaches, 202

Milk (for children), 163
Minerals, 120, *121*
Minors, sexual activity with, 320
"Miracle" cures, 61
Miscarriages, 496
Mixed emotions, 185
Modeling, 175
Moderate-intensity physical
    activities, *88*
Moles, 364
Mononucleosis, *640*
Mood, 76, 227
Mood disorders, 226–227
Mood swings, 185, 203, 226
Morphine, 608
Motor impairment, 697
Motorcycle safety, 724
Mourning, 240
Mouth, 368–370, 430, 431
Moving, 283
Multiple sclerosis, 408
Multiplier effect, 569
Muscle cramps, 102, 750
Muscle injuries, 749–750
Muscle mass, 158
Muscle tone, 396
Muscles, 152, 395, *396*
Muscular dystrophy, 398
Muscular strength and endurance,
    80–82, 85
Muscular system, 102, 103, 394–398
Myelin sheath, 400
Myocardium, 417
Myopia, 374
MyPyramid, 124

N

Nail care, 366
Narcotics, 608
National Cancer Institute (NCI), 65
National health goals, 7, 336, 555,
    706, 736
National Institutes of Health (NIH),
    65, 532
Natural disasters, 241
Nausea, 450
Needs, 172–174, 275–276
Negative peer pressure, 308–312
Neglect, 288, *349*
Negligence, 61
Negotiation, 266
Neighborhood Watch program, 355
Nephritis, 456
Nephrons, 454
Nerve cells, 362
Nerve function, 126
Nerve impulse, 373, *400*
Nervous system, 75, 200, 399–409, 443
Neurons, 400
Nicotine, 540–542, 605
Nicotine substitute, 549
Nicotine withdrawal, 548–549
Noise pollution, 770–771
Noncommunicable diseases, 674
    allergies, 688–690
    arthritis, 693–694
    asthma, 690
    cancer, 681–687
    cardiovascular disease, 674–680
    diabetes, 691–693
    physical inactivity and, 77

Nonverbal communication, 29,
    184, 258
Nose, 430, 431
Nosebleeds, 753
Nuclear wastes, 773
Nutrient-dense foods, 148, 157, 158
Nutrients, 110, 114–121
    carbohydrates, 114–115
    cholesterol and, 118
    fats, 117
    minerals, 120, *121*
    product label claims for, 132–133
    proteins, 116
    vitamins, 119–120
    water, 120
Nutrition, 110–113
    dietary guidelines, 122–129
    Dietary Guidelines for Americans,
        122–126
    dietary supplements, 161
    fitness and, 94
    healthful eating plan, 127–129, 424
    importance of, 110
    influences on food choices, 111–113
    for performance, 157–159
    physical health and, 10
    during pregnancy, 493–494
    product labeling, 130–132
    for stress management, 208
    throughout life span, 113, 162–163
    for vegetarians, 159–161
Nutrition Facts panel, 126, 127,
    130–132
Nutritional supplements, 94, 95

O

Obesity, 78, 113, 117, 146
Obsessive-compulsive disorder, 226
Occupational choices, 522
Occupational Safety and Health
    Administration (OSHA), 65, 713
Oil contamination, 775
Older adults, 163, 533
Oncologist, 701
Online shopping, 52, 53
Open dating (product labels), 133
Open wounds, 738
Opportunistic infections, 659, *663*
Optic nerve, 371
Organic foods, *132*
Organic mental disorders, 225
Ossification, 387
Osteoarthritis, 693
Osteoporosis, 78, 86, 113, 391
Ova, 515
Ovarian cancer, 479
Ovarian cysts, 479
Ovaries, 465, 474, *475*
Over-the-counter (OTC) medicines,
    59, 590, 591
Overdose, 594
Overeaters Anonymous (OA), 165
Overeating, 78. *See also* Eating disorders
Overexertion, 99
Overload, 90
Overweight, 78, 83, 146, 147
Ovo vegetarianism, 159
Ovulation, 474
OxyContin, 608

PHOTOGRAPHS/ILLUSTRATIONS
Cover:
Joe Michl/Workbookstock.com (top)
Ed Bock/Corbis (bottom)

A.D.A.M., Inc. 741, Jack Affleck/Superstock 100, Age Fotostock 480, AFP/CORBIS 473, Jim Arbogast 354, AP Photo-Staff Sgt. Bill Lisbon, U.S. Marine Corps 642, Bill Aron/PhotoEdit 173, 435, Art Bank/Photonica 164, Bruce Ayres/Stone/Getty Images 294, Bill BSIP/Photo Researchers 656, Bachmann/PhotoEdit 315, Jean Marc Barey/Vandystadt/Photo Researchers 147, Paul Barton/CORBIS 251, 512, 531, 537, Scott Bauer/ARS/USDA 624, Lester V. Bergman/CORBIS 741, Nathan Bilow/All Sport/Getty Images 93, Biophoto Associates/Photo Researchers 365, 500, 542, Ed Bock/CORBIS 295, Bohemian Nomad Picturemakers/CORBIS 5, John Boykin/PhotoEdit 305, Robert Brenner/PhotoEdit 27, 175, Michelle D. Bridwell/PhotoEdit 59, 92, 145, 275, 385, 581, 633, Dan Bridy/Wilkinson Studios 125, 125, 125, 125, 125, 159, 159, 159, 159, 564, 571, 571, 707, 707, 707, 707, 707, 709, 709, 710, 710, 711, 711, 711, 711, 711, 711, 711, 711, 711, 711, Keith Brofsky/Getty Images 461, Keith Brofsky/PhotoDisc/Getty Images 617, Gareth Brown/CORBIS 248, Rolf Bruderer/CORBIS 306, 521, Cleve Bryant/PhotoEdit 136, David Buffington/Getty Images 237, Burke/Triolo/Brand X Pictures/PictureQuest 598, Mark C. Burnett/Photo Researchers 576, 667, Jason Burns/Dr. Ryder/Phototake 468, Gary Buss/Getty Images 782, William Thomas Cain/Getty Images 64, CC Studios/Science Photo Library/Photo Researchers 152, Guy Call/Stock Connection/PictureQuest 724, Jose Carillo/PhotoEdit 638, Carolina Biological Supply Company/PhotoTake 675, 675, Ken Cavanagh/Photo Researchers 162, Jonathan Cavendish/CORBIS 307, Ron Chapple/Taxi/Getty Images 399, Cleo Photography/PhotoEdit 629, Anna Clopet/CORBIS 346, Stewart Cohen/Index Stock Imagery 337, Dean Conger/CORBIS 766, Paul Conklin/PhotoEdit 183, Gary Conner/PhotoEdit 643, W. Perry Conway/Corbis 772, CORBIS/Royalty-free 158, 232, 255, 419, 717, Corbis Stock Market/CORBIS 246, 296, CORBIS/PictureQuest 590, Jim Cummins/CORBIS 476, 628, Anne Cusek/Los Angeles Times/Newscom, 68, Custom Medical Stock 55, 139, 414, 489, 677, 677, 690, 690, 747, Bob Daemerich/Stock, Boston/PictureQuest 319, 585, Renee Daily/HK Portfolio 200, 712, 717, 717, 737, 739, 740, 743, 743, 744, 744, 746, 746, 746, 746, 746, 748, 748, 751, 756, 756, 756, 756, Michael Kevin Daly/CORBIS 467, Mary Kate Denny/PhotoEdit 8, 14, 40, 182, 193, 216, 281, 335, 381, 517, 563, 614, Digital Vision/Getty

Images 144, DiMaggio/Kalish/CORBIS 103, George DiSario/CORBIS 371, Duomo/CORBIS 466, Laura Dwight/CORBIS 511, Laura Dwight/PhotoEdit 221, 505, Dennis Dzielak 743, Rachel Epstein/PhotoEdit 568, Miles Ertman/MasterFile 328, Robert Essel NYC/CORBIS 783, Amy Etra/PhotoEdit 349, 527, Brian Evans/Photo Researchers Inc. 436, EyeWire Collection/Getty Images 719, David Falconer/Superstock 551, Myrleen Ferguson Cate/Index Stock Imagery 195, Myrleen Ferguson Cate/PhotoEdit 30, 172, 179, 198, 333, 350, 390, 436, 506, First Light/Image State 406, Todd France 700, Tony Freeman/PhotoEdit 17, 56, 151, 151, 275, 284, 328, 344, 347, 431, 440, 601, 602, 603, 605, 714, 718, 731, 753, Fotosearch.com 108, 233, 245, 669, GCA/Photo-Take 677, G.D.T./Stone/Getty Images 188, Rob Gage/Getty Images 404, Edward Gajdel 22, Mark Garvin 408, Garry Gay/Image State 124, Getty Images 164, 380, 668, Keerle Georges De/CORBIS 332, 332, Lowell Georgia/CORBIS 727, Patrik Giardino/CORBIS 38, Mark Giolas/Index Stock Imagery 439, Pascal Goetgheluck/Science Photo Library/Photo Researchers 606, Rick Gomez/CORBIS 36, 521, Carla R. Gonzalez/The Mazer Corporation 755, Stevie Grand/Photo Researchers 494, Stevie Grand/Science Photo Library/Photo Researchers 741, Spencer Grant/PhotoEdit 48, 58, 133, 179, 308, 597, 742, Spencer Grant/Stock Boston/PictureQuest 365, Jeff Greenberg/Index Stock Imagery 299, Jeff Greenberg/PhotoEdit 20, 45, 399, 464, 505, 703, Jeff Greenberg/Photo Researchers 172, 212, Jeff Greenberg/Visuals Unlimited 215, 566, Annie Griffiths Belt/CORBIS 496, David M. Grossman/PhotoTake 426, Klaus Guldbrandsen/Science Photo Library/Photo Researchers 663, HIRB/Index Stock Imagery 129, 763, Bruce Hands/Stone/Getty Images 540, Will Hart/PhotoEdit 184, 342, 383, 652, Aaron Haupt/Stock, Boston/PictureQuest 576, Richard Heinzen/Superstock 360, John Henley/CORBIS 18, 656, Jack Holtel/Photographik Company 238, 254, 541, 572, 586, 681, Brent Humphries 730, Richard Hutchings/PhotoEdit 10, ISM/PhotoTake 134, Iconos Explorer/Photo Researchers 175, ImageState/FotoSearch.com 262, Index Stock 242, 410, International Stock/Image State 74, 169, 275, 313, 411, 424, 484, 522, 547, 570, 577, 584, 592, 729, 736, R.W. Jones/CORBIS 530, Phil Jude/Science Photo Library/Photo Researchers 365, Zigy Kaluzny/Getty Images 218, Bonnie Kamin/PhotoEdit 25, 706, 758, Catherine Karnow/CORBIS 583, Michael Keller/CORBIS 54, 101, 535, 738, Michael Keller/Index Stock Imagery 689, David Kelly Crow/PhotoEdit 685, Dan Kenyon/Getty Images 230, Anja Kroencke 104, Anders Krusberg 556, Dennis

Kunkel/PhotoTake 474, 690, John Lamb/Getty Images 654, Lee White Photography 764, Lisette Le Bon/SuperStock 137, 685, Rick Leckrone/Index Stock Imagery 781, Lester Lefkowitz/CORBIS 677, Joe Lertalan 508, Rob Lewine/CORBIS 552, Robert Llewellyn/CORBIS 351, Patti Longmire/WirePix/The Image Works 556, Bill Losh/Getty Images 635, Damien Lovegrove/Science Photo Library/Photo Researchers 596, Ken Lucas/Getty Images 225, Jeaneen Lund 442, LWA-Dann Tardiff/CORBIS 61, LWA-Stephen Welstead/CORBIS 478, 697, Dennis MacDonald/PhotoEdit 38, 105, 733, Jeff Maloney/PhotoDisc/Getty Images 553, P. Marazzi/Science Photo Library/Photo Researchers 365, 365, John Marquette/Getty Images 693, Doug Martin/Photo Researchers 172, Phil Martin/PhotoEdit 41, Don Mason/CORBIS 164, 613, Matt Meadows Photography 43, 46, 47, 60, 81, 82, 82, 83, 85, 85, 85, 86, 91, 115, 116, 117, 118, 120, 127, 127, 128, 134, 155, 161, 201, 261, 283, 286, 358, 440, 457, 462, 538, 561, 685, 728, Matt Meadows Photography and Diyanni Homes, Reynoldsburg, OH 142, 316, 443, 451, 626, Buddy Mays/CORBIS 759, Maxmilian Stock Ltd./Science Photo Library/Photo Researchers 114, Will and Deni McIntyre/Photo Researchers 12, 53, 165, 266, 437, 658, Carolyn A. McKeone/Photo Researchers 648, Eric McNatt 668, Ryan McVay/Getty Images 113, 720, Oliver Meckes/Photo Researchers 655, Warren Morgan/CORBIS 384, Roy Morsch/CORBIS 287, 515, 526, Nash Design and Color Vision Store 375, National Institute on Drug Abuse 606, Joseph Nettis/Photo Researchers 179, Alex Newhall 324, Michael Newman/PhotoEdit 32, 99, 148, 167, 210, 213, 219, 250, 257, 330, 338, 355, 357, 358, 373, 409, 416, 459, 481, 504, 524, 560, 566, 699, 752, Dwayne Newton/PhotoEdit 624, Jonathan Nourok/PhotoEdit 171, 199, 205, 501, 647, NOVASTOCK/PhotoEdit 725, Richard T. Nowitz/Photo Researchers 156, 156, Linda Nye 102, 361, 368, 372, 377, 387, 388, 388, 389, 395, 396, 396, 400, 401, 401, 402, 405,405, 405, 418, 418, 420, 429, 444, 445, 454, 454, 465, 465, 470, 470, 475, 475, 476, 476, 476, 476, 487, 491, 491, 491, 499, 516, 543, 575, 575, 603, 622, 622, 622, 623, 623, 628, 629, 630, 632, 659, 664, 674, 740, Richard T. Nowitz/PhotoTake 695, Roy Ooms/MasterFile 422, Charles Orrico/SuperStock 778, Lisa Peardon/Getty Images 268, Michael Pawlyk/Index Stock 760, Frank Pedrick/Index Stock Imagery 376, Lori Adamski Peek/Getty Images 192, Jose Luis Pelaaz, Inc./CORBIS 109, 589, Kevin Peterson/Getty Images 520, Petit Format/Nestle/Photo Researchers 488, Petit Format/Nestle/Science Source/Photo Researchers 489, David M. Phillips/Photo Researchers 486, PhotoDisc/Getty Images 500, PhotoTake 456, Javier Pierini/Getty Images 148, Charlene Potts 571, 571, Tom Prettyman/PhotoEdit 673, Steven Puetzer/Photonica 405, Punchstock 534, Kevin Radford/SuperStock 277,

A. Ramey/PhotoEdit 662, Donovan Reese/PhotoDisc/Getty Images 226, Reuters NewMedia Inc./CORBIS 544, Mark Richards/PhotoEdit 519, 698, Jon Riley/Stone/Getty Images 557, John A. Rizzo/PhotoDisc/Getty Images 44, Robert Essel NYC/CORBIS 783, ROB & SAS/CORBIS 509, Rommel/MasterFile 600, Elena Rooraid/PhotoEdit 696, Tom Rosenthal/Superstock 485, Martin M. Rotker/Photo Researchers 574, Nicolas Russell/The Image Bank/Getty Images 214, Salisbury District Hospital/Photo Researchers 490, Pete Saloutos/CORBIS 197, 573, 676, Chuck Savage/CORBIS 168, 174, Lawrence M. Sawyer/PhotoDisc/Getty Images 448, Norbert Schaefer/CORBIS 385, 458, Phil Schermeister/CORBIS 414, Mark Scott/Getty Images 172, Lazslo Selly/FoodPix 138, James Shaffer/PhotoEdit 327, Francis Sheehan/Photo Researchers 665, George Shelley/CORBIS 528, Rhoda Sidney/PhotoEdit 353, Rhoda Sidney/Stock, Boston/PictureQuest 285, Frank Simonetti/Index Stock Imagery 320, Frank Siteman/Stock, Boston/PictureQuest 325, SIU/Photo Researchers 542, 574, Ariel Skelley/CORBIS 301, 492, 649, 761, Steve Skjold/PhotoEdit 749, Don Smetzer/PhotoEdit 685, Adam Smith/Superstock 33, Howard Sochurek/CORBIS 423, 677, 677, Joseph Sohm, Chromosohm Inc./CORBIS 785, Mary Steinbacher/PhotoEdit 588, Tom Stewart/CORBIS 23, 189, 302, 750, Barbara Stitzer/PhotoEdit 31, 322, StockImage/ImageState 163, David Stoecklein/CORBIS 627, 715, Stone/Getty Images 4, 57, 243, 609, 672, 775, Superstock 318, 341, 391, Nicola Sutton/Life File/PhotoDisc/Getty Images 303, SW Production/Index Stock Imagery 94, SW Productions/PhotoDisc/Getty Images 170, 177, 185, 186, 209, 520, 704, Jacob Taposchaner/Getty Images 89, Taxi/Getty Images 701, The Image Bank/Getty Images 713, Courtesy Texans Standing Tall 580, ThinkStock/Superstock 704, Arthur Tilley/Getty Images 505, Derek Trask/CORBIS 722, David Turnley/CORBIS 774, Lon Tweeten 616, U.S. Department of Health and Human Services 7, 579, Susan Van Etten/PhotoEdit 202, VCL/Stone/Getty Images 645, Merritt Vincent/PhotoEdit 204, Rudi Von Briel/PhotoEdit 75, Cath Wadforth/Science Photo Library/Photo Researchers 656, Karl Weatherly/Getty Images 72, David Weintraub/Photo Researchers 759, 759, Dana White/PhotoEdit 764, Jim Whitmer/Visuals Unlimited 178, Terry Whittaker/Photo Researchers 97, Dusty Wilson/Image State 505, Paul Windsor/Getty Images 690, Wolf/Jerrican/Photo Researchers 172, Brad Wrobleski/MasterFile 394, Mel Yates/Taxi/Getty Images 196, David Young-Wolff/PhotoEdit 6, 9, 21, 34, 65, 71, 79, 80, 87, 98, 102, 135, 141, 142, 150, 154, 157, 181, 241, 260, 276, 279, 280, 331, 340, 366, 452, 493, 512, 514, 521, 523, 545, 559, 562, 594, 611, 688, 691, 723, 777, David Young-Wolff/Stone/Getty Images 498, ZEFA/MasterFile 469, Zephyr/ImageState 442